Readings in Mathematical Psychology

Volume I

Readings in

Volume I

New York and London

Mathematical Psychology

EDITED BY

R. Duncan Luce, *University of Pennsylvania*

Robert R. Bush, *University of Pennsylvania*

Eugene Galanter, *University of Washington*

John Wiley and Sons, Inc.

Preface

The two volumes of *Readings in Mathematical Psychology*, of which this is the first, are designed as source materials to accompany the three-volume *Handbook of Mathematical Psychology*. The *Handbook* authors were asked to suggest journal references that they considered particularly important in their fields; from these suggestions the articles appearing in the *Readings* were selected. Because of space limitations and our own evaluations, we took considerable liberty in the selection process.

This volume focuses on two main areas of psychology: psychophysics and learning. Part I consists of 14 papers on measurement, psychophysics, and reaction time, and Part II consists of 21 papers on learning and related mathematical and statistical topics. These papers are referenced in Chapters 1–6 and 8–10 of the *Handbook*. Volume II of the *Readings* contains papers relevant to other *Handbook* chapters.

Papers that have appeared in hard-cover publications, such as *Decision Processes* (Wiley, 1954) and *Studies in Mathematical Learning Theory* (Stanford, 1959), were intentionally excluded from the present *Readings*. It is our view that every mathematical psychologist should have such books on his bookshelf. They are listed after the preface to Volume I of the *Handbook*.

Of the 35 papers reproduced in this volume, 11 are from *Psychometrika*, 10 are from *Psychological Review*, 3 from the *Journal of Experimental Psychology*, 3 from the *Journal of the Acoustical Society of America*, 2 from the *Pacific Journal of Mathematics*, and one each from the *Bulletin of Mathematical Biophysics*, the *Proceedings of the National Academy of Sciences*, *Transactions of the Institute of Radio Engineers*, the *Journal of Symbolic Logic*, the *Annals of Mathematical Statistics*, and a private document of the U.S. Air Force. Gratitude is expressed for permissions to reproduce these papers here.

The 35 papers represent the work of 30 different contributors. It may be of interest to note that 17 of these are professional psychologists, 8 are mathematicians or statisticians, 3 are engineers, and 2 are philosophers. One of the papers was published in 1947, and the others are rather uniformly spread over the years 1950–1962.

The compilation of a book of this sort requires a surprising amount of correspondence. For handling this and other details, the editors wish to thank Miss Ada Katz.

R. Duncan Luce
Robert R. Bush
Eugene Galanter

Philadelphia, Pennsylvania
March, 1963

v

Contents

PART I

MEASUREMENT, PSYCHOPHYSICS,
AND REACTION TIME

AN AXIOMATIC FORMULATION AND GENERALIZATION OF SUCCESSIVE INTERVALS SCALING*

ERNEST ADAMS

UNIVERSITY OF CALIFORNIA, BERKELEY

AND

SAMUEL MESSICK

EDUCATIONAL TESTING SERVICE

A formal set of axioms is presented for the method of successive intervals, and directly testable consequences of the scaling assumptions are derived. Then by a systematic modification of basic axioms the scaling model is generalized to non-normal stimulus distributions of both specified and unspecified form.

Thurstone's scaling models of successive intervals [7, 21] and paired comparisons [17, 24] have been severely criticized because of their dependence upon an apparently untestable assumption of normality. This objection was recently summarized by Stevens [22], who insisted that the procedure of using the variability of a psychological measure to equalize scale units "smacks of a kind of magic—a rope trick for climbing the hierarchy of scales. The rope in this case is the *assumption* that in the sample of individuals tested the trait in question has a canonical distribution, (e.g., 'normal') ⋯ . There are those who believe that the psychologists who make assumptions whose validity is beyond test are hoist with their own petard ⋯ ." Luce [13] has also viewed these models as part of an "extensive and unsightly literature which has been largely ignored by outsiders, who have correctly condemned the *ad hoc* nature of the assumptions."

Gulliksen [11], on the other hand, has explicitly discussed the testability of these models and has suggested alternative procedures for handling data which do not satisfy the checks. Empirical tests of the scaling theory were also mentioned or implied in several other accounts of the methods [e.g., 8, 9, 12, 15, 21, 25]. Criteria of goodness of fit have been presented [8, 18], which, if met by the data, would indicate satisfactory scaling within an acceptable error. Random errors and sampling fluctuations, as well as systematic deviations from scaling assumptions, are thereby evaluated by these

*This paper was written while the authors were attending the 1957 Social Science Research Council Summer Institute on Applications of Mathematics in Social Science. The research was supported in part by Stanford University under Contract NR 171-034 with Group Psychology Branch, Office of Naval Research, by Social Science Research Council, and by Educational Testing Service. The authors wish to thank Dr. Patrick Suppes for his interest and encouragement throughout the writing of the report and Dr. Harold Gulliksen for his helpful and instructive comments on the manuscript.

This article appeared in *Psychometrika*, 1958, **23**, 355–368. Reprinted with permission.

over-all internal consistency checks. However, tests of the scaling assumptions, and in particular the normality hypothesis, have not yet been explicitly derived in terms of the necessary and sufficient conditions required to satisfy the model. Recently Rozeboom and Jones [20] and Mosteller [16] have investigated the sensitivity of successive intervals and paired comparisons, respectively, to a normality requirement, indicating that departures from normality in the data are not too disruptive of scale values with respect to goodness of fit, but direct empirical consequences of the assumptions of the model were not specified as such.

The present axiomatic characterization of a well-established scaling model was attempted because of certain advantages which might accrue: (a) an ease of generalization that follows from a precise knowledge of formal properties by systematically modifying axioms, and (b) an ease in making comparisons between the properties of different models. The next section deals with the axioms for successive intervals and serves as the basis for the ensuing section, in which the model is generalized to non-normal stimulus distributions. One outcome of the following formalization which should again be highlighted is that the assumption of normality has directly verifiable consequences and should not be characterized as an untestable supposition.

Thurstone's Successive Intervals Scaling Model

The Experimental Method

In the method of successive intervals subjects are presented with a set of n stimuli and asked to sort them into k ordered categories with respect to some attribute. The proportion of times f_{si} that a given stimulus s is placed in category i is determined from the responses. If it is assumed that a category actually represents a certain interval of stimulus values for a subject, then the relative frequency with which a given stimulus is placed in a particular category should represent the probability that the subject estimates the stimulus value to lie within the interval corresponding to the category. This probability is in turn simply the area under the distribution curve inside the interval. So far scale values for the end points of the intervals are unknown, but if the observed probabilities for a given stimulus are taken to represent areas under a normal curve, then scale values may be obtained for both the category boundaries and the stimulus.

Scale values for interval boundaries are determined by this model, and interval widths are not assumed equal, as in the method of equal appearing intervals. Essentially equivalent procedures for obtaining successive intervals scale values have been presented by Saffir [21], Guilford [10], Mosier [15], Bishop [3], Attneave [2], Garner and Hake [9], Edwards [7], Burros [5], and Rimoldi [19]. The basic rationale of the method had been previously outlined by Thurstone in his absolute scaling of educational tests [23, 26]. Gulliksen

[12], Diederich, Messick, and Tucker [6], and Bock [4] have described least square solutions for successive intervals, and Rozeboom and Jones [20] presented a derivation for scale values which utilized weights to minimize sampling errors. Most of these papers contain the notion that the assumption of normality can be checked by considering more than one stimulus. Although one distribution of relative frequencies can always be converted to a normal curve, it is by no means always possible to normalize simultaneously all of the stimulus distributions, allowing unequal means and variances, on the same base line. The specification of exact conditions under which this is possible will now be attempted. In all that follows, the problem of sampling fluctuations is largely ignored, and the model is presented for the errorless case.

The Formal Model

The set of stimuli, denoted S, has elements $r, s, u, v, \cdots$. There is no limit upon the admissible number of stimuli, although for the purpose of testing the model, S must have at least two members. For each stimulus s in S, and each category $i = 1, 2, \cdots, k$, the relative frequency $f_{s,i}$ with which stimulus s is placed in category i is given. Formally f is a function from the Cartesian product of $S \times \{1, 2, \cdots, k\}$ to the real numbers. More specifically, it will be the case that for each s in S, f_s will be a probability distribution over the set $\{1, 2, \cdots, k\}$. For the sake of an explicit statement of the assumptions of the model, this fact will appear as an axiom, although it must be satisfied by virtue of the method of determining the values of $f_{s,i}$.

AxIOM 1. f is a function mapping $S \times \{1, \cdots, k\}$ into the real numbers such that for each s in S, f_s is a probability distribution over $\{1, \cdots, k\}$; i.e., for each s in S and $i = 1, \cdots, k$, $0 \leq f_{s,i} \leq 1$ and $\sum_{i=1}^{k} f_{s,i} = 1$.

The set S and the function f constitute the *observables* of the model. Two more concepts which are not directly observed remain to be introduced. The first of these is a set of numbers $t_1, \cdots, t_{(k-1)}$, which are the end points of the intervals corresponding to the categories. It is assumed that these intervals are adjacent and that they cover the entire real line. Formally, it will simply be assumed that $t_1, \cdots, t_{(k-1)}$ are an increasing series of real numbers.

AxIOM 2. Interval boundaries $t_1, \cdots, t_{(k-1)}$ are real numbers, and for $i = 2, \cdots, (k-1)$, $t_{(i-1)} \leq t_i$.

Finally, the distribution corresponding to each stimulus s in S is represented by a normal distribution function N_s.

AxIOM 3. N is a function mapping S into normal distribution functions over the real line.

Axioms 1–3 do not state fully the mathematical properties required for the set S, the numbers $t_1, \cdots, t_{(k-1)}$, and the functions N_s. In the interests of completeness, these will be stated in the following Axiom 0, which for formal purposes should be referred to instead of Axioms 1–3.

AXIOM 0. S is a non-empty set. k is a positive integer. f is a function mapping $S \times \{1, \cdots, k\}$ into the closed interval $[0, 1]$, such that for each s in S, $\sum_{i=1}^{k} f_{s,i} = 1$. For $i = 1, \cdots, (k - 1)$, t_i is a real number, and for $i = 1, \cdots, (k - 2)$, $t_i \leq t_{i+1}$. N is a function mapping S into the set of normal distribution functions over the real numbers.

Axioms 2 and 3 state only the set-theoretical character of the elements t_i and N_s, and have no intuitive empirical content. The central hypothesis of the theory states the connection between the observed relative frequencies $f_{s,i}$ and the assumed underlying distributions N_s.

AXIOM 4. (Fundamental hypothesis) For each s in S and $i = 1, \cdots, k$,

$$f_{s,i} = \int_{t_{i-1}}^{t_i} N_s(\alpha) \, d\alpha.$$

(Note that if $i = 1$, $t_{(i-1)}$ is set equal to $-\infty$, and if $i = k$, $t_i = \infty$.)

Axioms 1–4 state the formal assumptions of the theory although, because the fundamental hypothesis (Axiom 4) involves the unobservables N_s and t_i, it is not directly testable in these terms. The question of testing the model will be discussed in the next section. Scale values for the stimuli have not yet been introduced. These are defined to be equal to the means of the distributions N_s, and hence are easily derived. The function v will represent the scale values of the stimuli.

DEFINITION 1. v is the function mapping S into the real numbers such that for each s in S, v_s is the mean of N_s; i.e.,

$$v_s = \int_{-\infty}^{\infty} \alpha N_s(\alpha) \, d\alpha.$$

Testing the Model

The model will be said to fit exactly if all of the testable consequences of Axioms 1–4 are verified. Testable consequences of these axioms will be those consequences which are formulated solely in terms of the observable concepts S and f, or of concepts which are definable in terms of S and f. If no further assumptions are made about an independent determination of $t_1, \cdots, t_{(k-1)}$ and N, then the testable consequences are just those which follow about f and S from the assumption that there *exist* numbers $t_1, \cdots, t_{(k-1)}$ and functions N_s which satisfy Axioms 1–4. In this model, it is possible to give an exhaustive description of the testable consequences; hence this theory is axiomatizable in the sense that it is possible to formulate observable conditions which are necessary and sufficient to insure the existence of the numbers t_i and functions N_s. The derivation of these conditions will proceed by stages.

Let $p_{s,i}$ be the cumulative distribution of the function f for stimulus s and interval i.

DEFINITION 2. For each s in S and $i = 1, \cdots, k$,

$$p_{s,i} = \sum_{j=1}^{i} f_{s,j} \, .$$

It follows from this definition and Axiom 4 that for each s in S and $i = 1, \cdots, k$,

$$(1) \qquad p_{s,i} = \int_{-\infty}^{t_i} N_s(\alpha) \, d\alpha.$$

Using the table for the cumulative distribution of the normal curve with zero mean and unit variance, the numbers $z_{s,i}$ may be determined such that

$$(2) \qquad p_{s,i} = \frac{1}{\sqrt{2\pi}} \int_{-\infty}^{z_{s,i}} e^{-1/2x^2} \, dx.$$

(Note that for $i = k$, $z_{s,i}$ will be infinite.) N_s is a normal distribution function and must have the form:

$$(3) \qquad N_s(\alpha) = \frac{1}{\sigma_s \sqrt{2\pi}} \exp\left[-\frac{1}{2\sigma_s^2}(\alpha - v_s)^2\right],$$

where σ_s^2 is the variance of N_s about its mean v_s. Equations (1), (2), and (3) yield the conclusion that for each s in S and $i = 1, \cdots, k$,

$$(4) \qquad z_{s,i} = (t_i - v_s)/\sigma_s \, .$$

In (4) the numbers $z_{s,i}$ on the left are known transformations of the observed proportions $f_{s,i}$, while the numbers t_i, v_s and σ_s are unknown. Suppose however that r is a fixed member of the class S of stimuli; it is possible to solve (4) for all the unknowns in terms of the known z's, and v_r and σ_r, the mean and standard deviation of the fixed stimulus r. These solutions are

$$(5) \qquad t_i = \sigma_r z_{r,i} + v_r \quad \text{for} \quad i = 1, \cdots, (k-1);$$

$$(6) \qquad \sigma_s = \sigma_r \left(\frac{z_{r,i} - z_{r,j}}{z_{s,i} - z_{s,j}}\right) \quad \text{for} \quad s \in S, \quad \text{and} \quad i \neq j;$$

$$(7) \qquad v_s = \sigma_r \left[z_{r,i} - \left(\frac{z_{r,i} - z_{r,j}}{z_{s,i} - z_{s,j}}\right)z_{s,i}\right] + v_r \, .$$

The necessary and sufficient condition that the system of equations (4) have a solution, and hence that t_i, v_s and σ_s be determinable using (5), (6), and (7), is that all $z_{s,i}$ be linear functions of each other in the following sense. For all r and s in S, there exist real numbers $a_{r,s}$ and $b_{r,s}$ such that for each $i = 1, \cdots, k$,

$$(8) \qquad\qquad z_{s,i} = a_{r,s}z_{r,i} + b_{r,s} .$$

The required numbers $a_{r,s}$ and $b_{r,s}$ exist if and only if for each r and s, the ratio

$$(9) \qquad\qquad \frac{z_{r,i} - z_{r,j}}{z_{s,i} - z_{s,j}} = a_{s,r} = \frac{1}{a_{r,s}}$$

is independent of i and j.

If constants $a_{r,s}$ and $b_{r,s}$ satisfying (8) exist, then they are related to the scale values v_r and the standard deviations σ_r in a simple way. For each r, s in S,

$$(10) \qquad\qquad a_{r,s} = \sigma_r/\sigma_s ,$$

and

$$(11) \qquad\qquad b_{r,s} = (v_r - v_s)/\sigma_s .$$

Clearly the arbitrary choice of the constants v_r and σ_r in (5), (6), and (7) represents the arbitrary choice of origin and unit in the scale. Since scale values of t_i and v_s are uniquely determined once v_r and σ_r are chosen, the scale values are unique up to a linear transformation; i.e., an interval scale of measurement has been determined. It should be noted that this model does not require equality of standard deviations (or what Thurstone has called discriminal dispersions [25]) but provides for their determination from the data by equation (6). This adds powerful flexibility in its possible applications.

It remains only to make a remark about the necessary and sufficient condition which a set of observed relative frequencies $f_{s,i}$ must fulfill in order to satisfy the model. This necessary and sufficient condition is simply that the numbers $z_{s,i}$, which are defined in terms of the observed relative frequencies, be linearly related as expressed in (8). This can be determined by seeing if the ratios computed from (9) are independent of i and j, or by evaluating for all s, r the linearity of the plots of $z_{s,i}$ against $z_{r,i}$. Hence for this model there is a simple decision procedure for determining whether or not a given set of errorless data fits.

If $z_{s,i}$ and $z_{r,i}$ are found to be linearly related for all s, r in S, the assumptions of the scaling model are verified for that data. If the z's are not linearly related, then assumptions have been violated. For example, the normal curve may not be an appropriate distribution function for the stimuli and some other function might yield a better fit [cf. 11, 12]. Or perhaps the responses cannot be summarized unidimensionally in terms of projections on the real line representing the attribute [11]. If the stimuli are actually distributed in a multidimensional space, then judgments of projections on one of the attributes may be differentially distorted by the presence of variations in other dimensions. This does not mean that stimuli varying in several dimensions may not be scaled satisfactorily by the method of successive intervals, but rather that if the model does not fit, such distortion effects might be operating. A multidimensional scaling model [14] might prove more appropriate in such cases.

In practice the set of points $(z_{r,i}, z_{s,i})$ for $i = 2, \cdots, (k-1)$ will never exactly fit the straight line of (8) but will fluctuate about it. It remains to be decided whether this fluctuation represents systematic departure from the model or error variance. In the absence of a statistical test for linearity, the decision is not precise, although the linearity of the plots may still be evaluated, even if only by eye. One approach is to fit the obtained points to a straight line by the method of least squares and then evaluate the size of the obtained minimum error [4, 6, 12]. In any event, the test of the model is exact in the errorless case, and the incorporation of a suitable sampling theory would provide decision criteria for direct experimental applications.

A Generalization of the Successive Intervals Model

The successive intervals model discussed in the previous section can be generalized in a number of ways. One generalization, treated in detail by Torgerson [27], considers each interval boundary t_i to be the mean of a subjective distribution with positive variance. Another approach toward generalizing the model is to weaken the requirement of normal distributions of stimulus scale values. Formally, this generalization amounts to enlarging the class of admissible distribution functions. Instead of specifying exactly which distribution functions are allowed in the generalization, assume an arbitrary set ψ of distributions over the real line, to which it is required that the stimulus distributions belong. In formalizing the model, ψ is characterized simply as a set of distribution functions over the real line. Axiom 3 may be replaced by a new axiom specifying the nature of the class ψ and stating that C is a function mapping S into elements of ψ; i.e., for each s in S, C_s (interpreted as the distribution of the stimulus s) is a member of ψ.

One final assumption about the class ψ needs to be added: namely, if ψ contains a distribution function C, then it must contain all *linear transformations* of C. A linear transformation of a distribution function C is defined as any other distribution function C' which can be obtained from C by a shift of origin and a scale transformation of the horizontal axis. A stretch along the horizontal axis must be compensated for by a contraction on the vertical axis in order that the transformed function also be a probability density function. Algebraically, these transformations have the following form. Let D and D' be distribution functions, then D' is a linear transformation of D if there exists a positive real number a and a real number b such that for all x,

$$D'(x) = aD(ax + b).$$

This is not truly a linear transformation because of multiplication by a on the ordinate, but for lack of a better term this phrase is used. The reason for requiring that the class ψ of distribution functions be closed under linear transformations is to insure that in any determination of stimulus scale values it will be possible to convert them by a linear transformation into another admissible set of scale values; i.e., the stimulus values obtained are to form an interval scale. If the set ψ is not closed under linear transformations, in general it will not be possible to alter the scale by an arbitrary linear transformation.

AXIOM 3′. ψ is a set of distribution functions over the real numbers, and C is a function mapping S into ψ. For all D in ψ, if a is a positive real number and b is a real number, then the function D' such that for all x,

$$D'(x) = aD(ax + b)$$

is a member of ψ.

It is to be observed that the set of normal distributions has the required property of being closed under linear transformations. This set is in fact a minimal class of this type, in the sense that all normal distribution functions can be generated from a single normal distribution function by linear transformations.

Finally, Axiom 4 is replaced by an obvious generalization which specifies the connection between the observed $f_{s,i}$, the distribution functions C_s , and the interval end points t_i .

AXIOM 4′. For each s in S and $i = 1, \cdots , k$,

$$f_{s,i} = \int_{t_{i-1}}^{t_i} C_s(x) \, dx.$$

(Here again $t_0 = -\infty$ and $t_k = \infty$.) The stimulus values are defined as before to be the means of the distribution functions C_s .

DEFINITION 1′. v is the function mapping S into the real numbers such that for each s in S, v_s is the mean of C_s , i.e.,

$$v_s = \int_{-\infty}^{\infty} xC_s(x) \, dx.$$

The problem now is to specify the class of admissible distribution functions ψ. Each specification of this class amounts to a theory about the underlying stimulus distributions. If the hypothesis of normality is altered or weakened, what assumptions can replace it? Omitting any assumption about the form of the distribution functions would amount to letting ψ be the set of all distribution functions over real numbers. If no assumption whatever is made about the forms of C_s, then the theory is very weak. Every set of data will fit the theory, and the scale values of t_i can be determined only on an ordinal scale. It is always possible to determine distribution functions C_s satisfying Axiom 4' for arbitrarily specified t_i. To show this it is only necessary to construct them in accordance with the following definition.

$$C_s(x) = \begin{cases} \dfrac{f_{s,i}}{t_i - t_{i-1}}, & i-1 < x < i, \quad i = 1, \cdots, k, \\ 0 & \text{otherwise.} \end{cases}$$

Non-normal Distributions of Specified Form

It is clearly necessary to make some restrictions on ψ if the scale values are to be determined uniquely up to a linear transformation. It will next be shown that any minimal class of distribution functions, in the sense of a class all of whose members are generated from a single member by linear transformations, has the desired property of generating a linear scale of stimulus values when the model fits. For the present assume that ψ is a minimal class of distribution functions.

ASSUMPTION 1. There exists a distribution function D such that for all distribution functions D' in ψ there exists a positive real number a and a real number b such that for all x,

$$D'(x) = aD(ax + b).$$

To show that if Assumption 1 is satisfied the scale values are obtained on an interval scale, we proceed as follows. Axiom 3' and Assumption 1 imply that for all s in S, there exists a positive real number a_s and a real number b_s such that for all x,

$$(12) \qquad C_s(x) = a_s D(a_s x + b_s),$$

where the function D on the right side of (12) is a fixed function of some specified form linearly related to all the functions D' in ψ. According to Axiom 4', then, for each s in S, and $i = 1, \cdots, k$,

$$(13) \qquad f_{s,i} = \int_{t_{i-1}}^{t_i} a_s D(a_s x + b_s)\, dx.$$

If π is the cumulative distribution corresponding to D, and the cumulative distributions $p_{s,i}$ are defined as before, then

$$(14) \qquad p_{s,i} = \int_{-\infty}^{t_i} a_s D(a_s x + b_s)\, dx$$

$$= \pi(a_s t_i + b_s).$$

Assuming that the function π is strictly monotone increasing, then, knowing the form of function D, it is possible to determine uniquely the numbers $z_{s,i}$ such that for each s in S and $i = 1, \cdots, k$,

$$(15) \qquad\qquad p_{s,i} = \pi(z_{s,i}).$$

Equations (14) and (15) imply immediately that

$$(16) \qquad\qquad z_{s,i} = a_s t_i + b_s$$

for all s in S and $i = 1, \cdots, k$. It is clear from (15) why it is necessary to assume that π is strictly monotone increasing. If it were not, there would not in general be a unique $z_{s,i}$ determined by (15); hence the scale values based on $z_{s,i}$ would not be unique. It is also seen that (4), relating $z_{s,i}$ to t_i, v_s and σ_s in the normal distribution model, is simply a particular case of (16) here. The connection between a_s, b_s and σ_s and v_s is

$$\sigma_s = 1/a_s, \qquad v_s = -b_s/a_s.$$

In (15), as in the corresponding set of equations obtained from the normality assumption, the numbers on the left are known, and the numbers on the right are unknown. As before, if two numbers a_r and b_r are arbitrarily determined for a fixed stimulus r, then the t_i are uniquely determined by the following equation.

$$(17) \qquad\qquad t_i = (z_{r,i} - b_r)/a_r, \qquad i = 1, \cdots, k.$$

The scale values for the stimuli, however, cannot be directly determined from the coefficients $z_{s,i}$, a_r and b_r without first specifying the mean m of the basic distribution D. If m is the mean of D, then v_s, which was defined as the mean of C_s, is determined by

$$(18) \qquad\qquad v_s = (m - b_s)/a_s.$$

Both the a_s and the b_s in (17) can be determined in terms of $z_{s,i}$, a_r and b_r, (19) and (20); hence v_s is immediately determinable in terms of just these quantities by (18).

$$(19) \qquad\qquad a_s = a_r \frac{z_{s,i} - z_{s,j}}{z_{r,i} - z_{r,i}},$$

$$(20) \qquad\qquad b_s = z_{s,i} - \left(\frac{z_{s,i} - z_{s,i}}{z_{r,i} - z_{r,i}}\right)(z_{r,i} - b_r).$$

It is clear then that the scale values t_i and v_s are determined up to a linear transformation. Furthermore, necessary and sufficient conditions that a set of data fit the model are simply that the ratios of differences in z's on the right in (19) be independent of i and j; i.e., that the z's be linearly related.

The Forms of the Distributions Unspecified

A final generalization to be considered is one in which Assumption 1 holds, but where the form of the generating function D is not specified; i.e., it is assumed that the underlying distributions all belong to one minimal class, but that the class can be generated by any distribution function D. Interestingly enough, in this case it is still possible to test the model and to obtain more than ordinal information about the scale values. If it is assumed that the stimulus distributions all belong to one minimal family generated by a function D, but D is unknown, all of the deductions up through (14) go through, although in this case the function π is also unknown. Now, of course, it is impossible to discover the numbers $z_{s,i}$ by solving (15), but if it is postulated that the function π is strictly monotone increasing, it is still possible to obtain some information about the numbers $(a_s t_i + b_s)$. Since π is a cumulative distribution it is monotone increasing; however, it will only be strictly monotone increasing in case the distribution function D is never zero. This assumption is made explicit in Assumption 2.

ASSUMPTION 2. For all x, $D(x) > 0$.

Now, if π is strictly monotone increasing, then it follows that $\pi(x) \geq \pi(y)$ if and only if $x \geq y$. If (14) holds, then it will be the case that for all r, s in S and $i, j = 1, \cdots, k$,

$$(21) \qquad p_{s,i} \geq p_{r,j} \quad \text{if and only if} \quad a_s t_i + b_s \geq a_r t_j + b_r \, .$$

Therefore from an ordering on the numbers $p_{s,i}$ one can obtain a system of inequalities involving the constants a_s, b_s, and t_i. If it is further specified (as is required for the conditions of the problem) that $a_s > 0$ for all S, then this set of inequalities will not in general have a solution.

However, whether or not a set of data fits the model may still be determined. The necessary and sufficient condition for fit is that there exist numbers a_s, t_i and b_s (where $a_s > 0$) satisfying the system of inequalities (21). If this set of inequalities has a solution, then the interval boundaries may be taken to be the t_i satisfying (21). To determine the scale values of the stimuli it is first necessary to construct a distribution function which can represent the data. This is done in the following way. A differentiable monotone increasing function $\pi(x)$ is constructed by connecting the discrete set of points

$$\pi(a_s t_i + b_s) = p_{s,i}$$

with any smooth, strictly monotone increasing curve. If, as is usual, there is only a finite number of stimuli, then such a curve can always be constructed. Finally, the distribution function D is defined by

$$(22) \qquad D(x) = \frac{d}{dx} \pi(x).$$

Then, if the mean of the distribution D is m, the values v_s of the stimuli are determined by (18), $v_s = (m - b_s)/a_s$. As far as the determination of the v_s is concerned, it can be seen that they depend solely on the previously determined a and b and on the mean m, which can be regarded as an additional arbitrary constant in the determination of the v_s.

The remaining point of discussion for this model is the determination of the degree of uniqueness of the scale values. Finding the set of all possible solutions to the inequalities (21) presents, in general, extreme difficulty. One thing that can be simply determined is the class of what might be called the *universal transformations* of the solutions of the system of inequalities. A universal transformation is one which, applied to a solution of any set of inequalities, yields another solution to the same set of inequalities. By noting a close connection between the theory of the inequalities (21) and a two-dimensional affine geometry with a distinguished set of horizontal and vertical lines, it can be shown [1] that the class of universal transformations for this model is a subset of the affine transformations. The universal transformations of the interval boundaries t_i are the linear ones, and of the a_s are multiplications by a positive constant. The b_s also are determined up to a linear transformation, and hence so are the scale values v_s (although the additional arbitrary constant m also enters into their determination).

There is also an interesting special case in which, even though there is only a finite number of observations, the scale values of the t_i are determined up to a linear transformation. This might be called the special case of equal intervals, in which differences in successive t_i are all the same. If, for example, there exist stimuli with such relations among corresponding p's as $p_{x,i} = p_{y,i+1} = p_{z,i+2}$, $p_{x,i+1} = p_{y,i+2}$, $p_{y,i} = p_{z,i+1}$, etc., it is possible to determine that successive intervals are equal [1].

The fact that scale values obtained in this model, at least under certain circumstances, are unique up to a linear transformation has two interesting consequences for the original successive intervals model based on the normality hypothesis. (i) If in the errorless case the original model fits, then *no other successive intervals model which assumes a different form for the distribution functions will fit*. The reason for this is that the forms of the distribution functions (or the cumulative distributions) are determined by the values of $p_{s,i}$ lying above the point t_i. Hence, if the t_i are determined up to linear transformation, so are the curves $p_{s,i}$. (ii) Where the normality assumption does not fit the data it is theoretically possible to use the present generalization to obtain a scale. Then the deviation of the scale values from those obtained under a normality requirement can be evaluated. This, at least in principle, provides a second kind of goodness of fit besides the usual least squares regression methods employed where the data do not exactly fit the Thurstone model.

REFERENCES

[1] Adams, E. and Messick, S. An axiomatization of Thurstone's successive intervals and paired comparisons scaling models. Stanford, Calif.: Stanford Univ., Applied Mathematics and Statistics Laboratory, ONR Technical Report No. 12, 1957.

[2] Attneave, F. A method of graded dichotomies for the scaling of judgments. *Psychol. Rev.*, 1949, **56**, 334–340.

[3] Bishop, R. Points of neutrality in social attitudes of delinquents and non-delinquents. *Psychometrika*, 1940, **5**, 35–45.

[4] Bock, R. D. Note on the least squares solution for the method of successive categories. *Psychometrika*, 1957, **22**, 231–240.

[5] Burros, R. H. The estimation of the discriminal dispersion in the method of successive intervals. *Psychometrika*, 1955, **20**, 299–305.

[6] Diederich, G., Messick, S., and Tucker, L. R. A general least squares solution for successive intervals. *Psychometrika*, 1957, **22**, 159–173.

[7] Edwards, A. L. The scaling of stimuli by the method of successive intervals. *J. appl. Psychol.*, 1952, **36**, 118–122.

[8] Edwards, A. L. and Thurstone, L. L. An internal consistency check for scale values determined by the method of successive intervals. *Psychometrika*, 1952, **17**, 169–180.

[9] Garner, W. R. and Hake, H. W. The amount of information in absolute judgments. *Psychol. Rev.*, 1951, **58**, 446–459.

[10] Guilford, J. P. The computation of psychological values from judgments in absolute categories. *J. exp. Psychol.*, 1938, **22**, 32–42.

[11] Gulliksen, H. Paired comparisons and the logic of measurement. *Psychol. Rev.*, 1946, **53**, 199–213.

[12] Gulliksen, H. A least squares solution for successive intervals assuming unequal standard deviations. *Psychometrika*, 1954, **19**, 117–139.

[13] Luce, R. D. A theory of individual choice behavior. Bureau Appl. Soc. Res., Columbia Univ., 1957. (Mimeo.)

[14] Messick, S. Some recent theoretical developments in multidimensional scaling. *Educ. psychol. Measmt*, 1956, **16**, 82–100.

[15] Mosier, C. I. A modification of the method of successive intervals. *Psychometrika*, 1940, **5**, 101–107.

[16] Mosteller, F. Some miscellaneous contributions to scale theory: Remarks on the method of paired comparisons. Cambridge: Harvard Univ., Lab. Soc. Relations, Report No. 10. Ch. III.

[17] Mosteller, F. Remarks on the method of paired comparisons: I. The least squares solution assuming equal standard deviations and equal correlations. *Psychometrika*, 1951, **16**, 3–9.

[18] Mosteller, F. Remarks on the method of paired comparisons: III. A test of significance for paired comparisons when equal standard deviations and equal correlations are assumed. *Psychometrika*, 1951, **16**, 207–218.

[19] Rimoldi, H. J. A. and Hormaeche, M. The law of comparative judgment in the successive intervals and graphic rating scale methods. *Psychometrika*, 1955, **20**, 307–318.

[20] Rozeboom, W. W. and Jones, L. V. The validity of the successive intervals method of psychometric scaling. *Psychometrika*, 1956, **21**, 165–183.

[21] Saffir, M. A comparative study of scales constructed by three psychophysical methods. *Psychometrika*, 1937, **2**, 179–198.

[22] Stevens, S. S. Mathematics, measurement, and psychophysics. In S. S. Stevens (Ed.), *Handbook of experimental psychology*. New York: Wiley, 1951.

[23] Thurstone, L. L. A method of scaling psychological and educational tests. *J. educ. Psychol.*, 1925, **16**, 433–451.

[24] Thurstone, L. L. Psychophysical analysis. *Amer. J. Psychol.*, 1927, **38**, 368–389.
[25] Thurstone, L. L. A law of comparative judgment. *Psychol. Rev.*, 1927, **34**, 424–432.
[26] Thurstone, L. L. The unit of measurement in educational scales. *J. educ. Psychol.*, 1927, **18**, 505–524.
[27] Torgerson, W. S. A law of categorical judgment. In L. S. Clark (Ed.), *Consumer behavior*. New York: New York Univ. Press, 1954.

Manuscript received 2/12/58
Revised manuscript received 4/21/58

DECISION STRUCTURE AND TIME RELATIONS IN SIMPLE CHOICE BEHAVIOR*

LEE S. CHRISTIE[†] AND R. DUNCAN LUCE[‡]

GROUP NETWORKS LABORATORY,
RESEARCH LABORATORY OF ELECTRONICS,
MASSACHUSETTS INSTITUTE OF TECHNOLOGY

The structure of simple decisions is considered in terms of a model which composes such decisions from hypothetical elementary decisions. It is argued that reaction-time data can be treated by the use of the Laplace transform so as to overcome difficulties which negated earlier attempts to analyze choice reactions. The general model leads to complex problems which are formulated but not solved. Two special cases of the model are worked out, and the statistical problem of evaluating the fit of the model is discussed. It is shown that treating decision processing as time-discrete leaves the essential features of the analysis unchanged. Two experimental proposals, to provide data which should be considered in further work on the model, are made.

I. *Introduction.* In this paper we propose a model for the way human beings organize the decisions required by simple choice situations into a collection of component decisions. It is our thesis that such an organization of decisions must be reflected in the distribution of reaction times and, therefore, that it may be possible to infer the organization from the reaction-time distribution. Although our thinking derives from empirical studies, we must describe this proposal as speculative, for the model is not firmly

* This work was carried out when the authors were consultants to the Control Systems Laboratory, University of Illinois. It is a revision of report R-53 of that laboratory issued April 1954, supported under contract DA-36-039-SC-56695.

[†]Present address: Operations Research Office, The Johns Hopkins University, Chevy Chase, Maryland.

[‡]Present address: Center for Advanced Study in the Behavioral Sciences, Stanford, California.

This article appeared in *Bull. math. Biophysics,* 1956, **18**, 89–112. Reprinted with permission.

based on such studies. However, the development of the model has led us to suggest two experiments which we believe may help to determine what merit it has. These experiments will also help to decide whether it is desirable to pursue further work in an attempt to modify the model to accord better with reality, for we have little hope that the particular details of the present model have any lasting value.

II. *Reaction Times*. Suppose that a subject receives a stimulus of a fixed type at time 0 and responds at time t with a fixed type of response. The time interval, t, between the stimulus and the response is called the *simple reaction time*. If the subject is presented with one of a set of stimuli and a choice of response contingent on the stimulus is required the corresponding time interval is known as the *disjunctive reaction time*. In either case, it is clear that to obtain stable and readily analyzable time distributions it is necessary that the stimulus be simple enough so that the mean reaction time is no more than a second or two. Otherwise unwanted stimuli may intervene between the test stimulus and the response, and the interaction among the stimuli will cause a distortion of the time distribution which will be very difficult to analyze.

The study of reaction times, including disjunctive reaction times, has a long history in the literature of psychology (cf. Woodworth, 1938, chap. xiv). In recent years, however, relatively little interest has been evident in reaction-time studies. We may attribute this loss of interest to two related causes. First, there has been a failure to separate the time to make a decision (decision latency*) from the other time lags involved in the total process. One attempt to make this separation involved measuring the subject's response to a stimulus when no decision was to be made and subtracting this time from the time required to respond to the same stimulus with the same motor action when a decision was involved. This technique has been considered unsatisfactory for the following reason. If the subject has no decision to make he is able to bring his motor readiness for the specified response to a much higher

---

* We use *reaction time* when referring to the time of a process timed from stimulus presentation to motor response; *latency* when referring to times of distinguished parts of such a process.

pitch than he can when he is required to make a disjunctive reaction; thus, the *base time*—the time to react in a choice situation excluding the time for the decision itself—cannot be equated to any simple reaction time. We may conclude that the base time will be determined, if at all, only from measurements taken when the subject is required to make a decision.

Second, suppose that in one way or another the pure decision latency distribution has been obtained—then what? It is true that if these distributions were found to be extremely simple, in that they could be well approximated by some class of elementary mathematical functions, the separation of non-choice latencies (base times) from decision latencies might be an end in itself. If, however, the resulting decision latency distribution were of a complex character, the challenge to account for it in more primitive terms would remain.

We describe these as related difficulties, for it is not unreasonable to suppose that the method used to tease out the non-choice latencies (base times) can also be used, or adapted, to decompose the decision latencies into more primitive terms. Such a decomposition of the observed reaction-time distribution may be an entirely formal mathematical process with no empirical correlate or it may be based on a model which purports to describe the way a human being composes the finally observed decision from certain more elementary ones. It is with such a model that we are concerned.

At the heart of our proposal is the idea that the mathematical technique of the Laplace transform may be employed usefully in the study of reaction times. Since it is unlikely that every one of our readers will be familiar with the Laplace transform, we have devoted the next section to its definition and to a list of those of its elementary properties which we shall need.

III. *The Laplace Transform.* Let F be a real-valued function of a real variable t such that $F(t) = 0$ for $t < 0$. The real-valued function $L(F)$ of the real variable s defined by the equation

$$L(F) = \int_0^\infty e^{-st} F(t) dt \tag{1}$$

is called the *Laplace transform* of F. There is essentially no loss of information about F in making this transformation [see equation

(4)], but because of some of the special properties of the transform there is sometimes a distinct advantage to working with transformed functions. We shall list a few of the elementary properties of the transform which we shall need later; no proofs will be given for they are well known (cf. Churchill, 1944).

i.
$$L\left\{\int_0^t F_1(\tau)\, F_2(t-\tau)\, d\tau\right\} = L(F_1)L(F_2).\tag{2}$$

ii.
$$L\left(\frac{dF}{dt}\right) = sL(F) + F(0).\tag{3}$$

iii. If $L(F) = L(G)$, then $F = G + N$, where N is some $\qquad$ (4) function with the property $\int_0^T N(t)dt = 0$ for all $T > 0$. If it is known that F and G are continuous, the N is continuous and so $N \equiv 0$, i.e., $F = G$.

iv. If a and b are constants,
$$L(aF + bG) = aL(F) + bL(G).\tag{5}$$

v. If $F(t) = \lambda e^{-\lambda t}$, where λ is a constant, then
$$L(F) = \frac{1}{\dfrac{s}{\lambda} + 1}.\tag{6}$$

IV. *The Model.* Our proposal is based on assumptions which are intuitively acceptable, but which at the moment do not appear to be susceptible of direct verification. It is our impression that any empirical verification of the model must deal with the full set of assumptions rather than with each in isolation.

Assumption I. It is possible, for a given experimental situation, to divide the observed reaction time t into two latency components t_b and t_c, called base time and choice time respectively, such that:

1. $t = t_b + t_c$.

2. The value of t_b depends only on the mode of stimulus presentation and on the motor actions required of the subject. Specifically, it is not directly dependent on the character of the choice demanded.

3. The value of t_c depends only on the choice demanded. Specifically, it is not directly dependent on the mode of stimulus presentation or the motor actions required.

Let the distributions of t, t_b, and t_c be denoted by f, f_b, and f_c respectively. Since conditions 2 and 3 imply that the two component latencies are independent for a fixed experimental situation, it follows from condition 1 that

$$f(t) = \int_0^t f_b(\tau) f_c(t-\tau)\, d\tau \ .$$

(7)

Our second major assumption concerns only the choice latencies and requires the distribution f_c to be composed from more elementary distributions. The basic idea is that the final decision made by a person is organized into a set of simpler decisions which are, in some appropriate sense, elementary decisions built into him. If such a structure exists in human decision making, it is analogous to the structure of a decision process in a computing machine, which may be thought of as composed from a set of decisions which are elementary relative to that machine, i.e., the elementary decision capabilities built into the machine by the engineer. The actual organization of these elementary decisions to form a more complex one is a function both of the individual man or machine and of the nature of the decision being made. This is true at least of the machine, and we shall suppose it is true of human beings. In addition, the breakdown of a complex decision is not, in general, restricted to a serial process where one elementary decision is followed by another, for in a machine different portions may be simultaneously employed on different parts of the problem. There seems every reason to suppose this is also true in a human being.

We shall describe the organization of decisions by a *directed graph*. (The terms *oriented graph* and *network* have also been employed in the mathematical literature and the term *flow diagram* is used in connection with computer coding.) A directed graph consists of a finite set of points which are called *nodes*, with directed lines between some pairs of them. Several examples are shown in Figure 1. It is possible, in general, for more than one directed line to connect two points, both in the sense that we may have two or more in the same direction as in Figure 2a, and in the sense that there may be lines with opposite directions as in Figure 2b. In this paper, when we use the term directed graph, we shall suppose that neither of these possibilities is allowed, that is, we shall suppose that between any pair of nodes there is at most one directed line.

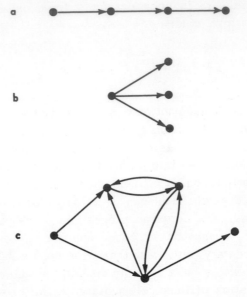

FIGURE 1

We shall employ a directed graph to represent the organization of decisions in the following way: At each node we shall assume that an "elementary decision" will take place, the latency distribution governing the decision at node i being denoted by f_i. The decision process is initiated at node i when, and only when, decisions have been made at each of those nodes j such that there is a directed line from j to i. We may think of the "demon" at node i waiting to begin making his decision until he has received the decisions of all the demons who precede him in the directed graph.

For the directed graphs we shall consider, there will be at least one node, possibly more, which is the terminal point of no line; these will be the decision points which are activated by the experimental stimulus at time 0. There will also be at least one node, and again possibly more, which initiates no directed line,

FIGURE 2

and it is only when the decisions at all these nodes have been taken that the motor actions, which signal the subject's response to the experimenter, are begun. It is clear that for any individual and for any stimulus situation it is possible to find at least one directed graph N and elementary latencies f_i which compose as described above to give f_c. For example, let N have but one node and let $f_i = f_c$. We shall, however, make stringent assumptions about N and f_c which, in general, exclude this trivial solution. It is some of these assumptions which most likely will be abandoned or modified if the present model cannot cope with experimental data.

Assumption II. It is possible to find for each stimulus situation, σ, a set of stimulus situations, S, which all have the same base-time distribution, f_b, and an elementary decision latency, f_e, such that:

1. σ is an element of S.

2. For each choice situation ρ in S there exists a directed graph N_ρ with the properties,

    a. each of the latency distributions at the nodes is the same, namely, f_e,

    b. the decision time at node i is independent of that at node j, $j \neq i$,

    c. f_c is a composition of N_ρ and f_e (as described above).

3. Among the stimulus situations in S there is one whose directed graph satisfying conditions II.2 is a single point.

In less formal terms, we require that there be groups of stimulus situations all of which have the same base-time distribution and which can be built up according to a directed graph from elementary and independent decisions which all have the same latency distribution f_e. In addition, among the stimulus situations in this class we assume that there is one which employs but a single elementary decision. The latter assumption can be weakened, if we choose, to the assumption that there is one stimulus situation whose directed graph we know a priori, but in what follows we shall take the stronger form that the graph is a single point.

V. *Comments*. The above assumptions comprise the formal structure of our model; there are a series of auxiliary comments which are necessary.

Even if we were able to show that these assumptions can be met for certain wide classes of experimental data, but that in so doing we obtain elementary decision distributions f_e which are extremely complicated, it is doubtful that we should accept the model as an adequate description of the decision process. Equally well, if the directed graphs required are excessively complex we should reject the model. The hope is that it is possible to subdivide the total process into a relatively small set of subprocesses which are practically identical. But we do not want to be forced to an analysis in terms of individual neurone firings. It is probable that Assumption II.3 effectively prevents this extremity by requiring the existence of a stimulus situation which demands but one elementary decision for its response.

It is also implicit in our thinking, although not a part of the formal model, that the sets S of "similar" stimulus situations will include as subsets those experimental situations we naturally think of as being similar. For example, suppose the subject is presented with n points, one of which is colored differently from the others and he is required to signal the location of that one. We should want to consider as "similar" the set of these situations generated as n ranges over the smaller integers. We should probably reject the model if they could not be put in the same set S, even if by great ingenuity we were able to find other less intuitively simple sets of situations for which the model held.

When the model is applied to experimental data we anticipate that the case of the directed graph being a single point will be identified with the intuitively "simplest" choice situation within the set of "similar" ones.

In some of the following sections we shall make the following explicit assumption as to the form of f_e:

$$f_e(t) = \begin{cases} \lambda e^{-\lambda t}, & t \geq 0, \\ 0 & , t < 0, \end{cases}$$

where λ is a positive constant. There are two grounds for supposing this might be an appropriate assumption. First, let us suppose that when no decision has been reached by time t following stimulation at time 0 then the probability that the decision will be reached between t and $t + \Delta t$, where Δt is small, is approximately proportional to Δt, with a constant of proportionality λ. In this case, it is not difficult to show that the distribution of decisions is exponential (Christie, 1952a, b). Whether this assumption is correct is an empirical problem, but it must be admitted that it has the virtue of simplicity. Second, and probably more relevant, it is a relatively common observation that as certain decision situations are made more and more simple, the observed latency is better and better approximated by an exponential distribution slightly displaced from the origin (Christie, 1952b; Luce, 1953). The main error is generally on the rising limb. If this change toward simplicity is actually toward a directed graph consisting of one point, and if our other assumptions hold, then it seems plausible that the elementary decision latency is actually exponential but that the observed distribution is smeared by the convolution of the base-time distribution and the decision-time distribution.

VI. *The Problem.* Let S be a set of choice situations which are presumed to satisfy the assumptions of the model, i.e., S is a set of the type described in Assumption II. Let f_σ denote the reaction-time distribution associated with a typical member of S. The problem is then to find distributions f_b and f_e and a set of directed graphs N_σ, where σ ranges over S, such that each of the triples (f_b, f_e, N_σ) when composed according to the assumptions of Section IV yields the distribution f_σ. There may, of course, be no, one, or many solutions to the problem, but one hopes that by an appropriate choice of S there will be exactly one solution.

It would appear that if the problem is to be solved in any degree of generality, it must be attacked somewhat indirectly. It may prove appropriate to solve first the following problem: Given a continuous distribution f, find the set of all triples (f_b, f_e, N), where f_b and f_e are continuous, which satisfy the assumptions and which compose to form f. It seems very plausible to suppose that, in general, there are many solutions to this problem. However, if f and f' are two distributions associated with choice situations from the same set S, then it will be necessary to accept only those triples with the same f_b and f_e present in both cases. Further stimulus situations should serve further to restrict the possibilities.

These problems will not be attacked, let alone solved, in this paper; they appear to be of considerable difficulty. We know of only one important lead in this direction, but we have not investigated it. In recent years, electrical engineers have been concerned with the problem of synthesizing in a systematic manner electrical networks to have preassigned transfer functions. If we identify the given reaction-time distribution with the transfer functions, the graph N with the electrical network, and f_e with component characteristic, there is an analogy between the two problems. This is probably worth investigation, but it is almost certain that solving our problem will prove to be a major research undertaking.

To some extent the problem we pose may be simplified by using some of our assumptions and the Laplace transform. Let f_σ be the observed distribution of reaction times for a given stimulus situation σ, then by Assumption II we know there exists a set S which includes σ and another stimulus situation whose directed graph consists of one point. Let f_1 denote the distribution of reaction times in the latter case. From Assumption I we may write

$$f_\sigma(t) = \int_0^t f_b(\tau)f_c(t - \tau)\,d\tau \; ,$$

$$(8)$$

$$f_1(t) = \int_0^t f_b(\tau)f_e(t - \tau)\,d\tau \; .$$

Taking the Laplace transform in each case and applying equation (2),

$$L(f_\sigma) = L(f_b)L(f_c) \; ,$$

$$L(f_1) = L(f_b)L(f_e) \; .$$

$$(9)$$

If we divide the first equation by the second in equation (9), we obtain

$$\frac{L(f_\sigma)}{L(f_1)} = \frac{L(f_c)}{L(f_e)} \; .$$

$$(10)$$

This is a fairly crucial consequence of our assumptions, for it is seen that all mention of the base time has been eliminated. It is an equation relating the empirical data to f_e and N_σ.

At this point we should raise an important practical problem. Empirically, one does not obtain estimates of the distribution f, but rather approximations to the cumulative distribution

$$F(t) = \int_0^t f(\tau)\,d\tau \; .$$

(Throughout we shall use small Latin letters to denote distributions and the corresponding capitals to denote their cumulatives.) Now, while approximations to F may be reasonably accurate, it is well known that numerical differentiation of data tends to magnify errors and is, therefore, to be avoided. So the question arises whether we can translate our results, in particular equation (10), into statements about the cumulative distributions. From equation (3) we have

$$L(f) = sL(F) + F(0) .$$

Since we are speaking of empirical data we may assume $F(0) = 0$, and so equation (10) becomes

$$\frac{L(F_\sigma)}{L(F_1)} = \frac{L(f_c)}{L(f_e)} . \tag{11}$$

Having eliminated f_b from our discussion, the problem of determining it remains. Since our division in equation (11) assumes f_b is the same in the several cases, it will suffice to determine it from any one. The simplest, of course, is the case where the graph consists of one point, in which case

$$L(f_b) = \frac{L(f_1)}{L(f_e)} = \frac{L(F_1)}{L(F_e)} . \tag{12}$$

As an example of how equation (12) may be used, suppose f_e is exponential with time constant λ. Then by equation (6),

$$L(f_e) = \frac{1}{\dfrac{s}{\lambda} + 1} ,$$

and so equation (12) becomes

$$L(f_b) = \frac{s}{\lambda} L(f_1) + L(f_1) .$$

If we make the reasonable assumption that $f_1(0) = 0$, then from equations (3) and (5) we find

$$L(f_b) = \frac{1}{\lambda} L\left(\frac{df_1}{dt}\right) + L(f_1) = L\left(\frac{1}{\lambda} \frac{df_1}{dt} + f_1\right) .$$

Assuming that f_b is continuous and that f_1 has a continuous derivative, equation (4) implies

$$f_b = \frac{1}{\lambda} \frac{df_1}{dt} + f_1 \; ,$$

or integrating from 0 to t,

$$F_b = \frac{1}{\lambda} f_1 + F_1 \; . \tag{13}$$

Since f_1 must be determined from empirical data, it is clear from equation (13) that considerable data will be necessary to obtain accurate estimates of F_b.

VII. *Serial Decision Process.* An alternative program to solving the general problem discussed in Section VI is to discover the consequences of certain explicit assumptions about the directed graph N and the elementary latency f_e. The results of this alternative program will, unfortunately, be much weaker than a solution of the general problem, but they may have considerable heuristic value. We may choose such extra assumptions on intuitive grounds, with the hope that they may be relevant for some experimental data. We shall examine two cases which are, in a sense, the two most extreme forms of the directed graph N. The first, the topic of this section, is the general serial case shown in Figure 3a, and the second, which will be discussed in Section VIII, is the parallel case shown in Figure 3b.

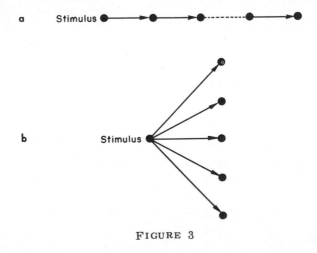

FIGURE 3

It follows immediately from Assumptions I and II.2.b that the observed distribution f_n of a serial process having n nodes is given by

$$f_n(t) = \int_0^t \cdots \int_0^{t_3} \int_0^{t_2} f_b(t_1) f_e(t_2 - t_1) \ldots f_e(t - t_n)\, dt_1\, dt_2 \ldots dt_n \,. \quad (14)$$

Applying the Laplace transform to equation (14) and using equation (2) we have

$$L(f_n) = L(f_b)L(f_e)^n \,, \quad (15)$$

or dividing by the case $n = 1$,

$$\frac{L(f_n)}{L(f_1)} = L(f_e)^{n-1} = \frac{L(F_n)}{L(F_1)} \,. \quad (16)$$

Equation (16) is the explicit form of equation (11) for the serial case. Clearly, if we have given numerical data we may determine (possibly numerically) f_e for each value of n.

As an example of how this might be done when we know the general form of f_e, suppose f_e is exponential with the time constant λ. In that case, equation (16) becomes

$$\frac{L(F_n)}{L(F_1)} = \frac{1}{\left(\dfrac{s}{\lambda} + 1\right)^{n-1}} \,. \quad (17)$$

In Figure 4 we have presented plots of $\dfrac{1}{\left(\dfrac{s}{\lambda} + 1\right)^n}$ vs. $\dfrac{s}{\lambda}$ for small values of n.

A second equation may be obtained by observing that the mean, $\mu_1(n)$, of a serial process with n exponential elementary decisions is given by

$$\mu_1(n) = \mu_1(b) + \frac{n}{\lambda} \,, \quad (18)$$

where $\mu_1(b)$ is the mean base time. Thus,

$$\mu_1(n) - \mu_1(1) = \frac{n-1}{\lambda} \,. \quad (19)$$

We may now use equations (17) and (19) to attempt to decide whether a given set of data is adequately fit by the assumptions of the model, plus the added assumptions of a serial directed graph and exponential elementary latencies. There are serious statistical questions as to how this may best be done, but the following

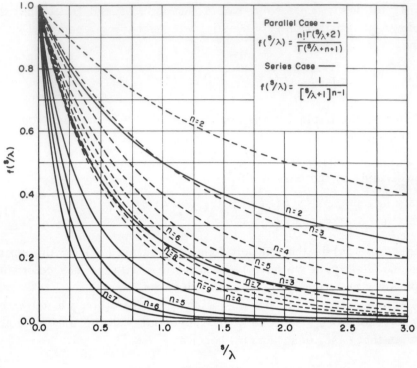

FIGURE 4

ready method may suffice until the statistical problems are formu-lated and solved. From the data we compute $\dfrac{L(F_n)}{L(F_1)}$ as a function of s; this we may assume is in the form of a plot, which we shall call plot A. For each (reasonable) value of n and for some value of $\dfrac{s}{\lambda}$, say $\dfrac{s}{\lambda} = \dfrac{1}{2}$, find in Figure 4 the corresponding value of $\dfrac{1}{\left(\dfrac{s}{\lambda}+1\right)^{n-1}}$.

We know from equation (17) that this must be equal to $\dfrac{L(F_n)}{L(F_1)}$ if our assumptions are correct and if the correct value of n has been chosen. We thus enter plot A at this point and determine the value of s. Since we selected $\lambda = 2s$, this determines λ. But equation (19) presents a relation between the observed means, λ, and n which will be satisfied if our assumptions are valid. We choose the value of n such that the error between the observed means [the left side of equation (19)] and $(n-1)/\lambda$ is a minimum; this yields the best possible fit at the point $s/\lambda = 1/2$ for the model with the added assumptions of a serial graph and exponential f_e. Using these values of λ and n, one may add the theoretical curve $\dfrac{1}{\left(\dfrac{s}{\lambda} + 1\right)^{n-1}}$ vs. s to plot A, and a comparison between the two curves will give some indication of the adequacy of the assumptions. Clearly, a less subjective criterion of the quality of this fit is needed.

VIII. *Parallel Decision Process.* If we suppose that the n elementary decision processes are carried out in parallel (see Figure 3b), the choice latency distribution is the distribution of the largest of n selections, one from each of the elementary distributions. This is known to be given by

$$\frac{d}{dt} \prod_{i=1}^{n} F_i(t) \;,$$

which in the case when all the elementary distributions are the same, namely F_e, reduces to

$$n f_e(t) [F_e(t)]^{n-1} \;.$$

If we denote the observed reaction-time distribution for the parallel case by g_n, then it follows from equation (7) that

$$g_n(t) = \int_0^t f_b(\tau) n f_e(t - \tau) [F_e(t - \tau)]^{n-1} d\tau \;. \tag{20}$$

Applying the Laplace transform and equation (2),

$$L(g_n) = L(f_b) L(n f_e F_e^{\,n-1}) \;. \tag{21}$$

As before, we may divide by $L(g_1)$ to eliminate $L(f_b)$.

To proceed further, we assume f_e is exponential, then

$$L(n f_e F_e^{\,n-1}) = n\lambda \int_0^\infty e^{-st} e^{-\lambda t} [1 - e^{-\lambda t}]^{n-1} dt \;,$$

$$= n\lambda \int_0^\infty e^{-(s + \lambda)t} \sum_{k=0}^{n-1} \binom{n-1}{k} (-1)^k e^{-k\lambda t} dt \;,$$

$$= n \sum_{k=0}^{n-1} \binom{n-1}{k} (-1)^k \frac{1}{\dfrac{s}{\lambda} + k + 1} \;.$$

To evaluate the above sum, consider the function

$$\Phi(x) = \sum_{k=0}^{n-1} \binom{n-1}{k}(-1)^k x^{\frac{s}{\lambda}} x^k = x^{\frac{s}{\lambda}}(1-x)^{n-1} .$$

Observe that

$$n\int_0^1 \Phi(x)\,dx = n\sum_{k=0}^{n-1}\binom{n-1}{k}(-1)^k \int_0^1 x^{\left(\frac{s}{\lambda}+k\right)}\,dx ,$$

$$= n\sum_{k=0}^{n-1}\binom{n-1}{k}(-1)^k \frac{1}{\frac{s}{\lambda}+k+1} ,$$

$$= L\left(nf_e F_e^{\,n-1}\right) ,$$

and that

$$n\int_0^1 \Phi(x)\,dx = n\int_0^1 x^{s/\lambda}(1-x)^{n-1}\,dx ,$$

$$= nB\left(\frac{s}{\lambda}+1,\,n\right) ,$$

$$= \frac{n\Gamma\left(\frac{s}{\lambda}+1\right)\Gamma(n)}{\Gamma\left(\frac{s}{\lambda}+n+1\right)} ,$$

where $B(m,\,n)$ is the Beta function and $\Gamma(n)$ is the Gamma function. From these results we easily obtain

$$\frac{L(g_n)}{L(g_1)} = \frac{nB\left(\frac{s}{\lambda}+1,\,n\right)}{B\left(\frac{s}{\lambda}+1,\,1\right)} ,$$

$$= \frac{n!\,\Gamma\left(\frac{s}{\lambda}+2\right)}{\Gamma\left(\frac{s}{\lambda}+n+1\right)} . \tag{22}$$

In Figure 4 we have also presented plots of $\dfrac{n!\,\Gamma\left(\frac{s}{\lambda}+2\right)}{\Gamma\left(\frac{s}{\lambda}+n+1\right)}$ vs. $\dfrac{s}{\lambda}$ for small values of n.

The mean of the parallel process can be shown to be given by

$$\mu_1(n) = \mu_1(b) + \frac{1}{\lambda} \sum_{i=1}^{n} \frac{1}{i}$$ and thus we have, as in the serial case, a

second relation which must be met

$$\mu_1(n) - \mu_1(1) = \frac{1}{\lambda} \sum_{i=2}^{n} \frac{1}{i}. \tag{23}$$

The procedure for curve fitting is the same as described for the serial case except that $\frac{s}{\lambda} = 1$ seems to be a more favorable place to enter the graph than is $\frac{s}{\lambda} = \frac{1}{2}$.

IX. *Model Selection.* Without a solution to the general problem described in Section VI, there arise statistical problems as to how well a particular set of assumptions, such as serial directed graph and exponential f_e, fit the data and whether another set of similar assumptions is better or not. In addition, within any one set of assumptions there are undetermined constants, such as λ and n, and there is a question as how best to choose them. We have indicated one procedure (end of Section VII) to determine the constants, but it is almost certain that such an *ad hoc* procedure is not optimal.

The difficulty of making a selection among different sets of assumptions is evidently quite serious for it can be seen from Figure 4 that for almost any small value of n in one there is an n' in the other such that the two curves are fairly similar. Presumably, any other directed graph will produce curves which, in some sense, lie between these two extreme cases. Thus, the shape of the empirical data curves will not be extremely revealing of the proper directed graph to use—an unfortunate situation.

It is clear that there are a number of difficult statistical problems here, but in all likelihood it will prove to be more efficient first to do some experimental exploring using subjective judgments as to goodness-of-fit before trying to formulate and to solve the statistical problems.

X. *The Perceptual Moment.* In Section II we remarked that in reaction-time studies the mean reaction time should be of the order of one second if unwanted interactions with other stimuli are to be avoided. This means that the data will be in a range where certain peculiar phenomena have been observed. To explain these observations, it has been proposed that a subject processes information very rapidly at certain discrete times and that he is in a refractory period between them. The period from the beginning of one such hypothetical event to the beginning of the next has been termed the perceptual moment (Stroud, 1949a, b). Unfortunately, relatively little direct experimentation has been conducted on this problem, and so it is not possible at this time to give a formal statement of the properties of the moment. Indeed, there are investigators who doubt its existence. In the case that it does exist, our analysis will be applied to situations where it most probably will have an effect. It is, therefore, of interest whether the analysis can be adapted to cope with it. In this section we shall make a simple hypothesis as to the nature of the moment, not with any belief that it is correct, but only to indicate that the general features of the analysis remain unchanged.

Let us assume the moment is of fixed duration, say δ seconds, and that while a person may receive information at any time during that period it will only serve as a stimulus at the end of the period. Furthermore, we will assume that all intermediate (elementary) decisions occur at multiples of δ. Since we may assume that there is no correlation between the stimulus presentation and the timing of the moment, we may assume the stimulus is presented according to a uniform distribution h in the interval 0 to δ. This assumption may be inappropriate, for it may happen that a person is only able to assimilate information during part of the moment; we shall return to this point later.

The question now arises as to the discrete form we should assume for the elementary decision process. In the continuous case we took it to be exponential, and so we shall use the discrete analogue. We assume that if no decision has been reached by the ith moment following the presentation, i.e., at time $i\delta$, then the probability of a decision in the ith moment is $\lambda\delta$. If we call the probability of a response by the ith moment P_i, then

$$P_i = P_{i-1} + [1 - P_{i-1}]\lambda\delta ,$$

$$= (1 - \lambda\delta)P_{i-1} + \lambda\delta .$$

(24)

With the initial condition $P_0 = 0$, the difference equation (24) is solved by

$$P_i = 1 - (1 - \lambda\delta)^i .$$

The probability of a decision in the ith moment is obviously

$$[1 - P_{i-1}]\lambda\delta ;$$

hence, we have

$$\lambda\delta(1 - \lambda\delta)^{i-1} , \tag{25}$$

as our distribution f_e.

If we replace this discrete distribution, equation (25), by a continuous one Φ_ϵ which has rectangles of width ϵ and height $\dfrac{\lambda\delta(1 - \lambda\delta)^{i-1}}{\epsilon}$ centered about the point $i\delta$, then it is clear that in the limit as $\epsilon \to o$ this becomes the discrete distribution.

Let the base-time distribution be denoted by f_b as before, then the observed data in the discrete serial case is given by

$$f_n(t) = \lim_{\epsilon \to o} \int_0^t \cdots \int_0^t \int_0^t f_b(t_1) h(t_2 - t_1) \Phi_\epsilon(t_3 - t_2) \cdots$$
$$\tag{26}$$
$$\Phi_\epsilon(t - t_{n+1}) dt_1 \cdots dt_{n+1} .$$

Applying the Laplace transform and using equation (2),

$$L(f_n) = \lim_{\epsilon \to o} L(f_b) L(h) L(\Phi_\epsilon)^n = L(f_b) L(h) \left[\lim_{\epsilon \to o} L(\Phi_\epsilon) \right]^n . \tag{27}$$

Observe,

$$L(\Phi_\epsilon) = \int e^{-st} \Phi_\epsilon(t) dt ,$$

$$= \sum_{i=1}^\infty \int_{i\delta - \frac{\epsilon}{2}}^{i\delta + \frac{\epsilon}{2}} e^{-st} \frac{\lambda\delta(1 - \lambda\delta)^{i-1}}{\epsilon} dt ,$$

$$= \frac{e^{\frac{s}{2}\epsilon} - e^{-\frac{s}{2}\epsilon}}{s\epsilon} \sum_{i=1}^\infty \lambda\delta(1 - \lambda\delta)^{i-1} e^{-is\delta} ,$$

$$= \frac{e^{\frac{s}{2}\epsilon} - e^{-\frac{s}{2}\epsilon}}{s\epsilon} \lambda\delta(1 - \lambda\delta)^{-1} \sum_{i=1}^\infty \{(1 - \lambda\delta) e^{-s\delta}\}^i .$$

But,

$$\lim_{\epsilon \to o} \frac{e^{\frac{s}{2}\epsilon} - e^{-\frac{s}{2}\epsilon}}{s\epsilon} = 1 \; ,$$

so,

$$\lim_{\epsilon \to o} L(\Phi_\epsilon) = \frac{\lambda \delta e^{-s\delta}}{1 - (1 - \lambda\delta) e^{-s\delta}} \; .$$

Substituting in equation (27) and dividing by the case $n = 1$, we have

$$\frac{L(f_n)}{L(f_1)} = \left[\frac{\lambda \delta e^{-s\delta}}{1 - (1 - \lambda\delta) e^{-s\delta}} \right]^{n-1} , \qquad (28)$$

which is the crucial equation for the discrete serial case. The mean of the discrete distribution f_e is given by

$$\sum_{i=1}^{\infty} i\delta\lambda\delta (1 - \lambda\delta)^{i-1} = \frac{1}{\lambda} \; . \qquad (29)$$

Thus, the relation between observed means is

$$\mu_1(n) - \mu_1(1) = \frac{n-1}{\lambda} \; . \qquad (30)$$

Now, if we know the value of δ, i.e., the length of the moment, then these two sets of equations may be used in exactly the same fashion as were equations (17) and (19) of Section VII. We have no theoretical value of δ, so it will be necessary to perform independent measurements of it. It is clear that if the perceptual moment is a real phenomenon it will be important to ascertain its properties prior to analyzing experiments on reaction time.

One further comment of some interest: If we ignore f_b and let $n = 1$, the convolution of h and Φ_ϵ, when $\epsilon \to 0$, is a step function such as that shown in Figure 5. The convolution of this function with f_b, for reasonable f_b, will serve to smear the steps but it will not utterly destroy them. Smearing will also result if n is larger than 1, the amount depending on the value of n. Thus, if our assumption as to the moment is roughly correct, we should expect, at least for comparatively simple situations, to find the observed latency distribution somewhat lumpy. Indeed, in the literature (cf. Woodworth, 1938) it has been remarked not only that the data are lumpy but that there is an oscillation superimposed on the distribu-

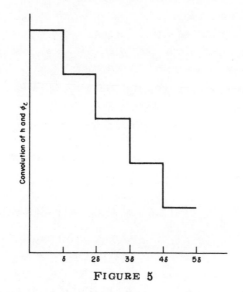

FIGURE 5

tion curve. This effect could easily be obtained analytically if we were to assume h uniform over only a small portion of the interval 0 to δ, in other words, if we assume the vast majority of the moment is truly a refractory period during which there is no intake of information. These considerations bring out even more strongly the need for comprehensive experiments to determine the properties of the moment.

We shall not attempt, as before, to study the parallel case. The reasons are that the mathematical problem is rather complex and with so little information on the nature of the moment it hardly seems worthwhile to carry out the analysis. Furthermore, we are of the opinion that it is unlikely that information accepted in different moments is dealt with other than serially. It may happen, however, that the information accepted in one moment is processed in parallel. The latter remark is a possible hint for developing an explanation of the effect of changing the number of "psychological dimensions" in an information display.

XI. *Experimental Proposals.* The key assumption in our analysis is that elementary decision processes can be found of such a sort that complex decisions can be built up from them in a way which leaves their characteristic λ value invariant. One should like to present experimental subjects with stimuli which vary in several dimensions but for which decisions on each of the dimensions have identical time characteristics. If one uses conceptually different dimensions, we run into the difficulty of possibly introducing several different λ values. If we use several objects with the same dimension relevant for each and with identical characteristics in every other respect, we have the difficulty that the reception of the stimulus may not be unitary, but broken down into several parts separated by receptor orienting acts such as eye movements. The first of the two following proposals suffers from the latter difficulty; the second from the former.

1st Experiment: Digit Difference Perception

Stimuli: White 3" × 5" cards with a triple-spaced typed, horizontal row of vertically aligned pairs of digits, 0 and 1, on each. The number of pairs per card to vary from one to sixteen. On each card either one pair or no pairs will be unlike digits, i.e., (0,1) or (1,0); the remainder like pairs, i.e., (1,1) or (0,0). The place of the unlike pair in the series of pairs to vary from the initial to the final position. Cards with the unlike pair in each of the positions from one to n will be included in the set with equal frequency, and cards with no unlike pair will be included with the same frequency. The assignment of (1,1) or (0,0) to the remaining places will be made on an equiprobable random basis, and the choice of (0,1) or (1,0) for the unlike pair will be made on the same basis.

Responses: Experimenter will announce prior to each stimulus presentation how many pairs the card to be shown bears. Subject will respond *yes* or *no*, depending on whether the card does or does not bear an unlike pair, by pressing the appropriate one of two keys. The subject will be told that an unlike pair in each of the possible positions, including in *no* position, are equally likely events, and will be instructed to read the lines of pairs from left to right. The data of primary interest will be the latencies of the *no* response to the cards which bear no unlike pair and the latencies of the *yes* response to the cards which bear an unlike pair in the nth position.

Apparatus: 1. Stimulus cards as described above,
                2. Light projector with fast shutter,

3. Three telegraph keys: (a) for the subjects to rest their fingers on prior to response so that the response will always start from the same situation. (b) for *yes* responses (c) for *no* responses.
4. A buzzer of ½ sec duration as a warning signal to be sounded ending 1 sec before shutter opens to illuminate stimulus.
5. Recording chronoscope accurate to at least ± 10 millisec.
6. Timer for ready signal and shutter operation with silent starting key for the experimenter.

2nd Experiment: Multi-attribute Perception

Stimuli: Ten decks of 32 cards each to be prepared using two values on each of five attributes according to the following scheme:

Attribute	Values
1. Number of spots	2; 3
2. Color of spots	Red; black
3. Shape of spots	Round; square
4. Arrangement of spots	Horizontal line; vertical line
5. Background color	White; green

Responses: Experimenter will announce what pattern of attributes is to be responded to positively prior to each stimulus presentation. Subject to make a *yes* or *no* response by pressing the appropriate one of two keys as exemplified below:

Experimenter Says	Stimulus Presented	S to Respond
1. Round red	Two black squares in horizontal line on white card	No
2. Vertical line of squares on green card	Three red squares in vertical line on green card	Yes

The instruction-stimulus pairs which call for a negative response should be half of the total number of stimuli presented in each attribute-pattern category so that the uncertainty of response prior to stimulus presentation will be equalized at the maximum. The data of primary interest will be the latencies of response to the set-stimulus pairs calling for a *yes* response.

Apparatus: Same as for the first experiment except for the stimulus cards.

LITERATURE

Christie, L. S. 1952a. "The Measurement of Discriminative Behavior." *Psychol. Rev.*, **59**, 443–52.

Christie, L. S., R. D. Luce, and J. Macy, Jr. 1952b. "Communication and Learning in Task-Oriented Groups." (Technical Report No. 231.) Cambridge: Research Laboratory of Electronics, Massachusetts Institute of Technology.

Churchill, R. V. 1944. *Modern Operational Mathematics in Engineering.* New York: McGraw Hill.

Luce, R. D., J. Macy, Jr., L. S. Christie, and H. Hay. 1953. "Information Flow in Task-Oriented Groups." (Technical Report No. 264.) Cambridge: Research Laboratory of Electronics, Massachusetts Institute of Technology.

Stroud, J. B. 1949a. "The Moment Function Hypothesis." M. S. Thesis. Stanford University.

Stroud, J. B. 1949b. "The Psychological Moment in Perception." H. von Forrester, Ed. *Sixth Conference on Cybernetics*, Josiah Macy, Jr. Foundation, 27–63.

Woodworth, R. S. 1938. *Experimental Psychology.* New York: Holt.

RECEIVED 5-5-55

PSYCHOACOUSTICS AND DETECTION THEORY*†

David M. Green

MASSACHUSETTS INSTITUTE OF TECHNOLOGY,
CAMBRIDGE, MASSACHUSETTS

This paper presents a fairly complete review of detection theory as it is applied to certain psychoacoustic data. Detection theory is treated as a combination of two theoretical structures: decision theory and the concept of ideal observer. The paper discusses how statistical decision theory has been used to analyze the auditory threshold process. By treating the threshold process as an instance of hypothesis testing, two determinants of the process are recognized: (1) the detectability of the signal and (2) the criterion level of the observer. The theory provides a technic of analysis which allows one to obtain a quantitative estimate of both factors. The measure of signal detectability appears to be independent of the psychophysical procedure when the physical parameters of signal and noise are held constant. The concept of ideal observer is reviewed with special emphasis on the assumptions of the derivation. The usefulness of this concept is illustrated by considering the shape of the psychophysical function—the function relating the detectability of the signal to its intensity. A rather general model based on the concept of signal uncertainty is presented which attempts to explain this relationship.

Introduction

There are two very striking characteristics of the field of psychoacoustics. One is the breadth and variety of research skills and techniques used to study hearing. The techniques range from hydrodynamic studies of the cochlea to analysis of the perception of vowel forms. This multidisciplinary approach is a fortunate one since it reduces the chances that any really significant aspect of the sensory system is being overlooked. However, it creates a diversity which makes integration of these areas most difficult.

A second characteristic of the field is the lack of any integrative structure from which to view the rapidly expanding experimental literature. If some basic theoretical structure existed, these new data might easily be integrated with the old. Psychoacoustics, however, does not have any complete comprehensive theory. A reflection of this deficit is the lack of consensus on methodology. Often, even where a general consensus seems to exist in some area of the field, a new paper may force a complete re-examination of the entire measurement procedure. A recent example of the latter

This article appeared in *J. Acoust. Soc. Amer.*, 1960, **32**, 1189–1203. Reprinted with permission.

* *Editor's Note.*—This is the first of a series of tutorial papers on aspects of acoustics of recent interest. Its publication is supported in part by a grant from the National Science Foundation. Other papers of this kind will follow in subsequent issues.

† This paper was partially supported by the U.S. Air Force under contract, monitored by the Operational Applications Office, Air Force Cambridge Research Center, Laurance G. Hanscom Field, Bedford, Massachusetts, and administered by the Research Laboratory of Electronics, M.I.T. This is Tech. Rept. No. AFCCDD TR-60-20.

may be found in the exchanges of Garner[1] and Stevens[2] on the quantitative scale of loudness. Such a situation compounds the problem of integration.

This paper, therefore, makes no attempt at broad coverage. The author hopes that by concentrating on one rather limited topic some positive contribution can be made. This topic is the detection of signals in noise. In recent years a general theoretical structure (detection theory) has been used to analyze such experiments. Unfortunately, there appears to be some confusion both about the theory itself and the manner of its application. The main objective of this paper will be to clarify these two questions. Part of the confusion about the theory arises from the fact that detection theory is a combination of two distinct theoretical structures: decision theory and the theory of ideal observers. Before we begin a detailed discussion of these two aspects of detection theory, we will briefly outline them and relate them to psychoacoustic problems.

Decision theory provides an analysis of the process which generates the dichotomy between stimuli the subject reports he does and does not hear. The theory recognizes that *a priori* probabilities, *values*, and *costs* of correct and incorrect decisions, as well as the physical parameters of the signal, play a decisive role in establishing this dichotomy. We will find that this dichotomy is determined by an adjustable criterion. The theory shows how a quantitative estimate of the criterion can be obtained from the data.

There are many psychoacousticians whose only interest in this criterion is as a constant parameter from which to obtain substantive relations between two physical parameters, for example, the absolute threshold energy as a function of frequency, or the just detectable change in power as a function of power (ΔI vs I). To them this aspect of detection theory will be of methodological interest only. Yet clearly, if factors such as *a priori* probability, *values*, and *costs* do play a role in determining the threshold, their control in substantive experiments is imperative.

The second part of detection theory is more directly related to substantive matters—it is the theory of ideal observers. Briefly, the theory provides a collection of ideal mathematical models which relates the detectability of the signal to definite physical characteristics of the stimulus. There is a collection of such models because one may make different restrictions on the nature of the detection device. These theoretical observers are rarely used as actual models of the hearing mechanism. Most often, they are used for the sake of comparing human performance with that of the ideal observer in order to specify the nature and amount of discrepancy. This comparison, in turn, suggests either a new and hopefully more accurate representation of the hearing mechanism, or new experiments to clarify further the exact nature of the discrepancy. This will be illustrated in a later section of the paper.

Decision Theory

We shall demonstrate, under quite general assumptions, how a transformation of the subject's responses can be utilized to determine both the subject's criterion and the detectability of the signal. This analysis requires an understanding of several basic concepts which are rather complex. We might skip over these fundamentals and start,

---

[1] W. R. Garner, *J. Acoust. Soc. Am.*, 1958, **30**, 1005.
[2] S. S. Stevens, *J. Acoust. Soc. Am.*, 1959, **31**, 995.

as some previous expositions have, with some assumptions about Gaussian distributions and parameters of these distributions. Such a procedure would be unfortunate because it robs the analysis of its generality and implies that strong assumptions are needed to justify its applicability. Such is not the case.

Typically, psychoacousticians try to analyze the subject's responses by making some assumptions about the way in which the sound is processed by the hearing mechanism. One assumes, for example, that the cochlea either makes a frequency analysis of the waveform or that it does not, etc. We wish to postpone temporarily such substantive issues. Let us, for the present, merely assume that each sound may be represented by a series of numbers. These numbers might be the values of a series of attributes, or various states of the nervous system. Whatever the representation, let us call this abstraction an *observation*.

The problem we wish to consider is this: Given an observation, what response alternative should be chosen? What is a good choice and how can we analyze these choices? We shall attempt to answer these questions by considering a single example. The example is obviously specific; the generality rests in the concepts. The single motive in presenting this example is to enable us to discuss these concepts—*likelihood ratio, decision rule*, and *criterion*—with some precision and yet avoid formalism.[3-5] After this theoretical discussion, we shall investigate the applicability of these concepts to a psychoacoustic experiment.

An example of decision theory

Let us assume we have 10 observations, each observation (X_i) represented by three numbers [$X_i = (x_1, x_2, x_3)$], and that we have two hypotheses, H_1, H_2, about the observations. Given an observation, we wish to decide whether the observation is an instance of H_1 or H_2.[6] We shall assume we have complete information about the probability of each observation given each hypothesis.

By limiting the example to 10 observations we can work with probabilities directly. The reader should note that the three numbers (x_1, x_2, x_3) could have been extended to three hundred. Everything that follows is independent of the dimensionality of the observation. The variables (x) of the observation could be quantitative (integers or real numbers) or qualitative (red, blue, or green). They are simply descriptions of the observation.

Likelihood ratio. In Table I, we have listed the observations and the three numbers corresponding to each observation. The next two columns provide the data

[3] These concepts come from the topic of statistical decision theory and the theory of inference. Most of the key theorems were first presented by Wald, who extended the basic principle which originated with Neyman and Pearson.

[4] A. Wald, *Statistical decision functions*, New York: Wiley, 1950.

[5] J. Neyman and E. S. Pearson, *Phil. Trans. Roy. Soc. London*, 1933, **A231**, 289.

[6] For a concrete interpretation of the example, the reader might think of the observation as a sealed package, the three numbers as the length, width, and depth of the package, and the hypothesis as whether the package contains a toy car or animal. The problem, then, is this: Given the measurements of a package, guess whether it contains a car or an animal. Alternatively, one might think of the observation as a sound which can be specified by three numbers or attributes. The problem is: Decide from the three numbers whether the sound is a consonant or a vowel.

TABLE I

Description of the Observations (X_i) and the Probability of Obtaining
That Observation Given Either Hypothesis (H_1 or H_2).

Observation	x_1	x_2	x_3	$P_{H_1}(x_1, x_2, x_3)$	$P_{H_2}(x_1, x_2, x_3)$	$l(x_1, x_2, x_3)$ $= \dfrac{P_{H_1}(x_1, x_2, x_3)}{P_{H_2}(x_1, x_2, x_3)}$
X_1	4	3	3	0.14	0.01	14.00
X_2	3	3	5	0.01	0.01	1.00
X_3	2	2	4	0.03	0.30	0.10
X_4	3	3	3	0.30	0.10	3.00
X_5	2	3	3	0.02	0.04	0.50
X_6	5	2	2	0.09	0.01	9.00
X_7	2	5	5	0.10	0.08	1.25
X_8	3	4	5	0.20	0.05	4.00
X_9	3	2	5	0.06	0.30	0.20
X_{10}	4	2	5	0.05	0.10	0.50
			Total	1.00	1.00	

on the probabilities of each observation on each hypothesis. The final column is simply the ratio of the fifth column to the sixth and represents the likelihood ratio. The likelihood ratio, then, is the probability that a particular observation resulted from H_1 divided by the probability that it resulted from H_2. The likelihood ratio gives what some call the "odds." If we have (X_6) we should be willing to wager nine cents to one that H_1 is correct. Note that the likelihood ratio is a *number*, not a probability, and that this number is a function of three variables (x_1, x_2, x_3). Thus we have taken an observation which is specified by three values (x_1, x_2, x_3), and related it to a single variable $l(x_1, x_2, x_3)$.

The reason we have performed this transformation is simply stated: We can make optimum decisions if we use the likelihood ratio. We have not stated what we mean by optimum, but let us take up this point a little later. First, let us show how we might use the likelihood ratio in making decisions.

Decision rule. If someone asks us to make a decision about a particular observation, whether it is an instance of H_1 or H_2, we would probably guess it was H_1 if the probability of that observation was greater on H_1 than on H_2. Such a statement is called a decision rule. In terms of likelihood ratio this decision can be expressed as follows: Choose H_1 if $l(X) \geqslant 1$. In effect, we have specified our decision rule by choosing one number; in this case, the number "one." This number is called a criterion or, more precisely, a likelihood-ratio criterion.

Suppose that, independent of any specific observation, H_2 was ten times as likely as H_1. Clearly, we would not maintain our previous criterion; even without knowing the characteristics of the observation, the odds are ten to one in favor of H_2. It turns out in this case that we should choose H_1 only if $l(X) \geqslant 10$. That is, we should choose H_1 only if, in our example, the specific observation is $X = (4, 3, 3)$.

Similarly, if we place asymmetrical values and costs on the various correct and incorrect decisions, we should change our criterion or likelihood ratio accordingly.

Monotonic functions of likelihood ratio. While we can state our decision procedure in terms of likelihood ratio, there are other exactly equivalent ways of stating
the decision rules. In the example, it so happens that the product x_1 times x_2 minus x_3
is also an optimum decision quantity. This is true because this quantity is monotonic
with the likelihood ratio. The criterion number is not the same as that we would use
on a likelihood-ratio scale, but there is always some number on this monotonic scale
which corresponds to the criterion number on likelihood ratio. For example, suppose
we select the alternative H_1 if $l(x_1, x_2, x_3) \geqslant 1.25$; then we would make identical
decisions using the decision rule, select H_1 if $(x_1 \cdot x_2 - x_3) \geqslant 5.00$.

In many cases, such as the application of this theory to psychoacoustics, the
decision axis is unobservable, and hence we are only interested in equivalent decision
procedures. To say the observer uses an optimum decision procedure means only that
he is using a monotonic transformation of likelihood ratio.

Optimum nature of likelihood ratio. We turn now to the very important question of the optimum nature of likelihood ratio. Clearly a decision procedure based on
likelihood ratio is only optimum if it best attains some specific objective. Let us list
some of these objectives to indicate their generality: (1) maximize the expected value
of decisions,[7] (2) minimize risk,[8] (3) estimate *a posteriori* probability,[9] (4) maximize the
percentage of correct decisions,[8] and (5) set the error rate on some decision alternative at some constant and maximize the number of correct decisions for the other
alternative.[5] The impressive fact is that a decision criterion based on likelihood ratio is
optimum under all the above objectives. Naturally this criterion may be different for
different objectives. The references listed with the objectives contain a more detailed
explanation of each objective and prove how a decision rule based on likelihood ratio,
or some monotonic transformation of that quantity, may be used to make the best
decisions.[10]

Distribution of likelihood ratio. We have seen how each observation, independent of the number of attributes included in the observation, can be reduced to a single
quantity—likelihood ratio. Likelihood ratio is simply a function of several variables
and for any single observation is simply a number. We may then properly consider a
probability defined on the variable likelihood ratio. Let us consider, in particular, the
probability that we shall obtain a particular value of likelihood ratio under H_1 and H_2
of the preceding example. Table II shows these probabilities and the corresponding
cumulative distributions for both hypotheses of our example. The likelihood ratio is
ranked from largest to smallest to facilitate the explanation of the *ROC* curve.[11]

ROC curves and their properties. We shall use Table II to construct an *ROC*
(Receiver Operating Characteristic) curve. To do this, let us assume the decision rule
is to accept H_1 if $l(x_1, x_2, x_3) \geqslant k$. If $k = 14$ we find that the probability of accepting

[7] W. W. Peterson, T. G. Birdsall, and W. C. Fox, *Trans. IRE*, 1954, **PGIT-4**, 171.

[8] T. W. Anderson, *An introduction to multivariate statistical analysis*, New York:
Wiley, 1958.

[9] P. M. Woodward, *Probability and information theory with applications to radar*,
New York: McGraw-Hill, 1955.

[10] To estimate *a posteriori* probability no criterion is involved. In this case the best
estimate of *a posteriori* probability is a simple monotonic transformation of likelihood ratio.

[11] Note that since two observations yield a likelihood ratio of 0.50, we have added the
probabilities under both hypotheses to obtain the probability of that likelihood ratio.

TABLE II

Probability under Each Hypothesis that
$l(X)$ Will Have a Certain Value.

$l(X)$	$P_{H_1}[l(X)]$	Cumulative	$P_{H_2}[l(X)]$	Cumulative
14.00	0.14	0.14	0.01	0.01
9.00	0.09	0.23	0.01	0.02
4.00	0.20	0.43	0.05	0.07
3.00	0.30	0.73	0.10	0.17
1.25	0.10	0.83	0.08	0.25
1.00	0.01	0.84	0.01	0.26
0.50	0.07	0.91	0.14	0.40
0.20	0.06	0.97	0.30	0.70
0.10	0.03	1.00	0.30	1.00

H_1 when it is true [$P_{H_1}(H_1)$] is 0.14 and the probability of accepting H_1 when it is false [$P_{H_2}(H_1)$] is 0.01. By decreasing k, we change both probabilities. The upper curve shown in Fig. 1 shows how the probabilities change as a function of k, and is called an *ROC* curve. The two probabilities completely represent the stimulus-response matrix in a two-alternative detection task since the complements of $P_{H_1}(H_1)$ and $P_{H_2}(H_1)$ are the two remaining cells in the stimulus-response matrix.

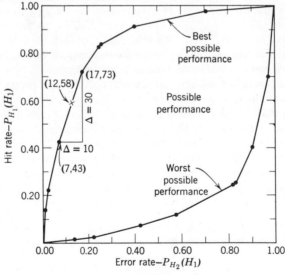

FIGURE 1

The receiver operating characteristic (*ROC*) curve of the example. The axes are $P_{H_1}(H_1)$, which is the probability of responding H_1 if the observation was from H_1, and $P_{H_2}(H_1)$, which is the probability of responding H_1 if the observation was from H_2. The points were plotted from Table II.

What if some decision procedure which is less than optimum were used? Let us consider an extremely poor decision procedure. The lower curve of the figure was generated by using the decision rule accepting H_1 if $l(x_1, x_2, x_3) \leqslant k$ for all k. This is the exact opposite of the first decision rule and hence generates the *ROC* curve for the worst possible decision rule.

The area included between the upper and lower bounds on performance represents attainable performance using any decision procedure in this task. Obviously any single decision is either right or wrong, but any decision rule whatever, in the long run, will produce some probability of "hit" and some probability of "miss" which lie within the bounds illustrated.[12] Other decision procedures do not necessarily involve likelihood ratio. One procedure would be to flip a coin and select the first alternative if the coin landed heads; if the coin were unbiased, this decision rule would achieve an error and hit rate of 0.5 Should the coin be biased, this decision procedure would produce performance located somewhere along the center diagonal of Fig. 1.

Another point to be noted involves the slope of the *ROC* curve based on the optimum decision axis. Notice that the slope between any two consecutive points is equal to the likelihood ratio of the higher point. Thus the slope must clearly diminish because each successive point represents a lower value for likelihood ratio. Any *ROC* curve which does not show a monotonically decreasing slope implies an incorrect decision rule. This means that the decision maker is accepting the first hypothesis when the likelihood exceeds a certain value and yet accepting the other hypothesis when likelihood ratio is some greater value. Any such inversion in slope for any *ROC* curve implies that better performance might be achieved by interchanging some of the points on the decision axis.

ROC curve and percent correct using forced choice. The *ROC* curve is useful in a situation where the subject's response is limited to selecting one or the other alternative. There are other ways in which the detection task may be structured; one involves the class of forced-choice procedures. For simplicity, we will consider a two-alternative forced-choice task. The extension to larger numbers of alternatives should be clear from the following discussion. A two alternative forced-choice procedure is one in which two stimuli are presented, one from each class, and the subject is asked, in effect, what was the order of the stimuli: H_1H_2 or H_2H_1?

We shall calculate the probability of a correct decision based on the following rule: Select the alternative H_1H_2 if the likelihood ratio on the first observation is greater than on the second. In effect, this rule says to pick the larger likelihood ratio and say H_1 for that observation. The reason for considering only this particular decision rule is that this assumption is often made in the analysis of forced-choice tests.[13]

Assuming the subject picks the larger of two likelihood ratios and says the

---

[12] It should also be noted that the lines connecting the points in the *ROC* curve do in fact represent attainable performance. For example, a point located midway between the points (7, 43) and (17, 73) is attainable by using a mixed-decision procedure, where H_1 is accepted if $l(X) > 3$, each alternative is selected half the time by some random procedure if $l(X) = 3$, and H_2 is selected if $l(X) < 3$.

[13] Were we to give a complete analysis of this situation we would first list all possible stimulus pairs (S_iS_j). Next we would consider the probabilities on the hypothesis that the pairs represented instances of H_1H_2 or H_2H_1, compute a likelihood ratio, and, in fact, derive an *ROC* curve based on these computations.

TABLE III

Calculation of the Probability of a Correct Response
in a Forced-Choice Test.

k	$P_{H_1}[l_1(X) = k]$	$P_{H_2}[l_2(X) < k]$	Product
14	0.14	0.99	0.1386
9	0.09	0.98	0.0882
4	0.20	0.93	0.1860
3	0.30	0.83	0.2490
1.25	0.10	0.75	0.0750
1.00	0.01	0.74	0.0074
0.50	0.07	0.60	0.0420
0.20	0.06	0.30	0.0180
0.10	0.03	0.00	0.0000
		Sum	0.8042

likelihood ratio was produced by H_1, we shall be correct if the larger likelihood was in fact produced by H_1 and the smaller was in fact produced by H_2. The probability of this occurrence is $P_{H_1}[l_1(X)] \cdot P_{H_2}[l_2(X)]$ where $l_1(X) > l_2(X)$. In fact, if the larger likelihood ratio is equal to k, the probability of a correct choice is simply: $P_{H_1}[l(X) = k] \cdot \Sigma_i P_{H_2}[l_i(X) < k]$.[14] To obtain the final result we need only summate over all the values of k, since any of these values might be the largest, except the lowest value of likelihood ratio itself.

Table III gives these calculations and the final answer (0.8042). While the method of calculating this probability is straightforward, often, especially in psychoacoustic experiments, one does not have numerical distributions on a likelihood-ratio scale. Two approaches could be used in these situations. The first, and the safest, since it makes no additional assumptions, would be to compute the probability from an experimentally determined ROC curve. If you look at Table III closely, you will see that the quantities used in the calculation are simply $\Delta P_{H_1}(H_1)$ times $[1 - P_{H_2}(H_1)]$ for each successive point on the ROC curve (Fig. 1). Obviously, the accuracy of such a procedure is heavily determined by the accuracy of the experimental estimate of the ROC curve. The merit of the technique is that no assumptions beyond that of the decision rule are necessary to predict forced-choice behavior from the ROC data.

A second procedure, one which has often been used, is to make some assumptions about the distributions which generated the ROC curve and then use these assumptions in predicting behavior in the forced-choice experiment. The most popular set of assumptions is that the distribution of observations on the likelihood-ratio axis, or some monotonic function of that axis, is normal or Gaussian under both hypotheses. The distributions are assumed to differ only in their means and, sometimes, in their standard deviations. Let us assume, for simplicity, that standard deviations are equal under both hypotheses, then the ROC curve can be characterized by one parameter;

[14] If more than two, say M, alternatives are used in the forced-choice test, the equation becomes

$$P(\text{correct}) = \sum_k P_{H_1}(l = k)\left[\sum_i P_{H_2}(l_i < k)\right]^{M-1}.$$

the difference in the means divided by the standard deviation ($\Delta M/\sigma$). This parameter is usually denoted by $d' = \Delta M/\sigma$. The calculations of the probability of a correct detection in a two-alternative forced-choice situation if these assumptions are made are quite simple. The probability that one likelihood is larger than another is the probability that the difference is greater than zero. Since, by assumption, some transformation of $l(X)$ is normal, the difference distribution is normal with a mean of ΔM and a variance equal to the sum of the original variances. Hence the probability of a correct decision is

$$P(\text{correct, 2 alternative}) = \Phi[\Delta M/(\sigma_1^2 + \sigma_2^2)^{\frac{1}{2}}] = \Phi[d'/(2)^{\frac{1}{2}}].$$

The probability of being correct for any number of alternatives is given in footnote reference 15.

We have now reviewed all the essential aspects of how detection theory uses decision theory in analyzing the process of detection. Let us now turn to some experimental results and see to what extent these notions are supported. Following this review of the experimental studies, we shall conclude this section with a discussion of the implications of these studies for psychoacoustic procedures in general.

Experimental results

ROC curve. One of the earlier studies[16] simply sought to determine experimentally the shape of the *ROC* curve in a simple psychoacoustic task. The signal was a 1/10 second of a 1000-cps sinusoid. White noise, the masking stimulus, was present continuously throughout the experimental session. A light occurred to mark the observation interval. During this interval either the signal was added to the noise (SN) or simply the noise was presented (N): these were the two hypotheses of the detection task. The subject gave one of two possible responses; he pressed one button if he believed the signal was present ("yes") or pressed a second button if he believed no signal was present ("no"). The physical parameters of the situation, including noise and signal levels, were held constant. The independent variable was the probability (*a priori*) of a signal being present. Five levels of *a priori* probability were selected (0.1, 0.3, 0.5, 0.7, 0.9) and the one used for a given session of 300 observations was announced to the subject. After the subject responded, he was given immediate information as to whether or not the signal had in fact been presented. The subject was awarded some fraction of a cent for each correct answer and fined an equal amount for each incorrect answer. He was instructed to make as much money as possible.

The results for one of the subjects are presented in Fig. 2. [$P_N(A)$ is the probability of saying "yes" when noise alone was presented.] The general trend of the data supports the decision-theory analysis. The curve drawn is generated by assuming the distributions on likelihood ratio are normal under both hypotheses. The normalized difference between the means is 0.92.

Threshold model and the ROC curve. Before considering whether or not the subjects adopted the proper criterion so as actually to maximize their payoff, let us consider one alternative explanation of the data. This is the so-called threshold model.

[15] P. B. Elliott, Electronic Defense Group, University of Michigan, Technical Report No. 97, 1959.

[16] W. P. Tanner, J. A. Swets, and D. M. Green, Electronic Defense Group, University of Michigan, Technical Report No. 30, 1956.

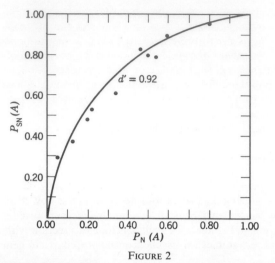

FIGURE 2

A sample of the *ROC* curve from an auditory detection experiment. See footnote 16. $P_N(A)$ is the probability of responding "yes" when noise alone was presented. $P_{SN}(A)$ is the probability of saying "yes" when signal-plus-noise was presented. These probabilities were estimated from the stimulus-response matrix. See text for details of the experiment.

The essentials of this model are that the signal, when added to the noise, augments some process within the organism, such that if the increment reaches a critical level called the threshold, the signal is heard and can be correctly detected. So far, we note no great difference with the decision-theory analysis except in semantics. If one calls the decision-theory criterion a threshold and the hypothetical process likelihood ratio, the correspondence is complete. The differences between the models appear when one considers "subthreshold" events and the procedures used to deal with these events. The threshold model assumes that should the signal increment fail to reach the threshold, the subject can only make a pure guess as to whether or not the signal is present. This is surely true since anything below the threshold is just that. If ordering is preserved below the threshold, the word has no meaning. The difference in terminology between criterion and threshold is important, for to say the subject adopts a criterion is to simply say an arbitrary cut point on a continuum is used as the decision rule.

Given that the subject guesses about events which are "subthreshold," he may, if blanks are ever employed, report the signal is present when it is not (false positive response). Two techniques, both consistent with the threshold assumption, might be employed if this occurs. One procedure widely used is to instruct the subject to be more careful; this can be interpreted as an attempt to instruct the subject to respond negatively to all "subthreshold" events. The implication of this procedure will be discussed in a later section. Another procedure, equally valid from the assumptions of this model, would be to employ a correction for guessing. This correction procedure assumes the guessing mechanism and the sensory mechanisms are independent. The excellent experiments of Smith and Wilson[17] were the first, I believe, to show the inadequacy of this second procedure. This fact led them to reconsider the entire notion

[17] M. Smith and E. A. Wilson, *Psychol. Monogr.*, 1953, **67,** Whole No. 359.

of the threshold and they presented, as an alternative model, one very similar to that suggested by decision-theory analysis. (See especially Sec. IV, footnote 17.) Munson and Karlin,[18] using an information-theory analysis, investigated the detection process under "absolute threshold conditions." In order to deal with false positive responses, they proposed a "discriminant level model." This model is also very similar to that suggested by decision-theory analysis.

The threshold model could still attempt to account for the data shown in Fig. 2. The argument would run as follows: Suppose the subject achieves some hit and false-alarm rate. If the situation is changed in some way, he can modify his behavior by simply giving more "yes" responses. Since this guessing rate is independent of the stimulus conditions (both noise and signal-plus-noise events are below the threshold) this will increase, by the same *relative* amounts, both the hit and false-alarm rates. In short, a linear function will result. In the extreme, the subject says "yes" all the time, hence this linear function must go through the point in the upper right-hand corner $[P_N(A) = 1.00, P_{SN}(A) = 1.00]$. Thus the threshold prediction for the data is a collection of lines having the upper right-hand corner as the common intercept, and a slope depending upon the detectability of the signal. No linear function which has this intercept as one value can fit more than a few of the data points for any value of the slope. The results of this first experiment, then, seriously conflict with this version of the threshold model and give some measure of support to the decision-theory analysis.

The conflict between some version of the threshold model and the decision analysis has been the subject of considerable experimental effort. There are other experimental results more damaging to the threshold position. These experiments attack the threshold concept directly because they suggest that ordering below the threshold value is indeed possible.[16] We shall drop this conflict and proceed to other questions.

Actual criterion and optimum criterion. Let us now return to the results displayed in Fig. 2 and discuss the question of the optimum criterion. It turns out that if one wishes to select an optimum criterion on likelihood ratio, it is equal to $\beta = P(N)/P(SN)$, where β is the criterion value on likelihood ratio and $P(N)$ and $P(SN)$ are the *a priori* probabilities of noise alone and signal-plus-noise, respectively. We can, of course, obtain a rough measure of the subject's criterion by measuring the slope of the *ROC* curve at the point nearest the experimental data point. This rough comparison is displayed in Fig. 3. Note that while there is a strong relation between the estimated and optimal criterion values, there is also a consistent departure from an exact correspondence. The general trend might be summarized by saying the subjects are conservative; they tend to adopt criteria which are not as different from $\beta = 1$ as they should be. This result is almost an inevitable consequence of the procedure. The way in which expected values change for various criterion levels is the crux of the problem. This topic is discussed in more detail in Appendix A.

Since these earlier investigations, other procedures have been utilized to vary the subject's criterion. One which seems more straightforward and is certainly successful is simply to instruct the subject verbally to adopt different criteria such as *lax* or *very strict*, or even to instruct the subject to maintain a certain value for $P_N(A)$.[19]

[18] W. A. Munson and J. E. Karlin, *J. Acoust. Soc. Am.*, 1956, **26**, 542.
[19] J. P. Egan, A. I. Schulman, and G. Z. Greenberg, *J. Acoust. Soc. Am.*, 1959, **31**, 768.

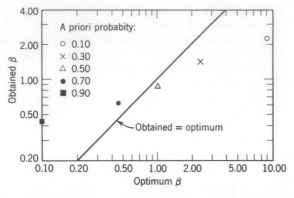

FIGURE 3

Comparison of the optimum and obtained criterion levels. This criterion level, β, is the equivalent of the criterion level on likelihood ratio. The optimum criterion is obtained by assuming normal statistics for both hypotheses. It is equal to $[1 - P(SN)]/P(SN)$, where $P(SN)$ is the *a priori* probability of the signal.

Measure of detectability. Let us turn now from the question of the criterion and its adjustment to another aspect of detection-theory analysis, the measure of detectability, and more specifically, whether or not this measure remains relatively invariant over different experimental procedures. How one can compare different measurements obtained using different experimental procedures is an important question, not only for psychoacousticians but for any scientific enterprise. Let us review the evidence on the extent to which detection-theory analysis has permitted such a comparison. If we make the usual assumption that the distribution of likelihood is normal with equal variance on both hypotheses, as in the situation outlined in the first experiment, then the measure of detectability is d'.

A paper by Swets[20] has considered the applicability of this detectability index for yes-no and forced-choice procedures; he has also compared predicted and obtained results using two, three, four, six, and eight alternatives in the forced-choice procedure. In general, these predictions based on d' hold up remarkably well. The worst failure reported seems to be about 1 db; no consistent error trend is evident in the data.

Another method of generating *ROC* curves, first suggested by Swets *et al.*[21] has been employed. Egan *et al.*[19] tested and compared this method with the standard yes-no procedure. In the single observation or yes-no procedure, the decision-theory analysis claims that the subject adopts a single criterion and this determines a "yes" or "no" response. The experimenter, then, is employing the subject as a threshold device. Alternatively, the experimenter could have the subject report a number after each observation such as likelihood ratio; from these numbers, the experimenter could construct an *ROC* curve by placing various criteria on the likelihood ratios reported.

The rating procedure is a compromise between these two extremes. The subject in the rating procedure is asked to place each observation in one of several categories;

[20] J. A. Swets, *J. Acoust. Soc. Am.*, 1959, **31**, 511.

[21] J. A. Swets, W. P. Tanner, and T. G. Birdsall, Electronic Defense Group, University of Michigan, Technical Report No. 40, 1955.

the top one being used for sureness of a signal's presence, the next for a lesser degree of sureness, and so forth. *ROC* curves are subsequently constructed. One can then compare the measure of signal detectability obtained from these two procedures, yes-no and rating. Egan *et al.*[19] found these two measures differed for his three subjects by 0.3, 0.4, and 0.1 db, differences probably well within the experimental error.

In summary then, we have seen how decision analysis allows one to predict within a fairly wide range of psychoacoustic procedures. The forced-choice procedures using two to eight alternatives and a single-interval procedure using two to four categories of response can be summarized by a single measure of detectability, a measure which, for practical purposes, is invariant.

Implications for psychoacoustic methods. The more traditional methods of psychoacoustics utilize some parameter of the signal such as the threshold energy. This value is obtained by an analysis of the subject's responses. Many of these methods do not allow one to determine directly the subject's criterion and in most methods it is presumed to be constant.

Let us investigate how variation in the subject's criterion, if it occurs, will affect the estimate of the threshold energy. Variation of the subject's criterion affects the false-alarm rate $P_N(A)$. Figure 4 shows how the probability distribution for signal-plus-noise must be varied as the false-alarm rate $P_N(A)$ is changed to maintain a constant value of signal detection $P_{SN}(A)$. We have assumed Gaussian distribution and equal variance to construct the solid line of the figure. The insert displays the essentials of the calculations and shows how a change in $P_N(A)$ of from 0.10 to 0.01 necessitates a change in the mean of the signal distribution from 1.3 to 3.1 in order to maintain $P_{SN}(A) = 0.50$. This value of $P_{SN}(A)$ is a reasonable one since it is often used as the

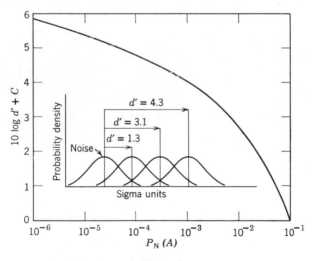

FIGURE 4

Evaluation of how a change in criterion will influence the size of the "threshold" signal. $P_N(A)$ is the false-alarm rate; a "yes" response to no signal. The hit rate, $P_{SN}(A)$, was held constant at 0.5. The mean of the signal distribution was varied (see insert) to achieve this hit rate for various values of $P_N(A)$. The constant, C, was chosen so that $10 \log 1.3 + C = 0$.

estimate of "threshold." Very small values of false-alarm rate were used because most methods control this parameter to the extent of keeping it very low.

We cannot say *generally* how this change in the mean of the signal distribution is related to any signal parameter. However, for sinusoidal signals in noise, d' is roughly proportional to signal energy; thus the "estimated threshold" may vary over a 6-db range depending on the criterion of the subject. (In other experiments d' varies with signal voltage—hence the range might be 12 db. See Fig. 7 and the discussion.)

This change in the estimated threshold, of say 6 db, will only occur if the subject's criterion changes. One may be willing to assume that it is approximately constant over the course of the experiment.[22] Then this number, 6 db, could be interpreted as a tolerable difference in comparing two sets of different measurements. The theory, then, is consistent with the rather wide-spread view in psychoacoustics; namely, that results obtained using different methods should not be expected to show exact congruence. Whether these differences are large enough to warrant concern depends both on the particular nature of the problem and the precision desired.

Decision analysis and speech research. The use of *ROC* curves and the measure d' has not been limited to detection experiments. Since some confusion has been generated by the multiplicity of d' measures, this issue deserves some attention.

Figure 5 displays an *ROC* curve taken from a report by Egan.[23] The similarity between this figure and Fig. 2 is apparent, even though measures employed to construct this graph differ greatly. The procedure here is as follows: A word is presented in noise to a listener who writes down the word he thinks was presented. He then checks whether or not he believes this identification response is correct. The conditional probabilities of the receiver saying he was correct on those words where he in fact was, and was not correct, define the ordinate and abscissa respectively of Fig. 5.

Egan's *ROC* curve, then, is constructed from a table of response-response contingencies rather than from stimulus-response contingencies, as was the *ROC* curve presented earlier. This difference, from the standpoint of analysis, is by no means trivial. The method used by Egan is really a two-stage decision process. First, the observer has to select (from several possibilities) the most likely word; second, he must evaluate this decision with respect to all other possibilities. Such a process produces mathematical expressions virtually impossible to evaluate except under the most doubtful set of simplifying assumptions.

This difficulty does not, of course, prevent one from summarizing the data presented in Fig. 5 by a single parameter. The line drawn to the data points is that generated by moving a criterion along two normal deviates of the same variance which differ only in means. This measure was, unfortunately, initially labeled d' because of its analogy to the detection measure. It is unfortunate because the detection measure d' has often been specifically related to physical measurements of signal and noise. No

---

[22] Obviously one can only assume it is constant because one cannot directly measure probabilities of the order 10^{-3}. If one is not willing to make this assumption, one must raise the false-alarm rate to a measurable value, $P_N(A) > 10^{-1}$, or use one of the other techniques discussed in the previous section. The signal energy necessary to obtain a certain d', say $d' = 1$, could then be used as the counterpart of the threshold energy.

[23] J. P. Egan, Hearing and Communication Laboratory, Indiana University, Technical Report under contract, 1957.

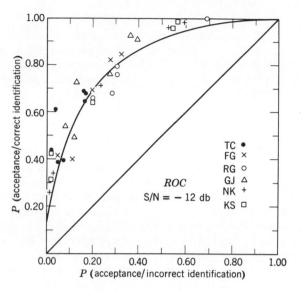

FIGURE 5
Some data taken from footnote 23. The signal-to-noise ratio refers to the peak signal power of the word compared with the noise power. The points represent different subjects. The subject listens to a word in noise, guesses what word it was, and then grades that response as either being correct (acceptance) or incorrect (rejection). The abscissa and ordinate refer to the probability of acceptance given the word was correctly or incorrectly identified.

such identification was ever intended in speech work, and therefore these measures obtained in speech research are presently denoted by various subscripts.[24]

The importance and usefulness of such measures is reviewed thoroughly in the monograph by Egan[23] and in the work of Pollack.[25-27] Basically, these measures are all aimed at specifying the subject's criterion. For an interesting example of how this value of the criterion affects the substantive conclusion one might draw, the paper by Pollack[28] is recommended. A recent paper by Clarke[29] has illustrated how confidence ratings may be utilized to supplement the usual articulation index.

[24] As yet, no standard notation has evolved. The following list of references contains many of the proposals that have been advanced to clarify this confusion. At present, one must very carefully determine how the detectability measure is defined in each experiment. Even subscripted measures, d_e' in particular, are defined differently in different experiments. See F. R. Clarke, T. G. Birdsall, and W. P. Tanner, *J. Acoust. Soc. Am.*, 1959, **31**, 629; J. P. Egan, G. Z. Greenberg, and A. I. Schulman, Hearing and Communication Laboratory, Indiana University, Technical Report under contract, 1959; and I. Pollack, *J. Acoust. Soc. Am.*, 1959, **31**, 1031.

[25] I. Pollack, *J. Acoust. Soc. Am.*, 1959, **31**, 1500.
[26] L. R. Decker and I. Pollack, *J. Acoust. Soc. Am.*, 1959, **31**, 1327.
[27] I. Pollack and L. R. Decker, *J. Acoust. Soc. Am.*, 1958, **30**, 286.
[28] I. Pollack, *J. Acoust. Soc. Am.*, 1959, **31**, 1509.
[29] F. R. Clarke, *J. Acoust. Soc. Am.*, 1960, **32**, 35.

Theory of Ideal Observers

In the most general sense, an ideal observer is simply a function relating an observation to the likelihood of that observation. Thus we have already specified an ideal observer for our simple example, since Table I accomplishes this task. This is not an interesting example, however, because the observations were already specified in terms of the probabilities under each hypothesis. A more interesting example of an ideal observer arises where the observations are waveforms and where the characteristics of the waveform differ under each hypothesis. The task of the ideal observer is, then, given a waveform, calculate likelihood ratio or some monotonic transformation of that quantity.

The ideal observer, strictly speaking, need not make any decisions. If likelihood ratio is computed, the problem of what decision rule to employ is determined by the specific objective in making the decisions. Various possible objectives have been discussed in the previous sections, where it was pointed out that these objectives could be attained by using a decision rule based on likelihood ratio. Although the calculation of likelihood ratio specifies the ideal observer for a given problem, such information is of little value unless we can evaluate this observer's performance. One general method of evaluating the ideal observer's performance is to determine *ROC* curves, but to obtain an *ROC* curve we must calculate two probabilities. Thus to evaluate completely the ideal observer we actually have to specify not only how likelihood is calculated but the probability distribution of likelihood ratio on both hypotheses.

Having established the general background of this problem, let us consider a specific example: the ideal observer for conditions of a signal which is known exactly.

Ideal observer for the signal known exactly (SKE)

Two hypotheses actually define this special case in which, given a waveform, one must select one of the following hypotheses:

H_1—the waveform is a sample of white Gaussian noise $n(t)$ with specified bandwidth (W) and noise power density (N_0).

H_2—the waveform is $n(t)$ plus some specified signal waveform $s(t)$. Everything is known about $s(t)$ if it occurs: its starting time, duration, and phase. It need not be a segment of a sine wave as long as it is specified, i.e., known exactly.

From these two hypotheses we wish to calculate likelihood ratio, and, if possible, derive the probability distribution of likelihood ratio on both hypotheses. Obviously such calculations will be of little use unless the final results can be fairly simply summarized in terms of some simple physical measurement of signal and noise. Happily, such is the case.

We shall not present the derivation here since it is not in itself particularly instructive and can be obtained elsewhere.[7] One assumption of the derivation will, however, be discussed, since an objection to this assumption has been recently raised; an objection which seriously questions the legitimacy of applying this result to any psychoacoustic experiment which has yet been conducted. Unfortunately, the alternative assumption suggested has a different but equally serious flaw.

Representation of the waveform

The assumption concerns the representation of the waveform. In order to compute likelihood ratio, one must find the probability of a certain waveform on each hypothesis. Since the waveform is simply a function of time, one must somehow associate a probability with this waveform, or somehow obtain a set of measures from the waveform and associate a probability with these measures.

But what exactly is the nature of the waveform? In order to compute these various probabilities we must make some very specific assumptions about the class of waveforms we will consider.

Peterson, Birdsall, and Fox[7] assumed that the waveforms were Fourier series-band limited. If the waveform is of this class it can be represented by $n = 2WT$ measures, where W is the "bandwidth" of the noise and T is the duration of the waveform. A series representation in terms of sine and cosine might be used. There are of course, many equivalent ways of writing this series to identify the n parameters, but these are all unique, and if the original waveform is indeed Fourier series-band limited, they will reproduce exactly the waveform in the interval $(0, T)$. Accepting this assumption, we find that a monotonic transformation of likelihood ratio (the logarithm) is normal under both hypotheses.

H_1: $\log l(x)$ is normal with mean $-E/N_0$, variance E/N_0,

H_2: $\log l(x)$ is normal with mean $+E/N_0$, variance E/N_0,

$d' = \Delta M/\sigma = (2E/N_0)^{\frac{1}{2}}$ where E is the signal energy, $\int_0^T [s(t)]^2 \, dt$, and N_0 is the noise power density. Naturally, if this assumption about the waveform is not made the preceding result is invalid. Mathews and David[30] have considered a slightly different assumption. They assumed the waveforms are Fourier integral-band limited. The conclusion resulting from this assumption is that the signal is perfectly detectable in the noise independent of the ratio E/N_0, as long as it is not zero. In short, d' is infinite for any nonzero value of E/N_0. Which of these assumptions is the more reasonable or applicable to a psychoacoustic experiment?

Neither assumption can be completely justified. In almost all psychoacoustic experiments, the noise voltage is actually produced by a special tube. The voltage produced by this tube is amplified and filtered. Such noise is not Fourier series-band limited, for the noise is clearly not periodic.[31] Although a Fourier series might serve

[30] M. V. Mathews and E. E. David, *J. Acoust. Soc. Am.*, 1959, **31**, 834(A).

[31] It is somewhat unfair to imply that Peterson, Birdsall, and Fox assumed the noise was periodic. Their assumption, strictly speaking, was that each waveform could be represented by a finite set of numbers. The way they obtained these numbers is through a sampling plan, which we cannot discuss in detail. It was not a simple Fourier expansion in terms of *sine* and *cosine*. This is a difficult and complex topic; for a discussion of the details in this area see footnote 7; D. Slepian, "Some comments on the detection of Gaussian signals in Gaussian noise," *Trans. IRE*, **PGIT-4**, 65 (1958); and W. B. Davenport and W. L. Root, *Random signals in noise*, New York: McGraw-Hill, 1958. Precise analysis of the situation where the noise is filtered, i.e., where the power spectrum of the noise is a polynomial, can be worked out in principle. The analysis is complex and exact answers can be obtained only in certain simple cases. One can show in general, however, that for practical situations the detectability of the signal is finite. (See Davenport and Root.)

as an excellent approximation to these waveforms in the interval $(0, T)$, it would not be an *exact* representation of the waveform. Similarly, an assumption of a Fourier integral limitation of the bandwidth cannot be correct, because the waveform does not have a sharp cutoff in the Fourier integral sense. If it did, the waveform would be analytic. If it were analytic, the ideal observer could sample at one point in time, obtain all the derivatives at that point, and know the exact form of the wave for all time. Such a result leads to the conclusion that the ideal observer, by observing one sample of the waveform at any time can, immediately, in principle, make his decision about all the waveforms the experimenter has presented in the past and all those he may ever decide to produce. This approach is therefore of little practical use.

The issue, while obviously only an academic one, has indicated one very important aspect of the problem. The ideal observer is, like all ideal concepts, only as good as the assumptions that generate it. Clearly, any such idealization of a practical situation is based on certain simplifying assumptions. It is always extremely important to understand what these assumptions are and even more important to realize the implications of a change in these assumptions. In short, there are many ideal observers, each generated by certain key assumptions about the essential nature of the detection task.

For the discussion which follows, we shall use the Peterson, Birdsall, and Fox[7] approach and assume that the waveforms can be completely represented by a finite number of measurements. A similar treatment is given by Van Meter and Middleton.[32] As more progress is made with the theory of ideal observers we should be able to state quite precisely how detection will vary if certain definite restrictions are imposed on the manner in which the observer operates. Peterson, Birdsall, and Fox have, in fact, considered several such cases and their results. Each case provides us with a framework from which we may evaluate and assess the performance of the subject. Such a comparison provides both qualitative aud quantitative guides for further research.[33] There are several areas we might select to illustrate this approach. The one we have selected was chosen because it is a general topic and because it has been slighted somewhat in psychoacoustics.

Shape of the psychophysical function

The psychophysical function is generally defined as the curve relating the percentage of correct detections of the signal (the ordinate) to some physical measure of the signal (the abscissa). If some variant of the constant stimuli method is used, the curve rises monotonically from zero to one hundred percent as the signal level is increased.

Generally, hypotheses about the form of this function arise from assumptions about the process of discrimination. Often these assumptions are sufficient to allow one to deduce the form of the psychophysical function to within two or three parameters which are then determined experimentally. Obviously, it is extremely important for the model to specify the exact transformation of the physical stimulus which is used as the abscissa of the psychophysical function; without such specification, the theory is incomplete.

In psychoacoustics, there has been comparatively little concern with the form of this function. Most theories of the auditory process have been content with attempting

[32] D. Van Meter and D. Middleton, *Trans. IRE*, 1954, **PGIT-4**, 119.

[33] W. P. Tanner and T. G. Birdsall, *J. Acoust. Soc. Am.*, 1958, **30**, 922.

to predict only one parameter of the psychophysical curve, usually the mean or threshold. As a result, it is nearly impossible to obtain from the literature information on the actual form of the psychophysical function.

The notable exception to the preceding statement is the neural-quantum hypothesis.[34] The authors of this theory say that it "enables us to predict the form and the slope of certain psychometric functions." It can be demonstrated from the model that the form of the function should be linear and this linear function is specified to within one parameter. The physical measure is never mentioned in the derivation of the theory and we find only after the data are presented that sound pressure and frequency are the appropriate physical measures. The authors remark in their paper that "strictly speaking, data yielding rectilinear psychometric functions when plotted against sound pressure do not show absolute rectilinearity when expressed in terms of sound energy, but calculation shows that the departure from rectilinearity is negligible." It is certainly true that pressure, pressure squared, and indeed pressure cubed, are all nearly linear for small values of pressure—but that is not entirely the point.

It is the location of this function that plays a crucial role in the theory. If the subject employs a two-quantum criterion then, according to the theory, the psychophysical function must be zero up to one quantum unit, show a linear increase to one hundred percent at two quantum units, and maintain this level for more quantum units. Where the curve breaks from zero percent reports and where it reaches one hundred percent reports is precisely specified by the theory. In general, if the subject requires n quanta to produce a positive report, the increasing linear function must extend from n to $n + 1$ quantum units. Now clearly, what appears to be a two-quantum subject (0% at one pressure unit, 100% at two pressure units), when the data are plotted in pressure units, cannot be interpreted as a two-quantum subject in energy units. In fact, he cannot be interpreted as an any-number-of-quantum subject. This is true no matter how small the values of pressure.

This criticism of the rather *post hoc* treatment of the physical scale is by no means limited to the neural-quantum hypothesis. Many hypotheses about the shape of the psychophysical function, including some formulations of the Gaussian hypothesis, neglect this rather crucial factor.

Detection theory stands in marked contrast with these theories. Models based on the ideal observer concept predict the form of the psychophysical function exactly. The proper physical dimensions are completely specified and there are no free parameters.

Obviously, one would not be surprised to find human observers somewhat less than optimum, but hopefully, the shape of the psychophysical function might at least be parallel to that obtained from the model. Often however, the obtained psychophysical function does not parallel that predicted by the model and this discrepancy deserves some discussion.

Signal uncertainty and ideal detectors.[35] In Fig. 6, we have plotted the percentage of correct detections in a two-alternative forced-choice procedure versus

[34] S. S. Stevens, C. T. Morgan, and J. Volkmann, *Am. J. Psychol.*, 1941, **54**, 315.

[35] The analysis of detection data from the viewpoint of signal uncertainty is very similar to some ideas expressed by Dr. W. P. Tanner. Although several details of the analysis differ, the essentials are the same. The author is indebted to Dr. Tanner for many long and lively conversations on this topic.

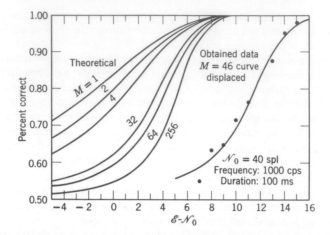

FIGURE 6

The theoretical psychophysical functions for the ideal observer detecting 1 of M-orthogonal signals. The parameter M is the number of possible orthogonal signals. The ideal detector need only detect the signal, not identify it. The abscissa is ten times the logarithm of signal energy to noise-power density. The ordinate is the percent correct detection in a two-alternative forced-choice test. The obtained data are compared with the theoretical function shifted about 10 db to the right.

$\mathscr{E}$-$\mathscr{N}_0$ for a typical subject and a series of mathematical models. The problem in all cases is simply to detect a sinusoidal signal added to a background of white noise.

We say "typical subject" because the shape of this function is remarkably invariant over both subjects and a range of physical parameters. For signal durations of 10 to 1000 msec[36] and signal frequencies from 250 to 4000 cps,[37] there appears to be no great change in the shape of the function when plotted against the scale shown in Fig. 6. Naturally, the exact location of the curve depends on the exact physical parameters of the signal, but except for this constant, which is a simple additive constant in logarithmic form, the shape is remarkably stable. The striking aspect of this function is its slope. We notice the slope of the observed function is steeper than most of the theoretical functions depicted in Fig. 6.

The class of theoretical functions is generated by assuming the detector has various uncertainties about the exact nature of the signal.[38] Each function is generated by assuming the detector knows only that the signal will be one of M-orthogonal signals. If the signal is known exactly ($M = 1$) there is no uncertainty. For sinusoidal signals, the nature of the uncertainty might be phase, time of occurrence of the signal, or signal frequency. The degree of uncertainty is reflected by the parameter M. As this

[36] D. M. Green, *J. Acoust. Soc. Am.*, 1959, **31**, 836(A).

[37] D. M. Green, M. J. McKey, and J. C. R. Licklider, *J. Acoust. Soc. Am.*, 1959, **31**, 1446.

[38] The details of this model may be found in footnote 7, p. 207. This particular model was selected because it has been presented in the literature. There are other models which assume signal uncertainty but which differ in details about the decision rule. The psychophysical functions produced by these models are similar to those displayed in Fig. 6, although the value of the parameter (M) would be changed somewhat.

uncertainty increases, the psychophysical function increases in slope. It therefore appears that there may exist a model with sufficient uncertainty about the signal to generate a function which is very similar to that displayed by the human observer.

Accepting for the moment the assumption that the extreme slope of the human observer's psychophysical function is due to some degree of uncertainty about the signal, we might try to manipulate this slope by various experimental procedures.

Preview technique. One general class of procedures would attempt to reduce the uncertainty by supplying the missing information through some form of cueing or preview technique. If, for example, the observer is uncertain about the frequency of the signal we might attempt to reduce this uncertainty by presenting the signal briefly at a high level just prior to the observation interval. Similarly, if the time of occurrence of the signal is uncertain we might increase the noise during the observation interval. If the noise was increased for all trials, whether or not the signal was presented, it would provide no information about the signal's presence but would convey direct information about the signal's starting time and duration. Both of these techniques have been utilized with only partial success. While it is impossible to assert that there was no change (the null hypothesis) the amount of change was very small, although in the proper direction.[39]

Another class of procedures which has been utilized to attempt to reduce the subject's uncertainty about the signal parameters involves changing the detection task so that some information is directly supplied. The procedures are like the preceding but actually include the information in the observation interval. For example, to remove frequency uncertainty, we might add a continuous sine wave to the noise. The continuous sine wave is adjusted to a level such that it is clearly evident in the noise. The signal is an increment added to this sine wave and the task is to detect this increment. The procedure definitely changes the slope of the subject's psychophysical function—it becomes less steep and the signal is easier to detect.[40]

This procedure of making the signal an increment to a continuous sine wave provides good frequency information but does not remove temporal uncertainty. Another procedure which minimizes practically all uncertainty is in fact a modification of a standard procedure used to investigate the *j.n.d.* for intensity. A two-alternative forced-choice procedure is employed. Two gated sinusoids occur in noise, one at standard level, the other at this level plus an increment. The subject's task is to select the interval containing the increment. If the standard signal is adjusted to a power level about equal to the noise-power density, the psychophysical function actually parallels that expected for the signal-known-exactly case.[41] It is from 3 to 6 db off optimum in absolute value, depending on the energy of the standard. (See Fig. 7. Note the change in scale between Figs. 6 and 7.)

Let us, at least tentatively, accept as the conclusion of these last results that the shape of the psychophysical function is in fact due primarily to various uncertainties about the signal parameter. If this is true, then we still have the problem of explaining

---

[39] Unpublished work of the author. Also see T. Marill, Ph.D. thesis, Massachusetts Institute of Technology, 1956, and J. C. R. Licklider and G. H. Flanagan, "On a methodological problem in audiometry," unpublished.

[40] W. P. Tanner, J. Bigelow, and D. M. Green, unpublished.

[41] W. P. Tanner, Electronic Defense Group, University of Michigan, Technical Report No. 47, 1958.

the lack of success evidenced when the previous techniques were employed. Should not a preview of the signal, preceding an observation, serve to reduce frequency uncertainty? The answer might be that such procedures do reduce uncertainty, but not enough relative to the uncertainty still remaining. From Fig. 6 we note that, as we introduce signal uncertainty, the slope of the psychophysical function increases very rapidly for small changes in uncertainty; then, as the uncertainty increases, the slope approaches some asymptotic value. A change in uncertainty from $M = 256$ to 64 may hardly affect the psychophysical function. This fact also probably explains why the psychophysical functions do not appear to change very much for a variety of signal parameters, such as signal duration and signal frequency. Undoubtedly, as the signal duration increases, the uncertainty about the time of occurrence of the signal is reduced. Due to the large initial uncertainty, this change is too small to be detected in the data.

Uncertain signal frequency. Still another manner of checking this general model is to vary the uncertainty of the signal and determine how this affects the subject's performance. One might, for example, select several different sinusoidal signals and select one at random as the signal used on a particular trial. The subject is simply asked to *detect* a signal, not identify it. Depending on the frequency separation and the number of signals used, one can directly manipulate signal uncertainty.

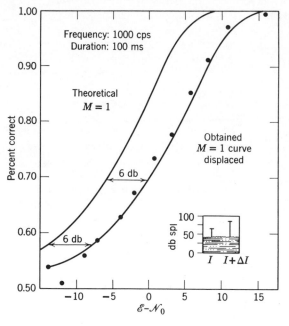

FIGURE 7

Observed data in the ΔI versus I experiment and the signal-known-exactly observer ($M = 1$). The abscissa and ordinate are the same as in Figure 6, but note the change in scale of the abscissa. The two curves differ by 6 db at each value of percent correct. The apparent convergence of the two curves at low values of percent correct is illusory. The insert shows the level of the noise; the lines show the level of I in power, and the maximum $I + \Delta I$ power.

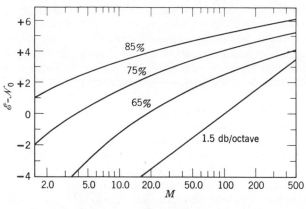

FIGURE 8
The variation of signal-to-noise level for some constant percent correct as a function of M. This curve is the same information presented in Figure 6 with M as the variable and percent correct at the parameter.

This in fact was a procedure used in an earlier study by Tanner et al.[16] A small decrement (1.0 to 1.5 db) in detectability was found if one compared a situation where a *single* fixed sinusoid was the signal and a situation where the signal was one of *two* sinusoids. Later results[42-44] show, however, that the decrement did not increase very much as more components were included in the set of possible signals. This result is consistent with the theoretical model we have been discussing. Figure 8 shows how, for a constant detectability, one must change the signal level as uncertainty (M) is increased. The decrement in signal detectability as a function of signal uncertainty changes very slowly after M reaches a value of 50 or so. The 1.5 db per octave decrement, suggested by some of the earlier models to account for the uncertain frequency data[45] is only a reasonable approximation for a rather limited range of M.[46]

While the preceding argument that the shape of the psychophysical function is largely due to signal uncertainty has some appeal, there still remain some problems with this interpretation. Another way to attack this problem of signal uncertainty is to use a signal where little information about the waveform is known, and compare the subject's performance with the theoretical optimum model in this situation. A specific case arises where the signal is a sample of noise. The most one can specify about the signal is the frequency region, starting time, duration, and power. The ideal detector for this signal can be specified—it simply measures signal energy in the signal band. But the

[42] F. A. Veniar, *J. Acoust. Soc. Am.*, 1958, **30**, 1020.

[43] F. A. Veniar, *J. Acoust. Soc. Am.*, 1958, **30**, 1075.

[44] C. D. Creelman, Electronic Defense Group, University of Michigan, Technical Memo. No. 71, 1959.

[45] D. M. Green, *J. Acoust. Soc. Am.*, 1958, **30**, 904. See also footnotes 16 and 44.

[46] J. P. Egan, G. Z. Greenberg, and A. I. Schulman, *J. Acoust. Soc. Am.*, 1959, **31**, 1579(A). Egan et al. have investigated how temporal uncertainty affects signal detectability. In one condition they present a fixed-frequency sinusoidal signal of 0.25 sec duration somewhere in an 8-sec interval. They did not report the results in detail, but the decrement in detectability due to temporal uncertainty was small (1 or 2 db).

psychophysical functions obtained with this type of signal are also slightly steeper than those predicted by the model.[47] Either partial time uncertainty still remains or signal uncertainty alone is not a sufficient explanation. The author feels that a better model would assume that the human observer utilizes some nonlinear detection rule. This assumption, coupled with the uncertainty explanation, could probably explain most of the results obtained thus far. The mathematical analysis of such devices, is however, complex.

Internal noise. Before summarizing, one final point must be considered. Often it is a temptation to invoke the concept of internal or neural noise when discussing the discrepancy between an ideal model and the human observer. There are good reasons for avoiding this temptation. While it would take us too far afield to cover this point in detail, the following remarks will illustrate the point.

Only if the model is of a particularly simple form can one hope to evaluate the specific effects of the assumption of internal noise. The signal-known-exactly observer is of this type. Here one can show how a specific type of internal noise can simply be treated as adding noise at the input of the detection device. Thus one can evaluate the psychophysical function and it will be shifted to the right by some number of decibels (see Fig. 6) due to the internal noise. But, of course, such an assumption can immediately be rejected since no shift in the psychophysical function can account for the data displayed in the figure.

With more complicated models, it is usually difficult to say exactly what internal noise will do. While it will obviously lower discrimination, the specific effects of the assumption are often impossible to evaluate. Unless these specific effects can be evaluated, the assumption simply rephrases the original problem of the discrepancy.

I am not suggesting that the human observer is perfect in any sense, nor attempting to minimize the importance of the concept of internal noise. What I am emphasizing is that the concept must be used with great care. If the concept is to have any importance it must be made specific. This implies that we have to (1) state exactly what this noise is, i.e., that we have to characterize it mathematically, (2) specify in what way it interacts with the detection or discrimination process, and (3) evaluate specifically what effect it will have on performance. Unless these steps can be carried out the *ad hoc* nature of the assumption vitiates its usefulness.

Summary and Conclusion

The main emphasis in this paper has been to explain detection theory and to illustrate how such a theory has been applied to certain areas of psychoacoustics. This method of analysis is simply one of many that are currently being used in an attempt to understand the process of hearing.

Two main aspects of this approach have been distinguished. The first, decision theory, emphasizes that the subject's criterion as well as the physical properties of the stimulus play a major role in determining the subject's responses. The theory indicates both the class of variables which determines the level of the criterion, and, more importantly, suggests an analytic technique for removing this source of variation. This technique leaves a relatively pure measure of the detectability of the signal. The invariance of this measure over several psychophysical procedures has already been demonstrated.

[47] D. M. Green, *J. Acoust. Soc. Am.*, 1960, **32**, 121.

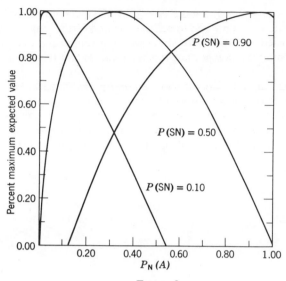

FIGURE 9

The normalized expected value as a function of changes in criterion. This is a theoretical curve based on the data presented in Figures 2 and 3. The appendix lists the assumptions used to construct the curve.

The second aspect, the theory of ideal observers, has also been discussed in some detail. The usefulness of such an analysis was illustrated by considering the form of the psychophysical function. No ideal observer provides a complete or comprehensive model even for the rather limited areas of psychoacoustics that we have discussed in this paper. The model provides a source of hypotheses and a standard against which experimental results can be evaluated. It is too early to attempt any complete evaluation of this approach. The mathematical models are relatively new and the application of these models to a sensory process began with Tanner and Swets[48] only about five years ago. There remain many problems to be solved both of a mathematical and experimental nature. As more progress is made in both areas, the theory should become more specific and concrete, then perhaps it will be able to interact more directly with the research from several other areas in psychoacoustics.

Appendix A

The inherent difficulty of comparing the optimum criterion value and that employed by the subject is the shape of the expected-value function. Let us investigate in detail a typical situation. We have assumed that the distribution on likelihood ratio is normal under both hypotheses, that the mean separation is one sigma unit, and that the values and costs of the various decision alternatives are all the same. From these assumptions we have constructed Fig. 9. This figure shows how the expected value varies with changes in *a priori* probability of signal $P(SN)$ and false-alarm rate $P_N(A)$. We see immediately that for extreme values of *a priori* probability, e.g., $P(SN) = 0.10$, the difference between optimum expected-value behavior [$P_N(A) = 0.004$] and

[48] W. P. Tanner and J. A. Swets, *Psychol. Rev.*, 1954, **61**, 401.

a pure strategy $[P_N(A) = 0.000]$ is less than 3%. In fact, the curves in the figure were somewhat exaggerated to allow one to see the location of the maximum. Since most subjects are instructed to avoid pure strategies in psychoacoustic experiments, this tends to force the subject to adopt more moderate values of $P_N(A)$ for extreme conditions.

On the other hand, if more moderate *a priori* probabilities are employed in the experiment [e.g., $P(SN) = 0.50$], we see that any value of $P_N(A)$ within a range from 0.15 to 0.50 will achieve at least 90% of the maximum expected payoff.

Thus any attempt to investigate, in any more than a correlational sense, the correspondence between obtained and optimum criteria appears extremely difficult.

Received June 23, 1960.

SOME COMMENTS AND A CORRECTION OF
"PSYCHOACOUSTICS AND DETECTION THEORY"*

DAVID M. GREEN

DEPARTMENT OF ECONOMICS AND RESEARCH LABORATORY OF ELECTRONICS,
MASSACHUSETTS INSTITUTE OF TECHNOLOGY, CAMBRIDGE, MASSACHUSETTS

Dr. S. S. Stevens has very kindly pointed out two items in my paper, "Psycho-acoustics and Detection Theory,"[1] that require further comment in order to avoid misunderstanding.

I called the function relating the percentage of correct detection responses to the physical intensity of the stimulus the *psychophysical* function. It is true that this function is more often called the *psychometric* function, a term probably introduced by Urban in 1908.[2]

Originally Fechner added up successive just-noticeable-differences (jnd's) to determine the relation between the magnitude of sensation and the physical intensity of the stimulus. The resulting relation is commonly called the psychophysical function. Since Fechner's time many other techniques for determining this relation have been devised and the results are also called psychophysical functions (e.g., Stevens' power law[3]). The newer methods do not involve determining jnd's and are not obtained by using any simple variant of the classical methods of psychophysics. We are therefore faced with the anomaly that psychometric functions are obtained by using psycho-physical methods and psychophysical functions are now determined by other, different techniques.

Personally I find the designation used in vision—frequency-of-seeing curve—even more distasteful than the term psychometric function. Some change in terminology would be most welcome. I am open for suggestions.

The second item is more crucial and concerns my remarks about the neural-quantum theory. I asserted that data that appear to indicate a two-quantum observer when plotted against pressure units cannot be interpreted as any kind of quantum observer when plotted against energy units. There is, however, a very straightforward interpretation of the scales of pressure and energy that makes this assertion incorrect. Unfortunately, this interpretation had never occurred to me, and I thereby did injustice to the authors of the neural-quantum theory. Let me explain this interpretation and the scale of pressure and energy units that I had in mind when I made my remarks.

In the neural-quantum procedure we have a continuous sinusoidal stimulus (call it the standard). At specific times we increase briefly the amplitude of this sinusoid and the observer's task is to detect these increments. If we measure the pressure of the standard, call it p, and measure the pressure of the standard plus the increment, call it

From *J. Acoust. Soc. Amer.*, 1961, **33**, 965. Reprinted with permission.

* The preparation of this letter was supported by the U.S. Army Signal Corps, the Air Force (Operational Applications Office and Office of Scientific Research), and the Office of Naval Research. This is Technical Note No. ESD TN 61-56.

[1] D. M. Green, *J. Acoust. Soc. Am.*, 1960, **32**, 1189.

[2] F. M. Urban, *The application of statistical methods to the problems of psychophysics*, Philadelphia: Psychological Clinic Press, 1908, p. 107.

[3] S. S. Stevens, *Psychol. Rev.*, 1957, **64**, 153.

$p + \Delta p$, then by subtracting the former from the latter we obtain on a pressure scale values of Δp. We may call this quantity Δp the increment of pressure.

Similarly, if we measure the power of the standard, a quantity proportional to p^2, and the power of the standard plus the increment a quantity proportional to $(p + \Delta p)^2$, we might subtract the former from the latter, and (since the constants of proportionality are the same) obtain the quantity, $(p^2 + 2\Delta pp + \Delta p^2 - p^2) = (2\Delta pp + \Delta p^2)$. The latter quantity is also proportional to energy, since the increment is of constant duration, and we may call this quantity the increment of energy. The important result is that these two quantities, the increment in pressure and the increment in energy, are nearly linear for values of Δp much less than p. If some data are exactly consistent with the predictions of the neural quantum theory on one scale, they would very nearly be consistent on the other scale.

When I made my remarks, I had in mind data plotted on a scale of *signal* pressure or *signal* energy. By *signal* I mean the waveform added to the standard that the observers are asked to detect. In this terminology, the pressure of the signal is proportional to Δp and the energy of signal is proportional to that quantity squared, Δp^2. Only data plotted on a scale of signal pressure as I have now defined it are in agreement with the predictions of neural quantum theory.

Part of the reason for my oversight undoubtedly arose from the fact that this measure of signal energy Δp^2 is the quantity I used in presenting some of the data reported later in my paper. There is, however, no inherent reason for using my partic-ular measure of the stimulus and I should have made my reference clear.

In some cases the two different scales of energy obtained from the pressure scale would be exactly the same. This would happen if the standard and signal are inco-herent; that is, if the middle term in the square of $(\Delta p + p)$ is zero. An example of this would be an increment in white noise. In the case at hand, this is not true and the quantity that I have called increment in energy and the quantity that I called signal energy are quite different.

The general point I was trying to make is that the neural-quantum theory does not specify in advance how the physical stimulus should be measured. It was my position that it is important for a theory of psychophysics to specify how the physical scale is related to the expected psychological results. This position is apparently not widely endorsed. I am particularly impressed with the number of theories that suggest that the psychometric function is Gaussian, log-Gaussian, Poisson, rectilinear, or logistic, but cannot specify in advance what particular transformation of the physical scale will yield these results. It is not hard to envision different circumstances in which all these assertions are true at least in the sense that deviations are within the range of experimental error. Somehow there never seems to be any resolution to these different findings.

One can, of course, simply ignore all this and go on measuring only one arbitrary parameter of the psychometric function such as the "threshold" value. While this position obviously has the merit of convenience, it would also appear important to demonstrate how all of these different results might come about from one single general theory. To accomplish the latter task one must have a theory which carefully specifies the physical part of the psychophysical theory.

Received April 14, 1961.

ON THE POSSIBLE PSYCHOPHYSICAL LAWS [1]

R. DUNCAN LUCE

Harvard University

This paper is concerned with the century-old effort to determine the functional relations that hold between subjective continua and the physical continua that are presumed to underlie them. The first, and easily the most influential, attempt to specify the possible relations was made by Fechner. It rests upon empirical knowledge of how discrimination varies with intensity along the physical continuum and upon the assumption that jnd's are subjectively equal throughout the continuum. When, for example, discrimination is proportional to intensity (Weber's law), Fechner claimed that the equal-jnd assumption leads to a logarithmic relation (Fechner's law).

This idea has always been subject to controversy, but recent attacks upon it have been particularly severe. At the theoretical level, Luce and Edwards

[1] This work has been supported in part by Grant M-2293 from the National Institute of Mental Health and in part by Grant NSF-G 5544 from the National Science Foundation.

Ward Edwards, E. H. Galanter, Frederick Mosteller, Frank Restle, S. S. Stevens, and Warren Torgerson have kindly given me their thoughtful comments on drafts of this paper, many of which are incorporated into this version. I am particularly indebted to S. S. Stevens for his very detailed substantive and stylistic criticisms of the last two drafts.

(1958) have pointed out that Fechner's mathematical reasoning was not sound. Among other things, his assumption is not sufficient to generate an interval scale. By recasting his problem somewhat—essentially by replacing the equal-jnd assumption with the somewhat stronger condition that "equally often noticed differences are equal, except when always or never noticed"— they were able to show that an interval scale results, and to present a mathematical expression for it. Their work has no practical import when Weber's law, or its linear generalization $\Delta x = ax + b$, is true, because the logarithm is still the solution, but their jnd scale differs from Fechner's integral when Weber's law is replaced by some other function relating stimulus jnd's to intensity.

At the empirical level, Stevens (1956, 1957) has argued that jnd's are unequal in subjective size on intensive, or what he calls prothetic, continua—a contention supported by considerable data—and that the relation between the subjective and physical continua is the power function αx^β, not the logarithm. Using such "direct" methods as magnitude estimation and ratio production, he and others (Stevens: 1956, 1957; Stevens & Galanter, 1957) have accumulated considerable evidence to but-

This article appeared in *Psychol. Rev.,* 1959, **66**, 81–95. Reprinted with permission.

tress the empirical generality of the power function. Were it not for the fact that some psychophysicists are uneasy about these methods, which seem to rest heavily upon our experience with the number system, the point would seem to be established. In an effort to bypass these objections, Stevens (1959) has recently had subjects match values between pairs of continua, and he finds that the resulting relations are power functions whose exponents can be predicted from the magnitude scales of the separate variables. Thus, although much remains to be learned about the "direct" methods of scaling, the resulting power functions appear to summarize an interesting body of data.

Given these empirical results, one is challenged to develop a suitable formal theory from which they can be shown to follow. There can be little doubt that, as a starting point, certain commonly made assumptions are inappropriate: equality of jnd's, equally often noticed differences, and Thurstone's equal variance assumption. Since, however, differences stand in the same —logarithmic—relation to ratios as Fechner's law does to the power function, a reasonable starting point might seem to be the assumption that the subjective ratio of stimuli one jnd apart is a constant independent of the stimulus intensity. Obvious as the procedure may seem, in my opinion it will not do. Although generations of psychologists have managed to convince themselves that the equal-jnd assumption is plausible, if not obvious, it is not and never has been particularly compelling; and in this respect, an equal-ratio assumption is not much different. This is not to deny that subjective continua may have the equal-ratio property—they must if the power law is correct and Weber's law holds— but rather to argue that such an as-

sumption is too special to be acceptable as a basic axiom in a deductive theory.

Elsewhere (Luce, in press), I have suggested another approach. An axiom, or possible law, of wide applicability in the study of choice behavior, may be taken in conjunction with the linear generalization of Weber's law to demonstrate the existence of a scale that is a power function of the physical continuum. Although that theory leads to what appears to be the correct form, it is open to two criticisms. First, the exponent predicted from discrimination data is at least an order of magnitude larger than that obtained by direct scaling methods. Second, the theory is based upon assumptions about discriminability, and these are not obviously relevant to a scale determined by another method. Scales of apparent magnitude may be related to jnd scales, but it would be unwise to take it for granted that they are.

The purpose of this paper is to outline still another approach to the problem, one that is not subject to the last criticism. The results have applicability far beyond the bounds of psychophysics, for they concern the general question of the relation between measurement and substantive theories.

TYPES OF SCALES

Although familiarity may by now have dulled our sense of its importance, Stevens' (1946, 1951) stress upon the transformation groups that leave certain specified scale properties invariant must, I think, be considered one of the more striking contributions to the discussion of measurement in the past few decades. Prior to his work, most writers had put extreme emphasis upon the property of "additivity," which is a characteristic of much physical measurement (Cohen & Nagel, 1934). It was held that this property is fundamental to scientific measurement and, indeed, the term "fundamental measurement" was applied only to these scales. This contention, however, puts the nonphysical sciences in a most peculiar fix. Since no one has yet discovered an "additive" psychological variable, it would seem that psychology can have no fundamental measures of its own. This conclusion might be acceptable if we could define psychological measures in terms of the fundamental physical scales, i.e., as "derived" scales, but few of the things we want to measure seem to be definable in this way. So either rigorous psychological measurement must be considered impossible or additive empirical operations must not be considered essential to measurement. What is important is not additivity itself, but the fact that, when it is coupled with other plausible assumptions, it sharply restricts the class of transformations that may be applied to the resulting scale. Specifically, it makes the scale unique except for multiplication by positive constants, i.e., changes of unit. Additivity is not the only property that an assignment of numbers to objects or events may have which sharply limits the admissible transformations. Some of these other properties appear applicable and relevant to psychological variables, and so in this sense psychological measurement appears to be possible.

By a *theory of measurement,* I shall mean the following. One or more operations and relations are specified over a set of objects or events (the variable), and they are characterized by a number of empirically testable assumptions. In addition, it must be possible to assign numbers to the objects and to identify numerical operations and relations with the empirical operations and relations in such a way that the numerical operations represent (are isomorphic to) the empirical ones. In other words, we have a measurement theory whenever (a) we have a system of rules for assigning numerical values to objects that are interrelated by assumptions about certain empirical operations involving them, and (b) these rules let us set up an isomorphic relation between some properties of the number system and some aspects of the empirical operations.

One of the simplest examples of a theory of measurement is a finite set (of goods) ordered by a binary (preference) relation P that is assumed to be antisymmetric and transitive. A scale u can be assigned to the set in such a manner that it represents P in the sense that xPy if and only if $u(x) > u(y)$.

By the *scale type,* I shall mean the group of transformations that result in other isomorphic representations of the measurement theory. In the preceding example any strictly monotonic increasing transformation will do, and scales of this type are known as ordinal. Any transformation chosen from the scale type will be said to be an *admissible transformation.*

It should be re-emphasized that quite divergent measurement theories may lead to the same scale type. For example, Case V of Thurstone's law of comparative judgment (1927) and the von Neumann-Morgenstern utility axioms (1947) both result in interval scales (of something), yet the basic terms and assumptions involved are totally different, even though both theories can be applied to the same subject matter. Of course, the resulting interval scales may not be linearly related, for they may be measuring different things.

A measurement theory may be contrasted with what I shall call a *substantive theory.* The former involves operations and assumptions only about a single class of objects which is treated as a unitary variable, whereas the latter involves relations among two or more variables. In practice, substantive theories are usually stated in terms of functional relations among the scales that result from the several measurement theories for the variables involved.

For a number of purposes, the scale type is much more crucial than the details of the measurement theory from which the scale is derived. For example, much attention has been paid to the limitations that the scale type places upon the statistics one may sensibly employ. If the interpretation of a particular statistic or statistical test is altered when admissible scale transformations are applied, then our substantive conclusions will depend upon which arbitrary representation of the scale we have used in making our calculations. Most scientists, when they understand the problem, feel that they should shun such statistics and rely only upon those that exhibit the appropriate invariances for the scale type at hand. Both the geometric and arithmetic means are legitimate in this sense for ratio scales (unit arbitrary), only the latter is legitimate for interval scales (unit and zero arbitrary), and neither for ordinal scales. For fuller discussions, see Stevens: 1946, 1951, 1955; for a somewhat less strict interpretation of the conclusions, see Mosteller, 1958.

A second place where the transformation group imposes limitations is in the construction of substantive theories. These limitations seem to have received far less attention than the statistical questions, even though they are undoubtedly more fundamental. The remainder of the paper will attempt to formulate the relation between scale types and functional laws, and to answer the question what psychophysical laws are possible. As already pointed out, these issues have scientific relevance beyond psychophysics.

A PRINCIPLE OF THEORY CONSTRUCTION

In physics one finds at least two classes of basic assumptions: specific empirical laws, such as the universal law of gravitation or Ohm's law, and a priori principles of theory construction, such as the requirement that the laws of mechanics should be invariant under uniform translations and rotations of the coordinate system. Other laws, such as the conservation of energy, seem to have changed from the empirical to the a priori category during the development of physics. In psychology more stress has been put on the discovery of empirical laws than on the formulation of guiding principles, and the search for empirical relations tends to be pursued without the benefit of explicit statements about what is and is not an acceptable theory.[2] Since such principles have been used effectively in physics to limit the possible physical laws, one wonders whether something similar may not be possible in psychology.

Without such principles, practically any relation is a priori possible, and the correct one is difficult to pin down by empirical means because of the ever present errors of observation. The error problem is particularly acute in the behavioral sciences. On the other hand, if a priori consideration about what constitutes an acceptable theory limits us to some rather small set of possible laws, then fairly crude obser-

[2] Two attempts to introduce and use such statements in behavioral problems are the combining of classes condition in stochastic learning theory (Bush, Mosteller, & Thompson, 1954) and some work on the form of the utility function for money which is based upon the demand that certain game theory solutions should remain unchanged when a constant sum of money is added to all the payoffs (Kemeny & Thompson, 1957). In neither case do the conditions seem particularly compelling.

vations may sometimes suffice to decide which law actually obtains.

The principle to be suggested appears to be a generalization of one used in physics. It may be stated as follows.

A substantive theory relating two or more variables and the measurement theories for these variables should be such that:

1. (*Consistency of substantive and measurement theories*) Admissible transformations of one or more of the independent variables shall lead, via the substantive theory, only to admissible transformations of the dependent variables.

2. (*Invariance of the substantive theory*) Except for the numerical values of parameters that reflect the effect on the dependent variables of admissible transformations of the independent variables, the mathematical structure of the substantive theory shall be independent of admissible transformations of the independent variables.

In this principle, and in what follows, the terms independent and dependent variables are used only to distinguish the variables to which arbitrary, admissible transformations are imposed from those for which the transformations are determined by the substantive theory. As will be seen, in some cases the labeling is truly arbitrary in the sense that the substantive theory can be written so that any variable appears either in the dependent or independent role, but in other cases there is a true asymmetry in the sense that some variables must be dependent and others independent if any substantive theory relates them at all.

One can hardly question the consistency part of the principle. If an admissible transformation of an independent variable leads to an inadmissible transformation of a dependent variable, then one is simply saying that the strictures imposed by the measurement theories are incompatible with those imposed by the substantive theory. Such a logical inconsistency must, I think, be interpreted as meaning that something is amiss in the total theoretical structure.

The invariance part is more subtle and controversial. It asserts that we should be able to state the substantive laws of the field without reference to the particular scales that are used to measure the variables. For example, we want to be able to say that Ohm's law states that voltage is proportional to the product of resistance and current without specifying the units that are used to measure voltage, resistance, or current. Put another way, we do not want to have one law when one set of units is used and another when a different set of units is used. Although this seems plausible, there are examples from physics that can be viewed as a particular sort of violation of Part 2; however, let us postpone the discussion of these until some consequences of the principle as stated have been derived.

The meaning of the principle may be clarified by examples that violate it. Suppose it is claimed that two ratio scales are related by a logarithmic law. An admissible transformation of the independent variable x is multiplication by a positive constant k, i.e., a change of unit. However, the fact that $\log kx = \log k + \log x$ means that an inadmissible transformation, namely, a change of zero, is effected on the dependent variable. Hence, the logarithm fails to meet the consistency requirement. Next, consider an exponential law, then the transformation leads to $e^{kx} = (e^x)^k$. This can be viewed either as a violation of consistency or of invariance. If the law is exponential, then the dependent variable is raised to a power, which is inconsistent with its being a ratio scale. Alternatively, the dependent variable may be taken to be a ratio scale, but then the law is not invariant because it is an exponential raised to a power that depends upon the unit of the independent variable.

An Application of the Principle

Most of the physical measures entering into psychophysics are idealized in physical theories in such a way that they form either ratio or interval scales. Mass, length, pressure, and time durations are measured on ratio scales, and physical time (not time durations), ordinary temperature, and entropy are measured on interval scales. Of course, differences and derivatives of interval scale values constitute ratio scales.

Although most psychological scales in current use can at best be considered to be ordinal, those who have worked on psychological measurement theories have attempted to arrive at scales that are either ratio or interval, preferably the former. Examples: the equally often noticed difference assumption and the closely related Case V of Thurstone's "law of comparative judgment" lead to interval scales; Stevens has argued that magnitude estimation methods result in ratio scales (but no measurement theory has been offered in support of this plausible belief); and I have given sufficient conditions to derive a ratio scale from discrimination data. Our question here, however, is not how well psychologists have succeeded in perfecting scales of one type or another, but what a knowledge of scale types can tell us about the relations among scales.

In addition to these two common types of scales, there is some interest in what have been called logarithmic interval scales (Stevens, 1957). In this case the admissible transformations are multiplications by positive constants and raising to positive powers, i.e., kx^c, where $k > 0$ and $c > 0$. The name applied to this scale type reflects the fact that $\log x$ is an interval scale, since the transformed scale goes into $c \log x + \log k$. We will consider all combinations of ratio, interval, and logarithmic interval scales.

Because this topic is more general than psychophysics, I shall refer to the variables as independent and dependent rather than physical and psychological. Both variables will be assumed to form numerical continua having more than one point. Let $x \geq 0$ denote a typical value of the independent variable and $u(x) \geq 0$ the corresponding value of the dependent variable, where u is the unknown functional law relating them. Suppose, first, that both variables form ratio scales. If the unit of the independent variable is changed by multiplying all values by a positive constant k, then according to the principle stated above only an admissible transformation of the dependent variable, namely multiplication by a positive constant, should result and the form of the functional law should be unaffected. That is to say, the changed unit of the dependent variable may depend upon k, but it shall not depend upon x, so we denote it by $K(k)$. Casting this into mathematical terms, we obtain the functional equation

$$u(kx) = K(k)u(x)$$

where $k > 0$ and $K(k) > 0$.

Functional equations for the other cases are arrived at in a similar manner. They are summarized in Table 1.

The question is: What do these nine functional equations, each of which embodies the principle, imply about

TABLE 1

THE FUNCTIONAL EQUATIONS FOR THE LAWS SATISFYING THE
PRINCIPLE OF THEORY CONSTRUCTION

Eq. No.	Scale Types		Functional Equation	Comments
	Independent Variable	Dependent Variable		
1	ratio	ratio	$u(kx) = K(k)u(x)$	$k>0,\ K(k)>0$
2	ratio	interval	$u(kx) = K(k)u(x) + C(k)$	$k>0,\ K(k)>0$
3	ratio	log interval	$u(kx) = K(k)u(x)^{C(k)}$	$k>0,\ K(k)>0,\ C(k)>0$
4	interval	ratio	$u(kx+c) = K(k,c)u(x)$	$k>0,\ K(k,c)>0$
5	interval	interval	$u(kx+c) = K(k,c)u(x)$ $+ C(k,c)$	$k>0,\ K(k,c)>0$
6	interval	log interval	$u(kx+c) = K(k,c)u(x)^{C(k,c)}$	$k>0,\ K(k,c)>0,\ C(k,c)>0$
7	log interval	ratio	$u(kx^c) = K(k,c)u(x)$	$k>0,\ c>0,\ K(k,c)>0$
8	log interval	interval	$u(kx^c) = K(k,c)u(x) + C(k,c)$	$k>0,\ c>0,\ K(k,c)>0$
9	log interval	log interval	$u(kx^c) = K(k,c)u(x)^{C(k,c)}$	$k>0,\ c>0,\ K(k,c)>0,$ $C(k,c)>0$

the form of u? We shall limit our consideration to theories where u is a continuous, nonconstant function of x.

Theorem 1. If the independent and dependent continua are both ratio scales, then $u(x) = \alpha x^\beta$, where β is independent of the units of both variables.[3]

Proof. Set $x = 1$ in Equation 1, then $u(k) = K(k)u(1)$. Because u is nonconstant we may choose k so that $u(k) > 0$, and because $K(k) > 0$, it follows that $u(1) > 0$, so $K(k) = u(k)/u(1)$. Thus, Equation 1 becomes $u(kx)$

[3] In this and in the following theorems, the statement can be made more general, if x is replaced by $x + \gamma$, where γ is a constant independent of x but having the same unit as x. The effect of this is to place the zero of u at some point different from the zero of x. In psychophysics the constant γ may be regarded as the threshold. The presence of such a constant means, of course, that a plot of log u vs. log x will not in general be a straight line. If, however, the independent variable is measured in terms of deviations from the threshold, the plot may become straight. Such nonlinear plots have been observed, and in at least some instances the degree of curvature seems to be correlated with the magnitude of the threshold. Further empirical work is needed to see whether this is a correct explanation of the curvature.

$= u(k)u(x)/u(1)$. Let $v = \log[u/u(1)]$, then

$$v(kx) = \log\left[u(kx)/u(1)\right]$$
$$= \log\frac{u(k)u(x)}{u(1)u(1)}$$
$$= \log\left[u(k)/u(1)\right]$$
$$+ \log\left[u(x)/u(1)\right]$$
$$= v(k) + v(x)$$

Since u is continuous, so is v, and it is well known that the only continuous solutions to the last functional equation are of the form

$$v(x) = \beta \log x$$
$$= \log x^\beta$$

Thus,

$$u(x) = \alpha e^{v(x)}$$
$$= \alpha x^\beta$$

where $\alpha = u(1)$.

We observe that since

$$u(kx) = \alpha k^\beta x^\beta = \alpha' x^\beta$$

β is independent of the unit of x, and it is clearly independent of the unit of u.

Theorem 2. If the independent continuum is a ratio scale and the depend-

ent continuum an interval scale, then either $u(x) = \alpha \log x + \beta$, where α is independent of the unit of the independent variable, or $u(x) = \alpha x^\beta + \delta$, where β is independent of the units of both variables and δ is independent of the unit of the independent variable.

Proof. In solving Equation 2, there are two possibilities to consider.

1. If $K(k) \equiv 1$, then define $v = e^u$. Equation 2 becomes $v(kx) = D(k)v(x)$, where $D(k) = e^{C(k)} > 0$ and v is continuous, positive, and nonconstant because u is. By Theorem 1, $v(x) = \delta x^\alpha$, where α is independent of the unit of x and where $\delta > 0$ because, by definition, $v > 0$. Taking logarithms, $u(x) = \alpha \log x + \beta$, where $\beta = \log \delta$.

2. If $K(k) \not\equiv 1$, then let u and u^* be two different solutions to the problem, and define $w = u^* - u$. It follows immediately from Equation 2 that w must satisfy the functional equation $w(kx) = K(k)w(x)$. Since both u and u^* are continuous, so is w; however, it may be a constant. Since $K(k) \not\equiv 1$, it is clear that the only constant solution is $w = 0$, and this is impossible since u and u^* were chosen to be different. Thus, by Theorem 1, $w(x) = ax^\beta$. Substituting this into the functional equation for w, it follows that $K(k) = k^\beta$. Then setting $x = 0$ in Equation 2, we obtain $C(k) = u(0) \times (1 - k^\beta)$. We now observe that $u(x) = \alpha x^\beta + \delta$, where $\delta = u(0)$, is a solution to Equation 2:

$$u(kx) = \alpha k^\beta x^\beta + \delta$$
$$= \alpha k^\beta x^\beta + u(0)k^\beta + u(0) - u(0)k^\beta$$
$$= k^\beta u(x) + u(0)(1 - k^\beta)$$
$$= K(k)u(x) + C(k)$$

Any other solution is of the same form because

$$u^*(x) = u(x) + w(x)$$
$$= \alpha x^\beta + \delta + ax^\beta$$
$$= (\alpha + a)x^\beta + \delta$$

It is easy to see that δ is independent of the unit of x and β is independent of both units.

A much simpler proof of this theorem can be given if we assume that u is differentiable in addition to being continuous. Since the derivative of an interval scale is a ratio scale, it follows immediately that du/dx satisfies Equation 1 and so, by Theorem 1, $\dfrac{du}{dx} = \alpha x^\beta$. Integrating, we get

$$u(x) = \begin{cases} \dfrac{\alpha}{\beta + 1}x^{\beta+1} + \delta & \text{if } \beta \neq -1 \\ \alpha \log x + \delta & \text{if } \beta = -1 \end{cases}$$

Theorem 3. If the independent continuum is a ratio scale and the dependent continuum is a logarithmic interval scale, then either $u(x) = \delta e^{\alpha x^\beta}$, where α is independent of the unit of the dependent variable, β is independent of the units of both variables and δ is independent of the unit of the independent variable, or $u(x) = \alpha x^\beta$, where β is independent of the units of both variables.

Proof. Take the logarithm of Equation 3 and let $v = \log u$:

$$v(kx) = K^*(k) + C(k)v(x)$$

where $K^*(k) = \log K(k)$. By Theorem 2, either

$$v(x) = \alpha x^\beta + \delta^* \text{ or } v(x) = \beta \log x + \alpha^*$$

Taking exponentials, either

$$u(x) = \delta e^{\alpha x^\beta} \quad \text{or} \quad u(x) = \alpha x^\beta$$

where $\delta = e^{\delta^*}$ and, in the second equation, $\alpha = e^{\alpha^*}$.

Theorem 4. If the independent continuum is an interval scale, then it is impossible for the dependent continuum to be a ratio scale.

Proof. Let $c = 0$ in Equation 4, then by Theorem 1 we know $u(x) = \alpha x^\beta$.

Now set $k = 1$ and $c \neq 0$ in Equation 3:

$$\alpha(x + c)^\beta = K(1,c)\alpha x^\beta$$

so

$$x + c = K(1,c)^{1/\beta}x$$

which implies x is a constant, contrary to our assumption that both continua have more than one point.

Theorem 5. *If the independent and dependent continua are both interval scales, then $u(x) = \alpha x + \beta$, where β is independent of the unit of the independent variable.*

Proof. If we let $c = 0$, then Equation 5 reduces to Equation 2 and so Theorem 2 applies. If $u(x) = \alpha \log x + \beta$, then choosing $k = 1$ and $c \neq 0$ in Equation 5 yields

$$\alpha \log (x + c) + \beta = K(1,c)\alpha \log x \\ + K(1,c)\beta + C(1,c)$$

By taking the derivative with respect to x, it is easy to see that x must be a constant, which is impossible.

Thus, we must conclude that $u(x) = \alpha x^\delta + \beta$. Again, set $k = 1$ and $c \neq 0$,

$$\alpha(x + c)^\delta = K(1,c)\alpha x^\delta \\ + K(1,c)\beta + C(1,c)$$

If $\delta \neq 1$, then differentiate with respect to x:

$$\alpha\delta(x + c)^{\delta-1} = K(1,c)\alpha\delta x^{\delta-1}$$

which implies x is a constant, so we must conclude $\delta = 1$. It is easy to see that $u(x) = \alpha x + \beta$ satisfies Equation 5.

Theorem 6. *If the independent continuum is an interval scale and the dependent continuum is a logarithmic interval scale, then $u(x) = \alpha e^{\beta x}$, where α is independent of the unit of the independent variable and β is independent of the unit of the dependent variable.*

Proof. Take the logarithm of Equation 6 and let $v = \log u$:

$$v(kx + c) = K^*(k,c) + C(k,c)v(x)$$

where $K^*(k,c) = \log K(k,c)$. By Theorem 5,

$$v(x) = \beta x + \alpha^*$$

so

$$u(x) = \alpha e^{\beta x}$$

where $\alpha = e^{\alpha^*}$.

Theorem 7. *If the independent continuum is a logarithmic interval scale, then it is impossible for the dependent continuum to be a ratio scale.*

Proof. Let $v(\log x) = u(x)$, i.e., $v(y) = u(e^y)$, then Equation 7 becomes

$$v(\log k + c \log x) = K(k,c)u(\log x)$$

Thus, $\log x$ is an interval scale and v is a ratio scale, which by Theorem 4 is impossible.

Theorem 8. *If the independent continuum is a logarithmic interval scale and the dependent continuum is an interval scale, then $u(x) = \alpha \log x + \beta$, where α is independent of the unit of the independent variable.*

Proof. Let $v(\log x) = u(x)$, then Equation 8 becomes

$$v(\log k + c \log x) \\ = K(k,c)v(\log x) + C(k,c)$$

so $\log x$ and v are both interval scales. By Theorem 5,

$$u(x) = v(\log x) \\ = \alpha \log x + \beta$$

Theorem 9. *If the independent and dependent continua are both logarithmic interval scales, then $u(x) = \alpha x^\beta$, where β is independent of the units of both the independent and dependent variables.*

Proof. Take the logarithm of Equation 9 and let $v = \log u$:

$$v(kx^c) = K^*(k,c) + C(k,c)v(x)$$

where $K^*(k,c) = \log K(k,c)$. By Theorem 8,

$$v(x) = \beta \log x + \alpha^*$$

so

$$u(x) = e^{v(x)}$$
$$= \alpha x^\beta$$

where $\alpha = e^{\alpha^*}$.

ILLUSTRATIONS

It may be useful, prior to discussing these results, to cite a few familiar laws that accord with some of them. The best source of examples is classical physics, where most of the fundamental variables are idealized as continua that form either ratio or interval scales. No attempt will be made to illustrate the results concerning logarithmic interval scales, because no actual use of scales of this type seems to have been made.

The variables entering into Coulomb's law, Ohm's law, and Newton's gravitation law are all ratio scales, and in each case the form of the law is a power function, as called for by Theorem 1. Additional examples of Theorem 1 can be found in geometry since length, area, and volume are ratio scales; thus the dependency of the volume of a sphere upon its radius or of the area of a square on its side are illustrations.

Other important variables such as energy and entropy form interval scales, and we can therefore anticipate that as dependent variables they will illustrate Theorem 2. If a body of constant mass is moving at velocity v, then its energy is of the form $\alpha v^2 + \delta$. If the temperature of a perfect gas is constant, then as a function of pressure p the entropy of the gas is of the

form $\alpha \log p + \beta$. No examples, of course, are possible for Theorem 4.

As an example of Theorem 5 we may consider ordinary temperature, which is frequently measured in terms of the length of a column of mercury. Although length as a measure forms a ratio scale, the length of a column of mercury used to measure temperature is an interval scale (subject to the added constraint that the length is positive), since we may choose any initial length to correspond to a given temperature, such as the freezing point of water. If the temperature scale is also an interval scale, as is usually assumed, then the only relation possible according to Theorem 5 is the linear one.

DISCUSSION

Some with whom I have discussed these theorems—which from a mathematical point of view are not new—have had strong misgivings about their interpretation; the feeling is that something of a substantive nature must have been smuggled into the formulation of the problem. They argue that practically any functional relation can hold between two variables and that it is an empirical, not a theoretical, matter to ascertain what the function may be in specific cases. To support this view and to challenge the theorems, they have cited examples from physics, such as the exponential law of radioactive decay or some sinusoidal function of time, which seem to violate the theorems stated above. We must, therefore, examine the ways in which these examples bypass the rather strong conclusions of the present theory.

All physical examples which have been suggested to me as counterexamples to the theorems have a common form: the independent variable is a ratio scale, but it enters into the equation in a dimensionless fashion. For example, some identifiable value of the variable is taken as the reference level x_0, and all other values are expressed in reference to it as x/x_0. The effect of this is to make the quantity x/x_0 independent of the unit used to measure the variable, since $kx/kx_0 = x/x_0$. In periodic functions of time, the period is often used as a reference level. Slightly more generally, the independent variable only appears multiplied by a constant c whose units are the inverse of those of x. Thus, whenever the unit of x is changed by multiplying all values by a constant $k > 0$, it is necessary to adjust the unit of c by multiplying it by $1/k$. But this means that the product is independent of k: $(c/k)(kx) = cx$. The time constant in the law of radioactive decay is of this nature.

There are two ways to view these examples in relation to the principle stated above. If the ratio scale x is taken to be the independent variable, then the invariance part of the principle is not satisfied by these laws. If, however, for the purpose of the law under consideration the dimensionless quantity cx is treated as the variable, then no violation has occurred. Although surprising at first glance, it is easy to see that the principle imposes no limitations upon the form of the law when the independent variable is dimensionless, i.e., when no transformations save the identity are admissible.

We are thus led to the following conclusion. Either the independent variable is a ratio scale that is multiplied by a dimensional constant that makes the product independent of the unit of the scale, in which case there is no restriction upon the laws into which it may enter, or the independent variable is not rendered dimensionless, in which case the laws must be of the form described by the above theorems. Both situations are found in classical physics, and one wonders if there is any fundamental difference between them. I have not seen any discussion of the matter, and I have only the most uncertain impression that there is a difference. In many physical situations where a dimensional constant multiplies the independent variable, the dependent variable is bounded. This is true of both the decay and periodic laws. Usually, the constant is expressed in some natural way in terms of the bounds, as, for example, the period of a periodic function. Whether dimensional constants can legitimately be used in other situations, or whether they can always be eliminated, is not at all apparent to me.

One may legitimately question which of these alternatives is applicable to psychophysics, and the answer is far from clear. The widespread use of, say, the threshold as a reference level seems at first to suggest that psychophysical laws are to be expressed in terms of dimensionless quantities; however, the fact that this is done mainly to present results in decibels may mean no more than that the given ratio scale is being transformed into an interval scale in accordance with Theorem 2:

$$y = \alpha \log x/x_0$$
$$= \alpha \log x + \beta$$

where

$$\beta = -\alpha \log x_0$$

In addition to dimensionless variables as a means of by-passing the restrictions imposed by scale types, three other possibilities deserve discussion.

First, the idealization that the scales form mathematical continua and that they are related by a continuous function may not reflect the actual state of affairs in the empirical world. It is certainly true that, in detail, physical continua are not mathematical continua, and there is ample reason to suspect that the same holds for psychological variables. But the assumptions that stimuli and responses both form continua are idealizations that are difficult to give up; to do so would mean casting out much of psychophysical theory. Alternatively, we could drop the demand that the function relating them be continuous, but it is doubtful if this would be of much help by itself. The discontinuous solutions to, say, Equation 1 are manifold and extremely wild in their behavior. They are so wild that it is difficult to say anything precise about them at all (see Hamel, 1905; Jones: 1942a, 1942b), and it is doubtful that such solutions represent empirical laws.

Second, casual observation suggests that it might be appropriate to assume that at least the dependent variable is bounded, e.g., that there is a psychologically maximum loudness. Although plausible, boundedness cannot be imposed by itself since, as is shown in the theorems, all the continuous solutions to the appropriate functional equations are unbounded if the functions are increasing, as they must be for empirical reasons. It seems clear that boundedness of the dependent variable is intimately tied up either with introducing a reference level so that the independent variable is an absolute scale or with some discontinuity in the formulation of the problem, possibly in the nature of the variables or possibly in the function relating them. Actually, one can establish that it must be in the nature of the variables. Suppose, on the contrary, that the variables are ratio scales that form numerical continua

and that they are related by a function u that is nonnegative, nonconstant, and monotonic increasing, but not necessarily continuous. We now need only show that u cannot be bounded to show that the discontinuity must exist in the variable. Suppose, therefore, that it is bounded and that the bound is M. By Equation 1, $u(kx) = K(k)u(x) \leq M$, so $u(x) \leq M/K(k)$. For $k \geq 1$, the monotonicity of u implies that $u(x) \leq u(kx) = K(k)u(x)$, so choosing $u(x) > 0$ we see that $K(k) \geq 1$. If for some $k \geq 1$, $K(k) > 1$, then K can be made arbitrarily large since, for any integer n, $K(k^n) = K(k)^n$, but since $u(x) \leq \dfrac{M}{K(k)}$, this implies $u \equiv 0$, contrary to assumption. Thus, for all $k \geq 1$, $K(k) = 1$, which by Equation 1, means $u(kx) = u(x)$, for all x and $k \geq 1$. This in turn implies u is a constant, which again is contrary to assumption. Thus, we have established our claim that some discontinuity must reside in the nature of the variables.

Third, in many situations, there are two or more independent variables; for example, both intensity and frequency determine loudness. Usually we hold all but one variable constant in our empirical investigations, but the fact remains that the others are there and that their presence may make some difference in the total range of possible laws. For example, suppose there are two independent variables, x and y, both of which form ratio scales and that the dependent variable u is also a ratio scale, then the analogue of Equation 1 is

$$u(kx,hy) = K(k,h)u(x,y)$$

where $k > 0$, $h > 0$, and $K(k,h) > 0$. We know by Theorem 1 that if we hold one variable, say y, fixed at some value and let $h = 1$, then the solution must be of the form

$$u(x,y) = \alpha(y)x^{\beta(y)}$$

But holding x constant and letting $k = 1$, we also know that it must be of the form

$$u(x,y) = \delta(x)y^{\epsilon(x)}$$

Thus,

$$\alpha(y)x^{\beta(y)} = \delta(x)y^{\epsilon(x)}$$

If we restrict ourselves to u's having partial derivatives of both variables, this equation can be shown (see Section 2.C.2 of Luce [in press]) to have solutions only of the form:

$$u(x,y) = ax^{b}y^{c+d\ \log\ x}$$

Thus, the principle again severely restricts the possible laws, even when we admit more than one independent variable.[4]

It must be emphasized that the remark in Footnote 3 does not apply here. If a function that depends upon one independent variable is added to the other, e.g.,

$$u(x,y) = \alpha(y)[x + \gamma(y)]^{\beta(y)}$$

then wholly new solution possibilities exist (see Section 2.C.3 of Luce [in press]).

In sum, there appear to be two ways around the restrictions set forth in the theorems. The first can be viewed either as a rejection of Part 2 of the principle or as the creation of a dimensionless independent variable from a ratio scale; it involves the presence of dimensional constants that cancel out the dimensions of the independent variables. This appears to be particularly appropriate if the dependent variable has a true, well-defined bound. The second is to reject the idealization of the variables as numerical continua and, possibly, to assume that they are bounded.

On the other hand, if the theorems are applicable, then the possible psychophysical (and other) laws become severely limited. Indeed, they are so limited that one can argue that the important question is not to determine the forms of the laws, but rather to create empirically testable measurement theories for the several psychophysical methods in order that we may know for certain what types of scales are being obtained. Once this is known, the form of the psychophysical functions is determined except for some numerical constants. In the meantime, however, experimental determinations of the form of the psychophysical functions by methods for which no measurement theories exist provides at least indirect evidence of the type of scale being obtained. For example, the magnitude methods seem to result in power functions, which suggests that the psychological measure is either a ratio or a logarithmic interval scale, not an interval scale. Since the results from cross-modality matchings tend to eliminate the logarithmic interval scale as a possibility, there is presumptive evidence that these methods yield ratio scales, as Stevens has claimed.

SUMMARY

The following problem was considered. What are the possible forms of a substantive theory that relates a dependent variable in a continuous manner to an independent variable? Each variable is idealized as a nu-

[4] The use of this argument to arrive at the form of $u(x,y)$ seems much more satisfactory and convincing than the heuristic development given in Section 2.C of Luce (in press), and the empirical suggestions given there should gain correspondingly in interest as a result of the present work.

TABLE 2

The Possible Laws Satisfying the Principle of Theory Construction

Scale Types		Possible Laws	Comments[a]
Independent Variable	Dependent Variable		
ratio	ratio	$u(x) = \alpha x^\beta$	$\beta/x; \beta/u$
ratio	interval	$u(x) = \alpha \log x + \beta$	α/x
		$u(x) = \alpha x^\beta + \delta$	$\beta/x; \beta/u; \delta/x$
ratio	log interval	$u(x) = \delta e^{\alpha x \beta}$	$\alpha/u; \beta/x; \beta/u; \delta/x$
		$u(x) = \alpha x^\beta$	$\beta/x; \beta/u$
interval	ratio	impossible	
interval	interval	$u(x) = \alpha x + \beta$	β/x
interval	log interval	$u(x) = \alpha e^{\beta x}$	$\alpha/x; \beta/u$
log interval	ratio	impossible	
log interval	interval	$u(x) = \alpha \log x + \beta$	α/x
log interval	log interval	$u(x) = \alpha x^\beta$	$\beta/x; \beta/u$

[a] The notation α/x means "α is independent of the unit of x."

merical continuum and is restricted by its measurement theory to being either a ratio, an interval, or a logarithmic interval scale. As a principle of theory construction, it is suggested that transformations of the independent variable that are admissible under its measurement theory shall not result in inadmissible transformations of the dependent variable (consistency) and that the form of the functional relation between the two variables shall not be altered by admissible transformation of the independent variable (invariance). This principle limits significantly the possible laws relating the two continua, as shown in Table 2.

These results do not hold in two important circumstances. First, if the independent variable is a ratio scale that is rendered dimensionless by multiplying it by a constant having units reciprocal to those of the independent variable, then either the principle has no content or it is violated, depending upon how one wishes to look at the matter. Second, if the variables are discrete rather than continuous, or if the functional relation is discontinuous, then laws other than those given in Table 2 are possible.

REFERENCES

Bush, R. R., Mosteller, F., & Thompson, G. L. A formal structure for multiple-choice situations. In R. M. Thrall, C. H. Coombs, & R. L. Davis (Eds.), *Decision processes.* New York: Wiley, 1954. Pp. 99–126.

Cohen, M. R., & Nagel, E. *An introduction to logic and scientific method.* New York: Harcourt, Brace, 1934.

Hamel, G. Eine Basis aller Zahlen und die unstetigen Lösungen der Funktionalgleichung: $f(x + y) = f(x) + f(y)$. *Math. Annalen,* 1905, 60, 459–462.

Jones, F. B. Connected and disconnected plane sets and the functional equation $f(x) + f(y) = f(x + y)$. *Bull. Amer. Math. Soc.,* 1942, 48, 115–120. (a)

Jones, F. B. Measure and other properties of a Hamel basis. *Bull. Amer. Math. Soc.,* 1942, 48, 472–481. (b)

Kemeny, J. G., & Thompson, G. L. The effect of psychological attitudes on the outcomes of games. In M. Dresher, A. W. Tucker, & P. Wolfe (Eds.), *Contributions to the theory of games, III.* Princeton: Princeton Univer. Press, 1957. Pp. 273–298.

Luce, R. D. *Individual choice behavior: A theoretical analysis.* New York: Wiley, in press.

Luce, R. D., & Edwards, W. The derivation of subjective scales from just noticeable differences. *Psychol. Rev.,* 1958, 65, 222–237.

Mosteller, F. The mystery of the missing corpus. *Psychometrika,* 1958, 23, 279–289.

STEVENS, S. S. On the theory of scales of measurement. *Science*, 1946, **103**, 677–680.

STEVENS, S. S. Mathematics, measurement and psychophysics. In S. S. Stevens (Ed.), *Handbook of experimental psychology*. New York: Wiley, 1951. Pp. 1–49.

STEVENS, S. S. On the averaging of data. *Science*, 1955, **121**, 113–116.

STEVENS, S. S. The direct estimation of sensory magnitudes—loudness. *Amer. J. Psychol.*, 1956, **69**, 1–25.

STEVENS, S. S. On the psychophysical law. *Psychol. Rev.*, 1957, **64**, 153–181.

STEVENS, S. S. Cross-modality validation of subjective scales for loudness, vibration, and electric shock. *J. exp. Psychol.*, 1959, **57**, 201–209.

STEVENS, S. S., & GALANTER, E. H. Ratio scales and category scales for a dozen perceptual continua. *J. exp. Psychol.*, 1957, **54**, 377–411.

THURSTONE, L. L. A law of comparative judgment. *Psychol. Rev.*, 1927, **34**, 273–286.

VON NEUMANN, J., & MORGENSTERN, O. *The theory of games and economic behavior*. (2nd ed.) Princeton: Princeton Univer. Press, 1947.

(Received December 2, 1958)

MULTIVARIATE INFORMATION TRANSMISSION*†

WILLIAM J. McGILL

MASSACHUSETTS INSTITUTE OF TECHNOLOGY

A multivariate analysis based on transmitted information is presented. It is shown that sample transmitted information provides a simple method for measuring and testing association in multi-dimensional contingency tables. Relations with analysis of variance are pointed out, and statistical tests are described.

Several recent articles in the psychological journals have shown how ideas derived from communication theory are being applied in psychology.

It is not widely understood, however, that the tools made available by communication theory are useful for analyzing data whether or not we believe the human organism is best described as a communications system.

This paper will present an extension of Shannon's (**10**) measure of transmitted information. It will be shown that transmitted information leads to a simple multivariate analysis of contingency data, and to appropriate statistical tests.

1. Basic Definitions

Let us consider a communication channel and its input and output. Transmitted information measures the amount of association between the input and output of the channel. If input and output are perfectly correlated, all the input information is transmitted. On the other hand, if input and output are independent, no information is transmitted. Naturally most cases of information transmission are found between these extremes. There is some uncertainty at the receiver about what was sent. Some information is transmitted and some does not get through.

We are interested not in what the transmitted information is, but in the amount of information transmitted. Suppose that we have a discrete input variable, x, and a discrete output variable, y. Since x is discrete, it takes on values or signals $k = 1, 2, 3, \cdots, X$ with probabilities indicated by $p(k)$. Similarly, y assumes values $m = 1, 2, 3, \cdots, Y$ with probabilities $p(m)$. If it happens that k is sent and m is received, we can speak of the joint input-output event (k,m). This joint event has probability $p(k,m)$.

*This work was supported in part by the Air Force Human Factors Operations Research Laboratories, and in part jointly by the Army, Navy, and Air Force under contract with the Massachusetts Institute of Technology.

†Several of the indices and tests discussed in this paper have been developed independently by J. E. Keith Smith (**11**) at the University of Michigan, and by W. R. Garner at Johns Hopkins University.

This article appeared in *Psychometrika*, 1954, **19**, 97–116. Reprinted with permission.

The rules governing the selection of signals at either end of the channel must be constructed so that

$$\sum_{k=1}^{k=X} p(k) = \sum_{m=1}^{m=Y} p(m) = \sum_{k,m} p(k,m) = 1.$$

Under these conditions, assuming successive signals are independent, the amount of information transmitted in "bits" per signal is defined as

$$T(x;y) = H(x) + H(y) - H(x,y), \tag{1}$$

where

$$H(x) = -\sum_{k} p(k) \log_2 p(k),$$

$$H(y) = -\sum_{m} p(m) \log_2 p(m),$$

$$H(x,y) = -\sum_{k,m} p(k,m) \log_2 p(k,m).$$

One "bit" is equal to $-\log_2 (\frac{1}{2})$ and represents the information conveyed by a choice between two equally probable alternatives. Our development will use the bit as a unit, since this is the convention in information theory, but any convenient unit may be substituted by changing the base of the logarithm.

If there is a relation between x and y, $H(x) + H(y) > H(x,y)$ and the size of the inequality is just $T(x;y)$. On the other hand, if x and y are independent, $H(x,y) = H(x) + H(y)$ and $T(x;y)$ is zero. It can be shown that $T(x;y)$ is never negative.

The presentation to this point has been an outline of the properties of the measure of transmitted information as set forth by Shannon (10). These properties may be summarized by stating that the amount of information transmitted is a bivariate, positive quantity that measures the association between input and output of a channel. There are, however, very few restrictions on how a channel may be defined. The input-output relations that occur in many psychological contexts are certainly possible channels. Consequently we can measure transmitted information in these contexts and anticipate that the results will be interesting.

2. Sample Information

Our development will be based on sample measures of information, i.e., on measures of information constructed from relative frequencies.

Suppose that we make n observations of events (k,m). We identify n_{km} as the number of times that k was sent and m was received. This means that

$$n_k = \sum_{m} n_{km},$$

$$n_m = \sum_{k} n_{km},$$

$$n = \sum_{k,m} n_{km},$$

where n_k is the number of times that k was sent, n_m is the number of times that m was received, and n is the total number of observations. A particular experiment can then be represented by a contingency table with XY cells and entries n_{km} .

We may estimate the probabilities, $p(k)$, $p(m)$, and $p(k,m)$ with n_k/n, n_m/n, and n_{km}/n, respectively. Sample transmitted information, $T'(x;y)$, is defined as

$$T'(x;y) = H'(x) + H'(y) - H'(x,y), \tag{2}$$

where $H'(x)$, $H'(y)$ and $H'(x,y)$ are constructed from relative frequencies instead of from probabilities. [Throughout the paper a prime is used over a quantity to indicate the maximum likelihood estimator of the same quantity without the prime, e.g., $T'(x;y)$ is an estimator for $T(x;y)$.] As before, $T'(x;y)$ is the amount of transmitted information (in the sample) measured in "bits" per signal.

Since it is difficult to manipulate logs of relative frequencies, we will introduce an easier notation:

$$s_{km} = \frac{1}{n} \sum_{k,m} n_{km} \log_2 n_{km} ,$$

$$s_k = \frac{1}{n} \sum_{k} n_k \log_2 n_k ,$$

$$s_m = \frac{1}{n} \sum_{m} n_m \log_2 n_m ,$$

$$s = \log_2 n.$$

Expressions involving sample measures of information are easier to handle in this notation. For example, $T'(x;y)$ becomes

$$T'(x;y) = s - s_k - s_m + s_{km} . \tag{3}$$

Equations (2) and (3) are equivalent expressions for $T'(x;y)$. When we write equations like (3), we shall say that these equations are written in s-notation. Thus (3) is (2) in s-notation.

3. Three-Dimensional Transmitted Information

Now let us extend the definition of transmitted information to include two sources, u and v, that transmit to y. To accomplish this we replace x in equation (2) with u, v and we find that

$$T'(u,v;y) = H'(u,v) + H'(y) - H'(u,v,y), \tag{4}$$

where x has been subdivided into two classes, u and v. The possible values of u are $i = 1, 2, 3, \cdots , U$, while v assumes values $j = 1, 2, 3, \cdots , V$. The subdivision is arranged so that the range of values of u and v jointly constitute the possible values of x. This means that the input event, k, can be replaced by the joint input event (i,j). Consequently we have

$$n_k = n_{ij} ,$$

and the direct substitution of u,v for x in (2) is legitimate.

Our new term, $T'(u,v;y)$, measures the amount of information transmitted when u and v transmit to y. It is evident, however, that the direction of transmission is irrelevant, for examination of (4) reveals that

$$T'(u,v;y) = T'(y;u,v).$$

This means that nothing is gained formally by distinguishing transmitters from receivers. The amount of information transmitted is a measure of association between variables. It does not respect the direction in which the information is travelling. On the other hand, we cannot permute symbols at will, for

$$T'(u,y;v) = H'(u,y) + H'(v) - H'(u,v,y),$$

and this is not necessarily equal to $T'(u,v;y)$.

Our aim now is to measure $T'(u,v;y)$ and then to express $T''(u,v;y)$ as a function of the bivariate transmissions between u and y, and v and y. Computation of $T''(u,v;y)$ is not difficult. Our observations of the joint event (i,j,m) organize themselves into a three-dimensional contingency table with UVY cells and entries n_{ijm} . We can compute the quantities in (4) from this table, or we can write

$$T'(u,v;y) = s - s_m - s_{ij} + s_{ijm} , \tag{5}$$

where

$$s_{ijm} = \frac{1}{n} \sum_{i,j,m} n_{ijm} \log_2 n_{ijm} ,$$

and the other s-terms are defined by analogy with the s-terms in equation (3).

Now suppose we want to study transmission between u and y. We may eliminate v in two ways. First let us reduce the three-dimensional contingency table to two dimensions by summing over v. The entries in the reduced table are

$$n_{im} = \sum_{j} n_{ijm} .$$

We have for the transmitted information between u and y,

$$T'(u;y) = s - s_i - s_m + s_{im} . \tag{6}$$

The second way to eliminate v is to compute the transmission between u and y separately for each value of v and then average these together. This transmitted information will be called $T'_v(u;y)$, where

$$T'_v(u;y) = \sum_j \frac{n_j}{n} [T'_j(u;y)], \tag{7}$$

and $T'_j(u;y)$ is information transmitted between u and y for a single value of v, namely j. It is readily shown that

$$T'_v(u;y) = s_j - s_{ij} - s_{jm} + s_{ijm} . \tag{8}$$

We see that $T'_v(u;y)$ is written in the same way as $T'(u;y)$ except that the subscript j is added to each of the s-terms.

There are three different pairs of variables in a three-dimensional contingency table. For example, the two equations for transmission between v and y are written

$$T'(v;y) = s - s_j - s_m + s_{jm} , \tag{9}$$

$$T'_u(v;y) = s_i - s_{ij} - s_{im} + s_{ijm} . \tag{10}$$

Finally we may study transmission between u and v, i.e.,

$$T'(u;v) = s - s_i - s_j + s_{ij} , \tag{11}$$

$$T'_v(u;v) = s_m - s_{im} - s_{jm} + s_{ijm} . \tag{12}$$

With these results in mind let us reconsider the information transmitted between u and y. If v has an effect on transmission between u and y, then $T'_v(u;y) \neq T'(u;y)$. One way to measure the size of the effect is by

$$A'(uvy) = T'_v(u;y) - T'(u;y),$$

$$A'(uvy) = -s + s_i + s_j + s_m - s_{ij} - s_{im} - s_{jm} + s_{ijm} . \tag{13}$$

A few more substitutions will show that

$$A'(uvy) = T'_v(u;y) - T'(u;y),$$

$$= T'_u(v;y) - T'(v;y), \tag{14}$$

$$= T'_v(u;v) - T'(u;v).$$

In view of this symmetry, we may call $A'(uvy)$ the $u \cdot v \cdot y$ interaction information. We see that $A'(uvy)$ is the gain (or loss) in sample information transmitted between any two of the variables, due to additional knowledge of the third variable.

Now we can express the three-dimensional information transmitted from u,v to y, i.e., $T'(u,v;y)$, as a function of its bivariate components, for

$$T'(u,v;y) = T'(u;y) + T'(v;y) + A'(uvy), \tag{15}$$

$$T'(u,v;y) = T'_v(u;y) + T'_u(v;y) - A'(uvy). \tag{16}$$

Equations (15) and (16) taken together mean that $T''(u,v;y)$ can be represented by a diagram with overlapping circles as shown in Figure 1. The diagram assumes what we shall call "positive" interaction between u,v and y. Inter-

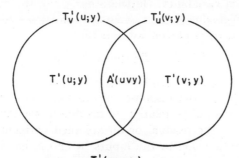

$$T'(u,v;y)$$

FIGURE 1

Schematic diagram of the components of three-dimensional transmitted information. The diagram shows that three-dimensional transmission can be analyzed into a pair of bivariate transmissions plus an interaction term. The meanings of the symbols are explained in the text.

action is positive when the effect of holding one of the interacting variables constant is to increase the amount of association between the other two. This means that $T'_v(u;y) > T'(u;y)$ and $T'_u(v;y) > T'(v;y)$. [Because of (14), if one of these inequalities holds, both must hold.] Later on, however, we shall show that interaction may be negative. When this happens, relations between the interacting variables are reversed, and the diagram in Figure 1 is no longer strictly correct.

4. *Components of Response Information*

The multivariate model of information transmission is useful to us because the situations treated by communication theory are not the same as those we deal with in psychological applications. The engineer is usually able to restrict himself to transmission from a single information source. He knows the statistical properties of the source, and when he speaks of noise he means random noise. This kind of precision is seldom available to us. In our experiments we generally do not know in advance how many sources are transmitting information. We must therefore be careful not to confuse statistical noise with the experimenter's ignorance.

The bivariate model of transmitted information provided by communication theory tells us to attribute to random noise whatever uncertainty there is in specifying the response when the stimulus is known (1). Consequently, if several sources transmit information to responses, the bivariate model will certainly fail to discriminate effects due to uncontrolled sources from those due to random variability. On the other hand, the multivariate model can measure the effects due to the various transmitting sources. For example, in three-dimensional transmission we find that

$$H'(y) = H'_{uv}(y) + T'(u;y) + T'(v;y) + A'(uvy), \qquad (17)$$

where $H'(y) = s - s_m$ and $H'_{uv}(y) = s_{ij} - s_{ijm}$.

We see that $H'(y)$, the response information, has been analyzed into an error term plus a set of correlation terms due to the input variables. The error term, $H'_{uv}(y)$, is the residual or unexplained variability in the output, y, after the information due to the inputs, u and v, has been removed. In bivariate information transmission, the response information is analyzed less precisely. For example, we may have

$$H'(y) = H'_u(y) + T'(u;y). \qquad (18)$$

In this case the error term is $H'_u(y)$ because only one input, u, is recorded. Shannon (10) showed that

$$H'_u(y) \geqq H'_{uv}(y).$$

In other words the error term, when only u is controlled, cannot be increased if we also control v. In fact

$$H'_u(y) = H'_{uv}(y) + T'_u(v;y). \qquad (19)$$

Equation (19) is proved by expanding both sides in s-notation. Thus if u and v are stimulus variables that transmit information via responses, y, we have an error term, $H'_u(y)$, provided we keep track of only one of the inputs, namely, u. However, this error term contains a still smaller error term as well as the information transmitted from v. Controlling v is thus seen to be equivalent to extracting the association between v and y from the noise. Multivariate transmitted information is essentially information analyzed from the noise part of bivariate transmission.

5. An Example

The kind of analysis that multivariate information transmission yields can be illustrated by a set of data obtained from one subject in an experiment on frequency judgment.

Four equally loud tones, 890, 925, 970, and 1005 cycles per second were presented to the subject one at a time in random order. Each tone was $\frac{1}{2}$ second long and separated by about 3 seconds from the next tone. During preliminary training the subject learned to identify the tones by pairing them with four response keys. In experimental sessions, a loud masking noise was turned on and a random sequence of 250 tones was presented against the noise background. A flashing light told the subject when the stimulus occurred, and he was instructed to guess if in doubt about which one of the four tones it was.

One object of the experiment was to find weights for both the frequency stimulus and the immediately preceding response in determining which key the subject would press. Tests were run at several signal-to-noise ratios. The data presented here were obtained when the signal-to-noise ratio was close to the masked threshold.

In order to calculate weights, we can consider the experiment as an example of three-dimensional transmission. Our analysis is based on the responses to the 125 even-numbered stimuli. The odd-numbered responses are considered as the context in which the subject judged the even-numbered stimuli. The odd-numbered stimuli are ignored in this analysis.

The stimuli will be designated as the variable u. Last previous responses are called "presponses" and they will be indicated by the variable v. These are the inputs. Current responses are represented by y. This is the output variable. Thus we can identify the joint event (i,j,m) as the occurrence of response m to stimulus i, following presponse j. Failure to respond is considered as a possible response. Consequently there are four stimulus categories and five response categories.

The subject's responses to the 125 test stimuli were sorted into a $4 \times 5 \times 5$ contingency table. Two of the reduced tables that were obtained from this master table are reproduced here in order to illustrate our com-

TABLE 1

Stimulus-Response Frequency Table

Stimulus

	1	2	3	4	
0	1	3	2	1	7
1	5	2	2	1	10
2	12	10	13	12	47
3	8	10	12	7	37
4	5	5	4	10	24
	31	30	33	31	125

(Response)

TABLE 2

Presponse-Response Frequency Table

Presponse

	0	1	2	3	4	
0	1	2	3	0	1	7
1	1	1	4	3	1	10
2	2	13	8	20	4	47
3	3	7	12	6	9	37
4	3	3	0	15	3	24
	10	26	27	44	18	125

putations. For example, the Stimulus-Response plot in Table 1 has entries n_{im}. The calculation for s_{im} goes as follows:

$$s_{im} = \frac{1}{125} [1 \log_2 1 + 5 \log_2 5 + 12 \log_2 12 + \cdots + 7 \log_2 7 + 10 \log_2 10],$$

$s_{im} = 374.05750/125,$

$s_{im} = 2.99246.$

In the same way, s_{jm} is computed from the figures for n_{jm} in the Presponse-Response table, Table 2:

$$s_{jm} = \frac{1}{125} [1 \log_2 1 + 1 \log_2 1 + 2 \log_2 2 + \cdots + 9 \log_2 9 + 3 \log_2 3],$$

$s_{jm} = 372.38710/125,$

$s_{jm} = 2.97910.$

We obtain the value for s_i from the n_i in the bottom marginal of Table 1:

$$s_i = \frac{1}{125} [31 \log_2 31 + 30 \log_2 30 + 33 \log_2 33 + 31 \log_2 31],$$

$s_i = 620.83188/125,$

$s_i = 4.96665.$

The computation for s is based on the total number of measurements:

$$s = \log_2 125 = 6.96579.$$

It is evident that these calculations are performed very easily with a table of $n \log_2 n$. If he wishes, the reader may also make the computations with tables of $p \log_2 p$ like those prepared by Newman (8), and Dolansky (3). The use of $p \log_2 p$ tables for analyzing discrete data is not recommended, however, because it leads to rounding errors that the table of $n \log_2 n$ avoids. The complete set of s-terms in the experiment on frequency judgment worked out as follows:

$$s_{ijm} = 1.45211 \qquad s_i = 4.96665$$
$$s_{ij} = 2.91389 \qquad s_j = 4.79269$$
$$s_{im} = 2.99246 \qquad s_m = 4.93380$$
$$s_{jm} = 2.97910 \qquad s = 6.96579$$

In section 4 it was shown that response information, $H'(y)$, can be analyzed into components

$$H'(y) = H'_{uv}(y) + T'(u;y) + T(v;y) + A'(uvy). \tag{17}$$

Since $H'(y) = s - s_m$, we see that $H'(y) = 2.03199$ bits. If the subject had used the four response keys equally often, this figure would have been at most 2 bits. The extra information shows that the subject sometimes did not respond. This can be verified from the right-hand marginals in Tables 1 and 2. The rest of the quantities in equation (17) are easily computed from s-terms. For example, $H'_{uv}(y)$ is computed from $s_{ij} - s_{ijm}$. We see that $H'_{uv}(y)$ is 1.46178 bits. This is the part of the response information that is not accounted for either by the auditory stimuli or the presponses. Consequently, $1.46178/2.03199$ or 72 per cent of the response information is unanalyzed error. Some 28 per cent of the response information must therefore be due to associations between the subject's responses and the two predicting variables.

If we consider the association between auditory stimuli (u) and responses (y), we have

$$T'(u;y) = s - s_i - s_m + s_{im} ,$$

$$T'(u;y) = .05780.$$

Thus only .058 bits are transmitted from the frequency stimuli, accounting for less than 3 per cent of the response information. This is not surprising because the signal-to-noise ratio was set near the masked threshold and the stimuli were difficult to hear.

If we consider the association between presponses (v) and current responses (y), we find a little more transmitted information:

$$T'(v;y) = s - s_i - s_m + s_{im} ,$$

$$T'(v;y) = .21840.$$

This value of .218 bits transmitted, amounts to some 11 per cent of the response information.

The last element in equation (17) is the stimulus $\times$ response $\times$ presponse interaction, $A'(uvy)$. This is computed from

$$A'(uvy) = -s + s_i + s_j + s_m - s_{ij} - s_{im} - s_{jm} + s_{ijm} ,$$

$$A'(uvy) = .29401.$$

We see that about 14 per cent of the response information is due to the interaction. Knowledge of the interaction also permits us to hold one of the inputs constant while measuring transmission from the other input. For example, the transmission from stimuli to responses with presponses held constant is:

$$T'_v(u;y) = s_i - s_{ij} - s_{im} + s_{ijm}$$

$$= T'(u;y) + A'(uvy)$$

$$= .35181.$$

Our calculations for the parts of the response information that we can analyze with the three-dimensional model, lead to weights of approximately 3, 11 and 14 per cent for stimuli, presponses and interaction respectively. These figures sum to 28 per cent, the amount of transmitted information we predicted from the size of the noise term. We can also obtain this total weight directly by computing the information transmitted from both inputs together. We have

$$T'(u,v;y) = s - s_m - s_{ij} + s_{ijm}$$

$$T'(u,v;y) = .57021.$$

If we now divide this three-dimensional transmitted information by the response information, we get back our figure of 28 per cent.

There are several points worth noting about our application of information theory to this experiment. The first is that the analysis is additive. The component measures of association plus the measure of error (or noise) sum to the response information. Furthermore, the analysis is exact. No approximations are involved. The process is very similar to the partition of a sum of squares in analysis of variance. As a matter of fact, a notation can be worked out in analysis of variance that is exactly parallel to the s-notation in multivariate information transmission (4).

The second point is that information transmission is made to order for contingency tables. Measures of transmitted information are zero when variables are independent in the contingency-sense (as opposed to the restriction to linear independence in analysis of variance). In addition, the analysis is designed for frequency data in discrete categories, while methods based on analysis of variance are not. No assumptions about linearity are introduced in multivariate information transmission. Furthermore, when statistical tests are developed in a later section, it will be shown that these tests are distribution-free in the sense that they are extensions of the familiar chi-square test of independence.

The measure of amount of information transmitted also has certain inherent advantages. Garner and Hake (2) and Miller (5) have pointed out that the amount of information transmitted is approximately the logarithm of the number of perfectly discriminated input-classes. In experiments on discrimination like the one we have discussed, the measure provides an immediate picture of the subject's discriminative ability. Miller has also discussed applications of this property in mental testing and in the general theory of measurement.

6. *Independence in Three-Dimensional Transmission*

It is evident from the definition of transmitted information that

$T'(u,v;y) = 0$ when the output is independent of the joint input, i.e., when

$$n_{ijm} = \frac{n_{ij} \cdot n_m}{n}. \tag{20}$$

With this kind of independence, we can show that

$$s_{ijm} = s_{ij} + s_m - s.$$

This expression for s_{ijm} may be substituted into (5) to confirm the fact that $T'(u,v;y) = 0$.

Now suppose that $T'(u,v;y) > 0$ but that v and y are independent, that is to say,

$$n_{jm} = \frac{n_j \cdot n_m}{n}. \tag{21}$$

This leads to

$$s_{jm} = s_j + s_m - s.$$

If we substitute for s_{jm} in equation (9), we find that $T'(v;y) = 0$. Equation (21) does not provide a unique condition for independence between v and y. To show this, let us pick some value of u and study the v-to-y transmission at that value of u. We now require that

$$n_{ijm} = \frac{n_{ij} \cdot n_{im}}{n_i}. \tag{22}$$

If we have (22) for all i, we must have

$$s_{ijm} = s_{ij} + s_{im} - s_i \, ,$$

and it follows from substitution in (10) that $T'_u(v;y) = 0$. This is the situation in which v and y are independent provided that u is held constant. It is an interesting case because we can show from (14) that if this kind of independence happens,

$$A'(uvy) = -T'(v;y).$$

The sign of $T'(v;y)$ must be positive or zero so that $-T'(v;y)$ must be negative or zero. Consequently, $A'(uvy)$ can be negative. We see that negative interaction information is produced when the information transmitted between a pair of variables is due to a regression on a third variable. Holding the interacting variable constant causes the transmitted information to disappear.

If we have the independence defined by (21), we may not necessarily have the independence defined by (22). Let us suppose that we have both, i.e., that we have

$$s_{jm} = s_j + s_m - s,$$

$$s_{ijm} = s_{ij} + s_{im} - s_i \, .$$

Now we substitute for s_{im} and s_{ijm} in equation (8).

$$T'_v(u;y) = s_i - s_{ij} - s_{im} + s_{ijm},$$

$$T'_v(u;y) = s_i - s_{ij} - s_j - s_m + s + s_{ij} + s_{im} - s_i,$$

$$T'_v(u;y) = s - s_i - s_m + s_{im},$$

$$T'_v(u;y) = T'(u;y).$$

Both kinds of independence, (21) and (22), together mean that v is not involved in transmission between u and y. When this happens we do not have three-dimensional transmission, since u is the only input variable (provided that no information is transmitted between u and v). As might be expected, both kinds of independence can be generated from a single restriction on the data, namely

$$n_{ijm} = \frac{n_{im}}{V},$$

where V is the number of classes in v.

We have studied the case where v is independent of y. We could have had u independent of y, or u independent of v. The results are analogous to those we have presented.

7. Correlated Sources of Information

Three-dimensional transmitted information, $T'(u,v;y)$, accounts for only part of the total amount of association in a three-dimensional contingency table. It does not exhaust all the association in the table because it neglects the association between the inputs. When this association is considered, i.e., when all the relations in the contingency table are represented, we are led to an equation that is very useful for generating the components of multivariate transmission. Consider

$$C'(u,v,y) = H'(u) + H'(v) + H'(y) - H'(u,v,y). \tag{23}$$

If we add and subtract $H'(u,v)$, we obtain

$$C'(u,v,y) = T'(u;v) + T'(u,v;y),$$

$$C'(u,v,y) = T'(u;v) + T'(u;y) + T'(v;y) + A'(uvy). \tag{24}$$

We see that $C'(u,v,y)$ generates all possible components of the three correlated information-sources, u, v, and y.

8. Four-Dimensional Transmitted Information

It will be instructive to extend our measures one step further, i.e., to transmitted information with three input variables, since from that point results can be generalized easily to an N-dimensional input. For simplicity we shall restrict our development to the case of a channel with a multivariate input and a univariate output. The more general case with N inputs and M outputs does not present any special problems, and can be constructed with no difficulty once the rules become clear.

Let us add a new variable w to the bivariate input, u,v. The joint input is now u,v,w. We suppose that w sends signals $h = 1, 2, 3, \cdots W$. This gives us four sources of information u,v,w, and y. We can proceed to define a four-way interaction information, $A'(uvwy)$, as follows:

$$A'(uvwy) = A'_w(uvy) - A'(uvy).$$

We have already defined $A'(uvy)$. The definition of $A'_w(uvy)$ will be similar except that the subscript w indicates that $A'(uvy)$ is to be averaged over w. As we have already noted, this is accomplished by adding the subscript h to each of the s-terms that make up $A'(uvy)$. Consequently

$$A'_w(uvy) = -s_h + s_{hi} + s_{hj} + s_{hm} - s_{hij} - s_{him} - s_{hjm} + s_{hijm} . \qquad (25)$$

It is readily shown that $A'(uvwy)$ is symmetrical in the sense that it does not matter which variable is chosen for averaging, i.e.,

$$
\begin{aligned}
A'(uvwy) &= A'_u(vwy) - A'(vwy), \\
&= A'_v(uwy) - A'(uwy), \\
&= A'_w(uvy) - A'(uvy), \\
&= A'_y(uvw) - A'(uvw).
\end{aligned}
\qquad (26)
$$

We see that $A'(uvwy)$ is the amount of information gained (or lost) in transmission by controlling a fourth variable when any three of the variables are already known.

If we examine all possible associations in a four-dimensional contingency table, we obtain

$$C'(u,v,w,y) = T'(u;v) + T'(u;w) + T'(u;y) + T'(v;w) + T'(v;y) + T'(w;y)$$

$$+ A'(uvw) + A'(uvy) + A'(uwy) + A'(vwy) + A'(uvwy), \qquad (27)$$

where

$$C'(u,v,w,y) = H'(u) + H'(v) + H'(w) + H'(y) - H'(u,v,w,y).$$

Equation (27) can be proved by expanding both sides in s-notation. It turns out that in the general case, $C'(u,v,w, \cdots , y)$ is expanded by writing down T-terms for all possible pairs of variables, and A-terms for all possible combinations of three, four variables and so on.

Four-dimensional transmitted information from u,v,w to y, i.e., $T'(u,v,w;y)$, can be written as follows:

$$T'(u,v,w;y) = H'(y) + H'(u,v,w) - H'(u,v,w,y). \qquad (28)$$

The same arguments are used to justify (28) as were used in the case of (4) in three-dimensional transmission. To find the components of $T'(u,v,w;y)$, we note that

$$T'(u,v,w;y) = C'(u,v,w,y) - C'(u,v,w). \qquad (29)$$

This means that $T'(u,v,w;y)$ contains all the components of $C'(u,v,w,y)$ except the correlations among the inputs. Consequently the components of $T'(u,v,w;y)$ are ·

$$T'(u,v,w;y) = T'(u;y) + T'(v;y) + T'(w;y)$$
$$+ A'(uvy) + A'(uwy) + A'(vwy) + A'(uvwy). \qquad (30)$$

The components of $T'(u,v,w;y)$ are shown in schematic form in Figure 2.

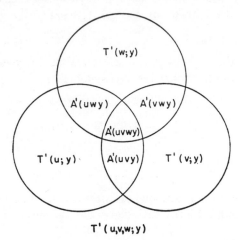

FIGURE 2

Schematic diagram of the components of four-dimensional transmitted information, with three transmitters and a single receiver.

If it happens that

$$n_{hijm} = n_{ijm}/W,$$

where W is the number of classes in w, all the components of $C'(u,v,w,y)$ that are functions of w drop out and $C'(u,v,w,y) = C'(u,v,y)$. In similar fashion, $C'(u,v,y)$ can be reduced to $C'(u,y)$. This is precisely what we did in the analysis of independence in three-dimensional transmitted information. Since $C'(u,y) = T'(u;y)$, we see that all cases of transmission with multivariate inputs can be related to the bivariate case.

With three inputs controlled, we are ready to extend the analysis of response information in section 4, a step further. We have

$$H'(y) = H'_{uvw}(y) + T'(u,v,w;y).$$ (31)

Equation (31) says that we can measure the effects in response information due to the three inputs. This is evident from the fact that (30) tells us how to expand $T'(u,v,w;y)$ in its components. In addition we know that

$$H'_{uv}(y) = H'_{uvw}(y) + T'_{uv}(w;y),$$ (32)

where

$$T'_{uv}(w;y) = T'(w;y) + A'(uwy) + A'(vwy) + A'(uvwy).$$ (33)

We see that controlling w in addition to u and v, enables us to rescue the information transmitted between w and y from the noise, and to replace $H'_{uv}(y)$ with a better estimate of noise information, namely $H'_{uvw}(y)$.

The transition to an N-dimensional input is now evident. In general, we have

$$H'(y) = H'_{uvw\cdots z}(y) + T'(u,v,w, \cdots, z;y).$$ (34)

The $(N + 1)$-dimensional transmitted information, $T'(u,v,w, \cdots, z;y)$ can then be expanded in its components in the manner that we have described.

9. *Asymptotic Distributions*

Miller and Madow (6) have shown that sample information is related to the likelihood ratio. Following Miller and Madow, we can show that the large sample distribution of the likelihood ratio may be used to find approximate distributions for the quantities involved in multivariate transmission.

Consider, for example, three-dimensional sample transmitted-information, $T'(u,v;y)$. We can test the hypothesis that $T(u,v;y)$ is equal to zero. This is equivalent to the hypothesis that

$$p(i,j,m) = p(i,j) \cdot p(m),$$ (35)

since $T(u,v;y)$ is zero when input and output are independent. This hypothesis leads to the likelihood ratio [see reference (7)],

$$\lambda = \frac{n^{-2n} \prod_{i,j} (n_{ij})^{n_{ij}} \prod_{m} (n_m)^{n_m}}{n^{-n} \prod_{i,j,m} (n_{ijm})^{n_{ijm}}}.$$ (36)

If we take logs, we obtain

$$\frac{-2 \log_e \lambda}{1.3863 \ n} = s - s_m - s_{ij} + s_{ijm} ;$$ (37)

$$-2 \log_e \lambda = 1.3863nT'(u,v;y).$$

For large samples, $-2 \log_e \lambda$ has approximately a χ^2 distribution with $(UV - 1)(Y - 1)$ degrees of freedom when the null hypothesis (35) is true. Thus $1.3863 \, nT'(u,v;y)$ is distributed approximately like χ^2 if $T(u,v;y)$ is equal to zero.

A more important problem involves testing suspected information sources. Suppose in our three-dimensional example, we assume that

$$p(i,j,m) = p(i) \cdot p(j) \cdot p(m). \tag{38}$$

This hypothesis leads to the likelihood ratio for complete independence in a three-dimensional contingency table,

$$\lambda = \frac{n^{-3n} \prod_i (n_i)^{n_i} \prod_j (n_j)^{n_j} \prod_m (n_m)^{n_m}}{n^{-n} \prod_{i,j,m} (n_{ijm})^{n_{ijm}}}. \tag{39}$$

After we take logs we find that

$$\begin{aligned} -2 \log_e \lambda &= 3s - s_i - s_j - s_m - s + s_{ijm} \\ &= H'(u) + H'(v) + H'(y) - H'(u,v,y) \tag{40} \\ &= 1.3863nC'(u,v,y). \end{aligned}$$

For large samples $-2 \log_e \lambda$ has approximately a χ^2 distribution with $(UVY - 1) - (U - 1) - (V - 1) - (Y - 1)$ degrees of freedom when the null hypothesis is true.

We also know that

$$C'(u,v,y) = T'(u;y) + T'(v;y) + T'_y(u;v). \tag{41}$$

The likelihood ratio can be used to show that $1.3863 \, nT'(u;y)$ and $1.3863 \, nT'(v;y)$ are asymptotically distributed like χ^2 with $(U - 1)(Y - 1)$ and $(V - 1)(Y - 1)$ degrees of freedom, respectively, if $T(u;y)$ and $T(v;y)$ are zero. To find the asymptotic distribution of $T'_y(u;v)$, we make the following hypothesis:

$$p(i,j,m) = p(i,m) \cdot p_m(j), \tag{42}$$

where $p_m(j)$ is the conditional probability of j given m.

Now we have the ratio

$$\lambda = \frac{n^{-n} \prod_{i,m} (n_{im})^{n_{im}} \prod_{j,m} \left(\frac{n_{jm}}{n_m}\right)^{n_{jm}}}{n^{-n} \prod_{i,j,m} (n_{ijm})^{n_{ijm}}}, \tag{43}$$

$$\frac{-2 \log_e \lambda}{1.3863 \, n} = s_m - s_{im} - s_{jm} + s_{ijm} , \tag{44}$$

$$-2 \log_e \lambda = 1.3863nT'_y(u;v).$$

In this case $-2 \log_e \lambda$ has $Y(U - 1)(V - 1)$ degrees of freedom. In view of (41) we can write

$$1.3863nC'(u,v,y) = 1.3863n[T'(u;y) + T'(v;y) + T'_y(u;v)]. \tag{45}$$

The quantities on the right side of (45) have degrees of freedom that sum to $(UVY - U - V - Y + 2)$. Since this is the same number of degrees of freedom as on the left hand side of (45), the quantities on the right side of (45) are asymptotically independent, if the null hypothesis,

$$p(i,j,m) = p(i) \cdot p(j) \cdot p(m),$$

is true.

This means that as an approximation we can test $T'(u;y)$, $T'(v;y)$ and $T'_y(u;v)$ simultaneously for significance under the null hypothesis we have stated. The test is very similar to an analysis of variance. We can see the similarity by applying the test to the data from our example in section 5. The significance tests will be made on the quantities in equation (45). To do this we need to compute $C'(u,v,y)$ and $T'_y(u;v)$, since these terms were not discussed in section 5. First we note that $C'(u,v,y)$ is the total amount of association in the stimulus $\times$ response $\times$ preponse table. We have

$$C'(u,v,y) = 2s + s_{i;m} - s_i - s_j - s_m \,,$$
$$C'(u,v,y) = .69055.$$

We also need $T'_y(u;v)$, the information transmitted from presponses to stimuli with responses held constant. This measures how successfully the presponses predict the auditory stimuli. Since stimuli were chosen at random, we do not expect much transmitted information here. The computation goes as follows:

$$T'_y(u;v) = s_m - s_{im} - s_{jm} + s_{i;m} \,,$$
$$= T'(u;v) + A'(uvy),$$
$$= .41435.$$

We may now put our computed values for $C'(u,v,y)$, $T'(u;y)$, $T'(v;y)$ and $T'_y(u;v)$ into equation (45) and perform the χ^2 tests. The results are summarized in Table 3. We have not attempted to calculate the significance level of $C'(u,v,y)$ because we do not have enough data to sustain the 88 degrees of freedom. The same criticism can probably be leveled at our test for $T'_y(u;v)$. In any case Table 3 shows that the only significant effect in the experiment is the presponse-response association.

One interesting fact that the analysis brings out clearly, is that we cannot decide whether an amount of transmitted information is big or small without knowing its degrees of freedom. In our example we find that $T'_y(u;v) = .414$ bits, while $T'(v;y) = .218$ bits. Yet $T'(v;y)$ is significant and $T'_y(u;v)$ is not. The reason lies in the difference in degrees of freedom. Miller and

TABLE 3

Table of Transmitted Information

Transmission	Component	$-2 \log_e \lambda$	d.f.	P
Stimulus-Response	$T'(u;y)$	10.016	12	>.50
Presponse-Response	$T'(v;y)$	37.844	16	<.01
Presponse-Stimulus	$T'_y(u;v)$	71.802	60	=.14
Total	$C'(u,v,y)$	119.664	88	

Madow (6) have discussed the amount of statistical bias in information measures due to degrees of freedom, and have suggested corrections.

In Table 3, we tested $T'_y(u;v)$, the association between presponses and stimuli with responses held constant. This association is broken down still

TABLE 4

Table of Transmitted Information

Transmission	Component	$-2 \log_e \lambda$	d.f.	P
Presponse-Stimulus	$T'(u;v)$	20.853	12	>.05
Interaction	$A'(uvy)$	50.948		**
Total	$T'_y(u;v)$	71.802	60	=.14

** Probability not estimated.

further in Table 4. No probability is estimated in Table 4 for the interaction term, $A'(uvy)$, because its asymptotic distribution is not chi-square. All A-terms are distributed like the difference of two variables each of which has the chi-square distribution. The distribution of this difference is evidently not chi-square because the difference can be negative. Its density function has been derived by Pearson, Stouffer, and David (9), but the writer has been unable to find a table of the integral. In some cases the problem can be circumvented by combining A-terms with T-terms to make new T-terms. [See, for example, equation (33).] However, in other cases, the interactions are genuinely interesting in their own right and should be tested directly. These cases can be treated when adequate tables become available.

REFERENCES

1. Fano, R. M. The transmission of information II. Research Laboratory of Electronics Tech. Report 149. Cambridge: Massachusetts Institute of Technology, 1950.
2. Garner, W. R. and Hake, H. W. Amount of information in absolute judgments. *Psychol. Rev.*, 1951, **58**, 446–459.
3. Dolansky, L. Table of $p \log p$. Research Laboratory of Electronics Tech. Report 227. Cambridge: Massachusetts Institute of Technology, 1952.
4. McGill, W. J. Multivariate transmission of information and its relation to analysis of variance. Human Factors Operations Research Laboratories Report 32. Cambridge: Massachusetts Institute of Technology, 1953.
5. Miller, G. A. What is information measurement? *Amer. Psychologist*, 1953, **8**, 3–11.
6. Miller, G. A. and Madow, W. J. Information measurement for the multinomial distribution (in preparation).
7. Mood, A. M. Introduction to the theory of statistics. New York: McGraw-Hill, 1950.
8. Newman, E. B. Computational methods useful in analyzing series of binary data. *Amer. J. Psychol.*, 1951, **64**, 252–262.
9. Pearson, K., Stouffer, S. A. and David, F. N. Further applications in statistics of the Bessel function. *Biometrika*, 1932, **24**, 293–350.
10. Shannon, C. E. and Weaver, W. The mathematical theory of communication. Urbana: University of Illinois Press, 1949.
11. Smith, J. E. Keith Multivariate attribute analysis (in preparation).
12. Stumper, F. L. A bibliography of information theory. Research Laboratory of Electronics Tech. Report, Cambridge: Massachusetts Institute of Technology, 1953.

Manuscript received 7/4/53

Revised manuscript received 10/23/53

RANDOM FLUCTUATIONS OF RESPONSE RATE*

WILLIAM J. McGILL

COLUMBIA UNIVERSITY

A simple model for fluctuating interresponse times is developed and studied. It involves a mechanism that generates regularly spaced excitations, each of which can trigger off a response after a random delay. The excitations are not observable, but their periodicity is reflected in a regular patterning of responses. The probability distribution of the time between responses is derived and its properties are analyzed. Several limiting cases are also examined.

A number of behavioral systems generate sequences of pulse-like responses that recur regularly in time. The constant beating of the heart is an illustration that springs immediately to mind. Another example is the optic nerve of the horseshoe crab, *limulus*, which is famous for the long trains of precisely timed action potentials it produces when its visual receptor is illuminated by a steady light [6]. Response sequences with comparable periodicity are also found in studies of operant conditioning when the rate of occurrence of a response is stabilized by reinforcing paced responding; (see [5], pp. 498–502). The essential point to bear in mind in each of these examples is the fact that the sequence of intervals between responses is not random. The intervals resemble the ticking of a watch more than the irregular fluctuations of a stream of electrons. Consequently the Poisson distribution, which is sometimes proposed [11] to deal with rate fluctuations, is not likely to be very helpful.

Under close scrutiny the timing of many of these periodic response systems reveals itself to be less than perfect, and the intervals between responses are seen to change in small amounts. The distribution of these changes is what interests us. We want to construct a model with both periodic and random components. Intervals generated by the model will then be more stable than a purely random sequence, but less stable than a completely periodic system. Moreover they will have the capacity to take on any one of the wide range of possibilities between these extremes. Since this seems to be a natural extension of the type of randomness found in physical systems to the more orderly behavior of biological processes, it is surprising that the problem has received so little attention.

This paper is an attempt to examine the properties of an elementary mechanism for producing noisy fluctuations in otherwise constant time

*This paper was completed while the writer was a visiting summer scientist at the Lincoln Laboratory, Lexington, Mass.

This article appeared in *Psychometrika*, 1962, **27**, 3–17. Reprinted with permission.

intervals. Despite its simplicity, the mechanism can duplicate a variety of observed phenomena, ranging from sharply peaked and symmetrical distributions of interresponse times to highly skewed distributions, and even completely random responding. Moreover, all these behaviors can be elicited from the same mechanism by altering the rate at which it is excited.

Periodic Excitation

We begin by examining interresponse times that are nearly constant. The key to this regularity, we assume, is some sort of periodic excitatory process that triggers a response after a short random delay. Even when the excitations are not observable their effects are seen in the regular intervals they impose between responses. The periodic mechanism proposed here is diagrammed in Fig. 1, which also illustrates our notation.

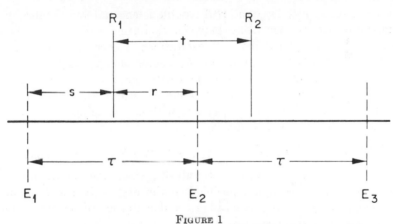

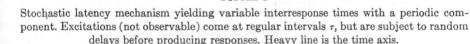

FIGURE 1

Stochastic latency mechanism yielding variable interresponse times with a periodic component. Excitations (not observable) come at regular intervals τ, but are subject to random delays before producing responses. Heavy line is the time axis.

E and R denote excitation and response respectively. The time interval between two successive responses is a random variable and is called t. The analogous interval (or period) between excitations is a fixed (unknown) constant τ. Excitation and response almost never coincide in time. Consequently a response will almost always be located between two excitations, and its distance from each excitation can be expressed as two location coordinates. The first of these, r, is the delay from a response to the next following excitation. The second, s, is the corresponding interval between a response and the excitation that immediately precedes it.

The basic random quantity in Fig. 1 is s, and our problem is to deduce the distribution of t when the distribution of s is known. Accordingly, suppose that s has an exponential distribution as would be the case if interresponse times were completely random. Let

$$(1) \qquad\qquad f(s) = \lambda e^{-\lambda s},$$

where $f(s)$ is the frequency function of s, and λ is a positive constant, i.e., the *time* constant. Equation (1) then describes a very simple delay process in which the probability of a response during any short interval of time Δs following excitation is constant and equal to $\lambda \Delta s$ (see Feller [4], p. 220). This defines what we mean by "completely" random; the instantaneous probability of response is independent of time.

We are in trouble immediately, for (1) is not strictly legitimate in view of the requirements just set down. This may be seen from the fact that the exponential is distributed on the interval $0 \leq s \leq \infty$, whereas the maximum value of s in Fig. 1 is τ.

If $\lambda \tau$ is sufficiently large, no real trouble is encountered because, in this circumstance, the average delay between excitation and response is small compared with the period between excitations. Hence the response to E_1 is practically certain to occur before E_2 comes along, and the tail of the distribution of s never really gets tangled with the next following excitation. When it happens that $\lambda \tau$ is not large, a simple adjustment of (1) is required in order to bound s between zero and τ, without changing its characterization as a completely random interval.

Distribution of Interresponse Times With a Periodic Component

Our main results are given in (2) and (3), which describe the probability distribution of the mechanism outlined in the first section and pictured in Fig. 1. The density function describing the distribution of the time interval t between two successive responses is

$$(2) \qquad f(t) = \begin{cases} \dfrac{\lambda \nu}{1 - \nu} \sinh \lambda t & t \leq \tau, \\[2ex] \dfrac{1 + \nu}{2\nu} \lambda e^{-\lambda t} & t \geq \tau, \end{cases}$$

in which ν is a constant given by $\nu = e^{-\lambda \tau}$. The distribution is evidently skewed and has a well-defined maximum over $t = \tau$.

Whenever $\lambda \tau$ happens to be large enough so that ν is negligibly small, the distribution of interresponse time in (2) simplifies to

$$(3) \qquad f(t - \tau) = \frac{\lambda}{2} e^{-\lambda |t - \tau|}, \qquad -\infty \leq t - \tau \leq \infty.$$

Equation (3) is the well-known Laplace density function [1]. It is symmetrical and sharply peaked over $t = \tau$, and describes the behavior of the latency mechanism when the intervals between successive responses are dominated by the periodic component τ. "Noise" introduced by the random component must then be small in comparison with the periodicity generated by the excitatory process.

The approximation in (3) is easily rationalized if $1/\lambda$ is considered as measuring the magnitude of the random component. In that case $1/\lambda\tau$ measures the size of the noisy perturbation relative to the period between excitations. Hence the parameter ν will go toward zero whenever the ratio $1/\lambda\tau$ gets small, i.e., whenever the random component is effectively small. It is not obvious that (2) approaches the Laplace distribution as ν disappears, but a brief study of (2) shows that this is in fact what happens.

Proof of the Distribution*

We shall now show that (2) is the correct form of the distribution of interresponse times when responses are triggered by periodic excitations as shown in Fig. 1.

First of all, (1) must be adjusted to hold s between zero and τ. This is easily handled. We begin with an excitation and simply cycle the exponential distribution back to the origin as soon as s reaches τ, letting the distribution continue to run down until it reaches τ again, and repeating the process ad infinitum. The ordinate corresponding to any point s between zero and τ will then be given by

$$f(s) = \lambda(e^{-\lambda s} + e^{-\lambda(s+\tau)} + e^{-\lambda(s+2\tau)} + \cdots)$$
$$= \lambda e^{-\lambda s}(1 + \nu + \nu^2 + \cdots).$$

Consequently the position of the response in the interval between excitations will be distributed as

(1a) $$f(s) = \frac{\lambda}{1-\nu} e^{-\lambda s}, \qquad 0 \leq s \leq \tau.$$

The distribution of r, the interval from the response to the next following excitation, is now determined, since, from Fig. 1, $s = \tau - r$. Substituting in (1a) yields

(4) $$f(r) = \frac{\lambda\nu}{1-\nu} e^{\lambda r}, \qquad 0 < r < \tau.$$

Evidently r and s are perfectly (and inversely) correlated in the same excitation period. On the other hand only one response can occur between two excitations. Hence, when intervals between responses are analyzed, r will belong to one excitation period and s will belong to a later one, thus making r and s independent for determining t.

It should be clear that t is not just the sum of r and s although a cursory

---

*The writer is indebted to a referee for suggesting several excellent ways to simplify the original proof.

examination of Fig. 1 leaves that impression. The trouble with the impression is that several excitation periods may separate R_1 from R_2. In other words, responses are not forced by excitations. A new excitation may come along before the response is emitted. We have drawn Fig. 1 as though response R_2 fell into the excitation period following R_1, but a moment's reflection suggests that things might not happen so neatly. To deal with this nasty eventuality, we shall define t as

$$(5) \qquad\qquad t = k\tau + r + s,$$

where r is taken as the time interval between R_1 and the next following excitation, s is the analogous interval between R_2 and the excitation immediately preceding it, and k is the number of periods in which no response occurs, i.e. the number of empty excitation periods between R_1 and R_2.

Equation (5) is now a unique specification of t in terms of quantities whose distributions are known as soon as λ and τ are fixed. The distributions of r and s have already been specified in (4) and (1a). Our next step is to find the distribution of $k\tau$.

An interval beginning with an excitation and terminating in a response may span several excitations before the response occurs. This latency is denoted by $k\tau + s$, where k takes on values 0, 1, 2, 3, etc. It is evident from the arguments leading up to (1a) that $k\tau + s$ has the exponential distribution out to infinity. Accordingly, the delay from an excitation to the first subsequent response can be resolved into two independent components: (i) the number of excitation periods passed, and (ii) the location of response R_2 in the period between the last two excitations. In view of the independence of k and s, we can write

$$\lambda e^{-\lambda(k\tau+s)} = P(k\tau)\,\frac{\lambda e^{-\lambda s}}{1-\nu}\,,$$

where $P(k\tau)$ is the probability of a particular value of $k\tau$. We find that

$$(6) \qquad\qquad P(k\tau) = \nu^k(1-\nu).$$

In other words, the distribution of $k\tau$ is geometric with ordinates spaced out at successive multiples of τ.

All three components of (5) are independent. Moreover, the variables r and s form a unit that is the same for each value of k. Consequently, (5) can be amended to read

$$(5a) \qquad\qquad t = k\tau + y,$$

where $0 \le y = r + s \le 2\tau$, and $k\tau$ has the geometric distribution given by (6).

The distribution of y is obtained from the convolution of r and s. After some simplification we find that

$$(7) \qquad\qquad f(y) = \begin{cases} c\sinh \lambda y & 0 \le y \le \tau, \\[2mm] c\sinh \lambda(2\tau - y) & \tau \le y \le 2\tau, \end{cases}$$

where

$$c = \frac{\lambda \nu}{(1 - \nu)^2}.$$

The distribution of t will depend on the number of excitations between the pair of responses that bound each interval. This number fixes k, and it follows that each change in k will define a new component of the distribution of t. It will be convenient to describe each component separately by linking it to the number of excitations in the interval. The density function of the kth harmonic component of $f(t)$ will be indicated as $f_k(y)$, since k and y determine t. Equations (5a) and (6) yield

$$(8) \qquad f_k(y) = \nu^k(1 - \nu)f(y).$$

For example, $f_0(y)$ is the density function of interresponse times with a single excitation between each pair of responses. This component of $f(t)$ has k equal to zero and is defined over the interval $0 \le t \le 2\tau$. The average interresponse time in the interval is τ.

The first harmonic component $f_1(y)$ refers to interresponse times with just two excitations between each pair of responses. Hence k is unity and $f_1(y)$ spans values of t between τ and 3τ. The average interresponse time is 2τ. Higher harmonic components are defined in the same way.

The foregoing makes it evident that for values of $t \ge \tau$ the density function has contributions from two harmonic components in each interval corresponding to the length of an excitation period. The pair of contributors will change as we proceed away from the origin in multiples of τ, but every element of density in $f(t)$ after $t = \tau$ will turn out to have two components. Specifically,

$$(9) \qquad f(t) = f_k(y) + f_{k+1}(y - \tau) \qquad\qquad \tau \le y \le 2\tau.$$

If the densities on the right-hand side of (9) are replaced by equivalent expressions determined from (8), it is easily shown that

$$(9a) \qquad f(t) = \frac{1 + \nu}{2\nu} \lambda e^{-\lambda(k\tau+\nu)}.$$

Now recall that $k\tau + y$ is simply another way of writing t, and it is apparent that the harmonic components of $f(t)$ interlace themselves in a way that produces a surprisingly simple expression for the distribution of t:

$$f(t) = \begin{cases} \dfrac{\lambda \nu}{1 - \nu} \sinh \lambda t & t \le \tau, \\[3mm] \dfrac{1 + \nu}{2\nu} \lambda e^{-\lambda t} & t \ge \tau. \end{cases}$$

This is (2) and the proof is complete.

TABLE 1

SUMMARY OF RESULTS

Variable	Description	Distribution	Moment Generating Function	Mean	Variance
r	Interval between response and nearest following excitation.	$\dfrac{\lambda\nu}{1-\nu}\,e^{\lambda r}$	$\dfrac{1}{1+\theta/\lambda}\cdot\dfrac{e^{\theta\tau}-\nu}{1-\nu}$	$\dfrac{\tau}{1-\nu}-\dfrac{1}{\lambda}$	$\dfrac{1}{\lambda^2}-\dfrac{\nu\tau^2}{(1-\nu)^2}$
s	Interval between response and nearest preceding excitation.	$\dfrac{\lambda}{1-\nu}\,e^{-\lambda s}$	$\dfrac{1}{1-\theta/\lambda}\cdot\dfrac{1-\nu e^{\theta\tau}}{1-\nu}$	$\dfrac{1}{\lambda}-\dfrac{\nu\tau}{1-\nu}$	$\dfrac{1}{\lambda^2}-\dfrac{\nu\tau^2}{(1-\nu)^2}$
y	Sum of $\underline{r}$ and $\underline{s}$, each taken from a different excitation period.	$c\sinh\begin{cases}\lambda y\\ \lambda(2\tau-y)\end{cases}$	$\dfrac{1}{1-(\theta/\lambda)^2}\cdot\dfrac{(e^{\theta\tau}-\nu)(1-\nu e^{\theta\tau})}{(1-\nu)^2}$	τ	$2\left(\dfrac{1}{\lambda^2}-\dfrac{\nu\tau^2}{(1-\nu)^2}\right)$
$k\tau$	Number of empty excitation periods between two responses.	$\nu^k(1-\nu)$	$\dfrac{1-\nu}{1-\nu e^{\theta\tau}}$	$\dfrac{\nu\tau}{1-\nu}$	$\dfrac{\nu\tau^2}{(1-\nu)^2}$
$k\tau+s$	Interval from excitation to first subsequent response.	$\nu^k\lambda e^{-\lambda s}$	$\dfrac{1}{1-\theta/\lambda}$	$\dfrac{1}{\lambda}$	$\dfrac{1}{\lambda^2}$
t	Interval between responses (i.e. $\underline{k\tau}+\underline{y}$).	$\begin{cases}\dfrac{\lambda\nu}{1-\nu}\sinh\lambda t\\[2mm] \dfrac{1+\nu}{2\nu}\lambda e^{-\lambda t}\end{cases}$	$\dfrac{1}{1-(\theta/\lambda)^2}\cdot\dfrac{e^{\theta\tau}-\nu}{1-\nu}$	$\dfrac{\tau}{1-\nu}$	$\dfrac{2}{\lambda^2}-\dfrac{\nu\tau^2}{(1-\nu)^2}$
$t-\tau$	Interval between responses (expressed as deviate from excitation period) in cases where $\underline{\lambda\tau}$ is large.	$\dfrac{\lambda}{2}\,e^{-\lambda|t-\tau|}$	$\dfrac{1}{1-(\theta/\lambda)^2}$	0	$\dfrac{2}{\lambda^2}$

Once the answer is known, a simpler proof can be established via a moment generating function. Table 1 gives the moment generating functions for r, s, and $k\tau$, all of which are easy to work out. The theorem governing moment generating functions for sums of random variables (see Hoel [8], or Mood [10]; our notation follows Hoel) allows us to write

$$(10) \qquad\qquad M_t(\theta) = M_{k\tau}(\theta) M_r(\theta) M_s(\theta),$$

where $M_t(\theta)$ is defined as

$$(11) \qquad\qquad M_t(\theta) = \int_0^\infty e^{\theta t} f(t)\, dt.$$

The generating functions in Table 1 are now substituted for the corresponding terms on the right-hand side of (10), and we obtain

$$(12) \qquad\qquad M_t(\theta) = \frac{1}{1 - (\theta/\lambda)^2} \cdot \frac{e^{\theta\tau} - \nu}{1 - \nu} .$$

This is the moment generating function of the distribution of interresponse times. It happens that it is also the m.g.f. of (2), a fact that is easily demonstrated by substituting (2) for $f(t)$ in (11). The properties of the Laplace transform assure that (2) will be the only continuous distribution having the required m.g.f. [12, 13].

The Laplace Distribution

An interesting limiting case of (2) occurs when the distribution of interresponse times is dominated by a strong periodic component. The net effect of this restriction is that (2) is transformed into the Laplace distribution. Consequently the Laplace distribution characterizes the "noise" in a class of simple timing devices. The essential feature of these devices is that they are self-compensating. Intervals that are too long tend to be followed immediately by intervals that are too short and vice versa. (The correlation between adjacent interresponse times for the mechanism pictured in Fig. 1 is $-.50$). This type of regulation is really what enables us to infer that regular excitations must be occurring.

The approach of (2) to the Laplace distribution is easily shown via its moment generating function. Consider (12) when ν goes to zero. We have immediately

$$(13) \qquad\qquad M_{t-\tau}(\theta) = \frac{1}{1 - (\theta/\lambda)^2} .$$

This is the m.g.f. of the Laplace distribution. More specifically, (3) has (13) as its m.g.f. The proof may be established by substituting (3) for $f(t)$ in (11).

The restriction $\nu = 0$, which leads from (2) to the Laplace distribution, implies that k, the number of empty excitation periods, must always be zero. This follows from the fact that the geometric distribution in (6) collapses when $\nu = 0$. Hence t in Fig. 1 will be just precisely the sum of r and s, and we can ignore the possibility of empty excitation periods. Two responses are necessary to define t. Hence there must also be two independent occurrences of s. Call them s_1 and s_2 corresponding to R_1 and R_2, respectively. Refer now to Fig. 1 and observe that

$$t = r + s_2 , \qquad \tau = r + s_1 , \qquad t - \tau = s_2 - s_1 .$$

Consequently, $t - \tau$ is distributed as the difference of two exponential variables and we can write its moment generating function as

$$M_{t-\tau}(\theta) = M_s(\theta)M_s(-\theta).$$

The m.g.f. of the exponential distribution is, of course, very familiar and is given in Table 1 for the variable $k\tau + s$. Substituting this exponential m.g.f. for $M_s(\theta)$, we obtain

$$M_{t-\tau}(\theta)^{-1} = (1 - \theta/\lambda)(1 + \theta/\lambda)$$
$$= 1 - (\theta/\lambda)^2,$$

which is, as we have already shown, the m.g.f. of the Laplace distribution. Evidently the Laplace density function (3) is in fact simply the distribution of the difference between two exponential variables. This simple point is ignored in most texts on statistics because, perhaps, no one imagines why anyone else would be interested. Our argument establishes a very good reason for being interested. The difference, and hence the Laplace distribution, provides a characterization of the error in a timing device that is under periodic excitation.

Continuous Excitation

The latency mechanism also behaves in an interesting way as the period between excitations gets very small. We now suppose that the delay part of the mechanism has a fairly slow response, but is bombarded by excitations following one another in rapid succession. The restriction is achieved symbolically by fixing the delay time constant, λ, while allowing τ to approach zero. Equation (2) for $f(t)$ immediately leads to:

(14) $$\lim_{\tau \to 0} f(t) = \lambda e^{-\lambda t}.$$

The result is almost obvious. The portion of $f(t)$ between $t = 0$ and $t = \tau$ must disappear as τ approaches zero. Meanwhile, the constant ν is approaching unity. Consequently the limit for $f(t)$ falls right out of the portion of (2) defined for $t \geq \tau$. The same exponential limit can be obtained by studying the behavior of the m.g.f. for $f(t)$ in (12) as τ approaches zero with λ fixed, or by analyzing the variance of $f(t)$ under these same limiting conditions.

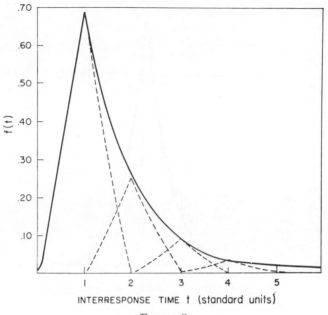

FIGURE 2

General distribution of interresponse times with arbitrary random and periodic parts. The curve is a plot of equation (2) in the text, with λ and $\tau = 1$. Dashed lines are harmonic components of the distribution.

Variances are given in Table 1. The formulas establish that the component *within* harmonics (i.e., the variance of y) disappears as τ vanishes, and the entire variance becomes concentrated in the *differences* between harmonics. This implies that the probability distribution of $f(t)$ must congeal around its harmonic peaks (see Fig. 2) when τ goes to zero, and that each peak then contributes a "line" of density to the resulting exponential distribution. Intuitively, the limit in (14) means that no delay can be contributed by the latency between a response and the next excitation. That excitation is instantly available. Hence r in Fig. 1 vanishes and the entire interval is consumed by the latency between excitation and response, which we have assumed to be exponential.

Applications

Fig. 3 presents a frequency distribution compiled from a long series of action potentials recorded on a single fiber of the optic nerve of *limulus*. The narrow distribution demonstrates that the data are periodic and the periodicity seems to originate in the refractory period of the nerve fiber. The mechanism, however, is not well understood. In this particular case, the regular sequence of action potentials was achieved by dissecting out a

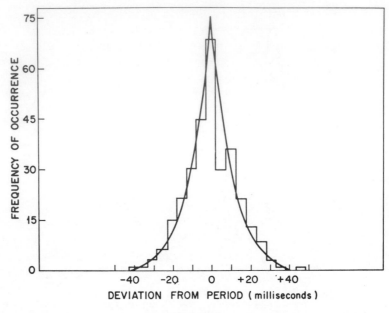

FIGURE 3

Frequency distribution of 303 interresponse times observed in a single fiber of the optic nerve of *limulus* when the eye was illuminated by a steady light. The nerve fiber adapted continuously to the illumination, resulting in a slow linear increase in period from 261 to 291 milliseconds. Measured intervals are deviations from the linear drift. Smooth curve is a Laplace distribution.

fiber of the optic nerve, and shining a beam of light on the receptor, i.e., the *ommatidium*, to which the fiber was attached. Under steady illumination, the nerve fiber produced a barrage of discrete responses which were then amplified and recorded on magnetic tape. Later on, the tape was played into the control gate of a digital counter, and time intervals between alternate pairs of responses were read out onto a permanent record. The timing signal passed through the gate was a 1000 cps sine wave generated by a calibrated tuning fork oscillator. Over-all accuracy of the measurements is of the order of ± 2 milliseconds, due to variations in the speed of the tape recorder.*

The nerve fiber adapted continuously to steady illumination, resulting in a slow increase in the basic period from about 261 milliseconds to 291 milliseconds. This change was isolated by averaging the data in blocks of 25 intervals, and fitting a line to the averages, which fortunately were quite linear. Measured intervals between responses were converted into deviations from this line, yielding the frequency distribution in Fig. 3. The fitted curve is a Laplace density function.

*The preparation and recording were made by C. G. Mueller. The data were recovered and analyzed by the writer with the assistance of Michael S. Kennedy.

A normal curve fitted to the same data would have high shoulders and a flat top. This fact then defines the distribution of interresponse time as being leptokurtic. Another illustration is provided in Fig. 4 and is taken from data reported by Hill [7]. The distribution was obtained by measuring intervals between successive bar-presses made by a white rat. The data were taken on the 93rd day of conditioning with a reinforcement schedule in which payoff was contingent on delaying at least 21 seconds from the last previous response. The normal approximation to Hill's data is shown in Fig. 4 by the dashed frequency distribution in the background. This normal curve was fitted by matching mean and variance to the data. Responses in the 0–3 second class interval were not used for this purpose because bursts of responses immediately after reinforcement are believed to be unrelated to the main effect. In any event the leptokurtic character of Hill's data is evident, and it suggests that the long regimen of training (184 hours) on the time discrimination problem made Hill's rat into a fairly accurate Laplace-type clock. We are led naturally to conjecture about how the rat constructs τ. Does it happen internally via some type of neurological clock or externally via a stereotyped sequence of movements?

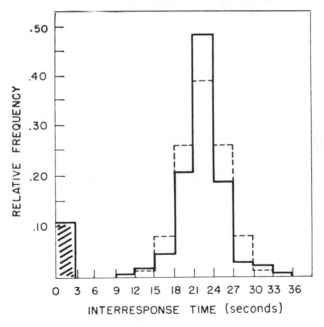

FIGURE 4

Distribution of interresponse times produced by a bar-pressing rat after a long period of conditioning on a schedule in which reinforcement is contingent on delaying at least 21 seconds from last previous response. Dotted curve is best fitting normal approximation and demonstrates peaking of empirical distribution. (Data from Hill).

Skewed distributions of interresponse times with the appearance of (2) (see Fig. 2) are found often in the literature, usually in connection with high speed responding. Fig. 5 is taken from Brandauer [2] who studied response sequences generated by a pigeon pecking at a small illuminated target. Reinforcement was controlled by a high speed flip-flop and the bird was reinforced whenever a peck happened to coincide in time with a particular one of the two states of the flip-flop. Consequently, the probability of reinforcement was determined by the proportion of time the flip-flop spent in that state, and the net result was that every response had the same (low) probability of reinforcement. The pigeon generated an average rate of 5.3 responses per second during the run shown in Fig. 5 which covers approximately 1000 responses. If the sharp peak in Fig. 5 is in fact created by a periodic excitatory mechanism, we would conclude that excitations were coming even faster than 5.3 times a second. This follows because the average length of the interval between responses is increased by the exponential tail which in turn reflects varying degrees of failure to follow excitation. In this case it is likely that the period τ is constructed by a pre-programmed rhythmic oscillation of the head something like the mechanism that humans use in order to generate high rates of tapping.

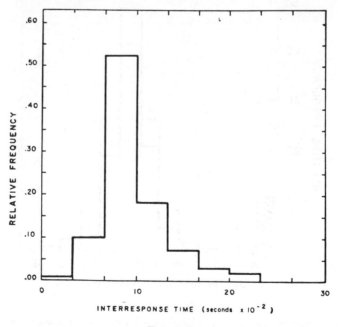

FIGURE 5

Frequency distribution of 1000 interresponse times recorded from a pigeon pecking at a high rate. Intervals longer than .23 seconds not shown. (Data from Brandauer).

In a recent paper, Hunt and Kuno [9] present several distributions of interresponse times recorded during spontaneous activity of single fibers in the spinal cord of the cat. The data run the gamut from the Laplace to the exponential, including several examples of what appears to be our skewed distribution (Fig. 2). The effect is exactly what might be expected, if the same general response system were subjected to varying rates of periodic excitation.

Discussion

It would be hard to find levels of behavior further apart than single fiber activity and overt responding. Yet the distributions of interresponse times presented in this paper seem applicable to both, and in the limited view afforded by a study of the time between responses, neither system looks more complicated or better organized than the other.

When we find stochastic mechanisms like Fig. 1 operating in overt responding, it probably means no more than that complicated systems of neurons can be organized to do very simple jobs. Even so, the noise in an organization may give a clue to the nature of the organization, and thus provide a way to study it. When we ask, as we did earlier, how the animal constructs τ, we have to find a way that is compatible with our conception of the mechanism as dictated by the noise.

The delineation of simple periodic mechanisms affords similar insights into information coding in single nerve fibers. Knowledge of the general form of the coding mechanism indicates what kind of noise higher centers have to face, and suggests possible ways for detecting periodicity in the noise. For instance, the Laplace distribution presents very interesting problems to a device attempting to estimate its parameters [1].

The latency mechanism considered in this paper barely scratches the surface of the possibilities. It turns out that our mechanism has indistinguishable excitations. Whenever a new excitation appears before there is a response to an earlier one, it makes no difference whether the new excitation replaces the old one and reactivates the response trigger, or is simply blocked by the excitation that is already working. Once this is clear other suggestions for summating excitations or for parallel channeling present themselves. For example, there are a number of *harmonic* distributions of interresponse times in the literature [3]. These distributions show clusterings of interresponse times at multiples of a fundamental period, and hence seem to closely related to (2) which also has harmonic components. But something else is required, and it is not entirely clear yet what that something else is.

REFERENCES

[1] Arley, N. and Buch, K. R. *Introduction to the theory of probability and statistics.* New York: Wiley, 1950.

[2] Brandauer, C. The effects of uniform probabilities of reinforcement upon the response rate of the pigeon. Unpublished doctoral thesis. Columbia University, 1958.

[3] Brink, F., Bronk, D., and Larrabee, M. Chemical excitation of nerve. *Ann. N. Y. Acad. Sci.*, 1946, **47**, 457–485.

[4] Feller, W. *Probability theory and its applications.* (1st ed.) New York: Wiley, 1950.

[5] Ferster, C. and Skinner, B. F. *Schedules of reinforcement.* New York: Appleton-Century-Crofts, 1957.

[6] Hartline, H. K. The nerve messages in the fibers of the visual pathway. *J. opt. Soc. Amer.*, 1940, **30**, 239–247.

[7] Hill, R. T. Operant behavior. Differential reinforcement of low rate responding. Report of Lederle Laboratories, American Cyanamid Co., Pearl River, N. Y., P. E. Vol. 4, 11/10/59, pp. 383–415.

[8] Hoel, P. G. *Introduction to mathematical statistics.* (2nd ed.) New York: Wiley, 1954.

[9] Hunt, C. C. and Kuno, M. Background discharge and evoked response of spinal interneurones. *J. Physiol.*, 1959, **147**, 364–384.

[10] Mood, A. *Introduction to the theory of statistics.* New York: McGraw-Hill, 1950.

[11] Mueller, C. G. Theoretical relationships among some measures of conditioning. *Proc. Nat. Acad. Sci.*, 1950, **36**, 123–130.

[12] Widder, D. *Advanced calculus.* New York: Prentice-Hall, 1947.

[13] Wilks, S. S. *Mathematical statistics.* Princeton: Princeton Univ. Press, 1943.

Manuscript received 12/14/59

Revised manuscript received 8/28/61

SENSITIVITY TO CHANGES IN THE INTENSITY
OF WHITE NOISE AND ITS RELATION TO
MASKING AND LOUDNESS[1]

GEORGE A. MILLER

Sensitivity to changes in the intensity of a random noise was determined over a wide range of intensities. The just detectable increment in the intensity of the noise is of the same order of magnitude as the just detectable increment in the intensity of pure tones. For intensities more than 30 db above the threshold of hearing for noise the size in decibels of the increment which can be heard 50 percent of the time is approximately constant (0.41 db). When the results of the experiment are regarded as measures of the masking of a noise by the noise itself, it can be shown that functions which describe intensity discrimination also describe the masking by white noise of pure tones and of speech. It is argued, therefore, that the determination of differential sensitivity to intensity is a special case of the more general masking experiment. The loudness of the noise was also determined, and just noticeable differences are shown to be unequal in subjective magnitude. A just noticeable difference at a low intensity produces a much smaller change in the apparent loudness than does a just noticeable difference at high intensity.

Differential sensitivity to intensity is one of the oldest and most important problems in the psychophysics of audition. But previous experiments have concerned themselves mainly with sensitivity to changes in the intensity of sinusoidal tones, and if we want to know the differential sensitivity for a complex sound, it is necessary either to extrapolate from existing information, or actually to conduct the experiment for the sound in question. This gap in our knowledge is due to expediency, not oversight. The realm of complex sounds includes an infinitude of acoustic compounds, and experimental parameters extend in many directions. Just which of these sounds we select for investigation is an arbitrary matter. Of the various possibilities, however, one of the most appropriate is random noise, a sound of persistent importance and one which marks a sort of ultimate on a scale of complexity.

Although the instantaneous amplitude varies randomly, white noise is perceived as a steady "hishing" sound, and it is quite possible to determine a listener's sensitivity to changes in its intensity.[2] The present paper reports the results of such determinations for a range of noise intensities.

Apparatus and Procedure

A white-noise voltage, produced by random ionization in a gas tube, was varied in intensity by shunting the line with known resistances provided by a General Radio

This article appeared in *J. Acoust. Soc. Amer.*, 1947, **19**, 609–619. Reprinted with permission.

[1] This research was conducted under contract with the U.S. Navy, Office of Naval Research (Contract N5ori-76, Report PNR-28).

[2] J. E. Karlin, *Auditory tests for the ability to discriminate the pitch and the loudness of noises*, OSRD Report No. 5294 (Psycho-Acoustic Laboratory, Harvard University, August 1, 1945) (available through the Office of Technical Services, U.S. Department of Commerce, Washington, D. C.).

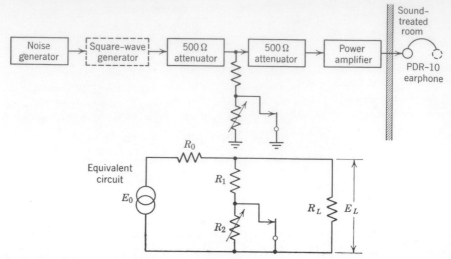

FIGURE 1

Schematic diagram of equipment with the equivalent circuit used in the computation of the size of the increment in intensity.

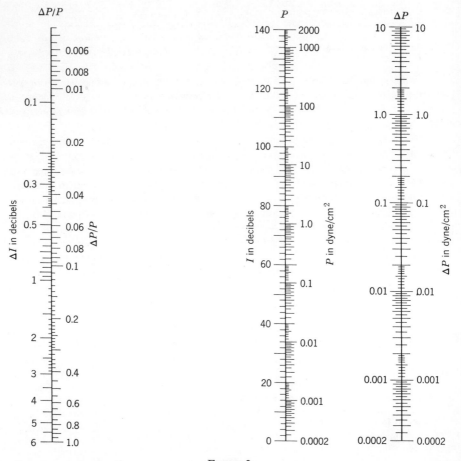

FIGURE 2

Nomogram to convert values of $\Delta P/P$ to ΔP when P is known.

Decade Resistance Box. A schematic diagram of the equipment is shown in Fig. 1. The attenuators were used to keep constant the values of source and load impedance, R_0 and R_L, surrounding the shunt resistances, R_1 and R_2, since these values must enter into the computation of the increment which is produced by the insertion of the variable resistance, R_2. The whole system can be represented by the equivalent circuit, also shown in Fig. 1. For this circuit, the size of an increment in voltage ΔE_L is given by

$$\frac{\Delta E_L}{E_L} = \frac{R_0 R_2 R_L}{R_1[R_0(R_1 + R_2 + R_3) + R_L(R_1 + R_2)]}.$$

If the system does not introduce amplitude distortion after the increments are produced, the increment in sound pressure, expressed in decibels, can be taken as $20 \log_{10}(1 + \Delta E_L/E_L)$.

Throughout the following discussion the intensity of the noise will be stated in terms of its sensation level—the number of decibels above the listener's absolute threshold for the noise. If the sound-pressure level of the noise is taken to be the level generated by a moving-coil earphone (Permoflux PDR-10) when the voltage across the earphone (measured by a thermocouple) is the same as the voltage required for a sinusoidal wave (1000 cycles) to generate the given sound pressure in a volume of 6 cc, then the absolute threshold for the noise corresponds to a sound pressure of approximately 10 db re 0.0002 dyne/cm². Thus the sensation level can be converted into sound-pressure level by the simple procedure of adding 10 db to the value given for the sensation level. The spectrum of the noise was relatively uniform (± 5 db) between 150 and 7000 c.p.s. The measurement and spectrum of the noise transduced by the earphone PDR-10 has been discussed in detail by Hawkins.[3]

Once the sound-pressure level and the relative size of the increment in decibels are known, the absolute value of the increment can be computed. Those interested in converting the decibels into dynes/cm² will find the nomogram of Fig. 2 a considerable convenience. A straight line which passes through a value of ΔI in decibels on the left-hand scale, and through a value of the sound pressure on the middle scale, will intersect the right-hand scale at the appropriate value of ΔP in dyne/cm². When the stimulus is a plane progressive sound wave, its acoustic intensity in watts/cm² is proportional to the square of the pressure: $I = kp^2$.

The peak amplitudes in the wave of a white noise are not constant. It is reasonable to expect, therefore, that the size of the just noticeable difference might vary as a function of the distribution of peak amplitudes in the wave. In order to evaluate this aspect of the stimulus, a second experiment was conducted. The noise voltage was passed through a square-wave generator (Hewlett Packard, Model 210-A) before the increments were introduced. The spectrum and subjective quality of the noise are not altered by the square-wave generator, but the peak amplitudes are "squared off" at a uniform level. The resulting wave form might be described as a square-wave modulated randomly in frequency.

---

[3] J. E. Hawkins, "The masking of pure tones and of speech by white noise," in a report entitled *The masking of signals by noise*, OSRD Report No. 5387 (Psycho-Acoustic Laboratory, Harvard University, October 1, 1945) (available through the Office of Technical Services, U.S. Department of Commerce, Washington, D.C.).

The experimental procedure for determining differential sensitivity was the same as that employed by Stevens, Morgan, and Volkmann.[4] The only difference was the omission of a signal light which they sometimes used to indicate the impending presentation of an increment. The observer, seated alone in a sound-treated room, listened to the noise monaurally through a high quality, dynamic earphone (PDR-10). The listener heard a continuous noise, to which an increment was added periodically. A series of 25 identical increments (1.5 sec. duration at intervals of 4.5 sec.) was presented, and the percentage heard was tabulated. Four such series were used to determine each

TABLE I

Differential Sensitivity for Intensity of Noise. Increments in Decibels Which Two Listeners Could Hear 50 Percent of the Time, as a Function of Sensation Level.

Sensation level	Random noise GM	SM	Square-wave noise GM	SM
3 db	3.20 db	3.20 db		
5	3.00	2.10		
10	1.17	1.17		
12			0.97 db	0.89 db
15	0.85	0.66		
20	0.49	0.55		
25	0.46	0.54		
32			0.40	0.39
35	0.40	0.50		
45	0.42	0.44		
52			0.40	0.46
55	0.39	0.50		
70	0.39	0.47		
82			0.32	0.47
85	0.33	0.48		
100	0.28	0.40		

of 5 to 8 points on a psychometric function, and from this function the differential threshold was obtained by linear interpolation. Thus 500 to 800 judgments by each of two experienced listeners were used to determine each differential threshold at the 16 different intensities.

Results

The increments in decibels which the two listeners could hear 50 percent of the time are presented in Table I as a function of the sensation level of the noise. It will be noted that the differential sensitivity for "square-wave noise" is not significantly greater than that for random noise. Apparently the fluctuations in the peak amplitude of the wave do not influence the size of the just noticeable increment. The response of the ear is probably too sluggish to follow these brief fluctuations. And since the difference between the two wave forms is essentially a matter of the phase relations

[4] S. S. Stevens, C. T. Morgan, and J. Volkmann, Theory of the neural quantum in the discrimination of loudness and pitch, *Am. J. Psychol.*, 1941, **54,** 315–335.

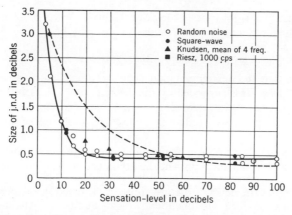

FIGURE 3

Increments in intensity heard 50 percent of the time are plotted as a function of the intensity of the noise in decibels above the threshold of hearing. Data for tones are presented for purposes of comparison. The solid line represents Eq. (2).

among the components, we may conclude that these phase relations have no important effect on differential sensitivity.

The data indicate that, for intensities 30 db or more above the absolute threshold, the relative differential threshold is approximately constant. At the highest intensities the value is about 0.41 db, which corresponds to a Weber-fraction of 0.099 for sound energy, or 0.048 for sound pressure. The range over which the increment is proportional to the level of stimulation is indicated by the horizontal portion of the solid curve in Fig. 3. The values over this range of intensities agree quite well with the values obtained by Karlin[2] with a group of 50 listeners.

For purposes of comparison, Fig. 3 includes data obtained by Riesz[5] and by Knudsen[6] for tones. Knudsen's results do not differ markedly from those obtained for noise, but Riesz's data are quite different, especially at low intensities. Possibly Knudsen's data represent sensitivity to the "noise" introduced by the abrupt onset of his tones, or possibly Riesz's data at low intensities are suspect because of his use of beats to produce increments in intensity. Data obtained by Stevens and Volkmann[7] for a single listener at four intensities of a 1000-cycle tone seem to agree more closely with the present results than with Riesz's, but their data are not complete enough to determine a function. Churcher, King, and Davies[8] have reported data with a tone of 800 c.p.s. which compare favorably with the function of Riesz. Taken together, all these studies indicate that the difference limen for intensity is of the same order of

[5] R. R. Riesz, Differential intensity sensitivity of the ear for pure tones, *Phys. Rev.*, 1928, **31**, 867–875.

[6] V. O. Knudsen, The sensibility of the ear to small differences in intensity and frequency, *Phys. Rev.*, 1923, **21**, 84–103.

[7] S. S. Stevens and J. Volkmann, The quantum of sensory discrimination, *Science*, 1940, **92**, 583–585.

[8] B. G. Churcher, A. J. King, and H. Davies, The minimum perceptible change of intensity of a pure tone, *Phil. Mag.*, 1934, **18**, 927–939.

magnitude for noise as it is for tones, at least at the higher levels of intensity.[9] At the lower intensities the discrimination for a noise stimulus may be somewhat more acute than for tones.

Implications for a Quantal Theory of Discrimination

The notion that the difference limen depends upon the activation of discrete neural units is not new. It is suggested by the discreteness of the sensory cells themselves. Only recently, however, has evidence been obtained to support the assumption that the basic neural processes mediating a discrimination are of an all-or-none character.

The principal evidence derives from the shape of the psychometric function. Stevens, Morgan, and Volkmann[10] present the argument in the following way:

We assume that the neural structures initially involved in the perception of a sensory continuum are divided into functionally distinct units. . . . The stimulus which excites a certain number of quanta will ordinarily do so with a little to spare—it will excite these quanta and leave a small surplus insufficient to excite some additional quantum. This surplus stimulation will contribute, along with the increment, ΔI, to bring into activity the added quantum needed for discrimination. . . . How much of this left-over stimulation or surplus excitation are we to expect? If [the over-all fluctuation in sensitivity] is large compared to the size of an individual quantum, it is evident that over the course of time all values of the surplus stimulation occur equally often. . . . From these considerations it follows that, if the increment is added instantaneously to the stimulus, it will be perceived a certain fraction of the time, and this fraction is directly proportional to the size of the increment itself.

When the increments are added to a continuous stimulus, however, the listener finds it difficult to distinguish one-quantum changes in the stimulus from the changes which are constantly occurring because of fluctuations in his sensitivity. In order to make reliable judgments, the listener is forced to ignore all one-quantum changes. Consequently, a stimulus increment under these conditions must activate at least two additional neural units in order that a difference will be perceived and reported. Thus, in effect, a constant error of one quantum is added to the psychometric function.

The psychometric function predicted by this line of reasoning can be described in the following way. When the stimulus increments to a steady sound are less than some value ΔI_Q, they are never reported, and over the range of increments from 0 to ΔI_Q the psychometric function remains at 0 percent. Between ΔI_Q and $2\Delta I_Q$ the proportion of the increments reported varies directly with the size of the increment, and reaches 100 percent at $2\Delta I_Q$. Such a function is illustrated by the solid line of Fig. 4.

It will be noted that the difference which is reported 50 percent of the time is equivalent to 1.5 times the quantal increment. If we take this value as defining a unit increment in the stimulus, all the psychometric functions obtained for the two listeners can be combined into a single function. In other words, we can adjust the individual intensity scales against which the functions are plotted in order to make all the functions coincide at the 50 percent point. In Fig. 4 the size of the relative increment in sound

[9] Of the modern investigations, only Dimmick's disagrees strikingly with the values reported here for the higher intensities. F. L. Dimmick and R. M. Olson, The intensive difference limen in audition, *J. acoust. Soc. Am.*, 1941, **12**, 517–525.

[10] See reference 4, p. 317.

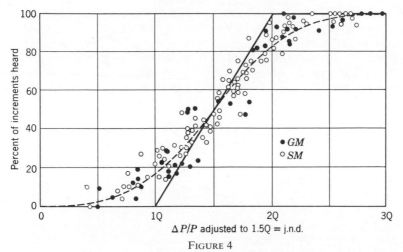

FIGURE 4

The 32 psychometric functions combined in a single graph. Values of $\Delta P/P$ heard 50 percent of the time are designated as $1.5Q$, and the datum points on each function are plotted relative to this value. Each point represents 100 judgments.

pressure, $\Delta P/P$, has been adjusted so that the increment which was heard 50 percent of the time is plotted as 1.5 times the quantal increment.

Figure 4 shows that the characteristic quantal function was not obtained in this experiment. The data are better described by the phi-function of gamma (the normal probability integral) indicated by the dashed line.

The classical argument for the application of the cumulative probability function to the difference limen assumes a number of small, indeterminate variables which are independent, and which combine according to chance. When these variables are controlled or eliminated, the step-wise, "quantal" relation is revealed.[11] If this reasoning is correct, then the deviations of the points in Fig. 4 from the quantal hypothesis should be attributable to the introduction of random variability into the listening situation.

Is there any obvious source of randomness in the experiment? Certainly there is, for white noise is a paradigm of randomness. The statistical nature of the noise means that the calculated value of the increment is merely the most probable value, and that a certain portion of the time the increment will depart from this probable value by an amount sufficient to affect the discrimination. And in view of the fluctuating level of the stimulus, it would be surprising indeed if the rigorous experimental requirements of the quantal hypothesis were fulfilled. This situation demonstrates the practical difficulty in obtaining the rectilinear functions predicted by the quantal hypothesis. Any source of variability tends to obscure the step-wise results and to produce the S-shaped normal probability integral.

It should be noted, however, that the shape of the psychometric function is only one of the implications of the quantal argument. According to the hypothesis, the slope

[11] G. A. Miller and W. R. Garner, Effect of random presentation on the psychometric function: Implications for a quantal theory of discrimination, *Am. J. Psychol.*, 1944, **57**, 451–467.

of the psychometric function is determined by the size of the difference limen for all values of stimulus-intensity. The present data accord with this second prediction. The standard deviations of the probability integrals which describe the data are approximately one-third the means (or $0.5\Delta I_Q$) for all the thresholds measured for both subjects. This invariance in the slope of the function is necessary but not sufficient evidence for a neural quantum, and it makes possible the representation of the results in the form shown in Fig. 4.

Symbolic Representation of the Data

In order to represent the experimental results in symbolic form, the following symbols will be used:

b numerical constant $= 1.333$,
c numerical constant $= 0.066 = \Delta I_Q/I$ when $I \gg I_0$,
DL difference limen (just noticeable difference) expressed in decibels,
f frequency in cycles per second,
I sound intensity (energy flow),
$I\sim$ sound intensity per cycle,
I_0 sound intensity which is just audible in quiet,
I_m sound intensity which is just masked in noise,
ΔI_Q quantal increment in sound intensity $= 0.667\Delta I_{50}$,
ΔI_{50} increment in sound intensity heard 50 percent of the time,
L loudness in sones,
M masking in decibels,
N_Q number of quantal increments above threshold,
R signal-to-noise ratio per cycle at any frequency,
Z effective level of noise at any frequency.

An adequate description of the data in Table I can be developed from the empirical equation

$$\Delta I_Q = cI + bI_0, \quad I \geq I_0, \tag{1}$$

where the quantal increment in the stimulus-energy is assumed to have a fixed and a variable component. Since ΔI_{50}—the increment which can be heard 50 percent of the time—equals $1.5\Delta I_Q$, we can write

$$DL = 10 \log_{10}(1 + \Delta I_{50}/I) = 10 \log_{10}[1 + 1.5c + 1.5b(I_0/I)]. \tag{2}$$

From (2) it is possible to compute the just noticeable increment in decibels as a function of sensation level, although we know only the ratio between I and I_0 and not their absolute values. When the computations are carried through, the values indicated by the solid curve in Fig. 3 are obtained. The fit of this curve to the data is good enough to justify the use of Eq. (2) to obtain smoothed values of the function.

It is interesting to note that at high intensities Eq. (1) is equivalent to the well-known "Weber's Law," which states that the size of a just noticeable difference is proportional to the intensity to which it is added. Differential sensitivity characteristically departs from Weber's Law at low intensities, and Fechner long ago suggested a modification of the law to the form expressed in Eq. (1).[12] The essential feature

[12] H. Helmholtz, *Treatise on physiological optics* (translated by P. C. Southall from 3rd German ed., Vol. II. The sensations of vision, 1911), Optical Society of America, 1924, pp. 172–181.

of this equation is the rectilinear relation between ΔI and I; the obvious difficulty is the explanation of the intercept value bI_0 which appears in Eq. (1) as an additive factor. Fechner supposed that this added term is attributable to intrinsic, interfering stimulation which cannot be eliminated in the measurement of the difference limen. Body noises, the spontaneous activity of the auditory nervous system, or the thermal noise of the air molecules have been suggested as possible sources of this background stimulation, but proof of these possibilities is still lacking. For the present, therefore, we must regard Eq. (1) as a purely empirical equation.

Relation to Masking

There is an operational similarity between experiments designed to study differential sensitivity for intensity and experiments devised to measure auditory masking. This similarity is usually obscured by a practical inclination to ignore the special case where one sound is masked by another sound identical with the first.

Suppose we want to know how much a white noise masks a white noise. What experimental procedures would we adopt? Obviously, the judgment we would ask the listener to make is the same judgment made in the present experiment. In the one case, however, we present the data to show the smallest detectable increment, while in the other we use the same data to determine the shift in threshold of the masked sound. When the masked and masking sounds are identical, the difference between masking and sensitivity to changes in intensity lies only in the way the story is told.

A striking example of this similarity is to be found in the work of Riesz. In order to produce gradual changes in intensity, Riesz used tones differing in frequency by 3 cycles and instructed his listeners to report the presence or absence of beats. Although his results are generally accepted as definitive measures of sensitivity to changes in the intensity of pure tones, it is equally correct to interpret them as measures of the masking of one tone by another tone differing in frequency by 3 cycles.

Let us, therefore, reconsider the data of Table I. In this table we have presented in decibels both the sensation level of the noise and the size of the increment which can be heard 50 percent of the time. How can these data be transformed to correspond with the definition of masking?

First, consider that we are mixing two noises in order to produce the total magnitude $I + \Delta I$. Since I is analogous to the intensity of the masking sound, $I + \Delta I$ must equal the intensity of the masking sound plus the intensity of the masked sound, $I + I_m$. Thus $I_m = \Delta I$, and from the definition of masking M we can write

$$M = 10 \log_{10}(I_m/I_0) = 10 \log_{10}(\Delta I/I_0). \tag{3}$$

Because there appears to be some basic significance to the quantal unit, whereas the criterion of hearing 50 percent of the increments is arbitrary, we will use the quantal increment ΔI_Q in Eq. (3). ΔI_Q is defined as 0.667 times the value of the increment which is heard 50 percent of the time.

$$M = 10 \log_{10}(\Delta I_Q/I_0). \tag{3a}$$

Equation (3a) tells us, then, that the logarithm of the ratio of the quantal increment to the absolute threshold is proportional to the masking of a sound by an identical sound.

TABLE II

Masking of White Noise by White Noise. Quantal Increments in Decibels and the Values of Masking Obtained for Two Listeners as a Function of the Sensation Level of the Masking Noise. Computed Values of Masking According to Eq. (4).

Sensation level	Quantal increment in decibels		Masking obtained		Masking computed
	GM	SM	GM	SM	
3 db	2.37 db	2.37 db	1.61 db	1.61 db	1.66 db
5	2.21	1.51	3.26	1.18	1.88
10	0.81	0.81	3.14	3.14	3.00
12	0.67	0.61	4.22	3.80	3.76
15	0.58	0.45	6.58	5.39	5.33
20	0.33	0.37	9.00	9.54	8.99
25	0.31	0.37	13.73	14.45	13.44
32	0.27	0.27	20.06	19.97	20.25
35	0.27	0.34	23.06	24.10	23.22
45	0.29	0.30	33.33	33.53	33.20
52	0.27	0.31	40.06	40.73	40.20
55	0.27	0.34	42.97	44.10	43.20
70	0.27	0.32	57.97	58.81	58.20
82	0.22	0.32	68.32	70.81	70.20
85	0.22	0.33	72.22	73.91	73.20
100	0.19	0.27	86.43	88.06	88.20

It is now possible to determine the values of ΔI_Q and I_0 from the information given in Table I, and to substitute these values into Eq. (3a). The results of converting the differential thresholds into quantal increments and then into masked thresholds are given in Table II for the two listeners, and are shown in Fig. 5 where masking is plotted as a function of the sensation level of the masking noise. In addition, Table II contains values of masking which are computed when Eqs. (1) and (3a) are combined:

$$M = 10 \log_{10}[(cI/I_0) + b]. \qquad (4)$$

For intensities 25 db or more above threshold, the masking noise is about 12 db more intense than the masked noise.

The obvious next step is to ask whether these results correspond to the functions obtained when noise is used to mask tones or human speech. Fortunately, we are able to answer this question. Hawkins[3] has measured the masking effects of noise on tones and speech with experimental conditions and equipment directly comparable with those used here.

Suppose, for purposes of comparison, we choose to mask a 1000-cycle tone. We find over a wide range of intensities that this particular white noise just masks a 1000-cycle tone which is 20 db less intense. Since the corresponding value is 12 db when this noise masks itself, we conclude that, for this specific noise spectrum, 8 db less energy is needed for audibility when the energy is concentrated at 1000 c.p.s. than when the energy is spread over the entire spectrum. In order to compare the forms of the two masking functions, therefore, we can subtract 8 db from the level of the noise which masks the 1000-cycle tone.

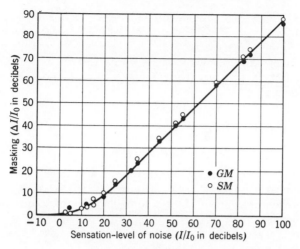

FIGURE 5
Discriminable increments in intensity of white noise plotted in a manner analogous to masking experiments. Solid line represents function obtained by Hawkins for the masking of tones and speech by white noise.

When we make this correction of 8 db in the noise level for Hawkins' data for a 1000-cycle tone and plot the masking of this tone as a function of the corrected noise intensity, we obtain the solid line shown in Fig. 5. The correspondence between this curve, taken from Hawkins' data, and the points obtained in the present experiment is remarkably close. The function computed from Eq. (4) falls too close to Hawkins' function to warrant its separate presentation in Fig. 5.

The choice of 1000 c.p.s. is not crucial to this correspondence. As Fletcher and Munson[13] have pointed out, a single function is adequate to describe the masking by noise of pure tones, if the intensity of the noise is corrected by a factor which is a function of the frequency of the masked tone. This factor is given at any frequency f by the ratio R of the intensity of the masked tone to the intensity per cycle of the noise at that frequency: $R = I_m/I\sim$. R is experimentally determined for all frequencies at intensities well above threshold—on the rectilinear portion of the function shown in Fig. 5.

For noises with continuous spectra, the masking of a tone of frequency f can be attributed to the noise in the band of frequencies immediately adjacent to f.[14] Consequently, it is convenient to relate the masking of a tone of frequency f to the intensity per cycle of the noise at f, and to express this intensity in decibels re the threshold of hearing at any frequency. This procedure gives $10 \log_{10}(I\sim/I_0)$, which can be regarded as the sensation level at f of a one-cycle band of noise. The effective level Z of the noise at that frequency is then defined as

$$Z = 10 \log_{10}(I\sim/I_0) + 10 \log_{10}R. \qquad (5)$$

[13] H. Fletcher and W. A. Munson, Relation between loudness and masking, *J. acous. Soc. Am.*, 1937, **9**, 1–10.

[14] H. Fletcher, Auditory patterns, *Rev. Mod. Phys.*, 1940, **12**, 47–65.

When the masking of pure tones is plotted as a function of Z, the relation between M and Z is found to be independent of frequency. A single function expresses the relation between M and Z for all frequencies.

When we compare the function relating M to Z with the function obtained in the present experiment, we find that the sensation level of the noise is equivalent to $Z + 11.8$ db. Therefore,

$$I/I_0 = 15.14R(I{\sim}/I_0).$$

Substituting this expression into Eq. (4) gives

$$M = 10 \log_{10}[R(I{\sim}/I_0) + b].   \tag{6}$$

This equation, along with the functions relating R and I_0 to frequency, enables us to compute the masking of pure tones by any random noise of known spectrum. When $10 \log_{10}(I{\sim}/I_0)$ is greater than about 15 db, b is negligible for all frequencies, and the masking can be computed more simply as $10 \log_{10}R + 10 \log_{10}(I{\sim}/I_0)$.

Hawkins' results show that the function of Eq. (4) can also be adapted to describe the masking of human speech by white noise.

Thus the correspondence seems complete. When the masking and the masked sounds are identical, masking and sensitivity to changes in intensity are equivalent. The results obtained with identical masking and masked noises are directly comparable to results obtained with different masked sounds. It is reasonable to conclude, therefore, that the determination of sensitivity to changes in intensity is a special case of the more general masking experiment.

It is worth noting that this interpretation of masking is also applicable to visual sensitivity to changes in the intensity of white light. Data obtained by Graham and Bartlett[15] provide an excellent basis for comparison, because of the similarity of their procedure to that of the masking experiment, and because they used homogeneous, rod-free, foveal areas of the retina. When these data are substituted into Eq. (3) and plotted as measures of visual masking, the result can be described by the same general function that we have used to express the auditory masking by noise of tones, speech, and noise.

Relation to Loudness

When Fechner adopted the just noticeable difference as the unit for sensory scales, he precipitated a controversy which is still alive today: Are equally-often-noticed differences subjectively equal? In the case of auditory loudness, the answer seems to be negative. Just noticeable differences (j.n.d.'s) at high intensities are subjectively much larger than j.n.d.'s at low intensities.

[15] C. H. Graham and N. R. Bartlett, The relation of stimulus and intensity in the human eye: III. The influence of area on foveal intensity discrimination, *J. exper. Psychol.*, 1940, **27**, 149–159.

Crozier has used similar visual data to demonstrate that the reciprocal of the just detectable increment is related to the logarithm of the light intensity by a normal probability integral. This is deduced on the assumption that sensitivity is determined by the not-already-excited portion of the total population of potentially excitable neural effects. Crozier's equations give an excellent description of the auditory data presented here. W. J. Crozier, On the law for minimal discrimination of intensities. IV. ΔI as a function of intensity, *Proc. Nat. Acad. Sci.*, 1940, **26**, 382–388.

In order to demonstrate that such is the case for noise as well as for pure tones, we need two kinds of information. We need to know the functions relating noise intensity to the number of distinguishable steps above threshold, and to the subjective loudness of the noise in sones. If these two functions correspond, Fechner was right and j.n.d.'s can be used as units on a subjective loudness-scale. If.they do not agree, Fechner was wrong, and the picture is more complex than he imagined.

TABLE III

Loudness and the Number of Quanta. Sensation-Level of Equally Loud 1000-Cycle Tone as a Function of Sensation-Level of Noise, with Corresponding Loudness in Sones. Data for 12 Listeners. The Last Column Gives the Corresponding Number of Quantal Units Above Threshold.

| Sensation-level of noise | Equally loud 1000 c.p.s. | | Loudness in sones | | No. of quanta above threshold |
	Sensation level	Stand. dev.	Mean	±Stand. dev.	
15 db	14.2 db	4.6 db	0.036	0.015– 0.081	13
30	38.1	6.9	0.83	0.40 – 1.6	58
45	57.9	9.1	4.8	2.3 – 9.7	111
60	74.2	8.2	17.0	9 –26	163
75	86.3	7.2	37	24 –47	216
90	97.9	3.1	76	62 –88	268

The number of differential quanta N_Q corresponding to a given sensation level of noise is readily obtained by "stepping off" the quantal increments against a scale of decibels. The procedure consists of finding the number of quantal increments per unit of intensity and then integrating:

$$N_Q = \int 1/\Delta I_Q \cdot dI. \tag{7}$$

If we substitute for the size of the quantal increment according to Eq. (1),

$$N_Q = \int \frac{1}{cI + bI_0} \cdot dI = \frac{1}{c} \ln \Delta I_Q + C. \tag{8}$$

When we convert to logarithms to the base 10, insert the values for the constants, and solve in terms of masking M, we find that

$$N_Q = 3.49M + K. \tag{9}$$

We assume that the number of quantal increments is zero when $I = I_0$, and at this point Eq. (4) indicates that $M = 1.46$ db. Therefore, $K = -5.1$. Values of N_Q obtained by Eq. (9) are given in Table III, and plotted in Fig. 7.

The loudness in sones was determined by requiring listeners to equate the loudness of the noise with the loudness of a 1000-cycle tone. The two sounds were presented alternately to the same ear, and the listener adjusted the intensity of the tone. Five equations were made by each of twelve listeners for the six noise-intensities studied. The result of this experiment—the level of the 1000-cycle tone which sounds equal in

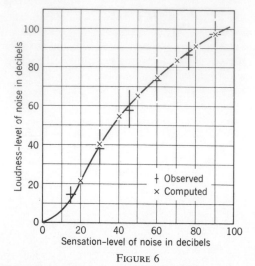

FIGURE 6

Observed and computed values of the loudness level of white noise. Standard deviations of the values for 15 listeners are indicated by the lengths of the vertical bars.

loudness to the noise—defines the loudness level of the noise. With these data, which are tabulated in Table III and plotted in Fig. 6, the loudness in sones is determined from the loudness-scale which has been constructed for the 1000-cycle tone. The values in sones from Stevens' loudness-scale[16] are included in Table III. Table III also gives the standard deviations of the distributions of loudness levels obtained for the 12 listeners.

Loudness can also be computed. Fletcher and Munson developed a procedure for calculating loudness from the masking which the sound produces. When this

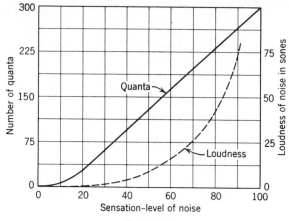

FIGURE 7

Comparison of the number of discriminatory quanta with the loudness of white noise. Just noticeable increments of intensity are not subjectively equal.

[16] S. S. Stevens and H. Davis, *Hearing*, New York: Wiley, 1938, p. 118.

procedure is applied to Hawkins' data for the masking of pure tones by noise, we get the computed values shown in Fig. 6. The agreement between computed and experimental results is quite satisfactory.

We are now equipped to present the two functions shown in Fig. 7. The solid curve shows the number of quantal units as a function of sensation level. The dashed

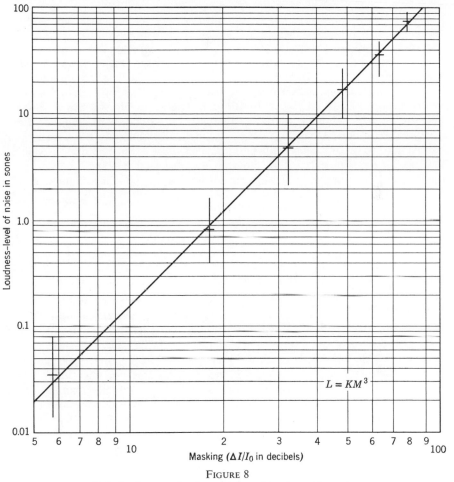

FIGURE 8
Relation between loudness and masking for white noise.

curve shows the loudness in sones. The discrepancy between these two curves affirms the error of Fechner's assumption. Loudness and the number of just noticeable differences are not linearly related.

When, as in the present case, two variables are both related to a third, it is possible to determine their relation to each other. Stevens[17] has used Riesz's data for

[17] S. S. Stevens, A scale for the measurement of a psychological magnitude: loudness, *Psychol. Rev.*, 1936, **43**, 405–416.

pure tones to arrive at the empirical equation $L = kN^{2.2}$, where L is the loudness of the tone in sones, k is the size in sones of the first step, and N is the number of distinguishable steps. When we parallel Stevens' computation with the data for noise presented in Table III, we find that $L = kN^3$ describes the relation rather well over most of the range. It is interesting that both turn out to be power functions, but why the exponent should be different for noise and tones is not apparent.

There is an alternative way to state the relation between differential sensitivity and loudness. In the preceding section we developed the notion that sensitivity to changes in intensity is a special case of masking, and we computed the masking of the noise on itself. Let us now examine the relation between masking, so defined, and the subjective loudness. In Fig. 5 and Table II masking is related to sensation level; in Fig. 7 and Table III loudness is related to sensation level. The relation of masking to loudness is obtained by combining these two functions. In Fig. 8 it can be seen that the expression $L = KM^3$ fits the data rather well. The loudness of a white noise increases in proportion to the third power of the masking produced by the noise on itself, i.e., the third power of the logarithm of the quantal increment in intensity. In whatever form we cast the empirical equation, however, it is obvious that faint j.n.d.'s are smaller than loud j.n.d.'s and that j.n.d.'s are not equal units along a scale of loudness.

Acknowledgment

The author wishes to express his gratitude to Miss Shirley Mitchell, who assisted in obtaining the experimental data, and to Professor S. S. Stevens, who contributed valuable criticism and advice during the preparation of this manuscript.

Correction

In 1963 D. H. Raab, E. Osman, and E. Rich noticed an error in Eq. (3), which is written as if the masked and masking noises had been generated independently. In fact, however, the two noises were perfectly correlated (cf. Fig. 1), so their sound pressures added in phase; their combined power was the square of their summed pressures, not the sum of their squared pressures. When the amount of masking is recomputed from Table I using $M = 20 \log_{10} (\Delta P / P_0)$, then for intensities 25 db or more above threshold, the masking noise is about 25 db more intense than the masked noise (not 12 db as stated on page 128). At sensation levels below about 25 db, therefore, there was facilitation (negative masking) instead of masking; listeners were able to hear in-phase increments which would have been inaudible if presented alone in the absence of the "masking" noise. This fact was verified directly by Raab, Osman, and Rich; a similar effect for sinusoids has been reported by S. M. Pfafflin and M. V. Mathews, Energy-detection model for monaural auditory detection, *J. acoust. Soc. Am.*, 1962, **34**, 1842–1853.

When this correction is made, of course, the relation shown in Fig. 8 no longer obtains.

THE MAGICAL NUMBER SEVEN, PLUS OR MINUS TWO: SOME LIMITS ON OUR CAPACITY FOR PROCESSING INFORMATION [1]

GEORGE A. MILLER

Harvard University

My problem is that I have been persecuted by an integer. For seven years this number has followed me around, has intruded in my most private data, and has assaulted me from the pages of our most public journals. This number assumes a variety of disguises, being sometimes a little larger and sometimes a little smaller than usual, but never changing so much as to be unrecognizable. The persistence with which this number plagues me is far more than a random accident. There is, to quote a famous senator, a design behind it, some pattern governing its appearances. Either there really is something unusual about the number or else I am suffering from delusions of persecution.

I shall begin my case history by telling you about some experiments that tested how accurately people can assign numbers to the magnitudes of various aspects of a stimulus. In the traditional language of psychology these would be called experiments in absolute judgment. Historical accident, however, has decreed that they should have another name. We now call them experiments on the capacity of people to transmit information. Since these experiments would not have been done without the appearance of information theory on the psychological scene, and since the results are analyzed in terms of the concepts of information theory, I shall have to preface my discussion with a few remarks about this theory.

INFORMATION MEASUREMENT

The "amount of information" is exactly the same concept that we have talked about for years under the name of "variance." The equations are different, but if we hold tight to the idea that anything that increases the variance also increases the amount of information we cannot go far astray.

The advantages of this new way of talking about variance are simple enough. Variance is always stated in terms of the unit of measurement— inches, pounds, volts, etc.—whereas the amount of information is a dimensionless quantity. Since the information in a discrete statistical distribution does not depend upon the unit of measurement, we can extend the concept to situations where we have no metric and we would not ordinarily think of using

[1] This paper was first read as an Invited Address before the Eastern Psychological Association in Philadelphia on April 15, 1955. Preparation of the paper was supported by the Harvard Psycho-Acoustic Laboratory under Contract N5ori-76 between Harvard University and the Office of Naval Research, U. S. Navy (Project NR142–201, Report PNR–174). Reproduction for any purpose of the U. S. Government is permitted.

This article appeared in *Psychol. Rev.*, 1956, **63**, 81–97. Reprinted with permission.

the variance. And it also enables us to compare results obtained in quite different experimental situations where it would be meaningless to compare variances based on different metrics. So there are some good reasons for adopting the newer concept.

The similarity of variance and amount of information might be explained this way: When we have a large variance, we are very ignorant about what is going to happen. If we are very ignorant, then when we make the observation it gives us a lot of information. On the other hand, if the variance is very small, we know in advance how our observation must come out, so we get little information from making the observation.

If you will now imagine a communication system, you will realize that there is a great deal of variability about what goes into the system and also a great deal of variability about what comes out. The input and the output can therefore be described in terms of their variance (or their information). If it is a good communication system, however, there must be some systematic relation between what goes in and what comes out. That is to say, the output will depend upon the input, or will be correlated with the input. If we measure this correlation, then we can say how much of the output variance is attributable to the input and how much is due to random fluctuations or "noise" introduced by the system during transmission. So we see that the measure of transmitted information is simply a measure of the input-output correlation.

There are two simple rules to follow. Whenever I refer to "amount of information," you will understand "variance." And whenever I refer to "amount of transmitted information," you will understand "covariance" or "correlation."

The situation can be described graphically by two partially overlapping circles. Then the left circle can be taken to represent the variance of the input, the right circle the variance of the output, and the overlap the covariance of input and output. I shall speak of the left circle as the amount of input information, the right circle as the amount of output information, and the overlap as the amount of transmitted information.

In the experiments on absolute judgment, the observer is considered to be a communication channel. Then the left circle would represent the amount of information in the stimuli, the right circle the amount of information in his responses, and the overlap the stimulus-response correlation as measured by the amount of transmitted information. The experimental problem is to increase the amount of input information and to measure the amount of transmitted information. If the observer's absolute judgments are quite accurate, then nearly all of the input information will be transmitted and will be recoverable from his responses. If he makes errors, then the transmitted information may be considerably less than the input. We expect that, as we increase the amount of input information, the observer will begin to make more and more errors; we can test the limits of accuracy of his absolute judgments. If the human observer is a reasonable kind of communication system, then when we increase the amount of input information the transmitted information will increase at first and will eventually level off at some asymptotic value. This asymptotic value we take to be the *channel capacity* of the observer: it represents the greatest amount of information that he can give us about the stimulus on the basis of an absolute judgment. The channel capacity is the upper limit on the extent to which the observer can match his responses to the stimuli we give him.

Now just a brief word about the *bit*

and we can begin to look at some data. One bit of information is the amount of information that we need to make a decision between two equally likely alternatives. If we must decide whether a man is less than six feet tall or more than six feet tall and if we know that the chances are 50–50, then we need one bit of information. Notice that this unit of information does not refer in any way to the unit of length that we use—feet, inches, centimeters, etc. However you measure the man's height, we still need just one bit of information.

Two bits of information enable us to decide among four equally likely alternatives. Three bits of information enable us to decide among eight equally likely alternatives. Four bits of information decide among 16 alternatives, five among 32, and so on. That is to say, if there are 32 equally likely alternatives, we must make five successive binary decisions, worth one bit each, before we know which alternative is correct. So the general rule is simple: every time the number of alternatives is increased by a factor of two, one bit of information is added.

There are two ways we might increase the amount of input information. We could increase the rate at which we give information to the observer, so that the amount of information per unit time would increase. Or we could ignore the time variable completely and increase the amount of input information by increasing the number of alternative stimuli. In the absolute judgment experiment we are interested in the second alternative. We give the observer as much time as he wants to make his response; we simply increase the number of alternative stimuli among which he must discriminate and look to see where confusions begin to occur. Confusions will appear near the point that we are calling his "channel capacity."

ABSOLUTE JUDGMENTS OF UNIDIMENSIONAL STIMULI

Now let us consider what happens when we make absolute judgments of tones. Pollack (17) asked listeners to identify tones by assigning numerals to them. The tones were different with respect to frequency, and covered the range from 100 to 8000 cps in equal logarithmic steps. A tone was sounded and the listener responded by giving a numeral. After the listener had made his response he was told the correct identification of the tone.

When only two or three tones were used the listeners never confused them. With four different tones confusions were quite rare, but with five or more tones confusions were frequent. With fourteen different tones the listeners made many mistakes.

These data are plotted in Fig. 1. Along the bottom is the amount of input information in bits per stimulus. As the number of alternative tones was increased from 2 to 14, the input information increased from 1 to 3.8 bits. On the ordinate is plotted the amount of

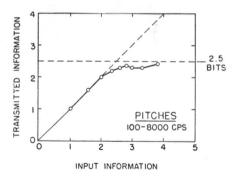

FIG. 1. Data from Pollack (17, 18) on the amount of information that is transmitted by listeners who make absolute judgments of auditory pitch. As the amount of input information is increased by increasing from 2 to 14 the number of different pitches to be judged, the amount of transmitted information approaches as its upper limit a channel capacity of about 2.5 bits per judgment.

transmitted information. The amount of transmitted information behaves in much the way we would expect a communication channel to behave; the transmitted information increases linearly up to about 2 bits and then bends off toward an asymptote at about 2.5 bits. This value, 2.5 bits, therefore, is what we are calling the channel capacity of the listener for absolute judgments of pitch.

So now we have the number 2.5 bits. What does it mean? First, note that 2.5 bits corresponds to about six equally likely alternatives. The result means that we cannot pick more than six different pitches that the listener will never confuse. Or, stated slightly differently, no matter how many alternative tones we ask him to judge, the best we can expect him to do is to assign them to about six different classes without error. Or, again, if we know that there were N alternative stimuli, then his judgment enables us to narrow down the particular stimulus to one out of $N/6$.

Most people are surprised that the number is as small as six. Of course, there is evidence that a musically sophisticated person with absolute pitch can identify accurately any one of 50 or 60 different pitches. Fortunately, I do not have time to discuss these remarkable exceptions. I say it is fortunate because I do not know how to explain their superior performance. So I shall stick to the more pedestrian fact that most of us can identify about one out of only five or six pitches before we begin to get confused.

It is interesting to consider that psychologists have been using seven-point rating scales for a long time, on the intuitive basis that trying to rate into finer categories does not really add much to the usefulness of the ratings. Pollack's results indicate that, at least for pitches, this intuition is fairly sound.

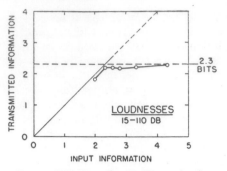

FIG. 2. Data from Garner (7) on the channel capacity for absolute judgments of auditory loudness.

Next you can ask how reproducible this result is. Does it depend on the spacing of the tones or the various conditions of judgment? Pollack varied these conditions in a number of ways. The range of frequencies can be changed by a factor of about 20 without changing the amount of information transmitted more than a small percentage. Different groupings of the pitches decreased the transmission, but the loss was small. For example, if you can discriminate five high-pitched tones in one series and five low-pitched tones in another series, it is reasonable to expect that you could combine all ten into a single series and still tell them all apart without error. When you try it, however, it does not work. The channel capacity for pitch seems to be about six and that is the best you can do.

While we are on tones, let us look next at Garner's (7) work on loudness. Garner's data for loudness are summarized in Fig. 2. Garner went to some trouble to get the best possible spacing of his tones over the intensity range from 15 to 110 db. He used 4, 5, 6, 7, 10, and 20 different stimulus intensities. The results shown in Fig. 2 take into account the differences among subjects and the sequential influence of the immediately preceding judgment. Again we find that there seems to be a limit.

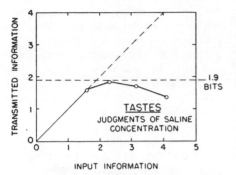

FIG. 3. Data from Beebe-Center, Rogers, and O'Connell (1) on the channel capacity for absolute judgments of saltiness.

The channel capacity for absolute judgments of loudness is 2.3 bits, or about five perfectly discriminable alternatives.

Since these two studies were done in different laboratories with slightly different techniques and methods of analysis, we are not in a good position to argue whether five loudnesses is significantly different from six pitches. Probably the difference is in the right direction, and absolute judgments of pitch are slightly more accurate than absolute judgments of loudness. The important point, however, is that the two answers are of the same order of magnitude.

The experiment has also been done for taste intensities. In Fig. 3 are the results obtained by Beebe-Center, Rogers, and O'Connell (1) for absolute judgments of the concentration of salt solutions. The concentrations ranged from 0.3 to 34.7 gm. NaCl per 100 cc. tap water in equal subjective steps. They used 3, 5, 9, and 17 different concentrations. The channel capacity is 1.9 bits, which is about four distinct concentrations. Thus taste intensities seem a little less distinctive than auditory stimuli, but again the order of magnitude is not far off.

On the other hand, the channel capacity for judgments of visual position seems to be significantly larger. Hake

and Garner (8) asked observers to interpolate visually between two scale markers. Their results are shown in Fig. 4. They did the experiment in two ways. In one version they let the observer use any number between zero and 100 to describe the position, although they presented stimuli at only 5, 10, 20, or 50 different positions. The results with this unlimited response technique are shown by the filled circles on the graph. In the other version the observers were limited in their responses to reporting just those stimulus values that were possible. That is to say, in the second version the number of different responses that the observer could make was exactly the same as the number of different stimuli that the experimenter might present. The results with this limited response technique are shown by the open circles on the graph. The two functions are so similar that it seems fair to conclude that the number of responses available to the observer had nothing to do with the channel capacity of 3.25 bits.

The Hake-Garner experiment has been repeated by Coonan and Klemmer. Although they have not yet published their results, they have given me permission to say that they obtained channel capacities ranging from 3.2 bits for

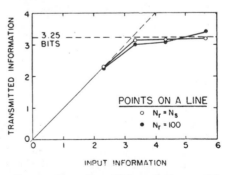

FIG. 4. Data from Hake and Garner (8) on the channel capacity for absolute judgments of the position of a pointer in a linear interval.

very short exposures of the pointer position to 3.9 bits for longer exposures. These values are slightly higher than Hake and Garner's, so we must conclude that there are between 10 and 15 distinct positions along a linear interval. This is the largest channel capacity that has been measured for any unidimensional variable.

At the present time these four experiments on absolute judgments of simple, unidimensional stimuli are all that have appeared in the psychological journals. However, a great deal of work on other stimulus variables has not yet appeared in the journals. For example, Eriksen and Hake (6) have found that the channel capacity for judging the sizes of squares is 2.2 bits, or about five categories, under a wide range of experimental conditions. In a separate experiment Eriksen (5) found 2.8 bits for size, 3.1 bits for hue, and 2.3 bits for brightness. Geldard has measured the channel capacity for the skin by placing vibrators on the chest region. A good observer can identify about four intensities, about five durations, and about seven locations.

One of the most active groups in this area has been the Air Force Operational Applications Laboratory. Pollack has been kind enough to furnish me with the results of their measurements for several aspects of visual displays. They made measurements for area and for the curvature, length, and direction of lines. In one set of experiments they used a very short exposure of the stimulus—$\frac{1}{40}$ second—and then they repeated the measurements with a 5-second exposure. For area they got 2.6 bits with the short exposure and 2.7 bits with the long exposure. For the length of a line they got about 2.6 bits with the short exposure and about 3.0 bits with the long exposure. Direction, or angle of inclination, gave 2.8 bits for the short exposure and 3.3 bits

for the long exposure. Curvature was apparently harder to judge. When the length of the arc was constant, the result at the short exposure duration was 2.2 bits, but when the length of the chord was constant, the result was only 1.6 bits. This last value is the lowest that anyone has measured to date. I should add, however, that these values are apt to be slightly too low because the data from all subjects were pooled before the transmitted information was computed.

Now let us see where we are. First, the channel capacity does seem to be a valid notion for describing human observers. Second, the channel capacities measured for these unidimensional variables range from 1.6 bits for curvature to 3.9 bits for positions in an interval. Although there is no question that the differences among the variables are real and meaningful, the more impressive fact to me is their considerable similarity. If I take the best estimates I can get of the channel capacities for all the stimulus variables I have mentioned, the mean is 2.6 bits and the standard deviation is only 0.6 bit. In terms of distinguishable alternatives, this mean corresponds to about 6.5 categories, one standard deviation includes from 4 to 10 categories, and the total range is from 3 to 15 categories. Considering the wide variety of different variables that have been studied, I find this to be a remarkably narrow range.

There seems to be some limitation built into us either by learning or by the design of our nervous systems, a limit that keeps our channel capacities in this general range. On the basis of the present evidence it seems safe to say that we possess a finite and rather small capacity for making such unidimensional judgments and that this capacity does not vary a great deal from one simple sensory attribute to another.

ABSOLUTE JUDGMENTS OF MULTI-DIMENSIONAL STIMULI

You may have noticed that I have been careful to say that this magical number seven applies to one-dimensional judgments. Everyday experience teaches us that we can identify accurately any one of several hundred faces, any one of several thousand words, any one of several thousand objects, etc. The story certainly would not be complete if we stopped at this point. We must have some understanding of why the one-dimensional variables we judge in the laboratory give results so far out of line with what we do constantly in our behavior outside the laboratory. A possible explanation lies in the number of independently variable attributes of the stimuli that are being judged. Objects, faces, words, and the like differ from one another in many ways, whereas the simple stimuli we have considered thus far differ from one another in only one respect.

Fortunately, there are a few data on what happens when we make absolute judgments of stimuli that differ from one another in several ways. Let us look first at the results Klemmer and Frick (13) have reported for the absolute judgment of the position of a dot in a square. In Fig. 5 we see their re-

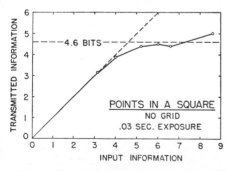

FIG. 5. Data from Klemmer and Frick (13) on the channel capacity for absolute judgments of the position of a dot in a square.

sults. Now the channel capacity seems to have increased to 4.6 bits, which means that people can identify accurately any one of 24 positions in the square.

The position of a dot in a square is clearly a two-dimensional proposition. Both its horizontal and its vertical position must be identified. Thus it seems natural to compare the 4.6-bit capacity for a square with the 3.25-bit capacity for the position of a point in an interval. The point in the square requires two judgments of the interval type. If we have a capacity of 3.25 bits for estimating intervals and we do this twice, we should get 6.5 bits as our capacity for locating points in a square. Adding the second independent dimension gives us an increase from 3.25 to 4.6, but it falls short of the perfect addition that would give 6.5 bits.

Another example is provided by Beebe-Center, Rogers, and O'Connell. When they asked people to identify both the saltiness and the sweetness of solutions containing various concentrations of salt and sucrose, they found that the channel capacity was 2.3 bits. Since the capacity for salt alone was 1.9, we might expect about 3.8 bits if the two aspects of the compound stimuli were judged independently. As with spatial locations, the second dimension adds a little to the capacity but not as much as it conceivably might.

A third example is provided by Pollack (18), who asked listeners to judge both the loudness and the pitch of pure tones. Since pitch gives 2.5 bits and loudness gives 2.3 bits, we might hope to get as much as 4.8 bits for pitch and loudness together. Pollack obtained 3.1 bits, which again indicates that the second dimension augments the channel capacity but not so much as it might.

A fourth example can be drawn from the work of Halsey and Chapanis (9) on confusions among colors of equal luminance. Although they did not analyze their results in informational terms, they estimate that there are about 11 to 15 identifiable colors, or, in our terms, about 3.6 bits. Since these colors varied in both hue and saturation, it is probably correct to regard this as a two-dimensional judgment. If we compare this with Eriksen's 3.1 bits for hue (which is a questionable comparison to draw), we again have something less than perfect addition when a second dimension is added.

It is still a long way, however, from these two-dimensional examples to the multidimensional stimuli provided by faces, words, etc. To fill this gap we have only one experiment, an auditory study done by Pollack and Ficks (19). They managed to get six different acoustic variables that they could change: frequency, intensity, rate of interruption, on-time fraction, total duration, and spatial location. Each one of these six variables could assume any one of five different values, so altogether there were 5^6, or 15,625 different tones that they could present. The listeners made a separate rating for each one of these six dimensions. Under these conditions the transmitted information was 7.2 bits, which corresponds to about 150 different categories that could be absolutely identified without error. Now we are beginning to get up into the range that ordinary experience would lead us to expect.

Suppose that we plot these data, fragmentary as they are, and make a guess about how the channel capacity changes with the dimensionality of the stimuli. The result is given in Fig. 6. In a moment of considerable daring I sketched the dotted line to indicate roughly the trend that the data seemed to be taking.

Clearly, the addition of independently variable attributes to the stimulus increases the channel capacity, but at a

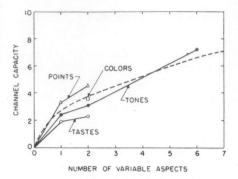

FIG. 6. The general form of the relation between channel capacity and the number of independently variable attributes of the stimuli.

decreasing rate. It is interesting to note that the channel capacity is increased even when the several variables are not independent. Eriksen (5) reports that, when size, brightness, and hue all vary together in perfect correlation, the transmitted information is 4.1 bits as compared with an average of about 2.7 bits when these attributes are varied one at a time. By confounding three attributes, Eriksen increased the dimensionality of the input without increasing the amount of input information; the result was an increase in channel capacity of about the amount that the dotted function in Fig. 6 would lead us to expect.

The point seems to be that, as we add more variables to the display, we increase the total capacity, but we decrease the accuracy for any particular variable. In other words, we can make relatively crude judgments of several things simultaneously.

We might argue that in the course of evolution those organisms were most successful that were responsive to the widest range of stimulus energies in their environment. In order to survive in a constantly fluctuating world, it was better to have a little information about a lot of things than to have a lot of information about a small segment of the environment. If a compromise was necessary, the one we seem to have made is clearly the more adaptive.

Pollack and Ficks's results are very strongly suggestive of an argument that linguists and phoneticians have been making for some time (11). According to the linguistic analysis of the sounds of human speech, there are about eight or ten dimensions—the linguists call them *distinctive features*—that distinguish one phoneme from another. These distinctive features are usually binary, or at most ternary, in nature. For example, a binary distinction is made between vowels and consonants, a binary decision is made between oral and nasal consonants, a ternary decision is made among front, middle, and back phonemes, etc. This approach gives us quite a different picture of speech perception than we might otherwise obtain from our studies of the speech spectrum and of the ear's ability to discriminate relative differences among pure tones. I am personally much interested in this new approach (15), and I regret that there is not time to discuss it here.

It was probably with this linguistic theory in mind that Pollack and Ficks conducted a test on a set of tonal stimuli that varied in eight dimensions, but required only a binary decision on each dimension. With these tones they measured the transmitted information at 6.9 bits, or about 120 recognizable kinds of sounds. It is an intriguing question, as yet unexplored, whether one can go on adding dimensions indefinitely in this way.

In human speech there is clearly a limit to the number of dimensions that we use. In this instance, however, it is not known whether the limit is imposed by the nature of the perceptual machinery that must recognize the sounds or by the nature of the speech machinery that must produce them. Somebody will have to do the experiment to find out. There is a limit, however, at about eight or nine distinctive features in every language that has been studied, and so when we talk we must resort to still another trick for increasing our channel capacity. Language uses sequences of phonemes, so we make several judgments successively when we listen to words and sentences. That is to say, we use both simultaneous and successive discriminations in order to expand the rather rigid limits imposed by the inaccuracy of our absolute judgments of simple magnitudes.

These multidimensional judgments are strongly reminiscent of the abstraction experiment of Külpe (14). As you may remember, Külpe showed that observers report more accurately on an attribute for which they are set than on attributes for which they are not set. For example, Chapman (4) used three different attributes and compared the results obtained when the observers were instructed before the tachistoscopic presentation with the results obtained when they were not told until after the presentation which one of the three attributes was to be reported. When the instruction was given in advance, the judgments were more accurate. When the instruction was given afterwards, the subjects presumably had to judge all three attributes in order to report on any one of them and the accuracy was correspondingly lower. This is in complete accord with the results we have just been considering, where the accuracy of judgment on each attribute decreased as more dimensions were added. The point is probably obvious, but I shall make it anyhow, that the abstraction experiments did *not* demonstrate that people can judge only one attribute at a time. They merely showed what seems quite reasonable, that people are less accurate if they must judge more than one attribute simultaneously.

SUBITIZING

I cannot leave this general area without mentioning, however briefly, the experiments conducted at Mount Holyoke College on the discrimination of number (12). In experiments by Kaufman, Lord, Reese, and Volkmann random patterns of dots were flashed on a screen for $\frac{1}{5}$ of a second. Anywhere from 1 to more than 200 dots could appear in the pattern. The subject's task was to report how many dots there were.

The first point to note is that on patterns containing up to five or six dots the subjects simply did not make errors. The performance on these small numbers of dots was so different from the performance with more dots that it was given a special name. Below seven the subjects were said to *subitize;* above seven they were said to *estimate.* This is, as you will recognize, what we once optimistically called "the span of attention."

This discontinuity at seven is, of course, suggestive. Is this the same basic process that limits our unidimensional judgments to about seven categories? The generalization is tempting, but not sound in my opinion. The data on number estimates have not been analyzed in informational terms; but on the basis of the published data I would guess that the subjects transmitted something more than four bits of information about the number of dots. Using the same arguments as before, we would conclude that there are about 20 or 30 distinguishable categories of numerousness. This is considerably more information than we would expect to get from a unidimensional display. It is, as a matter of fact, very much like a two-dimensional display. Although the dimensionality of the random dot patterns is not entirely clear, these results are in the same range as Klemmer and Frick's for their two-dimensional display of dots in a square. Perhaps the two dimensions of numerousness are area and density. When the subject can subitize, area and density may not be the significant variables, but when the subject must estimate perhaps they are significant. In any event, the comparison is not so simple as it might seem at first thought.

This is one of the ways in which the magical number seven has persecuted me. Here we have two closely related kinds of experiments, both of which point to the significance of the number seven as a limit on our capacities. And yet when we examine the matter more closely, there seems to be a reasonable suspicion that it is nothing more than a coincidence.

THE SPAN OF IMMEDIATE MEMORY

Let me summarize the situation in this way. There is a clear and definite limit to the accuracy with which we can identify absolutely the magnitude of a unidimensional stimulus variable. I would propose to call this limit the *span of absolute judgment,* and I maintain that for unidimensional judgments this span is usually somewhere in the neighborhood of seven. We are not completely at the mercy of this limited span, however, because we have a variety of techniques for getting around it and increasing the accuracy of our judgments. The three most important of these devices are (*a*) to make relative rather than absolute judgments; or, if that is not possible, (*b*) to increase the number of dimensions along which the stimuli can differ; or (*c*) to arrange the task in such a way that we make a sequence of several absolute judgments in a row.

The study of relative judgments is one of the oldest topics in experimental psychology, and I will not pause to review it now. The second device, increasing the dimensionality, we have just considered. It seems that by adding more dimensions and requiring crude, binary, yes-no judgments on each attribute we can extend the span of absolute judgment from seven to at least 150. Judging from our everyday behavior, the limit is probably in the thousands, if indeed there is a limit. In my opinion, we cannot go on compounding dimensions indefinitely. I suspect that there is also a *span of perceptual dimensionality* and that this span is somewhere in the neighborhood of ten, but I must add at once that there is no objective evidence to support this suspicion. This is a question sadly needing experimental exploration.

Concerning the third device, the use of successive judgments, I have quite a bit to say because this device introduces memory as the handmaiden of discrimination. And, since mnemonic processes are at least as complex as are perceptual processes, we can anticipate that their interactions will not be easily disentangled.

Suppose that we start by simply extending slightly the experimental procedure that we have been using. Up to this point we have presented a single stimulus and asked the observer to name it immediately thereafter. We can extend this procedure by requiring the observer to withhold his response until we have given him several stimuli in succession. At the end of the sequence of stimuli he then makes his response. We still have the same sort of input-output situation that is required for the measurement of transmitted information. But now we have passed from an experiment on absolute judgment to what is traditionally called an experiment on immediate memory.

Before we look at any data on this topic I feel I must give you a word of warning to help you avoid some obvious associations that can be confusing. Everybody knows that there is a finite span of immediate memory and that for a lot of different kinds of test materials this span is about seven items in length. I have just shown you that there is a span of absolute judgment that can distinguish about seven categories and that there is a span of attention that will encompass about six objects at a glance. What is more natural than to think that all three of these spans are different aspects of a single underlying process? And that is a fundamental mistake, as I shall be at some pains to demonstrate. This mistake is one of the malicious persecutions that the magical number seven has subjected me to.

My mistake went something like this. We have seen that the invariant feature in the span of absolute judgment is the amount of information that the observer can transmit. There is a real operational similarity between the absolute judgment experiment and the immediate memory experiment. If immediate memory is like absolute judgment, then it should follow that the invariant feature in the span of immediate memory is also the amount of information that an observer can retain. If the amount of information in the span of immediate memory is a constant, then the span should be short when the individual items contain a lot of information and the span should be long when the items contain little information. For example, decimal digits are worth 3.3 bits apiece. We can recall about seven of them, for a total of 23 bits of information. Isolated English words are worth about 10 bits apiece. If the total amount of information is to remain constant at 23 bits, then we should be able to remember only two or three words chosen at random. In this way I generated a theory about how the span of immediate memory should vary as a function of the amount of information per item in the test materials.

The measurements of memory span in the literature are suggestive on this question, but not definitive. And so it was necessary to do the experiment to see. Hayes (10) tried it out with five different kinds of test materials: binary digits, decimal digits, letters of the alphabet, letters plus decimal digits, and with 1,000 monosyllabic words. The lists were read aloud at the rate of one item per second and the subjects had as much time as they needed to give their responses. A procedure described by Woodworth (20) was used to score the responses.

The results are shown by the filled circles in Fig. 7. Here the dotted line indicates what the span should have been if the amount of information in the span were constant. The solid curves represent the data. Hayes repeated the experiment using test vocabularies of different sizes but all containing only English monosyllables (open circles in Fig. 7). This more homogeneous test material did not change the picture significantly. With binary items the span is about nine and, although it drops to about five with monosyllabic English words, the difference is far less than the hypothesis of constant information would require.

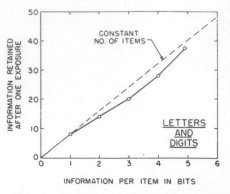

FIG. 8. Data from Pollack (16) on the amount of information retained after one presentation plotted as a function of the amount of information per item in the test materials.

There is nothing wrong with Hayes's experiment, because Pollack (16) repeated it much more elaborately and got essentially the same result. Pollack took pains to measure the amount of information transmitted and did not rely on the traditional procedure for scoring the responses. His results are plotted in Fig. 8. Here it is clear that the amount of information transmitted is not a constant, but increases almost linearly as the amount of information per item in the input is increased.

And so the outcome is perfectly clear. In spite of the coincidence that the magical number seven appears in both places, the span of absolute judgment and the span of immediate memory are quite different kinds of limitations that are imposed on our ability to process information. Absolute judgment is limited by the amount of information. Immediate memory is limited by the number of items. In order to capture this distinction in somewhat picturesque terms, I have fallen into the custom of distinguishing between *bits* of information and *chunks* of information. Then I can say that the number of bits of information is constant for absolute judgment and the number of chunks of informa-

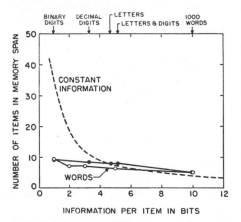

FIG. 7. Data from Hayes (10) on the span of immediate memory plotted as a function of the amount of information per item in the test materials.

tion is constant for immediate memory. The span of immediate memory seems to be almost independent of the number of bits per chunk, at least over the range that has been examined to date.

The contrast of the terms *bit* and *chunk* also serves to highlight the fact that we are not very definite about what constitutes a chunk of information. For example, the memory span of five words that Hayes obtained when each word was drawn at random from a set of 1000 English monosyllables might just as appropriately have been called a memory span of 15 phonemes, since each word had about three phonemes in it. Intuitively, it is clear that the subjects were recalling five words, not 15 phonemes, but the logical distinction is not immediately apparent. We are dealing here with a process of organizing or grouping the input into familiar units or chunks, and a great deal of learning has gone into the formation of these familiar units.

RECODING

In order to speak more precisely, therefore, we must recognize the importance of grouping or organizing the input sequence into units or chunks. Since the memory span is a fixed number of chunks, we can increase the number of bits of information that it contains simply by building larger and larger chunks, each chunk containing more information than before.

A man just beginning to learn radiotelegraphic code hears each *dit* and *dah* as a separate chunk. Soon he is able to organize these sounds into letters and then he can deal with the letters as chunks. Then the letters organize themselves as words, which are still larger chunks, and he begins to hear whole phrases. I do not mean that each step is a discrete process, or that plateaus must appear in his learning curve, for surely the levels of organization are achieved at different rates and overlap each other during the learning process. I am simply pointing to the obvious fact that the dits and dahs are organized by learning into patterns and that as these larger chunks emerge the amount of message that the operator can remember increases correspondingly. In the terms I am proposing to use, the operator learns to increase the bits per chunk.

In the jargon of communication theory, this process would be called *recoding*. The input is given in a code that contains many chunks with few bits per chunk. The operator recodes the input into another code that contains fewer chunks with more bits per chunk. There are many ways to do this recoding, but probably the simplest is to group the input events, apply a new name to the group, and then remember the new name rather than the original input events.

Since I am convinced that this process is a very general and important one for psychology, I want to tell you about a demonstration experiment that should make perfectly explicit what I am talking about. This experiment was conducted by Sidney Smith and was reported by him before the Eastern Psychological Association in 1954.

Begin with the observed fact that people can repeat back eight decimal digits, but only nine binary digits. Since there is a large discrepancy in the amount of information recalled in these two cases, we suspect at once that a recoding procedure could be used to increase the span of immediate memory for binary digits. In Table 1 a method for grouping and renaming is illustrated. Along the top is a sequence of 18 binary digits, far more than any subject was able to recall after a single presentation. In the next line these same binary digits are grouped by pairs. Four possible pairs can occur: 00 is renamed 0, 01 is renamed 1, 10 is renamed 2, and 11 is

TABLE 1

WAYS OF RECODING SEQUENCES OF BINARY DIGITS

Binary Digits (Bits)		1 0 1 0 0 0 1 0 0 1 1 1 0 0 1 1 1 0								
2:1	Chunks	10	10	00	10	01	11	00	11	10
	Recoding	2	2	0	2	1	3	0	3	2
3:1	Chunks	101		000	100	111		001	110	
	Recoding	5		0	4	7		1	6	
4:1	Chunks	1010		0010		0111		0011	10	
	Recoding	10		2		7		3		
5:1	Chunks	10100		01001		11001		110		
	Recoding	20		9		25				

renamed 3. That is to say, we recode from a base-two arithmetic to a base-four arithmetic. In the recoded sequence there are now just nine digits to remember, and this is almost within the span of immediate memory. In the next line the same sequence of binary digits is regrouped into chunks of three. There are eight possible sequences of three, so we give each sequence a new name between 0 and 7. Now we have recoded from a sequence of 18 binary digits into a sequence of 6 octal digits, and this is well within the span of immediate memory. In the last two lines the binary digits are grouped by fours and by fives and are given decimal-digit names from 0 to 15 and from 0 to 31.

It is reasonably obvious that this kind of recoding increases the bits per chunk, and packages the binary sequence into a form that can be retained within the span of immediate memory. So Smith assembled 20 subjects and measured their spans for binary and octal digits. The spans were 9 for binaries and 7 for octals. Then he gave each recoding scheme to five of the subjects. They studied the recoding until they said they understood it—for about 5 or 10 minutes. Then he tested their span for binary digits again while they tried to use the recoding schemes they had studied.

The recoding schemes increased their span for binary digits in every case. But the increase was not as large as we had expected on the basis of their span for octal digits. Since the discrepancy increased as the recoding ratio increased, we reasoned that the few minutes the subjects had spent learning the recoding schemes had not been sufficient. Apparently the translation from one code to the other must be almost automatic or the subject will lose part of the next group while he is trying to remember the translation of the last group.

Since the 4:1 and 5:1 ratios require considerable study, Smith decided to imitate Ebbinghaus and do the experiment on himself. With Germanic patience he drilled himself on each recoding successively, and obtained the results shown in Fig. 9. Here the data follow along rather nicely with the results you would predict on the basis of his span for octal digits. He could remember 12 octal digits. With the 2:1 recoding, these 12 chunks were worth 24 binary digits. With the 3:1 recoding they were worth 36 binary digits. With the 4:1 and 5:1 recodings, they were worth about 40 binary digits.

It is a little dramatic to watch a person get 40 binary digits in a row and then repeat them back without error. However, if you think of this merely as

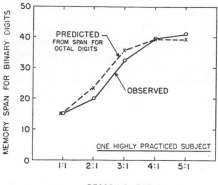

RECODING RATIO

FIG. 9. The span of immediate memory for binary digits is plotted as a function of the recoding procedure used. The predicted function is obtained by multiplying the span for octals by 2, 3 and 3.3 for recoding into base 4, base 8, and base 10, respectively.

a mnemonic trick for extending the memory span, you will miss the more important point that is implicit in nearly all such mnemonic devices. The point is that recoding is an extremely powerful weapon for increasing the amount of information that we can deal with. In one form or another we use recoding constantly in our daily behavior.

In my opinion the most customary kind of recoding that we do all the time is to translate into a verbal code. When there is a story or an argument or an idea that we want to remember, we usually try to rephrase it "in our own words." When we witness some event we want to remember, we make a verbal description of the event and then remember our verbalization. Upon recall we recreate by secondary elaboration the details that seem consistent with the particular verbal recoding we happen to have made. The well-known experiment by Carmichael, Hogan, and Walter (3) on the influence that names have on the recall of visual figures is one demonstration of the process.

The inaccuracy of the testimony of eyewitnesses is well known in legal psychology, but the distortions of testimony are not random—they follow naturally from the particular recoding that the witness used, and the particular recoding he used depends upon his whole life history. Our language is tremendously useful for repackaging material into a few chunks rich in information. I suspect that imagery is a form of recoding, too, but images seem much harder to get at operationally and to study experimentally than the more symbolic kinds of recoding.

It seems probable that even memorization can be studied in these terms. The process of memorizing may be simply the formation of chunks, or groups of items that go together, until there are few enough chunks so that we can recall all the items. The work by Bousfield and Cohen (2) on the occurrence of clustering in the recall of words is especially interesting in this respect.

SUMMARY

I have come to the end of the data that I wanted to present, so I would like now to make some summarizing remarks.

First, the span of absolute judgment and the span of immediate memory impose severe limitations on the amount of information that we are able to receive, process, and remember. By organizing the stimulus input simultaneously into several dimensions and successively into a sequence of chunks, we manage to break (or at least stretch) this informational bottleneck.

Second, the process of recoding is a very important one in human psychology and deserves much more explicit attention than it has received. In particular, the kind of linguistic recoding that people do seems to me to be the very lifeblood of the thought processes. Recoding procedures are a constant concern to clinicians, social psychologists, linguists, and anthropologists and yet, probably because recoding is less accessible to experimental manipulation than nonsense syllables or T mazes, the traditional experimental psychologist has contributed little or nothing to their analysis. Nevertheless, experimental techniques can be used, methods of recoding can be specified, behavioral indicants can be found. And I anticipate that we will find a very orderly set of relations describing what now seems an uncharted wilderness of individual differences.

Third, the concepts and measures provided by the theory of information provide a quantitative way of getting at some of these questions. The theory provides us with a yardstick for calibrating our stimulus materials and for measuring the performance of our subjects. In the interests of communication I have suppressed the technical details of information measurement and have tried to express the ideas in more familiar terms; I hope this paraphrase will not lead you to think they are not useful in research. Informational concepts have already proved valuable in the study of discrimination and of language; they promise a great deal in the study of learning and memory; and it has even been proposed that they can be useful in the study of concept formation. A lot of questions that seemed fruitless twenty or thirty years ago may now be worth another look. In fact, I feel that my story here must stop just as it begins to get really interesting.

And finally, what about the magical number seven? What about the seven wonders of the world, the seven seas, the seven deadly sins, the seven daughters of Atlas in the Pleiades, the seven ages of man, the seven levels of hell, the seven primary colors, the seven notes of the musical scale, and the seven days of the week? What about the seven-point rating scale, the seven categories for absolute judgment, the seven objects in the span of attention, and the seven digits in the span of immediate memory? For the present I propose to withhold judgment. Perhaps there is something deep and profound behind all these sevens, something just calling out for us to discover it. But I suspect that it is only a pernicious, Pythagorean coincidence.

REFERENCES

1. BEEBE-CENTER, J. G., ROGERS, M. S., & O'CONNELL, D. N. Transmission of information about sucrose and saline solutions through the sense of taste. *J. Psychol.*, 1955, **39**, 157–160.

2. BOUSFIELD, W. A., & COHEN, B. H. The occurrence of clustering in the recall of randomly arranged words of different frequencies-of-usage. *J. gen. Psychol.*, 1955, **52**, 83–95.

3. CARMICHAEL, L., HOGAN, H. P., & WALTER, A. A. An experimental study of the effect of language on the reproduction of visually perceived form. *J. exp. Psychol.*, 1932, **15**, 73–86.

4. CHAPMAN, D. W. Relative effects of determinate and indeterminate *Aufgaben*. *Amer. J. Psychol.*, 1932, **44**, 163–174.

5. ERIKSEN, C. W. Multidimensional stimulus differences and accuracy of discrimination. *USAF, WADC Tech. Rep.*, 1954, No. 54–165.

6. ERIKSEN, C. W., & HAKE, H. W. Absolute judgments as a function of the stimulus range and the number of stimulus and response categories. *J. exp. Psychol.*, 1955, **49**, 323–332.

7. GARNER, W. R. An informational analysis of absolute judgments of loudness. *J. exp. Psychol.*, 1953, **46**, 373–380.

8. HAKE, H. W., & GARNER, W. R. The effect of presenting various numbers of discrete steps on scale reading accuracy. *J. exp. Psychol.*, 1951, **42**, 358–366.

9. HALSEY, R. M., & CHAPANIS, A. Chromaticity-confusion contours in a complex viewing situation. *J. Opt. Soc. Amer.*, 1954, **44**, 442–454.

10. HAYES, J. R. M. Memory span for several vocabularies as a function of vocabulary size. In *Quarterly Progress Report*, Cambridge, Mass.: Acoustics Laboratory, Massachusetts Institute of Technology, Jan.–June, 1952.

11. JAKOBSON, R., FANT, C. G. M., & HALLE, M. *Preliminaries to speech analysis.* Cambridge, Mass.: Acoustics Laboratory, Massachusetts Institute of Technology, 1952. (Tech. Rep. No. 13.)

12. KAUFMAN, E. L., LORD, M. W., REESE, T. W., & VOLKMANN, J. The discrimination of visual number. *Amer. J. Psychol.,* 1949, **62**, 498–525.

13. KLEMMER, E. T., & FRICK, F. C. Assimilation of information from dot and matrix patterns. *J. exp. Psychol.,* 1953, **45**, 15–19.

14. KÜLPE, O. Versuche über Abstraktion. *Ber. ü. d. I Kongr. f. exper. Psychol.,* 1904, 56–68.

15. MILLER, G. A., & NICELY, P. E. An analysis of perceptual confusions among some English consonants. *J. Acoust. Soc. Amer.,* 1955, **27**, 338–352.

16. POLLACK, I. The assimilation of sequentially encoded information. *Amer. J. Psychol.,* 1953, **66**, 421–435.

17. POLLACK, I. The information of elementary auditory displays. *J. Acoust. Soc. Amer.,* 1952, **24**, 745–749.

18. POLLACK, I. The information of elementary auditory displays. II. *J. Acoust. Soc. Amer.,* 1953, **25**, 765–769.

19. POLLACK, I., & FICKS, L. Information of elementary multi-dimensional auditory displays. *J. Acoust. Soc. Amer.,* 1954, **26**, 155–158.

20. WOODWORTH, R. S. *Experimental psychology.* New York: Holt, 1938.

(Received May 4, 1955)

REMARKS ON THE METHOD OF PAIRED COMPARISONS:
I. THE LEAST SQUARES SOLUTION ASSUMING
EQUAL STANDARD DEVIATIONS
AND EQUAL CORRELATIONS*

FREDERICK MOSTELLER
HARVARD UNIVERSITY

Thurstone's Case V of the method of paired comparisons assumes equal standard deviations of sensations corresponding to stimuli and zero correlations between pairs of stimuli sensations. It is shown that the assumption of zero correlations can be relaxed to an assumption of equal correlations between pairs with no change in method. Further the usual approach to the method of paired comparisons Case V is shown to lead to a least squares estimate of the stimulus positions on the sensation scale.

1. *Introduction.* The fundamental notions underlying Thurstone's method of paired comparisons (4) are these:

(1)   There is a set of stimuli which can be located on a subjective continuum (a sensation scale, usually not having a measurable physical characteristic).

(2)   Each stimulus when presented to an individual gives rise to a sensation in the individual.

(3)   The distribution of sensations from a particular stimulus for a population of individuals is normal.

(4)   Stimuli are presented in pairs to an individual, thus giving rise to a sensation for each stimulus. The individual compares these sensations and reports which is greater.

(5)   It is possible for these paired sensations to be correlated.

(6)   Our task is to space the stimuli (the sensation means), except for a linear transformation.

*This research was performed in the Laboratory of Social Relations under a grant made available to Harvard University by the RAND Corporation under the Department of the Air Force, Project RAND.

This article appeared in *Psychometrika*, 1951, **16**, 3–9. Reprinted with permission.

There are numerous variations of the basic materials used in the analysis—for example, we may not have n different individuals, but only one individual who makes all comparisons several times; or several individuals may make all comparisons several times; the individuals need not be people.

Furthermore, there are "cases" to be discussed—for example, shall we assume all the intercorrelations equal, or shall we assume them zero? Shall we assume the standard deviations of the sensation distributions equal or not?

The case which has been discussed most fully is known as Thurstone's Case V. Thurstone has assumed in this case that the standard deviations of the sensation distributions are equal and that the correlations between pairs of stimulus sensations are zero. We shall discuss a standard method of ordering the stimuli for this Case V. Case V has been employed quite frequently and seems to fit empirical data rather well in the sense of reproducing the original proportions of the paired comparison table. The assumption of equal standard deviations is a reasonable first approximation. We will not stick to the assumption of zero correlations, because this does not seem to be essential for Case V.

2. *Ordering Stimuli with Error-Free Data.* We assume there are a number of objects or stimuli, O_1, O_2, $\cdots$, O_n. These stimuli give rise to sensations which lie on a single sensation continuum S. If X_i and X_j are single sensations evoked in an individual I by the ith and jth stimuli, then we assume X_i and X_j to be jointly normally distributed for the population of individuals with

$$
\begin{aligned}
&\text{mean of } X_i = S_i && (i = 1, 2, \cdots, n) \\
&\text{variance of } X_i = \sigma^2(X_i) = \sigma^2 && (i = 1, 2, \cdots, n) \\
&\text{correlation of } X_i \text{ and } X_j = \rho_{ij} = \rho && (i, j = 1, 2, \cdots, n).
\end{aligned} \tag{1}
$$

The marginal distributions of the X_i's appear as in Figure 1.

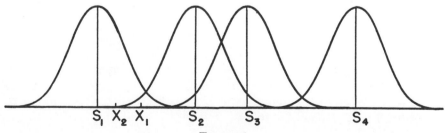

FIGURE 1

The Marginal Distributions of the Sensations Produced by the Separate Stimuli in Thurstone's Case V of the Method of Paired Comparisons.

The figure indicates the possibility that $X_2 < X_1$, even though $S_1 < S_2$. In fact this has to happen part of the time if we are to build anything more than a rank-order scale.

An individual I compares O_i and O_j and reports whether $X_i \gtrless X_j$ (no ties are allowed).

We can best see the tenor of the method for ordering the stimuli if we first work through the problem in the case of nonfallible data. For the case of nonfallible data we assume we know the true proportion of the time X_i exceeds X_j, and that the conditions given above (1) are exactly fulfilled.

Our problem is to find the spacing of the stimuli (or the spacing of the mean sensations produced by them, the $S_1 \cdots S_n$ points in Figure 1). Clearly we cannot hope to do this except within a linear transformation, for the data reported are merely the percentages of times X_i exceeds X_j, say p_{ij}.

$$p_{ij} = P(X_i > X_j) = \frac{1}{\sqrt{2\pi}\,\sigma(d_{ij})} \int_0^\infty e^{\frac{-[d_{ij} - (S_i - S_j)]^2}{2\,\sigma^2(d_{ij})}}\, dd_{ij} \quad (2)$$

where $d_{ij} = X_i - X_j$, and $\sigma^2(d_{ij}) = 2\sigma^2(1 - \rho)$. There will be no loss in generality in assigning the scale factor so that

$$2\sigma^2(1 - \rho) = 1. \tag{3}$$

It is at this point that we depart slightly from Thurstone, who characterized Case V as having equal variances and zero correlations. However, his derivations only assume the correlations are zero explicitly (and artificially), but are carried through implicitly with equal correlations (not necessarily zero). Actually this is a great easing of conditions. We can readily imagine a set of attitudinal items on the same continuum correlated .34, .38, .42, i.e., nearly equal. But it is difficult to imagine them all correlated zero with one another. Past uses of this method have all benefited from the fact that items were not *really* assumed to be uncorrelated. It was only *stated* that the model assumed the items were uncorrelated, but the model was unable to take cognizance of the statement. Guttman (2) has noticed this independently.

With the scale factor chosen in equation (3), we can rewrite equation (2)

$$p_{ij} = \frac{1}{\sqrt{2\pi}} \int_{-(S_i - S_j)}^{\infty} e^{-\frac{1}{2}y^2} \, dy. \qquad (4)$$

From (4), given any p_{ij} we can solve for $-(S_i - S_j)$ by use of a normal table of areas. Then if we arbitrarily assign as a location parameter $S_1 = 0$, we can compute all other S_i. Thus given the p_{ij} matrix we can find the S_i. The problem with fallible data is more complicated.

3. *Paired Comparison Scaling with Fallible Data.* When we have fallible data, we have p'_{ij} which are estimates of the true p_{ij}. Analogous to equation (4) we have

$$p'_{ij} = \frac{1}{\sqrt{2\pi}} \int_{-D'_{ij}}^{\infty} e^{-\frac{1}{2}y^2} \, dy, \qquad (5)$$

where the D'_{ij} are estimates of $D_{ij} = S_i - S_j$. We merely look up the normal deviate corresponding to p'_{ij} to get the matrix of D'_{ij}. We notice further that the D'_{ij} need not be consistent in the sense that the D_{ij} were; i.e.,

$$D_{ij} + D_{jk} = S_i - S_j + S_j - S_k = D_{ik},$$

does not hold for the D'_{ij}.

We conceive the problem as follows: from the D'_{ij} to construct a set of estimates of the S_i's called S'_i, such that

$$\Sigma = \sum_{i,j} [D'_{ij} - (S'_i - S'_j)]^2 \quad \text{is to be a minimum.} \qquad (6)$$

It will help to indicate another form of solution for nonfallible data. One can set up the $S_i - S_j$ matrix:

MATRIX OF $S_i - S_j$

	1	2	3	.....	n
1	$S_1 - S_1$	$S_1 - S_2$	$S_1 - S_3$		$S_1 - S_n$
2	$S_2 - S_1$	$S_2 - S_2$	$S_2 - S_3$		$S_2 - S_n$
3	$S_3 - S_1$	$S_3 - S_2$	$S_3 - S_3$		$S_3 - S_n$
.					
.					
.					
n	$S_n - S_1$	$S_n - S_2$	$S_n - S_3$		$S_n - S_n$
Totals	$\Sigma S_i - nS_1$	$\Sigma S_i - nS_2$	$\Sigma S_i - nS_3$		$\Sigma S_i - nS_n$
Means	$\bar{S} - S_1$	$\bar{S} - S_2$	$\bar{S} - S_3$		$\bar{S} - S_n$

Now by setting $S_1 = 0$, we get $S_2 = (\bar{S} - S_1) - (\bar{S} - S_2)$, $S_3 = (\bar{S} - S_1) - (\bar{S} - S_3)$, and so on. We will use this plan shortly for the S'_i.

If we wish to minimize expression (6) we take the partial derivative with respect to S'_i. Since $D'_{ij} = -D'_{ji}$ and $S'_i - S'_j = -(S'_j - S'_i)$ and $D'_{ii} = S'_i - S'_i = 0$, we need only concern ourselves with the sum of squares from above the main diagonal in the $D'_{ij} - (S'_i - S'_j)$ matrix, i.e., terms for which $i < j$. Differentiating with respect to S'_i we get:

$$\frac{\partial (\Sigma/2)}{\partial S'_i} = 2 \left[\sum_{j=1}^{i-1} (D'_{ji} - S'_j + S'_i) - \sum_{j=i+1}^{n} (D'_{ij} - S'_i + S'_j) \right] \quad (7)$$
$$(i = 1, 2, \cdots, n).$$

Setting this partial derivative equal to zero we have

$$+S'_1 + S'_2 \cdots + S'_{i-1} - (n-1)S'_i + S'_{i+1} + \cdots + S'_n \quad (8)$$

$$= \sum_{j=1}^{i-1} D'_{ji} - \sum_{j=i+1}^{n} D'_{ij} \quad (i = 1, 2, \cdots, n),$$

but $D'_{ij} = -D'_{ji}$, and $D'_{ii} = 0$; this makes the right side of (8)

$$\sum_{j=1}^{i-1} D'_{ji} + D'_{ii} + \sum_{j=i+1}^{n} D'_{ji} = \sum_{j=1}^{n} D'_{ji}.$$

Thus (8) can be written

$$\sum_{j=1}^{n} S'_j - nS'_i = \sum_{j=1}^{n} D'_{ji} \quad (i = 1, 2, \cdots, n). \quad (9)$$

The determinant of the coefficients of the left side of (9) vanishes. This is to be expected because we have only chosen our scale and have not assigned a location parameter. There are various ways to assign this location parameter, for example, by setting $\bar{S}' = 0$ or by setting $S'_1 = 0$. We choose to set $S'_1 = 0$. This means we will measure distances from S'_1. Then we try the solution (10) which is suggested by the similarity of the left side of (9) to the total column in the matrix of $S_i - S_j$.

$$S'_i = \sum_{j=1}^{n} D'_{j1}/n - \sum_{j=1}^{n} D'_{ji}/n. \quad (10)$$

Notice that when $i=1$, $S'_i = 0$ and that

$$\sum_{i=1}^{n} S'_i = \sum_{i=1}^{n} D'_{j1}$$

because

$$\sum_{i}\sum_{j} D'_{ji} = 0,$$

which happens because every term and its negative appear in this double sum. Therefore, substituting (10) in the left side of (9) we have

$$\sum_{i=1}^{n} D'_{j1} - n \left[\sum_{j=1}^{n} D'_{j1}/n - \sum_{j=1}^{n} D'_{ji}/n \right] = \sum_{j=1}^{n} D'_{ji}, \qquad (11)$$

which is an identity, and the equations are solved. Of course, any linear transformation of the solutions is equally satisfactory.

The point of this presentation is to provide a background for the theory of paired comparisons, to indicate that the assumption of zero correlations is unnecessary, and to show that the customary solution to paired comparisons is a least squares solution in the sense of condition (6). That this is a least squares solution seems not to be mentioned in the literature although it may have been known to Horst (3), since he worked closely along these lines.

This least squares solution is not entirely satisfactory because the p'_{ij} tend to zero and unity when extreme stimuli are compared. This introduces unsatisfactorily large numbers in the D'_{ij} table. This difficulty is usually met by excluding all numbers beyond, say, 2.0 from the table. After a preliminary arrangement of columns so that the S'_i will be in approximately proper order, the quantity

$$\sum (D'_{ij} - D'_{i,j+1})/k$$

is computed where the summation is over the k values of i for which entries appear in both column j and $j+1$. Then differences between such means are taken as the scale separations (see for example Guilford's discussion (1) of the method of paired comparisons). This method seems to give reasonable results. The computations for methods which take account of the differing variabilities of the p'_{ij} and therefore of the D'_{ij} seem to be unmercifully extensive.

It should also be remarked that this solution is not entirely a reasonable one because we really want to check our results against the original p'_{ij}. In other words, a more reasonable solution might be one such that once the S'_i are computed we can estimate the p'_{ij} by p''_{ij}, and minimize, say,

$$\sum (p'_{ij} - p''_{ij})^2$$

or perhaps

$$\sum (\text{arc sin } \sqrt{p'_{ij}} - \text{arc sin } \sqrt{p''_{ij}})^2.$$

Such a thing can no doubt be done, but the results of the author's attempts do not seem to differ enough from the results of the present method to be worth pursuing.

REFERENCES

1. Guilford, J. P. Psychometric Methods. New York: McGraw-Hill Book Co., 1936, 227-8.
2. Guttman, L. An approach for quantifying paired comparisons and rank order. *Annals of math. Stat.*, 1946, 17, 144-163.
3. Horst, P. A method for determining the absolute affective values of a series of stimulus situations. *J. educ. Psychol.*, 1932, 23, 418-440.
4. Thurstone, L. L. Psychophysical analysis. *Amer. J. Psychol.*, 1927, 38, 368-389.

Manuscript received 8/22/50

THEORETICAL RELATIONSHIPS AMONG SOME MEASURES OF CONDITIONING

By Conrad G. Mueller

Columbia University

Communicated by C. H. Graham, December 10, 1949

The relationships among the various measures of strength of conditioning constitute an important problem for conditioning theory. Many different measures have been used.[1] The measures *latency* and *magnitude* are based on the occurrence of a single response, while *number of responses in extinction* and *the rate of responding* in a "free-response" situation are based on more than one instance of a response. *Probability of response occurrence* is another term that is encountered in the literature; it is used most frequently in cases where more than one response is possible (e.g., right and left turns in a T maze) and in circumstances when it is possible to compute the frequency or the percentage of times that a specified response is given. Percentage of response occurrence is taken to be an estimate of the probability of obtaining the response.

Some theoretical formulations are concerned with one or two measures of strength; others are more inclusive. In only few cases has an attempt been made to present a theory of the relation among measures. In most treatments that consider several measures, the relations among the measures are empirically determined.

The purpose of the present note is to indicate one possible theoretical account of the relationships among latency of response, rate of responding and the probability of occurrence of a response. The last measure serves as the starting point for the discussion and provides the terms in which the other concepts are related.

Consider the Skinner bar-pressing situation[2] in which a rat's responses may occur at any time and at any rate during the period in which the animal is in the experimental cage. Assume that the responses under constant testing conditions are randomly distributed in time. Let the rate of occurrence of these responses be represented by r. It may then be shown that the probability, $P_{>t}$, of obtaining an interval between two responses greater than t is

$$P_{>t} = e^{-rt} \tag{1}$$

where e is the base of Naperian logarithms.[3] The probability of obtaining n responses in an interval, T, is

$$P_n = (rT)^n e^{-rT}/n! \tag{2}$$

Equation (1) gives us a statement of the distribution of time intervals associated with various rates of responding. For example, for the median

This article appeared in *Proc. natl. Acad. Sci.*, 1950, **36**, 123–130. Reprinted with permission.

time interval $P_{>t}$ is 0.5 and $-rt$ is $\log_e 0.5$ or the median t is $0.69/r$. Equation (2) gives the probability of various numbers of responses within some specified time interval. For example, the probability of getting exactly one response in an interval, T, is $(rT)e^{-rT}$. The relation between equations (1) and (2) is obvious when we consider the probability of getting no responses in an interval, T. In this case P_0 is e^{-rT}.

Equations (1) and (2) permit us to transform a rate measure into a probability measure. Since we are dealing with a continuous distribution (time), the probability of a response at any particular time is zero, but the probability of a response within given time intervals is finite and specifiable.

Latency usually refers to the time interval between a stimulus and a response and thus is not directly considered in the previous development. Assume, however, that the stimulus conditions are one determinant of the rate of responding, that is, that the rate has different values for different stimulus conditions. This assumption is consistent with the discussions by Skinner and others who have emphasized the measurement of rate; the assumption would presumably be an elementary requirement for any measure.

Under the circumstances of the assumption, t may be employed in discussing latency, since the latter would be the time interval between the beginning of the observation period (when a stimulus was presented) and the first response. Thus, on the assumption that stimulus conditions are a determinant of rate of responding and on the previous assumption that the responses are randomly distributed in time, a statement of the rate of responding under specified stimulus conditions implies a probability statement of the delay of length t between the presentation of the stimulus and the occurrence of the first response. This statement tells us not only of the distribution of latencies but also of the relationship between some representative value, say the median latency, and the rate of responding; for example, the probability of a response greater than the median latency, t_{md}, is 0.5; and from equation (1) we see that $-rt_{md} = \log_e 0.5$ or that the median latency equals $0.69/r$.

The preceding development does not imply any particular theory of conditioning but may be incorporated into a large class of theories. For example, if the foregoing discussion is combined with a theory that states that rate of responding is proportional to the number of responses that remain to be given in extinction, the measure of number of responses in extinction is immediately related to our latency and probability terms. In other words, if

$$r = k(N-n), \tag{3}$$

where N is the number of responses in extinction, n is the number of responses already given, and k is a constant, we may substitute $k(N-n)$ for r in equation (1) and obtain

$$P_{>t} = e^{-k(N-n)t}. \tag{4}$$

This equation may then be examined for relationships existing among the terms n, N, P and t.   In addition to the relationships among latency, rate and number of responses in extinction, equation (4) may be used to predict the distribution of responses in extinction for a constant strength and the distribution of time intervals between responses at various stages of extinction.

Since the present argument follows mainly from the assumption of a random distribution of responses in time, it is of interest to examine data

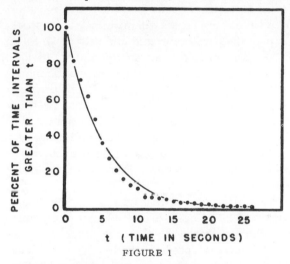

FIGURE 1

The percentage of inter-response time intervals greater than t, where t is time in seconds. The data are from an experiment with white rats in a bar-press situation as described in the text. The line drawn through the data is a plot of equation (1).

for direct evidence of randomness as well as for evidence relating to the above outlined consequences of randomness.

The data in figure 1 were taken from measurements obtained during the course of periodic reconditioning.[4]   The data represent the responses of a single animal during a 20-minute session of "three-minute" periodic reconditioning.   Within this observation period the rate of responding was approximately constant.   The question at issue is whether the responses in this interval are distributed randomly.   Equation (1) states that the probability of getting an interval between responses greater than t is e^{-rt}, where r is the rate of responding expressed in the same units as t.   In the

20-minute session, 238 responses were made, 237 time intervals were re-corded, and the rate in this session is 0.20 response per second. Thus, without direct reference to the distribution of time intervals, theory speci-fies the distribution of time intervals between responses uniquely. In this case the probability of getting a time interval greater than t (in seconds) is $e^{-0.20t}$. The ordinate of figure 1 shows the percentage of the intervals be-tween responses that were greater than the various time values specified on the abscissa. The solid line through the date in figure 1 represents the theoretical function. The data are consistent with the assumption that the measured responses occurred randomly in time.

Although the data of figure 1 may be representative of the agreement be-tween data and theory under the conditions specified, certain cases of sys-tematic deviations from theory may be noted. One class of deviations, for example, may be found in cases where animals show marked "holding" behavior, i.e., where the bar is depressed and held down for many seconds. Although the "holding" period is not a "refractory" period[3] in the usual sense of the term, it obviously affects the data in a similar way. During the "holding" period, the probability of response occurrence is zero. One complicating feature in analyzing responses characterized by "holding" is the fact that "holding" is of variable length. The data available at present do not warrant an extensive treatment of this problem, but the simplicity that may result from apparatus changes designed to eliminate the factor of "holding" and the advantages that may accrue from the additional response specification may be shown.

An example of a distribution showing systematic deviations from theory is shown in figure 2. The computations and plot are similar to those in figure 1. The ordinate represents the percentage of intervals between responses greater than the specified abscissa values. The solid line is theoretical. The constant of the line was determined, as in the case in figure 1, directly from the rate of responding without reference to the dis-tribution of time intervals. The fit is obviously poor; the function appears sigmoid and asymmetric.

Let us assume that the analysis leading to equation (1) and applied to figure 1 is correct when applied to all portions of the observation period except the time spent in "holding." An additional test may then be applied to the data from which figure 2 was obtained. Now we are inter-ested in the measurement of the time interval between the end of one re-sponse and the beginning of the next.[5] Figure 3 shows the results of such measurements in the form of a plot of the percentage of intervals between the end of one response and the beginning of the next that were greater than the specified abscissa values. The solid line through the data is theoretical when the rate term, r, is set equal to the ratio of the number of responses to the total time minus the "holding" time, i.e., to the number of responses

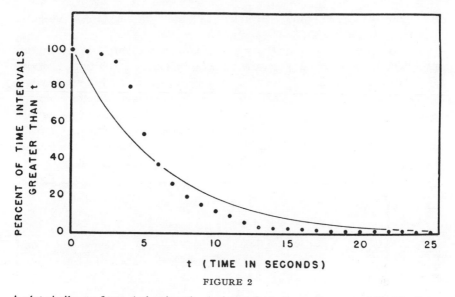

FIGURE 2

A plot similar to figure 1 showing the deviation from theory in cases of "holding" behavior.   The line drawn through the data is a plot of equation (1).

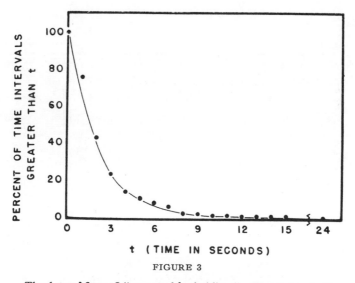

FIGURE 3

The data of figure 2 "corrected for holding."   The plot is similar to that in figures 1 and 2, except that the measured interval is the time between the end of one response and the beginning of the next response.   The line drawn through the data is a theoretical one described in the text.

per unit of "available" time.   As in figures 1 and 2 the constant is evaluated independently of the shape of the distribution of intervals.

Data relevant to the present analysis of latency measures are not numerous.   The agreement between the present theory and the data reported by Felsinger, Gladstone, Yamaguchi and Hull[6] is shown in figure 4, where the percentage of latencies greater than specified abscissa values are plotted. The solid line is the theoretical curve.   In the case of the latency data under consideration it is not possible to evaluate r independently of the distribution of time intervals.   In the case of figure 4 the constant was determined by the slope of a straight line fitted to a plot of $\log_e P_{>t}$ against t.

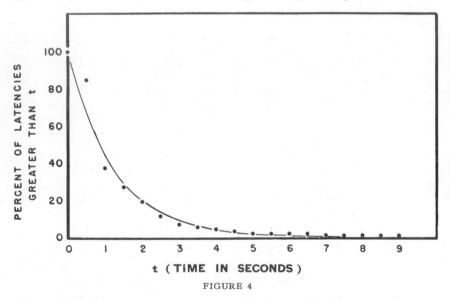

FIGURE 4

The percentage of latencies greater than t.   The data are from figure 1 of Felsinger, Gladstone, Yamaguchi and Hull.[6]

Probably little is to be gained at this time by further sampling of the consequences of equation (1), but many additional tests of the formulation may be made.   For some tests appropriate data are not available.   For the tests that have been tried the agreement between data and theory is promising.   One prediction that has been tested concerns the distribution of time intervals between responses for a number of animals at comparable stages in extinction.   The expectation is that at a specified stage in extinction the intervals between, say, response R_n and R_{n+1}, for a large number of animals, will be distributed in a manner similar to that shown in figure 1 and that the constant, r (therefore the steepness of drop of the curve) will vary systematically with n.   In other words, the steepness of the drop of a curve such as found in figure 1 will depend on where in extinction the intervals are measured. In fact this expectation seems to be borne out by the cases measured, although the number of measurements at each stage of extinction is not large.

Finally, it may be pointed out that the form of the present account has important consequences for the treatment of experimental data. Since one of the features of the account is the possibility of specifying the frequency distributions of the measures discussed it is possible to eliminate many of the problems associated with the arbitrary selection of representative values in summarizing data. On the basis of the preceding equations, one may state changes in one statistic, say the arithmetic mean, in terms of changes in another, say the geometric mean or the median. Therefore, data using different statistics are made comparable and the multiplicity of functions that may arise from the use of different descriptive statistics not only ceases to pose a difficult problem but is actually an aid to theory testing.

Summary.—A theoretical account of some relationships among measures of strength of conditioning has been considered. (1) If we assume that responses in a "free-response" situation are randomly distributed in time, we obtain directly a statement of the probability of occurrence of a response (or of any number of responses) within a specified time interval as a function of the length of the interval and of the rate of responding; we also obtain a statement of the probability of occurrence of inter-response time intervals of varying lengths. (2) If we assume that, for any specified stimulus condition, there corresponds some rate of responding, it turns out that the probability of occurrence of latencies of various lengths may be specified for various rates of responding, or, for a fixed probability value, the relation between latency and rate may be specified. (3) Finally, where these considerations are added to a theory specifying the relationship between rate of responding and number of responses yet to occur, the number of responses in extinction may be related to the latency and probability terms as well as to rate. In addition to statements about average values, the present formulation has consequences for the distribution of time intervals between responses and, by extension, for the distribution of latency measures.

[1] Hull, C. L., *Principles of Behavior*, D. Appleton-Century Co., New York, 1943.

[2] Skinner, B. F., *The Behavior of Organisms*, D. Appleton-Century Co., New York, 1938.

[3] A slightly different equation results if we assume that a "refractory" period exists, i.e., that immediately after a response there is a period during which the probability of getting a response is zero. If we assume that the transition from the "refractory" period to randomness is instantaneous, the probability of getting an interval greater than t is

$$P_{>t} = e^{-r(t-t_0)}$$

where t_0 is the "refractory" period.   The formulation is more complex if the transition is treated as a gradual one or if the "refractory" period has a variable length.

⁴ The data reported here were recorded by Mr. Michael Kaplan in the Psychological Laboratories of Columbia University.

⁵ This is merely a first approximation.   Subsequent analyses may show that the interval between the end of one response and the beginning of the next is not independent of the "holding" period.   The results of our procedure indicate that the approximation is useful for the present.

⁶ The experiment by Felsinger, Gladstone, Yamaguchi and Hull [*J. Exptl. Psychol.*, **37**, 214–228 (1947)] may not provide an optimal test of our formulation for two reasons. The first is that the data are reported in a frequency distribution with step intervals which begin at zero.   If the shortest latency were greater than zero, starting the step intervals at the lowest measure would be more appropriate.   The use of zero as a lower limit could easily make an exponential distribution more normal.   The method of summarizing the data may account for the deviation of the point at 0.5 second in figure 4. The deviation of this point is an expression of the fact that the distribution reported by Felsinger, Gladstone, Yamaguchi and Hull does not have a maximum frequency at the first step interval.

In the second place, it may be assumed that the many transient discriminative stimuli associated with the exposure of the bar may play a more important rôle than the continuous ones associated with the presence of the bar.   Although it is possible to extend the present notion to stimuli of short duration which end before the occurrence of the response, additional assumptions are required.   A less equivocal test of the present theory may be expected from a distribution of latencies obtained from an experimental procedure of the sort used by Skinner (op. cit.), Frick [*J. Psychol.*, **26**, 96–123 (1948)] and others.   After a period of, say, no light, a light is presented and stays on until one response occurs (Skinner) or stays on for some fixed period of time sufficiently long to insure the occurrence of many responses (Frick).   Such experimental procedures would minimize unspecified transient stimuli and would parallel more closely the notion that stimulus conditions determine a rate of responding.   The procedure used by Frick has the additional advantage of permitting the measurement of the time interval between the onset of the stimulus and the first response and the subsequent intervals between responses under "the same" stimulus conditions.

THE THEORY OF SIGNAL DETECTABILITY*

W. W. Peterson, T. G. Birdsall, and W. C. Fox

UNIVERSITY OF MICHIGAN

ANN ARBOR, MICHIGAN

The problem of signal detectability treated in this paper is the following: Suppose an observer is given a voltage varying with time during a prescribed observation interval and is asked to decide whether its source is noise or is signal plus noise. What method should the observer use to make this decision, and what receiver is a realization of that method? After giving a discussion of theoretical aspects of this problem, the paper presents specific derivations of the optimum receiver for a number of cases of practical interest.

The receiver whose output is the value of the likelihood ratio of the input voltage over the observation interval is the answer to the second question no matter which of the various optimum methods current in the literature is employed including the Neyman-Pearson observer, Siegert's ideal observer, and Woodward and Davies' "observer." An optimum observer required to give a yes or no answer simply chooses an operating level and concludes that the receiver input arose from signal plus noise only when this level is exceeded by the output of his likelihood ratio receiver.

Associated with each such operating level are conditional probabilities that the answer is a false alarm and the conditional probability of detection. Graphs of these quantities, called receiver operating characteristic, or ROC, curves are convenient for evaluating a receiver. If the detection problem is changed by varying, for example, the signal power, then a family of ROC curves is generated. Such things as betting curves can easily be obtained from such a family. The operating level to be used in a particular situation must be chosen by the observer. His choice will depend on such factors as the permissible false alarm rate, *a priori* probabilities, and relative importance of errors.

With these theoretical aspects serving as an introduction, attention is devoted to the derivation of explicit formulas for likelihood ratio, and for probability of detection and probability of false alarm, for a number of particular cases. Stationary, bandlimited, white Gaussian noise is assumed. The seven special cases which are presented were chosen from the simplest problems in signal detection which closely represent practical situations.

Two of the cases form a basis for the best available approximation to the important problem of finding probability of detection when the starting time of the signal, signal frequency, or both, are unknown. Furthermore, in these two cases uncertainty in the signal can be varied, and a quantitative relationship between uncertainty and ability to detect signals is presented for these two rather general cases. The variety of examples presented should serve to suggest methods for attacking other simple signal detection problems and to give insight into problems too complicated to allow a direct solution.

1. *Introduction*

The problem of signal detectability treated in this paper is that of determining a set of optimum instructions to be issued to an "observer" who is given a voltage varying with time during a prescribed observation interval and who must judge whether its source is "noise" or "signal plus noise." The nature of the "noise" and of the "signal plus noise" must be known to some extent by the observer.

From *Trans. IRE Professional Group in Information Theory*, 1954, PGIT 2-4, 171–212. Reprinted with permission.

* The work reported in this paper was done under U.S. Army Signal Corps Contract No. DA-36-039sc-15358.

Any equipment which the observer uses to make this judgment is called the "receiver." Therefore the voltage with which the observer is presented is called the "receiver input." The optimum instructions may consist primarily in specifying the "receiver" to be used by the observer.

The first three sections of this article survey the applications of statistical methods to this problem of signal detectability. They are intended to serve as an introduction to the subject for those who possess a minimum of mathematical training. Several definitions of "optimum" instructions have been proposed by other authors. Emphasis is placed here on the fact that these various definitions lead to essentially the same receiver. In subsequent sections the actual specification of the optimum receiver is carried out and its performance is evaluated numerically for some cases of practical interest [17].

1.1 *Population SN and N*

Either noise alone or the signal plus noise may be capable of producing many different receiver inputs. The totality of all possible receiver inputs when noise alone is present is called "Population N"; similarly, the collection of all receiver inputs when signal plus noise is present is called "Population SN." The observer is presented with a receiver input from one of the two populations, but he does not know from which population it came; indeed, he may not even know the probability that it arose from a particular population. The observer must judge from which population the receiver input came.

1.2 *Sampling plans*

A sampling plan is a system of making a sequence of measurements on the receiver input during the observation interval in such a way that it is possible to reconstruct the receiver input for the observation interval from the measurements. Mathematically, a sampling plan is a way of representing functions of time as sequences of numbers. The simplest way to describe this idea is to list a few examples.

A: Fourier series on an interval. Suppose that the observation interval begins at time t_0 and is T seconds long, and that each function in the population SN and N can be expanded in a Fourier series on the observation interval. The Fourier coefficients for each particular receiver input can be obtained by making measurements on that input, which can in turn be reconstructed from these measurements by the formula

$$x(t) = a_0 + \sum_{n=1}^{\infty} a_n \cos \frac{2\pi nt}{T} + b_n \sin \frac{2\pi nt}{T}, \qquad t_0 < t < t_0 + T. \tag{1}$$

Thus the process representing each function $x(t)$ by the sequence of its Fourier coefficients $(a_0, a_1, b_1, \ldots, a_n, b_n, \ldots)$ is a sampling plan in the sense described above.

The pair of terms in the Fourier series which involve the cosine and sine of $2\pi nt/T$ is of frequency n/T cycles per second. Suppose that for a particular population of receiver inputs the terms of frequency greater than n_0/T are zero; i.e., the population is bandlimited in the Fourier series sense or simply "series-bandlimited." For such a population the process of representing each receiver input $x(t)$ by the finite sequence $(a_0, a_1, b_1, \ldots, a_{n_0}, b_{n_0})$ is a finite sample plan.*

---

* A sampling plan is finite if there is a finite maximum length for the sequences for all receiver inputs in the population.

B: Shannon's sampling plan. Suppose that the observation interval includes all time and that the populations are "transform-bandlimited" to a band from 0 to W cycles per second, i.e., the Fourier transform of every receiver input is zero for frequencies greater than W. A sampling plan for this population is to represent each function $x(t)$ by its amplitude measured at times spaced $1/2W$ seconds apart, $(\ldots x(t_0 - n/2W), \ldots, x(t_0 - 1/2W), x(t_0), x(t_0 + 1/2W), \ldots x(t_0 + n/2W), \ldots)$. In this case the formula [2] for the reconstruction of the receiver input is

$$x(t) = \sum_{n=-\infty}^{\infty} x\left(t_0 + \frac{n}{2W}\right) \frac{\sin \pi[2W(t - t_0) - n]}{\pi[2W(t - t_0) - n]}. \tag{2}$$

The instants of time $t_0 + n/2W$ are called sampling-times. Each choice of t_0 between 0 and $1/2W$ yields a different sampling plan. If the observation interval again includes all time, but the populations are transform-bandlimited to a frequency band from $f_0 - W/2$ to $f_0 + W/2$ which does not contain zero frequency, then each receiver input $x(t)$ can be considered as an amplitude and frequency modulated waveform, $x(t) = r(t)\cos(2\pi f_0 t + \theta(t))$; $r(t)$ is the amplitude of the envelope and $\theta(t)$ is the instantaneous phase of the carrier. A sampling plan employing sampling-times is obtained in this case by representing each receiver input by the sequence $(\ldots r(t_0), \theta(t_0), \ldots, r(t_0 + n/W), \theta(t_0 + n/W), \ldots)$ of envelope amplitudes and carrier phases measured at sampling-times spaced by $1/W$ seconds apart [1]. The reconstruction of the receiver input from this sequence is given by

$$x(t) = \sum_{n=-\infty}^{\infty} r\left(t_0 + \frac{n}{W}\right) \cdot \cos\left[2\pi f_0 t + \theta\left(t_0 + \frac{n}{W}\right)\right] \frac{\sin \pi[W(t - t_0) - n]}{\pi[W(t - t_0) - n]}. \tag{3}$$

C: Sampling plan using sampling-times for a finite observation interval. Only functions known for all times have Fourier transforms, and therefore the hypothesis that the populations are transform-bandlimited applies only when the observation interval includes all time. If the observation interval is of finite length and if the populations are series-bandlimited, then there are sampling plans utilizing sampling-times which are similar to those described in paragraph *B* for transform-bandlimited populations and an infinite observation interval. Suppose that time is measured from the beginning of the observation interval, which is T seconds long, and suppose that the populations are series-bandlimited from 0 to W cycles per second. A finite sampling plan for this situation can be obtained by representing each receiver input by the sequence of its amplitudes measured $1/2W$ seconds apart [1]

$$\left[x(t_0), x\left(t_0 + \frac{1}{2W}\right), \ldots, x\left(t_0 + T - \frac{1}{2W}\right)\right] \tag{4}$$

and the reconstruction of the receiver input from this sequence is

$$x(t) = \sum_{n=0}^{2WT-1} x\left(t_0 + \frac{n}{2W}\right) \frac{\sin \pi[2W(t - t_0) - n]}{2WT \sin\left(\dfrac{2W(t - t_0) - n}{2WT} \pi\right)}, \quad 0 < t < T. \tag{5}$$

Again each choice of the (initial) sampling-time t_0 between 0 and $1/2W$ yields a different sampling plan. In a similar fashion, if the observation interval is unchanged but the populations are series-bandlimited on this interval to a frequency band from $f_0 - W/2$ to $f_0 + W/2$ which does not include zero frequency, then each receiver input can be represented by a finite sequence $[r(t_0), \theta(t_0), r(t_0 + 1/W), \theta(t_0 + 1/W), \ldots, r(t_0 + T - 1/W), \theta(t_0 + T - 1/W)]$ of envelope amplitudes and carrier phases measured at sample points $1/W$ seconds apart; t_0 is again used to denote the initial sampling time which may be chosen anywhere from 0 to $1/W$. The reconstruction of the receiver input from this sequence of measurements is given by

$$x(t) = \sum_{n=0}^{WT-1} r\left(t_0 + \frac{n}{W}\right) \cos\left[2\pi f_0 t + \theta\left(t_0 + \frac{n}{W}\right)\right] \frac{\sin \pi[W(t - t_0) - n]}{WT \sin\left[\pi \dfrac{W(t - t_0) - n}{WT}\right]},$$

$$0 < t < T. \quad (6)$$

From these examples it can be seen that there are a number of important differences between various sampling plans such as (a) the length of the observation interval, (b) whether sampling-times are employed, and (c) whether the measurements are all to be of the same kind, e.g., instantaneous amplitude measurements, or of different kinds, e.g., envelope amplitude and carrier phase. However, they all have in common the property that the receiver input can be reconstructed from the measurements made on it.

The role which the sampling plan plays in the theory presented in this paper is primarily one of mathematical convenience. The populations N and SN will be represented as sequences through the use of sampling plans in order to apply statistical methods. Once an answer is obtained concerning an "optimum" receiver, it is often possible to translate this answer back to the more familiar language of receiver inputs. If a finite-sampling plan is not available for a particular application of the theory, then recent work by Grenander [3] shows that the desired parameters of the "optimum" receiver can be approximated by using finite-sampling plans. Both for this reason and in order to simpify the exposition, the theory presented here is restricted to cases where finite-sampling plans are available.

2. *Optimum Tests on Fixed Observation Intervals*

2.1 *Probability density functions*

This part of the paper is concerned with a method of statistical analysis which requires for raw data a finite sequence of numbers $(x_1, x_2, \ldots, x_n)$, which is the result of the measurements made at the receiver input according to some particular finite-sampling plan. The sequence is often called a "sample" of the population from which it arose, and is denoted by a single letter; thus, if the receiver input is $x(t)$, and the sampling plan yields a sequence $(x_1, x_2, \ldots, x_n)$, then this sequence is called the sample X. The theory to be developed here is intended to specify an optimum receiver and is couched in the language of samples, $X = (x_1, x_2, \ldots, x_n)$. If n is very large, a receiver which had to make the measurements called for by a sampling plan would certainly be impractical. However, this practical difficulty is avoided when the specification of the receiver is translated back from the language of samples to the language of the receiver inputs; this can be done because it is possible to reconstruct the inputs from the samples.

For the purposes of the subsequent development any finite samping plan may be considered, provided enough properties are known of the associated sample X so that certain probabilities may be calculated. Specifically, the probability density functions $f_N(X)$ and $f_{SN}(X)$ of the sample variable X for the cases when X is drawn from populations N and SN, respectively, must be known.* The two basic properties of density functions are

$$f_N(X) \geq 0 \qquad \int f_N(X)\,dX = 1,$$

and   (7)

$$f_{SN}(X) \geq 0 \qquad \int f_{SN}(X)\,dX = 1$$

where the integration symbol represents the multiple integral taken over the entire range of the sample variable $X = (x_1, x_2, \ldots, x_n)$.

2.2 The concept of a criterion

Consider now an observer who has as available data the sample $X = (x_1, \ldots, x_n)$. The observer's job is to judge for each sample whether or not it was taken from population SN. Although it is not possible to determine the (probably subconscious) criterion used by the observer, it is quite possible to find an external manifestation of it. Ideally all that is necessary is to submit each possible sample to the observer and to record his judgment. This will yield a tabulation of those samples which the observer decided were drawn from population SN. If any other observer is given this tabulation and instructed to base his decisions on it, he will behave exactly as did the first observer. Thus, the tabulation of these responses can be used to replace the mental criterion employed by the observer. Such a tabulation will also be called a criterion and will be denoted by the letter A, which refers to the phraseology common in statistics of "Accepting the hypothesis that a signal is present." The tabulation of the remaining samples, those which the observer concluded were drawn from population N, will be denoted by B.

2.3 Probabilities associated with criteria

There are, of course, as many different criteria as there are observers. Among all possible criteria it is necessary to select those that are best for various purposes. To do so, certain numerical quantities must be associated with each criterion. It will be necessary to know the probability that a sample from one of the populations will be listed in a particular criterion A. According to the standard definitions, these probabilities are given by

$$P_{SN}(A) = \int f_{SN}(X)\,dX$$

and   (8)

$$P_N(A) = \int f_N(X)\,dX,$$

where the multiple integral is taken over all samples listed in the criterion A.

* In this discussion it should be kept in mind that "the event of the sample being drawn from population SN" corresponds to signal and noise being present at the receiver input. Also "the event of population SN being sampled" means the same thing.

For example, a particular sample plan might have a density function of the form $f_N(x_1, x_2, \ldots, x_n) = K \exp\left[-(x_1^2 + x_2^2 + \ldots + x_n^2)\right]$. A possible criterion would consist of those samples $X = (x_1, x_2, \ldots, x_n)$ which lie outside a sphere of radius 1 centered at the origin. Then the integral would be taken over the exterior of this sphere.

These probabilities have a special significance. $P_N(A)$ is the conditional probability that a sample from population N will be listed in criterion A; that is, will be judged as a sample from population SN. Thus $P_N(A) = F$ is the conditional false alarm probability. Also, $P_{SN}(A)$ is the conditional probability of a certain kind of correct response called a hit (that of judging correctly that a sample is from population SN). The conditional probability of judging falsely that a sample is from population SN is, therefore, given by $1 - P_{SN}(A) = M$, the conditional probability of a miss. The only errors which can occur are false alarms and misses; their conditional probabilities, F and M, are called briefly the error probabilities.

A reader familiar with the formal content of probability theory should note that these quantities are true conditional probabilities; the first is conditional on the sample being drawn from population SN; the second is conditional on its being drawn from population N. This is to distinguish them from *a priori* probabilities (the probabilities that a certain population will be sampled, for example) which are not as yet assumed known.

2.4 *Likelihood ratio and the ratio criteria*

It is convenient to introduce a new function called the likelihood ratio, $l(X)$, defined as the ratio $f_{SN}(X)/f_N(X)$ for sample points $X = (x_1, \ldots, x_n)$; $l(X)$ represents the likelihood that the sample X was drawn from SN relative to the likelihood that it was drawn from N. Hence, if $l(X)$ is sufficiently large, it would be reasonable to conclude that X was in fact drawn from population SN, i.e., that X should be listed in the desired "best" criterion. Thus, for each number $\beta \geq 0$, a certain criterion $A(\beta)$ will be selected; $A(\beta)$ is chosen by listing each sample X for which $l(X) \geq \beta$. The problem then reduces to that of making a wise choice of β; that is, to determine how large "sufficiently large" is. Criteria of the form $A(\beta)$ will be called ratio criteria.

A number of writers have presented varying definitions of a criterion being "optimum." It turns out that each of these optimum criteria can be expressed as a ratio criterion, so that a receiver designed to yield likelihood ratio as output could be used with any of them.

2.5 *Weighted combination criteria*

Suppose it is possible to assign a certain number w as a weighting factor representing the importance of a false alarm relative to a hit. Since $P_{SN}(A)$ is the probability of a hit, and $P_N(A)$ the probability of a false alarm, it would then be reasonable to find a criterion A which maximizes the quantity

$$P_{SN}(A) - wP_N(A). \tag{9}$$

But this quantity can be written as

$$\int_A [f_{SN}(X) - wf_N(X)] \, dX, \tag{10}$$

where the integration is taken over the sample points X listed in A. To maximize this integral, one would list in A every sample for which the integrand was not negative. Solving that inequality for w, one sees that A should contain those sample points X for which

$$l(X) = \frac{f_{SN}(X)}{f_N(X)} \geq w. \tag{11}$$

Thus the desired criterion A is simply $A(w)$, and so it is a ratio criterion.

2.6 *Neyman-Pearson criteria*

If it is critically important to keep the probability of a false alarm $P_N(A)$ below a certain level k, then it would be reasonable to choose from among such criteria that one which maximizes the probability of a hit. Thus Neyman and Pearson proposed [4] as a type of optimum criterion any criterion A_k for which

(1) $P_N(A_k) \leq k$, and

(2) $P_{SN}(A_k)$ is a maximum for all the criteria A with the property $P_N(A) \leq k$.

The A_k type criterion can also be expressed as a ratio criterion. This can be made plausible as follows. To begin with, it is necessary to consider only those criteria A for which $P_N(A) = k$, because A will be taken as large as possible in order to meet condition (2). Now consider the curve given parametrically by the equations

$$X = X(\beta) = P_N[A(\beta)]$$

and

$$Y = Y(\beta) = P_{SN}[A(\beta)]. \tag{12}$$

This curve will be called the Receiver Operating Characteristic (briefly, ROC) curve, for a receiver whose output is likelihood ratio and with which ratio criteria are being used.

The ROC curve passes through the points $(0, 0)$ and $(1, 1)$, the first at $\beta = \infty$, the second at $\beta = 0$. At $\beta = 0$, $l(X) \geq \beta = 0$ for all X, so $A(0)$ consists of all possible samples. Thus the observer will report that every sample is drawn from SN, so he will be certain to make a false alarm and to make a hit. (This assumes that the samples will not be drawn exclusively from one of the populations.) This can be verified, using the basic property of the density functions expressed by the following equations:

$$P_{SN}[A(0)] = \int f_{SN}(X)\, dX = 1$$

and

$$P_N[A(0)] = \int f_N(X)\, dX = 1, \tag{13}$$

where the integration is taken over all possible samples X. These equations mean that $X(0) = Y(0) = 1$. Moreover, $X(\infty) = Y(\infty) = 0$, because for $\beta = \infty$ there are no samples X with $l(X) \geq \infty$; i.e., $A(\infty)$ contains no samples at all and the operator will never report a signal is present. Therefore, the operator cannot possibly make a false alarm nor can he make a hit. Thus $P_{SN}[A(\infty)] = 0$ and $P_N[A(\infty)] = 0$.

These considerations, together with those of the next section, show that the ROC curve can be sketched somewhat as in Fig. 1.

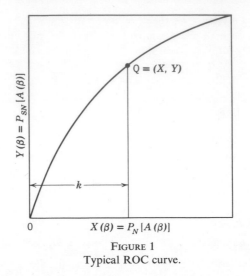

FIGURE 1
Typical ROC curve.

To determine the desired A_k, recall that all probabilities lie between zero and one, so that $P_N(A_k) = k$ is between zero and one. Then there is a point Q of the ROC curve which lies vertically above the point $(k, 0)$. The coordinates (X, Y) of Q are $X = P_N[A(\beta)] = k$ and $Y = P_{SN}[A(\beta)]$, for some β, which will be written β_k. Now $A(\beta_k)$ satisfies condition (1) because $P_N[A(\beta_k)] = k$, and therefore $A(\beta_k)$ will be the desired A_k if $P_{SN}(A) \leq P_{SN}[A(\beta_k)]$ for any criterion with the property that $P_N(A) = k$. From paragraph 2.5, it is clear that the ratio criterion $A(\beta_k)$ is an optimum weighted-combination criterion with the weighting factor $w = \beta_k$. Therefore, if $w = \beta_k$, the weighted combination using the criterion $A(\beta_k)$ is greater than or equal to the same weighted combination using any other criterion A, i.e.,

$$P_{SN}[A(\beta_k)] - \beta_k P_N[A(\beta_k)] \geq P_{SN}(A) - \beta_k P_N(A). \tag{14}$$

In this case both $P_N[A(\beta_k)]$ and $P_N(A)$ are equal to k. If this value is substituted into the inequality above, one obtains

$$P_{SN}[A(\beta_k)] \geq P_{SN}(A). \tag{15}$$

Therefore, the desired Neyman-Pearson criterion A_k should be chosen to be this particular ratio criterion, $A(\beta_k)$.

2.7 ROC curve

It is desirable to digress for a moment to study the ROC curve more closely. Its value lies in the fact that if the type of criterion chosen for a particular application is a ratio criterion, $A(\beta)$, then a complete description of the detection system's perform-ance can be read off the ROC curve. By the very definition of the ROC curve, the X coordinate is the conditional probability F, of false alarm, and the Y coordinate is the conditional probability of a hit. Similarly $(1 - X)$ is the conditional probability of being correct when noise alone is present, and $(1 - Y) = M$ is the conditional prob-ability of a miss. It will be shown in a moment that the operating level β for the ratio criterion $A(\beta)$ can also be determined from the ROC curve as the slope at the point

$$\{P_N[A(\beta)], \quad P_{SN}[A(\beta)]\}.$$

Since most proposed kinds of optimum criteria can be reduced to ratio criteria, the ROC curve assumes considerable importance.

In order to determine some of its geometric properties, it will be assumed that the parametric functions

$$X = X(\beta) = P_N[A(\beta)]$$

and   (16)

$$Y = Y(\beta) = P_{SN}[A(\beta)]$$

are differentiable functions of β. The slope of the tangent to the ROC curve is given by the quotient $(dY/d\beta)/(dX/d\beta)$. To calculate the slope at the point $[X(\beta_0), Y(\beta_0)]$, notice that among all criteria A, the quantity $P_{SN}(A) - \beta_0 P_N(A)$ is maximized by $A = A(\beta_0)$. Therefore, in particular, the function

$$Y(\beta) - \beta_0 X(\beta) = P_{SN}[A(\beta)] - \beta_0 P_N[A(\beta)] \tag{17}$$

has a maximum at $\beta = \beta_0$, so that its derivative must vanish there. Thus differentiating,

$$\frac{dY}{d\beta} - \beta_0 \frac{dX}{d\beta} = 0 \quad \text{at } \beta = \beta_0. \tag{18}$$

Solving for β_0, one obtains

$$\beta_0 = \frac{(dY/d\beta)_{\beta=\beta_0}}{(dX/d\beta)_{\beta=\beta_0}} = \text{the slope of the tangent to the}$$
$$\text{ROC curve at the point } [X(\beta_0), Y(\beta_0)]. \tag{19}$$

This shows that the slope of the ROC curve is given by its parameter β, and so is always positive. Hence the curve rises steadily. In addition, this means that $Y(\beta)$ can be written as a single valued function of $X(\beta)$, $Y = Y(X)$, which is monotone increasing, and where $Y(0) = 0$ and $Y(1) = 1$. These remarks make fully warranted the sketch of the ROC curve given in Fig. 1. The next two sections are concerned with determining the best value to use for the weighting factor w when *a priori* probabilities are known.

2.8 Siegert's "Ideal Observer's" criteria

Here it is necessary to know beforehand the *a priori* probabilities that population SN and that population N will be sampled. This is an additional assumption. These probabilities are denoted respectively by $P(SN)$ and $P(N)$. Moreover, $P(SN) + P(N) = 1$ because at least one of the populations must be sampled. The criterion associated with Siegert's Ideal Observer is usually defined as a criterion for which the *a priori* probability of error is minimized (or, equivalently, the *a priori* probability of a correct response is maximized) [5]. Frequently the only case considered is that where $P(SN)$ and $P(N)$ are equal, but this restriction is not necessary.

Since the conditional probability F of a false alarm is known as well as the *a priori* probability of the event (that population N was sampled) upon which F is conditional, then the probability of a false alarm is given by the product

$$P(N)F. \tag{20}$$

In the same way the probability of a miss is given by

$$P(SN)M. \tag{21}$$

Because an error E can occur in exactly these two ways, the probability of error is the sum of these quantities

$$P(E) = P(N)F + P(SN)M. \tag{22}$$

It has already been pointed out that $F = P_N(A)$ and $M = 1 - P_{SN}(A)$. If these are substituted into the expression for $P(E)$ a simple algebraic manipulation gives

$$P(E) = P(SN) - P(SN)\left[P_{SN}(A) - \frac{P(N)}{P(SN)} \cdot P_N(A)\right]. \tag{23}$$

It is desired to minimize $P(E)$. But from the last equation this is equivalent to maximizing the quantity

$$P_{SN}(A) - \frac{P(N)}{P(SN)} \cdot P_N(A), \tag{24}$$

and, of course, this will yield a weighted combination criterion with $w = P(N)/P(SN)$, which is known to be simply a ratio criterion $A(w)$.

2.9 Maximum expected-value criteria

Another way to assign a weighting factor w depends on knowing the "expected value" of each criterion. This can be determined if the a priori probabilities $P(SN)$ and $P(N)$ are known, and if numerical values can be assigned to the four alternatives. Let V_D be the value of detection and V_Q the value of being "quiet," that is, of correctly deciding that noise alone is present. The other two alternatives are also assigned values, V_M, the value of a miss, and V_F, the value of a false alarm. The expected value associated with a criterion can now be determined. In this case it is natural to define an optimum criterion as one which maximizes the expected value. It can be shown that such a criterion maximizes

$$P_{SN}(A) - \left[\frac{P(N)}{P(SN)} \cdot \frac{V_Q - V_F}{V_D - V_M}\right]P_N(A). \tag{25}$$

By definition (see paragraph 2.5), this criterion is a weighted combination criterion with weighting factor

$$w = \frac{P(N)}{P(SN)} \cdot \frac{V_Q - V_F}{V_D - V_M}, \tag{26}$$

and hence a likelihood ratio criterion. Siegert's "Ideal Observer" criterion is the special case for which $V_Q - V_F = V_D - V_M$.

2.10 A posteriori probability and signal detectability

Heretofore the observer has been limited to two possible answers, "signal plus noise is present" or "noise alone is present." Instead he may be asked what, to the best of his knowledge, is the probability that a signal is present. This approach has the advantage of getting more information from the receiving equipment. In fact, Woodward and Davies point out that if the observer makes the best possible estimate of this probability for each possible transmitted message, he is supplying all the information which his equipment can give him [6]. A good discussion of this approach is found in the original papers by Woodward and Davies [6, 7]. Their formula for the *a posteriori* probability, $P_X(SN)$, becomes, in the notation of this paper,

$$P_X(SN) = \frac{f_{SN}(X)P(SN)}{f_{SN}(X)P(SN) + (1 - P(SN))f_N(X)}, \tag{27}$$

or

$$P_X(SN) = \frac{l(X)P(SN)}{l(X)\,P(SN) + 1 - P(SN)}. \tag{28}$$

If a receiver which has likelihood ratio as its output can be built, and if the *a priori* probability $P(SN)$ is known, *a posteriori* probability can be calculated easily. The calculation could be built into the receiver calibration, since (28) is a monotonic function of $l(X)$; this would make the receiver an optimum receiver for obtaining *a posteriori* probability.

3. *Sequential Tests with Minimum Average Duration*

3.1 *Sequential testing*

The idea of sequential testing is this: make one measurement x_1 on the receiver input; if the evidence x_1 is sufficiently persuading, decide as to whether the receiver input was drawn from population SN or from population N. If the evidence is not so strong, make a second measurement x_2 and consider the evidence (x_1, x_2). Continue to make measurements until the resulting sequence of measurements is sufficiently persuading in favor of one population or the other. Obviously this involves the theoretical possibility of making arbitrarily many measurements before a final decision is made. This does not mean that infinitely many measurements must be made in an actual application, nor does it necessarily mean that the operation might entail an arbitrarily long interval of time. If, in a particular application, measurements are taken at evenly spaced times then the "time base" of such a measurement plan is infinite. However, another plan might call for measurements to be made at the instants $t = 0$, $t = 1/2, \ldots, t = (n - 1)/n$, and as these times all lie in the time interval from zero to one, such a measurement plan would have a time base of only one unit of time.

If the measurement plan has been carried out to the stage where n measurements $x_1, x_2, \ldots, x_n$ have been made, the variable $X_n = (x_1, x_2, \ldots, x_n)$ is called the nth stage sample variable. A specific plan for measurements will be considered only if for each possible stage n, the two density functions $f_{SN}(X_n)$ and $f_N(X_n)$ of the nth stage sample variable X_n are known; the first of these density functions is applicable when population SN is being sampled and the second is applicable when population N is being sampled. These density functions may very well differ at different stages, so that they should be written $f_N^n(X_n)$ and $f_{SN}^n(X_n)$; however, the n appearing in the argument X_n should always make the situation clear, and the superscript on the density functions themselves will be omitted.

3.2 *Sequential tests*

A sequential test will consist of two things:

(1) An (infinite) measurement plan with density functions $f_N(X_n)$ and $f_{SN}(X_n)$,

(2) An assignment of three criteria to each stage of the measurement plan.
These three criteria represent the three possible conclusions:

(A) Signal plus noise is present, i.e. the sample comes from population SN,

(B) Noise alone is present, i.e. the sample comes from population N,

(C) Another measurement should be made.

At the first stage of the measurement plan, any (real) number at all could theoretically result from the first measurement. This means that the first stage sample variable $X_1 = (x_1)$ ranges through the entire number system, which will be written S_1 to stand for the first stage sample space. Suppose the three first-stage criteria A_1, B_1, and C_1, have been chosen. If the sample X_1 is listed in A_1, the conclusion that a signal is present is drawn and the test is terminated. If it is listed in B_1, the conclusion is that noise alone is present, and again the test is terminated. If X_1 should be listed in C_1, another measurement will be made, and the test moves on to the second stage instead of terminating.

When the first stage criteria have been chosen, a limitation is placed on S_2, the space through which the second stage sample variable $X_2 = (x_1, x_2)$ ranges. The only way the test can proceed to the second stage is for $X_1 = (x_1)$ to be listed in C_1. Therefore, S_2 does not contain all possible second stage samples $X_2 = (x_1, x_2)$ but only those for which (x_1) is listed in C_1. Three second stage criteria, A_2, B_2, and C_2, must now be chosen from those samples X_2 listed in S_2. They must be chosen in such a way that there are no duplications in the listings and no sample in S_2 is omitted. These criteria carry exactly the same significance as those chosen in the first stage. That is, the three conclusions that a signal is or is not present, or that the test should be continued, are drawn when the sample X_2 is listed in A_2, B_2, or C_2 respectively.

The selection of criteria proceeds in the same way. If the nth stage criteria A_n, B_n, and C_n, have been chosen, then the next stage's sample space S_{n+1} consists of those samples $X_{n+1} = (x_1, x_2, \ldots, x_n, x_{n+1})$ for which $X_n = (x_1, x_2, \ldots, x_n)$ was listed in C_n. Then from S_{n+1} are drawn the three $(n + 1)$ stage criteria A_{n+1}, B_{n+1}, and C_{n+1}.

When an entire sequence

$$(A_1, B_1, C_1),$$

$$(A_2, B_2, C_2),$$

$$\cdot$$
$$\cdot$$
$$\cdot$$

$$(A_n, B_n, C_n),$$

$$\cdot$$
$$\cdot$$
$$\cdot$$

of criteria is selected, a "sequential test" has been determined. This does not mean of course that the test will necessarily be particularly useful. However, among all the possible ways of selecting a sequence of criteria and hence a sequential test, there may be particular ones which are very useful.

3.3 *Probabilities associated with sequential tests*

If Q_n is any nth stage criterion, then the quantities*

$$P_N(Q_n) = \int_{Q_n} f_N(X_n) \, dX_n$$

and   (29)

$$P_{SN}(Q_n) = \int_{Q_n} f_{SN}(X_n) \, dX_n$$

represent the (N or SN) conditional probabilities that an nth stage sample X_n will be listed in the criterion Q_n. Conditional probabilities of particular interest are:

(1) The nth stage conditional error probabilities:

If population N is sampled, then the probability that the sample variable X_n will be listed in A_n is $P_N(A_n)$. This is the N-conditional probability of a false alarm.

If population SN is sampled, then the probability that the sample variable X_n will be listed in B_n is $P_{SN}(B_n)$. This is the SN-conditional probability of a miss.

(2) The conditional error probabilities of the entire test:

$$F = \sum_{n=1}^{\infty} P_N(A_n), \text{ the } N\text{-conditional probability of a false alarm, and} \tag{30}$$

$$M = \sum_{n=1}^{\infty} P_{SN}(B_n), \text{ the } SN\text{-conditional probability of a miss,} \tag{31}$$

are merely the sums of the same error probabilities over all stages.

(3) The conditional probabilities of terminating at stage n are

$$T_N^n = P_N(A_n) + P_N(B_n), \tag{32}$$

and

$$T_{SN}^n = P_{SN}(A_n) + P_{SN}(B_n). \tag{33}$$

These equations can be justified by a simple argument. The only way the test can terminate at stage n is for the sample variable X_n to be listed in either A_n or B_n. The probability of this event is the sum of the probabilities of the component events which are mutually exclusive since X_n can be listed in at most one of A_n and B_n.

(4) The conditional probabilities that the entire test will terminate are

$$T_N = \sum_{n=1}^{\infty} T_N^n, \tag{34}$$

and

$$T_{SN} = \sum_{n=1}^{\infty} T_{SN}^n. \tag{35}$$

3.4. *Average sample numbers*

There are two other quantities which must be introduced. One feature of the sequential test is that it affords an opportunity of arriving at a decision early in the sampling process when the data happen to be unusually convincing. Thus one might

---

* The notation $\int_{Q_n}$ indicates that the integration is to be carried out over all sample points listed in Q_n.

expect that, on the average, the stage of termination of a well-constructed sequential test would be lower than could be achieved by an otherwise equal, good standard test. It is therefore important to obtain expressions for the average or expected value of the stage of termination. As with other probabilities, there will be two of these quantities: one conditional on population N being sampled; the other conditional on population SN being sampled. They are given by

$$E_N = \sum_{n=1}^{\infty} nT_N^n \tag{36}$$

and

$$E_{SN} = \sum_{n=1}^{\infty} nT_{SN}^n. \tag{37}$$

The letter E is used to refer to the term "expected value." The quantities E_N and E_{SN} are called the average sample numbers. The form these formulas take can be justified (somewhat freely) on the grounds that each value, n, which the variable "stage of termination" may take on must be weighted by the (conditional) probability that the variable will in fact take on that value.

It should be heavily emphasized that the average sample numbers are strictly average figures. In actual runs of a sequential test, the stages of termination will sometimes be less than the average sample numbers but will also be, upon occasion, much larger. Any sequential test whose average sample numbers are not finite would be useless for applications. Therefore the only ones to be considered are those with finite average sample numbers. Under this assumption,* it can be shown that $T_N = T_{SN} = 1$ so that the test is certain to terminate (in the sense of probability). On the other hand, if it is known that $T_N = T_{SN} = 1$ it does not always follow that the average sample numbers are finite. Such a situation would mean only that if a sequence of runs of the test were made, each run would probably terminate, but the average stage of termination would become arbitrarily large as more runs were made.

3.5 *Sequential ratio tests*

In studying non-sequential tests using finite samples it was found that the best criterion could always be expressed in terms of likelihood ratio. Therefore, it may be useful to introduce likelihood ratios at each stage of an infinite sample plan. The nth stage likelihood ratio function $l(X_n)$ is defined as the ratio $f_{SN}(X_n)/f_N(X_n)$. Optimum criteria in the finite-sample tests turned out to be criteria listing all samples X for which $l(X)$ is greater than or equal to a certain number. It should be possible to choose sequential criteria (A_n, B_n, C_n) in the same way. For each stage two numbers a_n and b_n with $b_n \leq a_n$ could be chosen. Then the criteria (A_n, B_n, C_n) determined by the numbers a_n and b_n would be

A_n lists all samples X_n of the sample space S_n for which $l(X_n) \geq a_n$,

B_n lists all samples X_n of the sample space S_n for which $l(X_n) \leq b_n$,

C_n lists all samples X_n of the sample space S_n for which $b_n < l(X_n) < a_n$.

* Remember that the sampling process is not assumed to yield independence among the X_i.

If criteria selected in this way meet the requirements that the average sample numbers be finite, then the resulting sequential test is called a "sequential ratio test."

3.6 Optimum sequential tests

It is customary [8] to define an optimum sequential test as that one for which the average sample numbers E_N and E_{SN} are minimum among all sequential tests with fixed error probabilities F and M.

In addition to the formulas given in Section 3.4, alternative formulas [9] for the average sample numbers are

$$E_N = 1 + \sum_{i=1}^{\infty} P_N(C_i) \tag{38}$$

and

$$E_{SN} = 1 + \sum_{i=1}^{\infty} P_{SN}(C_i). \tag{39}$$

Thus, if a set of sequential criteria (A_n^*, B_n^*, C_n^*) is presented as a possible optimum test, then its optimum character is decided by ascertaining whether the inequalities

$$\sum P_N(C_i^*) \leq \sum P_N(C_i) \tag{40}$$

and

$$\sum P_{SN}(C_i^*) \leq \sum P_{SN}(C_i) \tag{41}$$

hold for every other set of sequential criteria $\{(A_n, B_n, C_n)\}$ with the same error probabilities, i.e., with

$$\sum P_N(A_i^*) = \sum P_N(A_i) \tag{42}$$

and

$$\sum P_{SN}(B_i^*) = \sum P_{SN}(B_i). \tag{43}$$

The problem of constructing an optimum sequential test is difficult because the equalities (42) and (43) can be satisfied even when there is no apparent term-by-term relation between the sequences $\{P_N(C_i^*)\}$ and $\{P_N(C_i)\}$. Wald has proposed as optimum the tests in which each of the sequences $\{a_n\}$ and $\{b_n\}$ is constant, that is, $b_1 = b_n$ and $a_1 = a_n$ for all n. Moreover Wald and Wolfowitz [10] proved that these tests are optimum whenever the density functions at successive stages are independent, as can be the case for example when both noise and signal plus noise consist of "random noise." However, this "randomness" is not met with in most applications of the theory of signal detectability, at least not in the sense that the hypotheses of Wald and Wolfowitz are satisfied.

Consider a test of fixed length as described in Section 2, with error probabilities F and M. Although the optimum sequential test with these same error probabilities generally requires less time on the average, it has the disadvantage that it will sometimes use much more time than the fixed length test requires. In a conversation with the authors, Professor Mark Kac of Cornell University suggested that the dispersion, or variance, of the sample numbers may be so large as seriously to affect the usefulness of the sequential tests in applications to signal detectability. Certainly this matter should be investigated before a final decision is reached concerning the merits of sequential tests relative to tests on a fixed observation interval. However it is a difficult matter to calculate the variance of the sample numbers. Therefore an electronic simulator is being built at the University of Michigan which will simulate both types of tests and will provide data for ROC curves of both types as well as the distribution of the (sequential) sample numbers.

4. *Optimum Detection for Specific Cases*

4.1 *Introduction*

The chief conclusion obtained from the general theory of signal detectability presented in Section 2 of this paper is that a receiver which calculates the likelihood ratio for each receiver input is the optimum receiver for detecting signals in noise.

TABLE I

Section	Description of Signal Ensemble	Application
4.4	Signal known exactly*	Coherent radar with a target of known range and character
4.5	Signal known except for phase*	Ordinary pulse radar with no integration and with a target of known range and character
4.6	Signal a sample of white Gaussian noise	Detection of noise-like signals; detection of speech sounds in Gaussian noise
4.7	Detector output of a broad band receiver	Detecting a pulse of known starting time (such as a pulse from a radar beacon) with a crystal-video or other type broad band receiver
4.8	A radar case (A train of pulses with incoherent phase)	Ordinary pulse radar with integration and with a target of known range and character
4.10	Signal one of M orthogonal signals	Coherent radar where the target is at one of a finite number of non-overlapping positions
4.11	Signal one of M orthogonal signals known except for phase	Ordinary pulse radar with no integration and with a target which may appear at one of a finite number of non-overlapping positions

* Our treatment of these two fundamental cases is based upon Woodward and Davies' work, but here they are treated in terms of likelihood ratio, and hence apply to criterion type receivers as well as to *a posteriori* probability type receivers. These first two cases have been solved for the more general problem in which the noise is Gaussian but has an arbitrary spectrum [11,12]. Those solutions require the use of an infinite sampling plan and are considerably more involved than the corresponding derivations in this report.

It is the purpose of Section 4 to consider a number of different ensembles of signals with bandlimited white Gaussian noise. For each case, a possible receiver design is discussed. The primary emphasis, however, is on obtaining the probability of detection and probability of false alarm, and hence on estimates of optimum receiver performance for the various cases.

The cases which are presented were chosen from the simplest problems in signal detection which closely represent practical situations. They are listed in Table I along with examples of engineering problems in which they find application. In the last two cases the uncertainty in the signal can be varied, and some light is thrown on the relationship between uncertainty and the ability to detect signals. The variety of examples presented should serve to suggest methods for attacking other simple signal detection problems and to give insight into problems too complicated to allow a direct solution.

The reader will find the discussion of likelihood ratio and its distribution easier to follow if he keeps in mind the connection between a criterion type receiver and likelihood ratio. In an optimum criterion type system, the operator will say that a signal is present whenever the likelihood ratio is above a certain level β. He will say that only noise is present when the likelihood ratio is below β. For each operating level β, there is a false alarm probability and a probability of detection. The false alarm probability is the probability that the likelihood ratio $l(X)$ will be greater than β if no signal is sent; this is by definition the complementary distribution function $F_N(\beta)$. Likewise, the complementary distribution $F_{SN}(\beta)$ is the probability that $l(X)$ will be greater than β if there is signal plus noise, and hence $F_{SN}(\beta)$ is the probability of detection if a signal is sent.

4.2 *Gaussian noise*

In the remainder of this paper the receiver inputs will be assumed to be defined on a finite-observation interval, $0 < t < T$. It will further be assumed that the receiver inputs are series-bandlimited. By the sampling plan C (Section 1.2) any such receiver input $x(t)$ can be reconstructed from sample values of the function taken at points $1/2W$ apart throughout the observation interval, i.e.,

$$x(t) = \sum_{k=1}^{2WT} x_k \psi_k(t), \tag{44}$$

where

$$\psi_k(t) = \frac{\sin \pi 2WT\left(\dfrac{t}{T} - \dfrac{k}{2WT}\right)}{2WT \sin \pi\left(\dfrac{t}{T} - \dfrac{k}{2WT}\right)} \quad \text{and} \quad x_k = x\left(\dfrac{k}{2W}\right). \tag{45}$$

Therefore the receiver inputs can be represented by the sample $(x_1, x_2, \ldots, x_{2WT})$. In Section 4 the notation x will be used to denote either the receiver input function $x(t)$ or the sample $(x_1, x_2, \ldots, x_{2WT})$. Similarly the signal $s(t)$, or simply s, can be represented by the sample $(s_1, \ldots, s_{2WT})$, where $s_k = s(k/2W)$.

Only the probability distributions for receiver inputs $x(t)$ can be specified. The distribution must be given for the receiver inputs both with noise alone and with signal plus noise. The probability distributions are described by giving the probability density functions $f_{SN}(x)$ and $f_N(x)$ for the receiver inputs x.

The probability density function for the receiver inputs with noise alone are assumed to be

$$f_N(x) = \prod_{i=1}^{n} \left\{ \frac{1}{\sqrt{2\pi N}} \exp \left[-\frac{x_i^2}{2N} \right] \right\},$$

or   (46)

$$f_N(x) = \left(\frac{1}{2\pi N} \right)^{n/2} \exp \left[-\frac{1}{2N} \sum_{i=1}^{n} x_i^2 \right],$$

where n is $2WT$ and N is the noise power. It can be verified easily that this probability density function is the description of noise which has a Gaussian distribution of amplitude at every time, is stationary, and has the same average power in each of its Fourier components. Thus we shall refer to it as "stationary bandlimited white Gaussian noise."

The functions $\psi_k(t)$ are orthogonal and have energy $1/2W$, and therefore

$$\sum x_i^2 = 2W \int_0^T [x(t)]^2 \, dt, \tag{47}$$

so that

$$f_N(x) = \left(\frac{1}{2\pi N} \right)^{n/2} \exp \left[-\frac{1}{N_0} \int_0^T x(t)^2 \, dt \right], \tag{48}$$

where $N_0 = N/W$ is the noise power per unit bandwidth.

In a practical application, information is given about the signals as they would appear without noise at the receiver input, rather than about the signal plus noise probability density. Then $f_{SN}(x)$ must be calculated from this information and the probability density function $f_N(x)$ for the noise. The noise and the signals will be assumed independent of each other.

If the input to the receiver is the sum of the signal and the noise, then the receiver input $x(t)$ could have been caused by any signal $s(t)$ and noise $n(t) = x(t) - s(t)$. The probability density for the input x in signal plus noise is thus the probability (density) that $s(t)$ and $x(t) - s(t)$ will occur together, averaged over all possible $s(t)$. If the probability of the signals is described by a density function $f_S(s)$, then

$$f_{SN}(x) = \int f_N(x - s) f_S(s) \, ds, \tag{49}$$

where the integration is over the entire range of the sample variable s. A more general form is used when the probability of the signals is described by a probability measure P_S; the formula in this case is

$$f_{SN}(x) = \int f_N(x - s) \, dP_S(s). \tag{50}$$

This integral is a Lebesgue integral, and is essentially an "average" of $f_N(x - s)$ over all values of s weighted by the probability P_S. If $f_N(x)$ is taken from Eq. (46), this becomes

$$f_{SN}(x) = \int f_N(x - s) \, dP_S(s) = \left(\frac{1}{2\pi N}\right)^{n/2} \int \exp\left[-\frac{1}{2N} \sum_{i=1}^{n} (x_i - s_i)^2\right] dP_S(s)$$

(51)

$$= \left(\frac{1}{2\pi N}\right)^{n/2} \exp\left[-\frac{1}{2N} \sum_{i=1}^{n} x_i^2\right] \int \exp\left[-\frac{1}{2N} \sum_{i=1}^{n} s_i^2\right] \exp\left[\frac{1}{N} \sum_{i=1}^{n} x_i s_i\right] dP_S(s),$$

$$f_{SN}(x) = \int f_N(x - s) \, dP_S(s) = \left(\frac{1}{2\pi N}\right)^{n/2} \int \exp\left\{-\frac{1}{N_0} \int_0^T [x(t) - s(t)]^2 \, dt\right\} dP_S(s)$$

(52)

$$= \left(\frac{1}{2\pi N}\right)^{n/2} \exp\left[-\frac{1}{N_0} \int_0^T x^2 \, dt\right] \int \exp\left[-\frac{1}{N_0} \int_0^T s^2 \, dt\right] \exp\left[\frac{2}{N_0} \int_0^T xs \, dt\right] dP_S(s).$$

The factor $\exp\left[-(1/N_0) \int_0^T x^2(t) \, dt\right] = \exp\left[-(1/2N) \sum x_i^2\right]$ can be brought out of the integral since it does not depend on s, the variable of integration. Note that the integral

$$\int_0^T s(t)^2 \, dt = \frac{1}{2W} \sum s_i^2 = E(s)$$

(53)

is the energy* of the expected signal, while

$$\int_0^T x(t)s(t) \, dt = \frac{1}{2W} \sum x_i s_i$$

(54)

is the cross correlation between the expected signal and the receiver input.

4.3 Likelihood ratio with Gaussian noise

Likelihood ratio is defined as the ratio of the probability density functions $f_{SN}(x)$ and $f_N(x)$. With white Gaussian noise it is obtained by dividing Eq. (51) and (52) by (46) and (48) respectively:

$$l(x) = \int \exp\left[-\frac{E(s)}{N_0}\right] \exp\left[\frac{1}{N} \sum_{i=1}^{n} x_i s_i\right] dP_S(s),$$

(55)

or

$$l(x) = \int \exp\left[-\frac{E(s)}{N_0}\right] \exp\left[\frac{2}{N_0} \int_0^T x(t)s(t) \, dt\right] dP_S(s).$$

(56)

If the signal is known exactly or completely specified, the probability for that signal is unity, and the probability for any set of possible signals not containing s is zero. Then the likelihood ratio becomes

$$l_s(x) = \exp\left[-\frac{E(s)}{N_0}\right] \exp\left[\frac{1}{N} \sum_{i=1}^{n} x_i s_i\right],$$

(57)

or

$$l_s(x) = \exp\left[-\frac{E(s)}{N_0}\right] \exp\left[\frac{2}{N_0} \int_0^T x(t)s(t) \, dt\right].$$

(58)

Thus the general formulas (55) and (56) for likelihood ratio state that $l(x)$ is the weighted

* This assumes that the circuit impedance is normalized to one ohm.

average of $l_s(x)$ over the set of all signals, i.e.,

$$l(x) = \int l_s(x) \, dP_S(s). \tag{59}$$

An equipment which calculates the likelihood ratio $l(x)$ for each receiver input x is the optimum receiver. The form of equation (58) suggests one form which this equipment might take. First, for each possible expected signal s, the individual likelihood ratio $l_s(x)$ is calculated. Then these numbers are averaged. Since the set of expected signals is often infinite, this direct method is usually impractical. It is frequently possible in particular cases to obtain by mathematical operations on Eq. (58) a different form for $l(x)$ which can be recognized as the response of a realizable electronic equipment, simpler than the equipment specified by the direct method. It is essentially this which is done in the following paragraphs.

If the distribution function $P_S(s)$ depends on various parameters such as carrier phase, signal energy, or carrier frequency, and if the distributions in these parameters are independent, the expression for likelihood ratio can be simplified somewhat. If these parameters are indicated by $r_1, r_2, \ldots, r_n$, and the associated probability density functions are denoted by $f_1(r_1), f_2(r_2), \ldots, f_n(r_n)$, then

$$dP_S(s) = f_1(r_1) \cdots f_n(r_n) \, dr_1 \cdots dr_n.$$

The likelihood ratio becomes

$$l(x) = \int \cdots \int l_s(x) f_1(r_1) \cdots f_n(r_n) \, dr_1 \cdots dr_n$$

$$= \int \left\{ f_n(r_n) \cdots \left[\int f_1(r_1) l_s(x) \, dr_1 \right] \cdots \right\} dr_n. \tag{60}$$

Thus the likelihood ratio can be found by averaging $l_s(x)$ with respect to the parameters.

4.4 The case of a signal known exactly

The likelihood ratio for the case when the signal is known exactly has already been presented in Section 4.3:

$$l(x) = \exp \left[-\frac{E}{N_0} \right] \exp \left[\frac{1}{N} \sum_{i=1}^{n} x_i s_i \right], \tag{61}$$

$$l(x) = \exp \left[-\frac{E}{N_0} \right] \exp \left[\frac{2}{N_0} \int_0^T x(t) s(t) \, dt \right]. \tag{62}$$

As the first step in finding the distribution functions for $l(x)$, it is convenient to find the distribution for $(1/N) \sum x_i s_i$ when there is noise alone. Then the input $x = (x_1, x_2, \ldots, x_n)$ is due to white Gaussian noise. It can be seen from Eq. (46) that each x_i has a normal distribution with zero mean and variance $N = WN_0$ and that the x_i are independent. Because the s_i are constants depending on the signal to be detected, $s = (s_1, s_2, \ldots, s_n)$, each summand $(x_i s_i)/N$ has a normal distribution with mean s_i/N times the mean of x_i, and with variance $(s_i/N)^2$ times the variance of x_i, which are zero and s_i^2/N respectively. Because the x_i are independent, the summands $(s_i x_i)/N$ are independent, each with normal distribution, and therefore their sum has a normal distribution with mean the sum of the means—i.e., zero—and variance the sum of the variances.

$$\sum \frac{s_i^2}{N} = \frac{2WE(s)}{N} = \frac{2E}{N_0} = 2 \times \frac{\text{Signal Energy}}{\text{Noise Power Per Unit Bandwidth}}. \tag{63}$$

The distribution for $(1/N) \sum x_i s_i$ with noise alone is thus normal with zero mean and variance $2E/N_0$. Recalling from Eq. (61)

$$l(x) = \exp\left[-\frac{E}{N_0} + \frac{1}{N}\sum x_i s_i\right], \tag{64}$$

one sees that the distribution for $(1/N) \sum x_i s_i$ can be used directly by introducing α defined by

$$\beta = \exp\left[-\frac{E}{N_0} + \alpha\right], \quad \text{or} \quad \alpha = \frac{E}{N_0} + \ln \beta. \tag{65}$$

The inequality $l(x) \geq \beta$ is equivalent to $(1/N) \sum x_i s_i \geq \alpha$, and therefore

$$F_N(\beta) = \sqrt{\frac{N_0}{4\pi E}} \int_\alpha^\infty \exp\left[-\frac{1}{2}\frac{N_0}{2E}y^2\right] dy. \tag{66}$$

The distribution for the case of signal plus noise can be found by using Eq. (19), which states that

$$\left\{\frac{dP_{SN}[A(\beta)]}{dP_N[A(\beta)]}\right\}_{\text{at } \beta=\beta_0} = \beta_0. \tag{67}$$

Because these probabilities are equal to the complementary distribution functions for likelihood ratio, this can be written as

$$dF_{SN}(\beta) = \beta \, dF_N(\beta). \tag{68}$$

Differentiating Eq. (66),

$$dF_N(\beta) = -\sqrt{\frac{N_0}{4\pi E}} \exp\left[-\frac{N_0\alpha^2}{4E}\right] d\alpha, \tag{69}$$

and combining (65), (68), and (69), one obtains

$$dF_{SN}(\beta) = -\sqrt{\frac{N_0}{4\pi E}} \exp\left[-\frac{E}{N_0} + \alpha - \frac{N_0\alpha^2}{4E}\right] d\alpha. \tag{70}$$

Thus,

$$F_{SN}(\beta) = \sqrt{\frac{N_0}{4\pi E}} \int_\alpha^\infty \exp\left[-\frac{N_0}{4E}\left(y - \frac{2E}{N_0}\right)^2\right] dy. \tag{71}$$

In summary, α and therefore $\ln \beta$, have normal distributions with signal plus noise as well as with noise alone; the variance of each distribution is $2E/N_0$, and the difference of the means is $2E/N_0$.

The receiver operating characteristic curves in Figs. 2 and 3* are plotted for any case in which $\ln l$ has a normal distribution with the same variance both with noise alone and with signal plus noise. The parameter d in this figure is equal to the square of

* In Fig. 3, the receiver operating characteristic curves are plotted on "double-probability" paper. On this paper both axes are linear in the error function

$$\text{erf}(x) = (1/\sqrt{2\pi}) \cdot \int_{-\infty}^x \exp[-t^2/2]\, dt;$$

this makes the receiver operating characteristic straight lines.

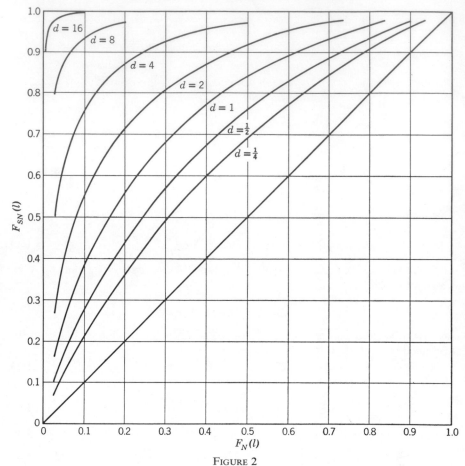

FIGURE 2

Receiver operating characteristic. ln l is a normal deviate with
$$\sigma_N^2 = \sigma_{SN}^2,\ (M_{SN} - M_N)^2 = d \cdot \sigma_N^2.$$

the difference of the means, divided by the variance. These receiver operating characteristic curves apply to the case of the signal known exactly, with $d = 2E/N_0$.

Eq. (62) describes what the ideal receiver should do for this case. The essential operation in the receiver is obtaining the correlation, $\int_0^T s(t)x(t)\,dt$. The other operations, multiplying by a constant, adding a constant, and taking the exponential function, can be taken care of simply in the calibration of the receiver output. Electronic means of obtaining cross correlation have been developed recently [13].

If the form of the signal is simple, there is a simple way to obtain this cross correlation [6, 7]. Suppose $h(t)$ is the impulse response of a filter. The response $e_0(t)$ of the filter to a voltage $x(t)$ is

$$e_0(t) = \int_{-\infty}^{t} x(\tau)\,h(t - \tau)\,d\tau. \tag{72}$$

If a filter can be synthesized so that

$$h(t) = s(T - t), \quad 0 \le t \le T$$

$$h(t) = 0, \quad \text{otherwise,}$$

(73)

then

$$e_0(T) = \int_0^T x(\tau)s(\tau)\, d\tau,$$

(74)

so that the response of this filter at time T is the cross correlation required. Thus, the ideal receiver consists simply of a filter and amplifiers.

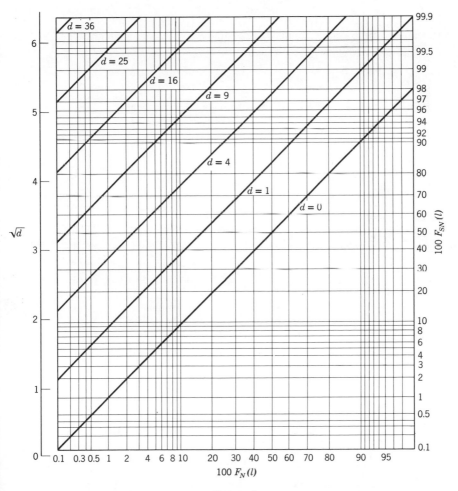

FIGURE 3

Receiver operating characteristic. ln l is a normal deviate, $\sigma_{SN}^2 = \sigma_N^2$, $(M_{SN} - M_N)^2 = d\sigma_N^2$.

It should be noted that this filter is the same, except for a constant factor, as that specified when one asks for the filter which maximizes peak signal to average noise-power ratio [14].

4.5 *Signal known except for carrier phase*

The signal ensemble considered in this section consists of all signals which differ from a given amplitude and frequency modulated signal only in their carrier phase, and all carrier phases are assumed equally likely.

$$s(t) = f(t) \cos [\omega t + \phi(t) - \theta]. \tag{75}$$

Since the unknown phase angle θ has a uniform distribution,

$$dP_S(\theta) = \frac{1}{2\pi} d\theta. \tag{76}$$

The likelihood ratio can be found by applying Eq. (56), and since the signal energy $E(s)$ is the same for all values of the carrier phase θ,

$$l(x) = \exp\left[-\frac{E}{N_0}\right] \int \exp\left[\frac{1}{N} \sum x_i s_i\right] dP_S(s). \tag{77}$$

Expanding s into the coefficients of $\cos \theta$ and $\sin \theta$ will be helpful:

$$s(t) = f(t) \cos [\omega t + \phi(t)] \cos \theta + f(t) \sin [\omega t + \phi(t)] \sin \theta, \tag{78}$$

and

$$\frac{1}{N} \sum x_i s_i = \cos \theta \frac{1}{N} \sum x_i f(t_i) \cos [\omega t_i + \phi(t_i)]$$

$$+ \sin \theta \frac{1}{N} \sum x_i f(t_i) \sin [\omega t_i + \phi(t_i)]. * \tag{79}$$

Because we wish to integrate with respect to θ to find the likelihood ratio, it is easiest to introduce parameters similar to polar coordinates (r, θ_0) such that

$$\frac{1}{N} r \cos \theta_0 = \frac{1}{N} \sum x_i f(t_i) \cos [\omega t_i + \phi(t_i)]$$

$$\frac{1}{N} r \sin \theta_0 = \frac{1}{N} \sum x_i f(t_i) \sin [\omega t_i + \phi(t_i)], \tag{80}$$

and therefore

$$\frac{1}{N} \sum x_i s_i = \frac{r}{N} \cos (\theta - \theta_0). \tag{81}$$

Using this form the likelihood ratio becomes

$$l(x) = \exp\left[-\frac{E}{N_0}\right] \int_0^{2\pi} \exp\left[\frac{r}{N} \cos (\theta - \theta_0)\right] \frac{d\theta}{2\pi}$$

$$= \exp\left[-\frac{E}{N_0}\right] I_0\left(\frac{r}{N}\right), \tag{82}$$

where I_0 is the Bessel function of zero order and pure imaginary argument.

* t_i denotes the ith sampling time, i.e., $t_i = i/2W$.

I_0 is a strictly monotone increasing function, and therefore the likelihood ratio will be greater than a value β if and only if r/N is greater than some value corresponding to β.

In the previous section it was shown that the sum $(1/N) \Sigma x_i s_i$ has a normal distribution with zero mean and variance $2E/N_0$ if the receiver input $x(t)$ is due to noise alone; E is the energy of the signal known exactly, $s(t)$, and N_0 is the noise power per cycle. Since $f(t) \cos [\omega t + \phi(t)]$ and $f(t) \sin [\omega t + \phi(t)]$ are signals known exactly, both $(r/N) \cos \phi_0$ and $(r/N) \sin \phi_0$ have normal distributions with zero mean and variance $2E/N_0$. The probability that due to noise alone

$$\frac{r}{N} = \sqrt{\left(\frac{r}{N} \cos \theta_0\right)^2 + \left(\frac{r}{N} \sin \theta_0\right)^2}$$

will exceed any fixed value, is given by the well known chi-square distribution for two degrees of freedom, $K_2(\alpha^2)$. The proper normalization yielding zero mean and unit variance requires that the variable be

$$\left(\frac{r}{N}\right) \sqrt{\frac{N_0}{2E(s)}},$$

that is

$$P_N\left(\frac{r}{N} \sqrt{\frac{N_0}{2E}} \geq \alpha\right) = K_2(\alpha^2) = \exp\left[-\frac{\alpha^2}{2}\right].^* \tag{83}$$

If α is defined by the equation

$$\beta = \exp\left[-\frac{E}{N_0}\right] I_0\left(\sqrt{\frac{2E}{N_0}} \alpha\right), \tag{84}$$

the distribution for $l(x)$ in the presence of noise alone is in the simple form

$$F_N(\beta) = \exp\left[-\frac{\alpha^2}{2}\right]. \tag{85}$$

It follows from (85) that

$$dF_N(\beta) = -\alpha \exp\left[-\frac{\alpha^2}{2}\right] d\alpha. \tag{86}$$

If in equation (68), namely

$$\beta \, dF_N(\beta) = dF_{SN}(\beta), \tag{87}$$

β is replaced by the expression given in (84) and $dF_N(\beta)$ is replaced by that given in (86), then

$$dF_{SN}(\beta) = -\exp\left[-\frac{E}{N_0}\right] \alpha \exp\left[-\frac{\alpha^2}{2}\right] I_0\left(\sqrt{\frac{2E}{N_0}} \alpha\right) d\alpha \tag{88}$$

is obtained. Integration of (88) yields

$$F_{SN}(\beta) = \exp\left[-\frac{E}{N_0}\right] \int_\alpha^\infty \alpha \exp\left[-\frac{\alpha^2}{2}\right] I_0\left(\sqrt{\frac{2E}{N_0}} \alpha\right) d\alpha. \tag{89}$$

* The symbol $P(x \geq \alpha)$ denotes the probability that the variable x is not less than the constant α.

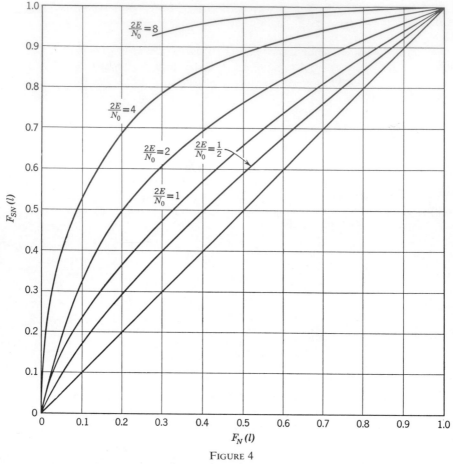

$$\text{FIGURE 4}$$

Receiver operating characteristic. Signal known except for phase.

Eqs. (85) and (89) yield the receiver operating characteristic in parametric form, and Eq. (84) gives the associated operating levels [15]. These are graphed in Fig. 4 for some of the same values of signal energy to noise power per unit bandwidth as were used when the phase angle was known exactly, Figs. 2 and 3, so that the effect of knowing the phase can be easily seen.

If the signal is sufficiently simple so that a filter could be synthesized to match the expected signal for a given carrier phase θ as in the case of a signal known exactly, then there is a simple way to design a receiver to obtain likelihood ratio. For simplicity let us consider only amplitude modulated signals $[\phi(t) = 0]$ in Eq. (75). Let us also choose $\theta = 0$. (Any phase could have been chosen.) Then the filter has impulse response

$$
\begin{aligned}
h(t) &= f(T - t) \cos [\omega(T - t)], & 0 \le t \le T, \\
&= 0, & \text{otherwise.}
\end{aligned}
\tag{90}
$$

The output of the filter in response to $x(t)$ is then

$$e_0(t) = \int_{-\infty}^{t} x(\tau)h(t - \tau)\, d\tau = \int_{t-T}^{t} x(\tau)f(\tau + T - t)\cos \omega(\tau + T - t)\, d\tau$$

$$= \cos \omega(T - t) \int_{t-T}^{t} x(\tau) f(\tau + T - t) \cos \omega\tau\, d\tau$$

$$- \sin \omega(T - t) \int_{t-T}^{t} x(\tau)f(\tau + T - t) \sin \omega\tau\, d\tau. \tag{91}$$

The envelope of the filter output will be the square root of the sum of the squares of the integrals,* and the envelope at time T will be proportional to r/N, since

$$\left(\frac{r}{2W}\right)^2 = \left[\int_0^T x(\tau) f(\tau) \cos \omega\tau\, d\tau\right]^2 + \left[\int_0^T x(\tau) f(\tau) \sin \omega\tau\, d\tau\right]^2, \tag{92}$$

which can be identified as the square of the envelope of $e_0(t)$ at time T. If the input $x(t)$ passes through the filter with an impulse response given by Eq. (90), then through a linear detector, the output will be $(N_0/2)r/N$ at time T. Because the likelihood ratio, Eq. (82), is a known monotone function of r/N, the output can be calibrated to read the likelihood ratio of the input.

4.6 Signal consisting of a sample of white Gaussian noise

Suppose the values of the signal voltage at the sample points are independent Gaussian random variables with zero mean and variance S, the signal power. The probability density due to signal plus noise is also Gaussian, since signal plus noise is the sum of two Gaussian random variables:

$$f_{SN}(x) = \left(\frac{1}{2\pi(N + S)}\right)^{n/2} \exp\left[-\frac{1}{2}\frac{1}{N + S}\sum x_i^2\right], \tag{93}$$

where $n = 2WT$.

The likelihood ratio is

$$l(x) = \left(\frac{N}{N + S}\right)^{n/2} \exp\left[\frac{1}{2}\frac{1}{N}\sum x_i^2 - \frac{1}{2}\frac{1}{N + S}\sum x_i^2\right]. \tag{94}$$

In determining the distribution functions for l, it is convenient to introduce the parameter α, defined by the equation

$$\beta = \left(\frac{N}{N + S}\right)^{n/2} \exp\left(\frac{S}{N + S}\frac{\alpha^2}{2}\right). \tag{95}$$

Then the condition $l(x) \geq \beta$ is equivalent to the condition that $(1/N) \sum x_i^2 \geq \alpha^2$. In the presence of noise alone the random variables $x_i/\sqrt{N}$ have zero mean and unit variance, and they are independent. Therefore, the probability that the sum of the squares of these variables will exceed α^2 is the chi-square distribution with n degrees of freedom, i.e.,

$$F_N(\beta) = K_n(\alpha^2). \tag{96}$$

* If the line spectrum of $s(t)$ is zero at zero frequency and at all frequencies equal to or greater than $2\omega/2\pi$, then it can be shown that these integrals contain no frequencies as high as $\omega/2\pi$.

Similarly, in the presence of signal plus noise the random variables $x_i/\sqrt{N+S}$ have zero mean and unit variance. The condition $(1/N)\sum x_i^2 \geq \alpha^2$ is the same as requiring that $[1/(N+S)]\sum x_i^2 \geq [N/(N+S)]\alpha^2$, and again making use of the chi-square distribution,

$$F_{SN}(\beta) = K_n\left(\frac{N}{N+S}\alpha^2\right). \tag{97}$$

For large values of n, the chi-square distribution is approximately normal over the center portion; more precisely [16], for $\alpha^2 \gg 0$,

$$F_N(\beta) = K_n(\alpha^2) \approx \frac{1}{\sqrt{2\pi}} \int_{\sqrt{2\alpha^2}-\sqrt{2n-1}}^{\infty} \exp\left[-\frac{1}{2}y^2\right] dy, \tag{98}$$

and

$$F_{SN}(\beta) = K_n\left(\frac{N}{N+S}\alpha^2\right) \approx \frac{1}{\sqrt{2\pi}} \int_{\sqrt{\frac{2N\alpha^2}{N+S}}-\sqrt{2n-1}}^{\infty} \exp\left[-\frac{1}{2}y^2\right] dy. \tag{99}$$

If the signal energy is small compared to that of the noise, $\sqrt{N/(N+S)}$ is nearly unity and both distributions have nearly the same variance. Then Figs. 2 and 3 apply to this case too, with the value of d given by

$$d = (2n-1)\left(1-\sqrt{\frac{N}{N+S}}\right)^2. \tag{100}$$

For these small signal to noise ratios and large samples, there is a simple relation between signal to noise ratio, the number of samples, and the detection index d.

$$1 - \sqrt{\frac{N}{N+S}} \approx \frac{1}{2}\frac{S}{N} \quad \text{for } \frac{S}{N} \ll 1,$$

and

$$d \approx \frac{nS^2}{2N^2} \tag{101}$$

Two signal to noise ratios, $(S/N)_1$ and $(S/N)_2$, will give approximately the same operating characteristic if the corresponding numbers of sample points, n_1 and n_2, satisfy

$$\frac{n_1}{n_2} = \frac{\left(\frac{S}{N}\right)_2^2}{\left(\frac{S}{N}\right)_1^2}. \tag{102}$$

By Eq. (94), the likelihood is a monotone function of $\sum x_i^2$. But the output of an energy detector,

$$e_0(t) = \int_0^T [x(t)]^2 \, dt = \frac{1}{2W}\sum x_i^2 \tag{103}$$

is proportional to $\sum x_i^2$. Therefore an energy detector can be calibrated to read likelihood ratio, and hence can be used as an optimum receiver in this case.

4.7 *Video design of a broad band receiver*

The problem considered in this section is represented schematically in Fig. 5. The signals and noise are assumed to have passed through a band pass filter, and at the output of the filter, point A on the diagram, they are assumed to be limited in spectrum to a band of width W and center frequency $\omega/2\pi > W/2$. The noise is assumed to be Gaussian noise with a uniform spectrum over the band. The signals and noise then pass through a linear detector. The output of the detector is the envelope of the signals and noise as they appeared at point A; all knowledge of the phase of the receiver input is lost at point B. The signals and noise as they appear at point B are considered receiver inputs, and the theory of signal detectability is applied to these video inputs to ascertain the best video design and the performance of such a system. The mathematical description of the signals and noise will be given for the signals and noise as they appear at point A. The envelope functions, which appear at point B, will be derived, and the likelihood ratio and its distribution will be found for these envelope functions.

The only case which will be considered here is the case in which the amplitude of the signal as it would appear at point A is a known function of time.

Any function at point A will be band limited to a band of width W and center frequency $\omega/2\pi > W/2$. Any such function $f(t)$ can be expanded as follows:

$$f(t) = x(t) \cos \omega t + y(t) \sin \omega t, \tag{105}$$

where $x(t)$ and $y(t)$ are band limited to frequencies no higher than $W/2$, and hence can themselves* be expanded by sampling plan C, yielding

$$f(t) = \sum_i \left[x\left(\frac{i}{W}\right) \psi_i(t) \cos \omega t + y\left(\frac{i}{W}\right) \psi_i(t) \sin \omega t \right]. \tag{106}$$

The amplitude of the function $f(t)$ is

$$r(t) = \sqrt{[x(t)]^2 + [y(t)]^2}, \tag{107}$$

and thus the amplitude at the ith sampling point is

$$r\left(\frac{i}{W}\right) = r_i = \sqrt{x_i^2 + y_i^2}. \tag{108}$$

The angle

$$\theta_i = \arctan \frac{y_i}{x_i} = \arccos \frac{x_i}{r_i} \tag{109}$$

might be considered the phase of $f(t)$ at the ith sampling point. The function $f(t)$ then might be described by giving the r_i and θ_i rather than the x_i and y_i.

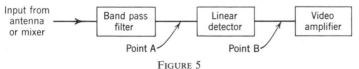

Input from antenna or mixer → Band pass filter → Linear detector → Video amplifier

Point A   Point B

FIGURE 5
Block diagram of a broad band receiver.

* Because any function $f(t)$ at A has no frequency greater than $(\omega/2\pi) + (W/2)$, the usual sampling plan C might have been used on $f(t)$. However, the distribution in noise alone, $f_N(x_i)$, would probably not be applicable.

Let us denote by x_i, y_i, or r_i, θ_i, the sample values for a receiver input after the filter (i.e., at the point A in Fig. 5). Let a_i, b_i, or f_i, ϕ_i, denote the sample values for the signal as it would appear at point A if there were no noise. The envelope of the signal, hence the amplitude sample values f_i, are assumed known. Let us denote by $F_S(\phi_1, \phi_2, \ldots, \phi_{n/2})$ the distribution function of the phase sample values ϕ_i. The probability density function for the input at A when there is white Gaussian noise and no signal, with $n = 2WT$, is

$$f_N(x, y) = \left(\frac{1}{2\pi N}\right)^{n/2} \exp\left[-\frac{1}{2N}\left(\sum_{i=1}^{n/2} x_i^2 + \sum_{i=1}^{n/2} y_i^2\right)\right], \tag{110}$$

and for signal plus noise, it is

$$f_{SN}(x, y) = \left(\frac{1}{2\pi N}\right)^{n/2} \int_R \exp\left[-\frac{1}{2N}\left(\sum_{i=1}^{n/2} (x_i - a_i)^2 + \sum_{i=1}^{n/2} (y_i - b_i)^2\right)\right] dP_S(a_i b_i). \tag{111}$$

Expressed in terms of the (r, θ) sample values, Eq. (110) and Eq. (111) become

$$f_N(r, \theta) = \left(\frac{1}{2\pi N}\right)^{n/2} \prod_{i=1}^{n/2} r_i \exp\left[-\frac{1}{2N}\sum_{i=1}^{n/2} r_i^2\right], \tag{112}$$

and

$$f_{SN}(r, \theta) = \left(\frac{1}{2\pi N}\right)^{n/2} \prod_{i=1}^{n/2} r_i \int_R \exp\left\{-\frac{1}{2N}\sum_{i=1}^{n/2} [r_i^2 + f_i^2 - 2r_i f_i \cos(\theta_i - \phi_i)]\right\}$$
$$dF_S(\phi_1, \ldots, \phi_{n/2}). \tag{113}$$

The factors Πr_i are introduced because they are the Jacobian of the transformation from the x, y sampling plan to the r, θ sampling plan [16].*

The probability density function for r alone, i.e., the density function for the output of the detector, is obtained simply by integrating the density functions for r and θ with respect to θ.

$$f_N(r) = \int_0^{2\pi} \int_0^{2\pi} \cdots \int_0^{2\pi} f_N(r_i, \theta_i)\, d\theta_1\, d\theta_2 \cdots d\theta_{n/2},$$

or

$$f_N(r) = \left(\frac{1}{N}\right)^{n/2} \prod_{i=1}^{n/2} r_i \exp\left[-\frac{1}{2N}\sum_{i=1}^{n/2} r_i^2\right], \tag{114}$$

and

$$f_{SN}(r) = \int_0^{2\pi} \int_0^{2\pi} \cdots \int_0^{2\pi} f_{SN}(r_i, \theta_i)\, d\theta_1\, d\theta_2 \cdots d\theta_{n/2},$$

or

$$f_{SN}(r) = \left(\frac{1}{N}\right)^{n/2} \int_R \prod_{i=1}^{n/2} r_i \exp\left[-\frac{1}{2N}\sum_{i=1}^{n/2} (r_i^2 + f_i^2)\right] \prod_{i=1}^{n/2} I_0\left(\frac{r_i f_i}{N}\right) dF(\phi_1, \phi_2 \cdots \phi_{n/2}),$$

or

$$f_{SN}(r) = \left(\frac{1}{N}\right)^{n/2} \prod_{i=1}^{n/2} r_i I_0\left(\frac{r_i f_i}{N}\right) \exp\left[-\frac{1}{2N}\sum_{i=1}^{n/2} (r_i^2 + f_i^2)\right]. \tag{115}$$

* For example, in two dimensions, $f_N(x, y)\, dx\, dy = f_N(r, \theta) r\, dr\, d\theta$.

Notice that the probability density for r is completely independent of the distribution which the ϕ_i had; all information about the phase of the signals has been lost.

The likelihood ratio for a video input, $r(t)$, is

$$l(r) = \frac{f_{SN}(r)}{f_N(r)} = \exp\left[-\frac{1}{2N}\sum_{i=1}^{n/2} f_i^2\right] \prod_{i=1}^{n/2} I_0\left(\frac{r_i f_i}{N}\right). \tag{116}$$

Again it is more convenient to work with the logarithm of the likelihood ratio. Thus,

$$\frac{1}{2N}\sum_{i=1}^{n/2} f_i^2 = \frac{W}{2N}\int [f(t)]^2\, dt = \frac{E}{N_0}, \quad \text{and} \tag{117}$$

$$\ln l(r) = -\frac{E}{N_0} + \sum_{i=1}^{n/2} \ln I_0\left(\frac{r_i f_i}{N}\right), \tag{118}$$

which is approximately

$$\ln l[r(t)] = -\frac{E}{N_0} + W\int_0^T \ln I_0\left[\frac{r(t) f(t)}{N}\right] dt. \tag{119}$$

The function $\ln I_0(x)$ is approximately the parabola $x^2/4$ for small values of x and is nearly linear for large values of x. Thus, the expression for likelihood ratio might be approximated by

$$\ln l[r(t)] = -\frac{E}{N_0} + \frac{W}{4N^2}\int_0^T [r(t)]^2 [f(t)]^2\, dt \tag{120}$$

for small signals, and by

$$\ln l[r(t)] = C_1 + C_2\int_0^T r(t) f(t)\, dt \tag{121}$$

for large signals, where C_1 and C_2 are chosen to approximate $\ln I_0$ best in the desired range.

The integrals in Eqs. (120) and (121) can be interpreted as cross correlations. Thus the optimum receiver for weak signals is a square law detector, followed by a correlator which finds the cross correlation between the detector output and $[f(t)]^2$, the square of the envelope of the expected signal. For the case of large signal to noise ratio, the optimum receiver is a linear detector, followed by a correlator which has for its output the cross correlation of the detector output and $f(t)$, the amplitude of the expected signal.

The distribution function for $l(r)$ cannot be found easily in this case. The approximation developed here will apply to the receiver designed for low signal to noise ratio, since this is the case of most interest in detection studies. An analogous approximation for the large signal to noise ratios would be even easier to derive.

First we shall find the mean and standard deviation for the distribution of the logarithm of the likelihood ratio as shown above,

$$\ln l(r) \approx -\frac{1}{2N}\sum f_i^2 + \frac{1}{4N^2}\sum_{i=1}^{n/2} r_i^2 f_i^2, \tag{122}$$

for the case of small signal to noise ratio. The probability density functions for each r_i are

$$g_{SN}(r_i) = \frac{r_i}{N} \exp\left[-\frac{r_i^2 + f_i^2}{2N}\right] I_0\left[\frac{r_i f_i}{N}\right],$$

and

$$g_N(r_i) = \frac{r_i}{N} \exp\left[-\frac{r_i^2}{2N}\right].$$

(123)

The notation $g_N(r_i)$ and $g_{SN}(r_i)$ is used to distinguish these from the joint distributions of all the r_i which were previously called $f_N(r)$ and $f_{SN}(r)$. The mean of each term $r_i^2 f_i^2 / 4N^2$ in the sum in Eq. (122) is

$$\mu_{SN}\left(\frac{r_i^2 f_i^2}{4N^2}\right) = \frac{f_i^2}{4N} \int_0^\infty \frac{r_i^2}{N} g_{SN}(r_i) \, dr_i,$$

(124)

or

$$\mu_{SN}\left(\frac{r_i^2 f_i^2}{4N^2}\right) = \frac{f_i^2}{4N} \int_0^\infty \frac{r_i^3}{N^2} \exp\left[-\frac{(r_i^2 + f_i^2)}{2N}\right] I_0\left(\frac{r_i f_i}{N}\right) \, dr_i.$$

Similarly,

(124)

$$\mu_N\left(\frac{r_i^2 f_i^2}{4N^2}\right) = \frac{f_i^2}{4N} \int_0^\infty \frac{r_i^2}{N} g_N(r_i) \, dr_i = \frac{f_i^2}{4N} \int_0^\infty \frac{r_i^3}{N^2} \exp\left[-\frac{r_i^2}{2N}\right] \, dr_i.$$

The second moment of each term $r_i^2 f_i^2 / 4N^2$ is

$$\mu_{SN}\left(\frac{r_i^4 f_i^4}{16N^4}\right) = \frac{f_i^4}{16N^2} \int_0^\infty \frac{r_i^4}{N^2} g_{SN}(r_i) \, dr_i,$$

or

$$\mu_{SN}\left(\frac{r_i^4 f_i^4}{16N^4}\right) = \frac{f_i^4}{16N^2} \int_0^\infty \frac{r_i^5}{N^3} \exp\left[\frac{-(r_i^2 + f_i^2)}{2N}\right] I_0\left(\frac{r_i f_i}{N}\right) \, dr_i.$$

(125)

Similarly,

$$\mu_N\left(\frac{r_i^4 f_i^4}{16N^4}\right) = \frac{f_i^4}{16N^2} \int_0^\infty \frac{r_i^4}{N^2} g_N(r_i) \, dr_i,$$

or

$$\mu_N\left(\frac{r_i^4 f_i^4}{16N^4}\right) = \frac{f_i^4}{16N^2} \int_0^\infty \frac{r_i^5}{N^3} \exp\left[-\frac{r_i^2}{2N}\right] \, dr_i.$$

The integrals for the case of noise alone can be evaluated easily:

$$\mu_N\left(\frac{r_i^2 f_i^2}{4N^2}\right) = \frac{f_i^2}{2N},$$

and

(126)

$$\mu_N\left(\frac{r_i^4 f_i^4}{16N^4}\right) = \frac{f_i^4}{2N^2}.$$

The integrals for the case of signal plus noise can be evaluated in terms of the confluent hypergeometric function, which turns out for the cases above to reduce to a simple polynomial. The required formulas are collected in convenient form in *Threshold Signals* [5] on page 174. The results are

$$\mu_{SN}\left(\frac{r_i^2 f_i^2}{4N^2}\right) = \frac{1}{2}\frac{f_i^2}{N}\left(1 + \frac{f_i^2}{2N}\right),$$

and (127)

$$\mu_{SN}\left(\frac{r_i^4 f_i^4}{16N^4}\right) = \frac{1}{2}\frac{f_i^4}{N^2}\left(1 + \frac{f_i^2}{N} + \frac{f_i^4}{8N^2}\right).$$

Since

$$\sigma^2(Z) = \mu(Z^2) - [\mu(Z)]^2, \tag{128}$$

the variances of $r_i^2 f_i^2/4N^2$ are

$$\sigma_{SN}^2\left(\frac{r_i^2 f_i^2}{4N^2}\right) = \frac{1}{4}\frac{f_i^4}{N^2}\left(1 + \frac{f_i^2}{N}\right),$$

and (129)

$$\sigma_N^2\left(\frac{r_i^2 f_i^2}{4N^2}\right) = \frac{f_i^4}{4N^2}.$$

For the sum of independent random variables, the mean is the sum of the means of the terms and the variance is the sum of the variances. Therefore the means of $\ln l(r)$ are

$$\mu_{SN}[\ln l(r)] = -\frac{1}{2N}\sum_{i=1}^{n/2} f_i^2 + \sum_{i=1}^{n/2}\left(\frac{1}{2}\frac{f_i^2}{N} + \frac{1}{4}\frac{f_i^4}{N^2}\right) = \sum_{i=1}^{n/2}\frac{f_i^4}{4N^2}$$

and (130)

$$\mu_N[\ln l(r)] = -\sum_{i=1}^{n/2}\frac{f_i^2}{2N} + \frac{1}{2}\sum_{i=1}^{n/2}\frac{f_i^2}{N} = 0,$$

and the variances of $\ln l(r)$ are

$$\sigma_{SN}^2[\ln l(r)] = \sum_{i=1}^{n/2}\left(\frac{1}{4}\frac{f_i^4}{N^2} + \frac{1}{4}\frac{f_i^6}{N^3}\right)$$

and (131)

$$\sigma_N^2[\ln l(r)] = \sum_{i=1}^{n/2}\frac{f_i^4}{4N^2}.$$

If the distribution functions of $\ln l(r)$ can be assumed to be normal, they can be obtained immediately from the mean and standard deviation of the logarithm of likelihood ratio.

Let us consider the case in which the incoming signal is a rectangular pulse which is M/W seconds long.* The energy of the pulse is half its duration times the amplitude squared of its envelope, for a normalized circuit impedance of one ohm.

* The problem of finding the distribution for the sum of M independent random variables, each with a probability density function $f(x) = x \exp\left[-(\frac{1}{2})(x^2 + a^2)\right]I_0(ax)$ arises in the unpublished report by J. I. Marcum, *A Statistical Theory of Target Detection by Pulsed Radar: Mathematical Appendix*, Project Rand Report R-113. Marcum gives an exact expression for this distribution which is useful only for small values of M, and an approximation in Gram-Charlier series which is more accurate than the normal approximation given here. Marcum's expressions could be used in this case, and in the case presented in Section 4.6.

Thus of the WT numbers (f_i), there are M consecutive ones which are not zero. These are given by

$$f_i = \sqrt{\frac{2EW}{M}}, \tag{132}$$

where E is the pulse energy at point A in Fig. 5 in the absence of noise. For this case, Eq. (130) and Eq. (131) become

$$\mu_{SN}[\ln l(r)] = \frac{1}{M} \frac{E^2}{N_0^2},$$

$$\mu_N[\ln l(r)] = 0, \tag{133}$$

$$\sigma_{SN}^2[\ln l(r)] = \frac{E^2}{MN_0^2}\left(1 + \frac{2}{M}\frac{E}{N_0}\right),$$

and

$$\sigma_N^2[\ln l(r)] = \frac{E^2}{MN_0^2}.$$

The distribution of $\ln l(r)$ is approximately normal if M is much larger than one, for, by the central limit theorem, the distribution of a sum of M independent random variables with a common distribution must approach the normal distribution as M becomes large. The actual distribution for the case of noise alone can be calculated in this case, since the convolution integral for the $g_N(r_i)$ with itself any number of times can be expressed in closed form. The distribution of $\ln l(r)$ for signal plus noise is more nearly normal than its distribution with noise alone, since the distributions $g_{SN}(r_i)$ are more nearly normal than $g_N(r_i)$.

The receiver operating characteristic for the case $M = 16$ is plotted in Fig. 6 using the normal distribution as approximation to the true distribution. In many cases it will be found that

$$\frac{1}{M} \cdot \frac{2E}{N_0} \ll 1. \tag{134}$$

In such a case the distributions have approximately the same variance. Assuming normal distribution then leads to the curves of Figs. 2 and 3, with

$$d = \frac{1}{4M}\left(\frac{2E}{N_0}\right)^2. \tag{135}$$

4.8 A radar case

This section deals with detecting a radar target at a given range. That is, we shall assume that the signal, if it occurs, consists of a train of M pulses whose time of occurrence and envelope shape are known. The carrier phase will be assumed to have a uniform distribution for each pulse independent of all others, i.e., the pulses are incoherent.

The set of signals can be described as follows:

$$s(t) = \sum_{m=0}^{M-1} f(t + m\tau) \cos(\omega t + \theta_i), \tag{136}$$

where the M angles θ_i have independent uniform distributions, and the function f,

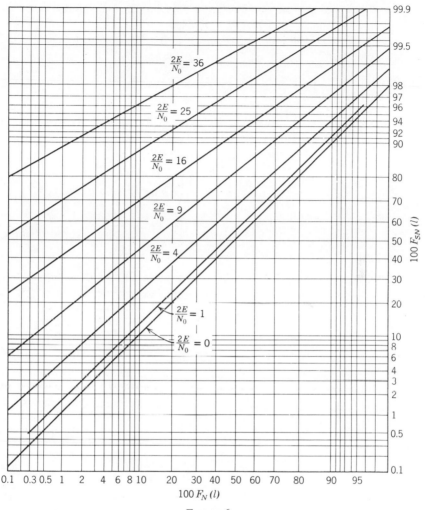

FIGURE 6

Receiver operating characteristic. Broad band receiver with optimum video design, $M = 16$.

which is the envelope of a single pulse, has the property that

$$\int_0^T f(t + i\tau) f(t + j\tau)\, dt = \frac{2E}{M}\, \delta_{ij}, \tag{137}$$

where δ_{ij} is the Kronecker delta function, which is zero if $i \neq j$, and unity if $i = j$. The time τ is the interval between pulses. Eq. (137) states that the pulses are spaced far enough so that they are orthogonal, and that the total signal energy is E.* The function $f(t)$ is also assumed to have no frequency components as high as $\omega/2\pi$.

* The factor 2 appears in (137) because $f(t)$ is the pulse envelope; the factor M appears because the total energy E is M times the energy of a single pulse.

The likelihood ratio can be obtained by applying Eq. (56). Then

$$l(x) = \int_R \exp\left[-\frac{E(s)}{N_0}\right] \exp\left[\frac{2}{N_0}\int_0^T s(t)x(t)\,dt\right] dP_S(s) \tag{138}$$

or

$$l(x) = \exp\left[-\frac{E}{N_0}\right]\int_0^{2\pi}\cdots\int_0^{2\pi}$$

$$\exp\left[\frac{2}{N_0}\int_0^T \sum_{m=0}^{M-1} f(t+m\tau)x(t)\cos(\omega t + \theta_m)\,dt\right] d\theta_0 \cdots d\theta_{M-1}. \tag{139}$$

The integral can be evaluated, as in Section 4.5, yielding

$$l(x) = \exp\left[-\frac{E}{N_0}\right]\prod_{m=0}^{M-1} I_0\left(\frac{r_m}{N}\right), \tag{140}$$

where

$$\left(\frac{r_m}{N}\right)^2 = \left[\frac{2}{N_0}\int_0^T f(t+m\tau)x(t)\cos\omega t\,dt\right]^2 + \left[\frac{2}{N_0}\int_0^T f(t+m\tau)x(t)\sin\omega t\,dt\right]^2. \tag{141}$$

This quantity r_m is almost identical with the quantity r which appeared in the discussion of the case of the signal known except for carrier phase, Section 4.5. In fact, each r_m could be obtained in a receiver in the manner described in that section. The quantity r_0 is connected with the first pulse; it could be obtained by designing an ideal filter for the signal

$$s_0(t) = f(t)\cos(\omega t + \theta) \tag{142}$$

for any value of the phase angle θ, and putting the output through a linear detector. The output will be $(N_0/2)r_0/N$ at some instant of time t_0 which is determined by the time delay of the filter. The other quantities r_m differ only in that they are associated with the pulses which come later. The output of the filter at time $t_0 + m\tau$ will be $(N_0/2)r_m/N$.

It is convenient to have the receiver calculate the logarithm of the likelihood ratio,

$$\ln l(x) = -\frac{E}{N_0} + \sum_{m=0}^{M-1} \ln I_0\left(\frac{r_m}{N}\right). \tag{143}$$

Thus the $\ln I_0(r_m/N)$ must be found for each r_m, and these M quantities must be added. As in the previous section, r_m/N will usually be small enough so that $\ln I_0(x)$ can be approximated by $x^2/4$. The quantities $\frac{1}{4}(r_m/N)^2$ can be found by using a square law detector rather than a linear detector, and the outputs of the square law detector at times $t_0, t_0 + \tau, \ldots, t_0 + (M-1)\tau$ then must be added. The ideal system thus consists of an *IF* amplifier with its passband matched to a single pulse,* a square law detector (for the threshold signal case), and an integrating device.

We shall find normal approximations for the distribution functions of the logarithm of the likelihood ratio using the approximation

$$\ln I_0\left(\frac{r_m}{N}\right) \approx \frac{r_m^2}{4N^2}, \tag{144}$$

---

* It is usually most convenient to make the ideal filter (or an approximation to it) a part of the *IF* amplifier.

which is valid for small values of r_m/N.* Substitution of (144) into (143) yields

$$\ln l \approx -\frac{E}{N_0} + \sum_{n=0}^{M-1} \frac{1}{4}\left(\frac{r_m}{N}\right)^2. \tag{145}$$

The distributions for the quantities r_m are independent; this follows from the fact that the individual pulse functions $f(t + m\tau)\cos(\omega t + \theta_m)$ are orthogonal. The distribution for each is the same as the distribution for the quantity r which appears in the discussion of the signal known except for phase; the same analysis applies to both cases. Thus, by Eq. (83)†

$$P_N\left(\frac{r_m}{N}\sqrt{\frac{N_0 M}{2E}} \geq \alpha\right) = \exp\left[-\frac{\alpha^2}{2}\right]$$

$$P_N\left(\frac{r_m}{N} \geq a\right) = \exp\left[-\frac{a^2 N_0 M}{2E}\right], \tag{146}$$

and by (89),

$$P_{SN}\left(\sqrt{\frac{N_0 M}{2E}}\frac{r_m}{N} \geq \alpha\right) = \exp\left[-\frac{E}{N_0}\right]\int_\alpha^\infty \alpha \exp\left[-\frac{\alpha^2}{2}\right]I_0\left(\alpha\sqrt{\frac{2E}{N_0 M}}\right)d\alpha, \tag{147}$$

or

$$P_{SN}\left(\frac{r_m}{N} \geq a\right) = \frac{N_0 M}{2E}\exp\left[-\frac{E}{N_0 M}\right]\int_a^\infty a \exp\left(-\frac{a^2 N_0 M}{4E}\right)I_0(a)\,da.$$

The density functions can be obtained by differentiating (146) and (147):

$$g_N\left(\frac{r_m}{N}\right) = \frac{MN_0}{2E}\left(\frac{r_m}{N}\right)\exp\left[-\left(\frac{r_m}{N}\right)^2\left(\frac{N_0 M}{4E}\right)\right],$$

$$g_{SN}\left(\frac{r_m}{N}\right) = \frac{MN_0}{2E}\left(\frac{r_m}{N}\right)\exp\left[-\frac{E}{MN_0}\right]\exp\left[-\left(\frac{r_m}{N}\right)^2\left(\frac{N_0 M}{4E}\right)\right]I_0\left(\frac{r_m}{N}\right). \tag{148}$$

This is the same situation, mathematically, as appeared in the previous section. The standard deviation and the mean for the logarithm of the likelihood ratio can be found in the same manner, and they are

$$\mu_{SN}(\ln l) = \frac{E^2}{MN_0^2},$$

$$\mu_N(\ln l) = 0,$$

$$\sigma_{SN}^2(\ln l) = \frac{E^2}{MN_0^2}\left(1 + \frac{2E}{MN_0}\right), \tag{149}$$

and

$$\sigma_N^2(\ln l) = \frac{E^2}{MN_0^2}.$$

If the distributions can be assumed normal, they are completely determined by their means and variances. These formulas are identical with the formulas (133) of the previous section. The problem is the same, mathematically, and the discussion and receiver operating characteristic curves at the end of Section 4.7 apply to both cases.

* See the footnote below equation (131).

† The M appears in the following equations because the energy of a single pulse is E/M rather than E.

4.9 *Approximate evaluation of an optimum receiver*

In order to obtain approximate results for the remaining two cases, the assumption is made that in these cases the receiver operating characteristic can be approximated by the curves of Figs. 2 and 3, i.e., that the logarithm of the likelihood ratio is approximately normal. This section discusses the approximation and a method for fitting the receiver operating characteristic to the curves of Figs. 2 and 3.

By (68), $F_{SN}(l)$ can be calculated if $F_N(l)$ is known. Furthermore, it can be seen that the nth moment of the distribution $F_N(l)$ is the $(n-1)$th moment of the distribution $F_{SN}(l)$. Hence, the mean of the likelihood ratio with noise alone is unity, and if the variance of the likelihood ratio with noise alone is σ_N^2, the second moment with noise alone, and hence the mean with signal plus noise, is $1 + \sigma_N^2$. Thus the difference between the means is equal to σ_N^2, which is the variance of the likelihood ratio with noise alone. Probably this number characterizes ability to detect signals better than any other single number.

Suppose the logarithm of the likelihood ratio has a normal distribution with noise alone, i.e.,

$$F_N(l) = \frac{1}{\sqrt{2\pi d}} \int_{\ln l}^{\infty} \exp\left[-\frac{(x-m)^2}{2d} \right] dx, \tag{150}$$

where m is the mean and d the variance of the logarithm of the likelihood ratio. The nth moment of the likelihood ratio can be found as follows:

$$\mu_N(l^n) = \int_0^{\infty} l^n dF_N(l) = \frac{1}{\sqrt{2\pi d}} \int_{-\infty}^{\infty} \exp[nx] \exp\left[-\frac{(x-m)^2}{2d} \right] dx, \tag{151}$$

where the substitution $l = \exp x$ has been made. The integral can be evaluated by completing the square in the exponent and using the fact that

$$\int_{-\infty}^{\infty} \exp\left[-\frac{x^2}{2d} \right] dx = \sqrt{2\pi d}.$$

Thus,   (152)

$$\mu_N(l^n) = \exp\left[\frac{n^2 d}{2} + mn \right].$$

In particular, the mean of $l(x)$, which must be unity, is

$$\mu_N(l) = 1 = \exp\left[\frac{d}{2} + m \right], \tag{153}$$

and therefore

$$m = -\frac{d}{2}. \tag{154}$$

The variance of $l(x)$ with noise alone is σ_N^2, and therefore the second moment of $l(x)$ is

$$\mu_N(l^2) = [\mu_N(l)]^2 + \sigma_N^2(l) = 1 + \sigma_N^2(l), \tag{155}$$

and this must agree with (152). It follows that

$$\mu_N(l^2) = 1 + \sigma_N^2 = \exp[2d + 2m] = \exp[d], \tag{156}$$

and therefore

$$d = \ln(1 + \sigma_N^2). \tag{157}$$

The distribution of likelihood ratio with signal plus noise can be found by applying Eq. (68). Thus

$$dF_{SN}(l) = l \, dF_N(l),$$

$$F_{SN}(l) = -\int_l^\infty l \, dF_N(l).$$

(158)

If $dF_N(l)$ is obtained from Eq. (150) and l is replaced by exp x, then

$$F_{SN}(l) = \frac{1}{\sqrt{2\pi d}} \int_{\ln l}^\infty \exp\left[x\right] \exp\left[-\frac{(x + d/2)^2}{2d}\right] dx$$

or

(159)

$$F_{SN}(l) = \frac{1}{\sqrt{2\pi d}} \int_{\ln l}^\infty \exp\left[-\frac{(x - d/2)^2}{2d}\right] dx.$$

Thus the distribution of ln l is normal also when there is signal plus noise, in this case with mean $d/2$ and variance d.

In summary, it is probable that the variance σ_N^2 of the likelihood ratio measures ability to detect signals better than any other single number. If the logarithm of likelihood ratio has a normal distribution with noise alone, then this distribution and that with signal plus noise are completely determined if σ_N^2 is given. The distribution of ln $l(x)$ is normal in both cases. Its variance in both cases is d, which is also the difference of the means. The receiver operating characteristic curves are those plotted in Fig. 2, with the parameter d related to σ_N^2 by the equation

$$d = \ln(1 + \sigma_N^2).$$

(160)

In the case of a signal known exactly, this is the distribution which occurs. In the cases of Section 4.6, Section 4.7, and Section 4.8 this distribution is found to be the limiting distribution when the number of sample points is large. Certainly in most cases the distribution has this general form. Thus it seems reasonable that useful approximate results could be obtained by calculating only σ_N^2 for a given case and assuming that the ability to detect signals is approximately the same as if the logarithm of the likelihood ratio has a normal distribution. On this basis, $\sigma_N^2(l)$ is calculated in the following sections for two cases, and the assertion is made that the receiver operating characteristic curves are approximated by those of Fig. 2 with $d = \ln(1 + \sigma_N^2)$.

4.10 Signal which is one of M orthogonal signals

Suppose that the set of expected signals includes just M functions $s_k(t)$, all of which have the same probability, the same energy E, and are orthogonal. That is,

$$\int_0^T s_k(t) s_q(t) \, dt = E\delta_{kq}.$$

(161)

Then the likelihood ratio can be found from Eq. (56) to be

$$l(x) = \sum_{k=1}^M \frac{1}{M} \exp\left[-\frac{E}{N_0}\right] \exp\left[\frac{1}{N} \sum_{i=1}^n x_i s_{ki}\right],$$

or

(162)

$$l(x) = \frac{1}{M} \sum_{k=1}^M \exp\left[\frac{1}{N} \sum_{i=1}^n x_i s_{ki} - \frac{E}{N_0}\right],$$

where s_{ki} are the sample values of the function $s_k(t)$.

With noise alone, each term of the form

$$(1/N) \sum_{i=1}^{n} x_i s_{ki}$$

has a normal distribution with mean zero and variance

$$\sum_{i=1}^{n} \frac{s_{ki}^2}{N} = \frac{2E}{N_0} . \text{ *}$$

Furthermore, the M different quantities

$$\left(\frac{1}{N}\right) \sum_{i=1}^{n} x_i s_{ki}$$

are independent, since the functions $s_k(t)$ are orthogonal. It follows that the terms

$$\exp\left[\left(\frac{1}{N}\right) \sum_{i=1}^{n} x_i s_{ki} - \frac{E}{N_0} \right]$$

are independent.

Since the logarithm of each term

$$Z = \exp\left[\left(\frac{1}{N}\right) \sum_{i=1}^{n} x_i s_{ki} - \frac{E}{N_0} \right]$$

has a normal distribution with mean $(-E/N_0)$ and variance $2E/N_0$, the moments of the distribution can be found from Eq. (152). The nth moment is

$$\mu_N(Z^n) = \exp\left[n(n-1) \frac{E}{N_0} \right]. \tag{163}$$

It follows that the mean of each term is unity, and the variance is

$$\sigma_N^2(Z) = \mu(Z^2) - [\mu(Z)^2] = \exp\left[\frac{2E}{N_0} \right] - 1. \tag{164}$$

The variance of a sum of independent random variables is the sum of the variances of the terms. Therefore

$$\sigma_N^2(Ml) = M\left[\exp\left(\frac{2E}{N_0} \right) - 1 \right], \tag{165}$$

and it follows that the variance of the likelihood ratio is

$$\sigma_N^2(l) = \frac{1}{M}\left[\exp\left(\frac{2E}{N_0} \right) - 1 \right]. \tag{166}$$

It was pointed out in Section 4.9, that the receiver operating characteristic curves are approximately those of Fig. 2, with

$$d = \ln(1 + \sigma_N^2) = \ln\left[1 - \frac{1}{M} + \frac{1}{M} \exp\left(\frac{2E}{N_0} \right) \right]. \tag{167}$$

This equation can be solved for $2E/N_0$:

$$\frac{2E}{N_0} = \ln[1 + M(e^d - 1)]. \tag{168}$$

* The reasoning is the same as that in Section 4.4.

Suppose it is desired to keep the false alarm probability and probability of detection constant. This requires that d be kept constant. Then from Eq. (168) it can be seen that if the number of possible signals M is increased, the signal energy E must also be increased.

4.11 *Signal which is one of M orthogonal signals with unknown carrier phase*

Consider the case in which the set of expected signals includes just M different amplitude-modulated signals which are known except for carrier phase. Denote the signals by

$$s_k(t) = f_k(t) \cos(\omega t + \theta). \tag{169}$$

It will be assumed further that the functions $f_k(t)$ all have the same energy E and are orthogonal, i.e.,

$$\int_0^T f_k(t) f_q(t)\, dt = 2E\delta_{kq}, \tag{170}$$

where the 2 is introduced because the f's are the signal amplitudes, not the actual signal functions. Also, let the $f_k(t)$ be band-limited to contain no frequencies as high as ω. Then it follows that any two signal functions with different envelope functions will be orthogonal. Let us assume also that the distribution of phase, θ, is uniform, and that the probability for each envelope function is $1/M$.

With these assumptions, the likelihood ratio can be obtained from Eq. (56), and it is given by

$$l(x) = \frac{1}{M} \sum_{k=1}^M \frac{1}{2\pi} \int_0^{2\pi} \exp\left[\frac{1}{N}\sum_{i=1}^n x_i s_{ki} - \frac{E}{N_0}\right] d\theta, \tag{171}$$

where s_{ki} are the sample values of $s_k(t)$, and hence depend upon the phase θ. The integration is the same as in the case of the signal known except for phase, and the result, obtained from Eq. (82), is

$$l(x) = \frac{1}{M} \sum_{k=1}^M \exp\left[-\frac{E}{N_0}\right] I_0\left(\frac{r_k}{N}\right), \tag{172}$$

where

$$r_k = \sqrt{\left(\sum_i x_i f_k(t_i) \cos \omega t_i\right)^2 + \left(\sum_i x_i f_k(t_i) \sin \omega t_i\right)^2}. \tag{173}$$

Now the problem is to find $\sigma_N^2(l)$. The variance of each term in the sum in Eq. (172) can be found since the distribution function with noise alone can be found in Section 4.5. Since the $f_k(t)$ are orthogonal, the distributions of the r_k are independent, and the terms in the sum in Eq. (172) are independent. Then the variance of the likelihood ratio, $\sigma_N^2(l)$, is the sum of the variances of the terms, divided by M^2.

The distribution function for each term $\exp(-E/N_0)I_0(r_k/N)$ is given in Section 4.5 by Eqs. (84) and (85). If α is defined by the equation

$$\beta = \exp\left[-\frac{E}{N_0}\right] I_0\left(\alpha\sqrt{\frac{2E}{N_0}}\right), \tag{174}$$

then the distribution function in the presence of noise for each term in Eq. (172) is

$$F_N^{(k)}(\beta) = \exp\left[-\frac{\alpha^2}{2}\right]. \tag{175}$$

The mean value of each term is

$$\mu_N^{(k)}(\beta) = \int_0^\infty \beta \, dF_N^{(k)}(\beta) = \int_0^\infty \exp\left[-\frac{E}{N_0}\right] I_0\left(\sqrt{\frac{2E}{N_0}}\,\alpha\right)\alpha \exp\left[-\frac{\alpha^2}{2}\right] d\alpha. \quad (176)$$

This can be evaluated as on page 174 of *Threshold Signals* [5], and the result is that $\mu^{(k)}(\beta) = 1$.

The second moment of each term is

$$\mu_N^{(k)}(\beta^2) = \int_0^\infty \beta^2 \, dF_N^{(k)}(\beta),$$

or   (177)

$$\mu_N^{(k)}(\beta^2) = \int_0^\infty \exp\left[-\frac{2E}{N_0}\right]\left[I_0\left(\alpha\sqrt{\frac{2E}{N_0}}\right)\right]^2 \alpha \exp\left[-\frac{\alpha^2}{2}\right] d\alpha.$$

The integral can be evaluated as in Appendix E of Part II of reference [17], and the result is

$$\mu_N^{(k)}(\beta^2) = I_0\left(\frac{2E}{N_0}\right). \quad (178)$$

The variance of each term in Eq. (172) is

$$[\sigma_N^{(k)}(\beta)]^2 = \mu^{(k)}(\beta^2) - [\mu^{(k)}(\beta)]^2 = I_0\left(\frac{2E}{N_0}\right) - 1. \quad (179)$$

It follows that the variance of Ml is

$$\sigma_N^2(Ml) = M\left[I_0\left(\frac{2E}{N_0}\right) - 1\right], \quad (180)$$

and therefore

$$\sigma_N^2(l) = \frac{1}{M}\left[I_0\left(\frac{2E}{N_0}\right) - 1\right], \quad (181)$$

since the variance for the sum of independent random variables is the sum of the variances.

If the approximation described in Section 4.9 is used, the receiver operating characteristic curves are approximately those of Fig. 2, with

$$d = \ln(1 + \sigma_N^2) = \ln\left[1 - \frac{1}{M} + \frac{1}{M}I_0\left(\frac{2E}{N_0}\right)\right]. \quad (182)$$

4.12 *The broad band receiver and the optimum receiver*

A few applications of the results of Section 4 are suggested in Table I, Section 4.1. Two further examples of practical knowledge obtainable from the theory are presented in this section and in the next.

One common method of detecting pulse signals in a frequency band of width B is to build a receiver which covers this entire frequency band. Such a receiver with a pulse signal of known starting time is studied in Section 4.7. This is not a truly optimum receiver; it would be interesting to compare it with an optimum receiver. We have been unable to find the distribution of likelihood ratio for the case of a signal which is a pulse of unknown carrier phase if the frequency is distributed evenly over a band. However, if the problem is changed slightly, so that the frequency is restricted to points spaced approximately the reciprocal of the pulse width apart, then pulses at different frequencies are approximately orthogonal, and the case of the signal which is one of M orthogonal signals known except for phase can be applied. Eq. (182) should be used with M equal to the ratio of the frequency band width B to the pulse band width. Since the band width of a pulse is approximately the reciprocal of its pulse width, the parameter M used in Section 4.7 also has this value. Curves showing $2E/N_0$ as a function of d are given in Fig. 7 for both the approximate optimum receiver

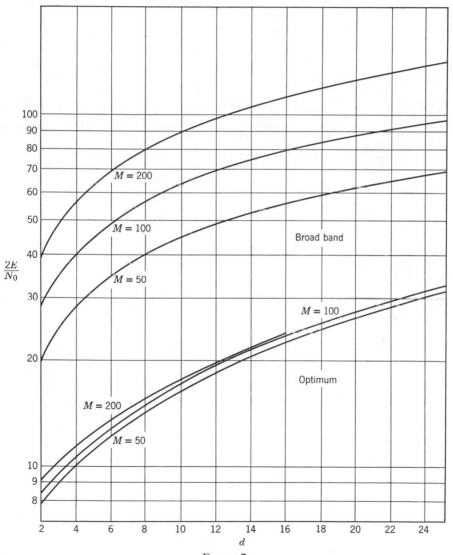

FIGURE 7

Comparison of optimum and broad band receivers.

and the broad band receiver for several values of M. In the figure, d is calculated from Eq. (135) and Eq. (182), which hold for large values of M.

4.13 *Uncertainty and signal detectability*

In the two cases where the signal considered is one of M orthogonal signals, the uncertainty of the signal is a function of M. This provides an opportunity to study the effect of uncertainty on signal detectability. In the approximate evaluation of the optimum receiver when the signal is one of M orthogonal functions, the ROC curves of Figs. 2 and 3 are used with the detection index d given by

$$d = \ln\left[1 - \frac{1}{M} + \frac{1}{M}\exp\left(\frac{2E}{N_0}\right)\right].$$ (167)

This equation can be solved for the signal energy, yielding

$$\frac{2E}{N_0} = \ln[1 - M + Me^d] \approx \ln M + \ln(e^d - 1),$$ (175)

the approximation holding for large $2E/N_0$.* From this equation it can be seen that the signal energy is approximately a linear function of $\ln M$ when the detection index d, and hence the ability to detect signals, is kept constant. It might be suspected that $2E/N_0$ is a linear function of the entropy, $-\Sigma\, p_i \ln p_i$, where p_i is the probability of the ith signal. The linear relation holds only when all the p_i are equal. The expression which occurs in this more general case is:

$$\frac{2E}{N_0} \approx -\ln(\sum p_i^2) + \ln(e^d - 1).$$ (176)

REFERENCES

[1] S. Goldman. *Information theory.* New York: Prentice-Hall, 1953. Chapter II, pp. 65–84, is devoted to sampling plans.

[2] C. E. Shannon. Communication in the presence of noise. *Proc. IRE*, January, 1949, **37**, 10–21.

[3] U. Grenander. Stochastic processes and statistical inference. *Arkiv för Mathematik*, 1950, Bd 1 nr 17, p. 195.

[4] J. Neyman, and E. S. Pearson. On the problems of the most efficient tests of statistical hypotheses. *Philosophical Transactions of the Royal Society of London*, 1933, **231**, Series A, 289.

[5] J. L. Lawson and G. E. Uhlenbeck. *Threshold signals.* New York: McGraw-Hill, 1950.

[6] P. M. Woodward and I. L. Davies. Information theory and inverse probability in telecommunications. *Proc. I.E.E.* (London), March, 1952, **99**, Part III, 37–44.

[7] I. L. Davies. On determining the presence of signals in noise. *Proc. I.E.E.* (London), March, 1952, **99**, Part III, 45–51.

[8] A. Wald. *Sequential analysis.* New York: Wiley, 1947.

[9] W. C. Fox. Signal detectability: A unified description of statistical methods employing fixed and sequential observation processes. Electronic Defense Group, University of Michigan, Technical Report No. 19 (unclassified).

[10] A. Wald and J. Wolfowitz. Optimum character of the sequential probability ratio test. *Ann. Math. Stat.*, September, 1948, **19**, 326.

* If $2E/N_0 > 3$, the error is less than 10%.

[11] E. Reich and P. Swerling. The detection of a sine wave in Gaussian noise, *Journal Applied Physics*, March, 1953, **24**, 289.

[12] R. C. Davis. On the detection of sure signals in noise, *Journal Applied Physics*, January, 1954, **25**, 76–82.

[13] J. V. Harrington and T. F. Rogers. Signal-to-noise improvement through integration in a storage tube, *Proc. I.R.E.*, October, 1950, 38, 1197.
   A. E. Harting and J. E. Meade. A device for computing correlation functions, *Rev. Sci. Instr.*, 1952, **23**, 347.
   Y. W. Lee, T. P. Cheatham, Jr., and J. B. Wiesner. Applications of correlation analysis to the detection of periodic signals in noise. *Proc. I.R.E.*, October, 1950, **38**, 1165.
   M. J. Levin and J. F. Reintjes. A five channel electronic analog correlator. *Proc. Nat. El. Conf.* 1952, **8**.

[14] D. O. North. An analysis of the factors which determine signal-noise discrimination in pulsed carrier systems. RCA Laboratory Rpt PTR-6C, 1943.
   See also reference [5], p. 206.

[15] Graphs of values of the integral (89) along with approximate expressions for small and for large values of α appear in S. O. Rice, Mathematical analysis of random noise, *B.S.T.J.*, 1944–1945, **23**, 282–332 and **24**, 46–156. Tables of this function have been compiled by: J. I. Marcum in an unpublished report of the Rand Corporation, Table of Q-functions, Project Rand Report RM-399.

[16] P. G. Hoel. *Introduction to mathematical statistics*. New York: Wiley, 1947, p. 246.

[17] The material of Sections 2 and 3 of this paper is drawn from reference [9] above and from Part I of W. W. Peterson, and T. G. Birdsall, The theory of signal detectability, Electronic Defense Group, University of Michigan, Technical Report No. 13 (unclassified), July, 1953. Part II of that report contains the material in Section 4 of this paper. Other work in this field may be found in D. Middleton, Statistical criteria for the detection of pulsed carriers in noise, *Journal Applied Physics*, 24, 371, April, 1953; D. Middleton, The statistical theory of detection. I: Optimum detection of signals in noise, M.I.T. Lincoln Laboratory. Technical Report No. 35, November 2, 1953; D. Middleton, Statistical theory of signal detection, *Trans. IRE.*, PGIT-3, p. 26, March, 1954; D. Middleton, W. W. Peterson, and T. G. Birdsall, Discussion of 'statistical criteria for the detection of pulsed carriers in noise. I, II', *Journal Applied Physics*, January, 1954, **25**, 128–130.

FOUNDATIONAL ASPECTS OF THEORIES OF MEASUREMENT [1]

DANA SCOTT and PATRICK SUPPES

1. Definition of measurement. It is a scientific platitude that there can be neither precise control nor prediction of phenomena without measurement. Disciplines as diverse as cosmology and social psychology provide evidence that it is nearly useless to have an exactly formulated quantitative theory if empirically feasible methods of measurement cannot be developed for a substantial portion of the quantitative concepts of the theory. Given a physical concept like that of mass or a psychological concept like that of habit strength, the point of a theory of measurement is to lay bare the structure of a collection of empirical relations which may be used to measure the characteristic of empirical phenomena corresponding to the concept. Why a collection of relations? From an abstract standpoint a set of empirical data consists of a collection of relations between specified objects. For example, data on the relative weights of a set of physical objects are easily represented by an ordering relation on the set; additional data, and a fortiori an additional relation, are needed to yield a satisfactory quantitative measurement of the masses of the objects.

The major source of difficulty in providing an adequate theory of measurement is to construct relations which have an exact and reasonable numerical interpretation and yet also have a technically practical empirical interpretation. The classical analyses of the measurement of mass, for instance, have the embarrassing consequence that the basic set of objects measured must be infinite. Here the relations postulated have acceptable numerical interpretations, but are utterly unsuitable empirically. Conversely, as we shall see in the last section of this paper, the structure of relations which have a sound empirical meaning often cannot be succinctly characterized so as to guarantee a desired numerical interpretation.

Nevertheless this major source of difficulty will not here be carefully scrutinized in a variety of empirical contexts. The main point of the present paper is to show how foundational analyses of measurement may be grounded in the general theory of models, and to indicate the kind of problems relevant to measurement which may then be stated (and perhaps answered) in a precise manner.

Received September 24, 1957.

[1] We would like to record here our indebteness to Professor Alfred Tarski whose clear and precise formulation of the mathematical theory of models has greatly influenced our presentation (see [7]). Although our theories of measurement do not constitute special cases of the arithmetical classes of Tarski, the notions are closely related, and we have made use of results and methods from the theory of models. This research was supported under Contract NR 171–034, Group Psychology Branch, Office of Naval Research.

This article appeared in *J. symbolic Logic*, 1958, **23**, 113–128.

Before turning to problems connected with construction of theories of measurement, we want to give a precise set-theoretical meaning to the notions involved. To begin with, we treat sets of empirical data as being (finitary) relational systems, that is to say, finite sequences of the form $\mathfrak{A} = \langle A, R_1, \ldots, R_n \rangle$, where A is a non-empty set of elements called the *domain* of the relational system $\mathfrak{A}$, and $R_1, \ldots, R_n$ are finitary relations on A. The relational system $\mathfrak{A}$ is called *finite* if the set A is finite; otherwise, *infinite*. It should be obvious from this definition that we are mainly considering *qualitative* empirical data. Intuitively we may think of each particular relation R_i (an m_i-ary relation, say) as representing a complete set of "yes" or "no" answers to a question asked of every m_i-termed sequence of objects in A. The point of this paper is not to consider that aspect of measurement connected with the actual collection of data, but rather the analysis of relational systems and their numerical interpretations.

If $s = \langle m_1, \ldots, m_n \rangle$ is an n-termed sequence of positive integers, then a relational system $\mathfrak{A} = \langle A, R_1, \ldots, R_n \rangle$ is of *type s* if for each $i = 1, \ldots, n$ the relation R_i is an m_i-ary relation. Two relational systems are *similar* if there is a sequence s of positive integers such that they are both of type s. Notice that the type of a relational system is uniquely determined only if all the relations are non-empty; the avoiding of this ambiguity is not worthwhile. Suppose that two relational systems $\mathfrak{A} = \langle A, R_1, \ldots, R_n \rangle$ and $\mathfrak{B} = \langle B, S_1, \ldots, S_n \rangle$ are of type $s = \langle m_1, \ldots, m_n \rangle$. Then $\mathfrak{B}$ is a *homomorphic image of* $\mathfrak{A}$ if there is a function f from A onto B such that, for each $i = 1, \ldots, n$ and for each sequence $\langle a_1, \ldots, a_{m_i} \rangle$ of elements of A, $R_i(a_1, \ldots, a_{m_i})$ *if and only if* $S_i(f(a_1), \ldots, f(a_{m_i}))$. If the function f is one-one, then $\mathfrak{B}$ is an *isomorphic image of* $\mathfrak{A}$, or simply $\mathfrak{A}$ and $\mathfrak{B}$ are *isomorphic*. $\mathfrak{A}$ is a *subsystem* of $\mathfrak{B}$ if $A \supseteq B$ and, for each $i = 1, \ldots, n$, the relation R_i is the restriction of the relation S_i to A. $\mathfrak{A}$ is *imbeddable* in $\mathfrak{B}$ if some subsystem of $\mathfrak{B}$ is a homomorphic image of $\mathfrak{A}$. [2] A *numerical relational system* is simply a relational system whose domain of elements is the set Re of all real numbers. A *numerical assignment* for a relational system $\mathfrak{A}$ with respect to a numerical relational system $\mathfrak{N}$ is a function which imbeds $\mathfrak{A}$ in $\mathfrak{N}$. A numerical assignment is not required to be one-one.

Within the framework of the preceding formal definitions it is now possible to give an exact characterization of a theory of measurement. First of all the general outlines of a theory are determined by fixing a finite sequence s of positive integers and only considering relational systems of type s. Next a numerical relational system $\mathfrak{N}$ of type s is selected which

---

[2] Although in most mathematical contexts imbeddability is defined in terms of isomorphism rather than homomorphism, for theories of measurement this is too restrictive. However, the notion of homomorphism used here is actually closely connected with isomorphic imbeddability and the facts are explained in detail in Section 2.

corresponds to the intended numerical interpretation of the theory, and only relational systems imbeddable in $\mathfrak{N}$ are permitted. Moreover the theory need not concern all relational systems of type s imbeddable in $\mathfrak{N}$ but only a distinguished subclass. Since it is reasonable that no special set of objects be preferred, we require that the distinguished subclass be closed under isomorphism. We thus arrive at the following characterization of theories of measurement as definite entities: a theory of measurement *is* a class K of relational systems closed under isomorphism for which there exists a finite sequence s of positive integers and a numerical relational system $\mathfrak{N}$ of type s such that all relational systems in K are of type s and imbeddable in $\mathfrak{N}$. [3]

Some readers may object that the definition of theories of measurement should be linguistic rather than set-theoretical in character, since a theory is ordinarily thought of as a linguistic entity. To be sure, many theories of measurement have a natural formalization in first-order predicate logic with identity. Notice, however, that first-order axioms by themselves are not adequate, for if they admit one infinite relational system as a model then they have models of every infinite cardinality, and it is difficult to see how any natural connection can be established between numerical models and models of arbitrary cardinality. Even neglecting this criticism first-order axioms are not adequate to express properties involving arbitrary natural numbers, for example, that a relational system is finite or that as an ordering it has Archimedean properties. Any linguistic definition of theories which will permit expression of these more general properties would require extensive machinery and be immediately involved in some of the deepest problems of modern metamathematics. On the other hand, we do not wish to give the impression that we reject any linguistic questions. In fact, we use our set-theoretical definition as a point of departure for asking just such questions.

On the basis of the definition of theories of measurement adopted, two questions naturally arise, to each of which we devote a section. In the first place, is a given class of relational systems a theory of measurement? And in the second place, given a theory of measurement, in what sense can it be axiomatized?

2. Existence of measurement.

A simple counterexample shows that not every class of relational systems of a given type closed under isomorphism is a theory of measurement. Let O be the class of all relational systems of type $\langle 2 \rangle$ that are simple orderings. Let $\langle A, R \rangle$ be a system in O where R

[3] In some contexts we shall say that the class K is *a theory of measurement of type s relative to* $\mathfrak{N}$. Notice that a consequence of this definition is that, if K is a theory of measurement, then so is every subclass of K closed under isomorphism. Moreover, the class of all systems imbeddable in members of K is also a theory of measurement

well-orders A and A has a power not equal to or less than that of the continuum. Such a relational system can be proved to exist even without the help of the axiom of choice, but of course with aid of this axiom the existence is obvious. By way of contradiction suppose that O is a theory of measurement relative to a numerical relational system $\langle \text{Re}, S \rangle$. From the definition it follows that $\langle A, R \rangle$ is imbeddable in $\langle \text{Re}, S \rangle$ and that there is a numerical assignment f mapping A onto a subset of Re such that xRy *if and only if* $f(x) \, S \, f(y)$ for all elements $x, y \in A$. Let a, b be elements of A such that $f(a) = f(b)$. From the hypothesis that R is a simple ordering, we can assume without loss of generality that aRb. Hence, we have $f(a) \, S \, f(b)$, and then $f(b) \, S \, f(a)$, and finally bRa. R is antisymmetric, and so $a = b$. This argument shows that the function f is one-one. Hence A has the same power as a subset of Re, which is impossible. This proof shows that every theory of measurement included in the class O contains only relational systems of power at most that of the continuum. It is an unsolved problem of set-theory closely connected with the continuum hypothesis whether the class O restricted to systems of power at most that of the continuum is actually a theory of measurement. [4] At least it can be very easily shown that O so restricted is not a theory of measurement relative to the system $\langle \text{Re}, \leq \rangle$, where the relation $\leq$ is the usual ordering of the real numbers. [5] Indeed, the exact condition that a relational system in O must satisfy to be imbeddable in $\langle \text{Re}, \leq \rangle$ is not really elementary, and the proof of the necessity involves the axiom of choice. [6]

Let O' be O restricted to countable relational systems. [7] It was proved by Cantor that O' is a theory of measurement relative to $\langle \text{Re}, \leq \rangle$, to formulate somewhat irreverently his classical result in the terminology of this paper. This restriction to countable relational systems is always sufficient. For it can be shown that the class of *all* countable relational systems of a given type is a theory of measurement; however, the numerical relational system required is so bizarre as to be of no practical value.

A primary aim of measurement is to provide a means of convenient computation. Practical control or prediction of empirical phenomena requires that unified, widely applicable methods of analyzing the important relationships between the phenomena be developed. Imbedding the dis-

---

[4] In this connection see Sierpinski [5], Section 7, pp. 141 ff., in particular *Proposition* C_{75}, where of course different terminology is used.

[5] It is sufficient here to consider a relational system isomorphic to the ordering of the ordinals of the second number class or to the lexicographical ordering of all pairs of real numbers.

[6] A simple ordering is imbeddable in $\langle \text{Re}, \leq \rangle$ if and only if it contains a countable dense subset. For the exact formulation and a sketch of a proof, see Birkhoff [1], pp. 31–32, Theorem 2.

[7] The word 'countable' means at most denumerable and it refers to the cardinality of the domains of the relational systems.

covered relations in various numerical relational systems is the most important such unifying method that has yet been found. But among the morass of all possible numerical relational systems only a very few are of any computational value, indeed only those definable in terms of the ordinary arithmetical notions. From an empirical standpoint most sets of qualitative data can find numerical interpretation by relations defined in terms of addition and ordering alone. By way of example we may cite the measurement of masses, distances, sensation intensities, and subjective probabilities. Frequently the consideration of weighted averages requires also the use of the multiplication of numbers. However, in the examples given in this paper we shall restrict ourselves to the notions of addition and ordering.

No natural scientific situation would seem strictly to require the consideration of sets of infinite data. This state of affairs suggests that theories of measurement containing only finite relational systems would suffice for empirical purposes. The problem is delicate, however, for the measurement of a meteorological quantity such as temperature by an automatic recording device is usually treated as continuous both in its own scale and in time. Yet the important problem of measurement does not really lie in the correct use of such recording devices but rather in their initial calibration, a process proceeding from a finite number of qualitative decisions. Because of the awkwardness of the uniform application of finite relational systems, we shall not generally make this restriction.

Further remarks about establishing the existence of measurement are best motivated by reference to a concrete example. In a recent paper [4], Luce has introduced a generalization of simple orderings which he calls *semiorders*. A *semiorder* is a relational system $\langle A, P \rangle$ of type $\langle 2 \rangle$ which satisfies the following axioms for all $x, y, z, w \in A$:

S1. *Not xPx.*
S2. *If xPy and zPw, then either xPw or zPy.*
S3. *If xPy and zPx, then either wPy or zPw.* [8]

Such relations are most likely to occur in situations where objects are to be arranged in order and where it is difficult to say exactly when two objects are indifferent. For example, to say that xPy might be interpreted as meaning that the pitch of the sound x is *definitely higher* than the pitch of y, or that the hue of color x is *definitely brighter* than the hue of color y, or that the weight of the object x is *noticeably greater* than that of y, etc. *Indifference* between two objects x and y (in symbols: xIy) is defined as not xPy, and not yPx. The point of Luce's axioms is that the relation I of

---

[8] See [4], Section 2, p. 181. The axioms given here are actually a simplification of those given by Luce.

indifference is not always transitive, a fact easily appreciated for each of the intuitive interpretations given above.

In his paper Luce gives a certain numerical interpretation for certain kinds of semiorders, but he does not show that any particular class of semiorders is a theory of measurement in the sense used here, because his interpretations are not relative to a fixed numerical relation. However, in the finite case the situation becomes relatively simple. Let $\gg$ be that relation between real numbers defined by the condition: $x \gg y$ *if and only if* $x > y+1$. Clearly, if x and y are real numbers such that $x \gg y$, then it is fair to say that x is *definitely greater than* y, or better, x is *noticeably greater than* y. It is in fact a simple exercise to prove that the relational system $\langle \text{Re}, \gg \rangle$ is a semiorder. Further we shall give the proof of the following result:

The class of finite semiorders is a theory of measurement relative to the numerical relational system $\langle \text{Re}, \gg \rangle$.

Before presenting the proof of the above, it would be well to outline a general method in proofs of the existence of measurement which we shall call the *method of cosets*. Let $\mathfrak{A} = \langle A, R_1, \ldots, R_n \rangle$ be a relational system of type $\langle m_1, \ldots, m_n \rangle$. A uniquely determined equivalence relation E is introduced into $\mathfrak{A}$ by the condition: xEy *if and only if for each* $i = 1, \ldots, n$ *and each pair* $\langle z_1, \ldots, z_{m_i} \rangle$, $\langle w_1, \ldots, w_{m_i} \rangle$ *of m_i-termed sequences of elements of A, if* $z_j \neq w_j$ *implies* $\{z_j, w_j\} = \{x, y\}$ *for* $j = 1, \ldots, m_i$, *then* $R_i(z_1, \ldots, z_{m_i})$ *if and only if* $R_i(w_1, \ldots, w_{m_i})$.

Even though the above definition is complicated to state in general, the meaning of the relation xEy is simple: elements x and y stand in the relation E just when they are perfect substitutes for each other with respect to all the relations R_i. [9]

The notion of a weak ordering can serve as an example. Let $\mathfrak{A} = \langle A, R \rangle$ where the binary relation R is connected and transitive. Then xEy is equivalent to the condition: *For all* $z \in A$, xRz *if and only if* yRz, *and* zRx *if and only if* zRy. However, this simplifies finally to: xRy *and* yRx.

Returning now to the general case, define, for each $x \in A$, $[x]$ to be the class of all y such that xEy. $[x]$ is called the *coset* of x. Let A^* be the class of all $[x]$ for $x \in A$. Directly from the definition of E we can deduce that it is permissible to define m_i-ary relations R_i^* over A^* such that, for all $x_1, \ldots, x_{m_i} \in A$, $R_i^*([x_1], \ldots, [x_{m_i}])$ *if and only if* $R_i(x_1, \ldots, x_{m_i})$. The relational system $\mathfrak{A}^* = \langle A_1^*, R_1^*, \ldots, R_n^* \rangle$ is called the *reduction of $\mathfrak{A}$ by cosets*.

It is at once obvious that $\mathfrak{A}^*$ is a homomorphic image of $\mathfrak{A}$ and that $\mathfrak{A}^{**}$ is isomorphic with $\mathfrak{A}^*$. What is not quite obvious is the following:

If $\mathfrak{B}$ is a homomorphic image of $\mathfrak{A}$, then $\mathfrak{A}^*$ is a homomorphic image of $\mathfrak{B}$.

---

[9] The authors are indebted to the referee for pointing out the work by Hailperin in [3] which suggested this general definition.

By way of proof, let f be a homomorphism of $\mathfrak{A}$ onto $\mathfrak{B}$. We wish to show that if $f(x) = f(y)$, then $[x] = [y]$. Instead of the general case, assume for simplicity that $\mathfrak{A}$ and $\mathfrak{B}$ are of type $\langle 2 \rangle$ and $\mathfrak{A} = \langle A, R \rangle$, $\mathfrak{B} = \langle B, S \rangle$. We must show that if $f(x) = f(y)$, then xEy, or in other words, for all $z \in A$, xRz if and only if yRz, and zRx if and only if zRy. Assume xRz. It follows that $f(x) \, S \, f(z)$, and hence $f(y) \, S \, f(z)$, which implies that yRz. The argument is clearly symmetric. We have therefore shown that there is a function g from B onto A^* such that $g(f(x)) = [x]$ for $x \in A$. It is trivial to verify that g is a homomorphism of $\mathfrak{B}$ onto $\mathfrak{A}^*$.

Notice the following relation between the concepts of homomorphic image and subsystem: if $\mathfrak{B}$ is a homomorphic image of $\mathfrak{A}$, then $\mathfrak{B}$ is isomorphic to a subsystem of $\mathfrak{A}$. For let f be a homomorphism of $\mathfrak{A}$ onto $\mathfrak{B}$. Let g be any function from B into A such that $f(g(y)) = y$ for all $y \in B$. The restriction of $\mathfrak{A}$ to the range of g yields the subsystem of $\mathfrak{A}$ isomorphic with $\mathfrak{B}$.

Using the above remarks we can establish at once the equivalence: $\mathfrak{A}$ *is imbeddable in* $\mathfrak{B}$ *if and only if* $\mathfrak{A}^*$ *is imbeddable in* $\mathfrak{B}$.

Further, it follows that any function imbedding $\mathfrak{A}^*$ in $\mathfrak{B}$ is always an isomorphism of $\mathfrak{A}^*$ onto a subsystem of $\mathfrak{B}$, and of all homomorphic images of $\mathfrak{A}$ this property is characteristic of $\mathfrak{A}^*$.

Let K now be any class of relational systems closed under isomorphism. Let K^* be the class of all systems isomorphic to some $\mathfrak{A}^*$ for $\mathfrak{A} \in K$. In effect we have shown above:

(i) K is a theory of measurement relative to a numerical relational system $\mathfrak{N}$ if and only if K^* is also.

(ii) If K in addition is closed under the formation of subsystems, then K^* is the class of all systems in K possessing only one-one numerical assignments.

To use our example again, if K is the class of weak orders, then K^* is the class of simple orders. Notice that the proof in the first paragraph of this section is a special case of (ii).

It should be remarked that for a relational system $\mathfrak{A}$, $\mathfrak{A}$ and $\mathfrak{A}^*$ always satisfy exactly the same formulas of first-order logic not involving the notion of identity. Hence, if K is the class of all relational systems satisfying first-order axioms without identity, then K^* is the class of all systems satisfying the axioms for K and in addition satisfying the axiom:

(*) If xEy, then $x = y$.

The application of this remark to weak orderings and simple orderings is left to the reader.

Consider again the case of semiorders. Let S be the class of all finite semiorders. For any $\langle A, P \rangle \in S$, consider the relation I of indifference defined above. In terms of I one can establish a simplified characterization of E: *xEy if and only for if all* $z \in A$, *xIz if and only if yIz*.

Introduce (*) as a new axiom S4. The class of all $\mathfrak{A} \in S$ satisfying S4 is just the class S^*. Notice that unlike the pleasant situation with weak orderings and simple orderings, the class S^* is not closed under the formation of subsystems even though S is.

For any semiorder $\langle A, P \rangle$ introduce a further relation R as follows: *xRy if and only if for all z, if zPx then zPy, and if yPz then xPz.*

We leave to the reader the elementary verification of the fact that R is a weak ordering of A, and that xEy if and only if xRy and yRx. Thus, if $\langle A, P \rangle \in S^*$, then R is a simple ordering of A. The connection between P and R is clearer if one notices that xPy implies xRy, and that, if xRx_1, x_1Py_1, and y_1Ry, then xPy.

Now let $\mathfrak{A} = \langle A, P \rangle$ be a fixed member of S^*. We wish to show that $\mathfrak{A}$ has an assignment in $\langle \mathrm{Re}, \gg \rangle$. Under the relation R, A is simply ordered. Let $A = \{x_0, \ldots, x_n\}$ where $x_i R x_{i-1}$ and $x_i \neq x_{i-1}$. Define by a course of values recursion a sequence $a_0, \ldots, a_n$ of rational numbers determined uniquely by the following two conditions:

(1)   If $x_i I x_0$, then $a_i = \dfrac{i}{i+1}$.

(2)   If $x_i I x_j$ and $x_i P x_{j-1}$ where $j > 0$, then $a_i = \dfrac{i}{i+1} a_j + \dfrac{1}{i+1} a_{j-1} + 1$.

Notice that in (2) the hypothesis implies that $j \leq i$, while in the case $j = i$ the formula for a_i simplifies to $a_i = a_{i-1} + i + 1$. Notice further that every element x_i comes either under (1) or (2); for letting x_j be the first element such that $x_j I x_i$, there are two cases: $j = 0$, $j > 0$. Clearly we always have $a_i \geq 0$.

We show first that $a_i > a_{i-1}$ by induction on i. For case (1), this is obvious. Passing to (2), assume that $x_i I x_j$ and $x_i P x_{j-1}$. If $x_{i-1} I x_0$, then $a_{i-1} < 1$ while $a_i > 1$. Hence we can assume not $x_{i-1} I x_0$, or in other words $x_{i-1} P x_0$. Let x_k be the first element such that $x_{i-1} I x_k$ and $x_{i-1} P x_{k-1}$. By definition $a_{i-1} = \dfrac{i-1}{i} a_k + \dfrac{1}{i} a_{k-1} + 1$. If $j = i$, there is no problem. Assume then that $j < i$. Now $x_{i-1} R x_j$, $x_i R x_{i-1}$, and $x_j I x_i$, hence $x_j I x_{i-1}$, and so by our choice of k we have $k \leq j$. By the induction hypothesis on i, it follows that $a_j > a_{j-1}$ and $a_k > a_{k-1}$. If $k = j$, the required inequality is obvious. If $k \leq j-1$, then $a_i > a_{j-1} + 1$. Similarly $a_{i-1} < a_k + 1$, but again, by the induction hypothesis, $a_k \leq a_{j-1}$, and hence $a_i > a_{i-1}$.

The next step is to prove that, if $x_i P x_k$, then $a_i > a_k + 1$. Let x_j be the first element such that $x_i I x_j$ and $x_i P x_{j-1}$. We have $j-1 \geq k$, and, in view of the preceding argument, $a_{j-1} \geq a_k$. But $a_{j-1} + 1 < a_i$, whence $a_i > a_k + 1$.

Conversely we must show that, if $a_i > a_k + 1$, then $x_i P x_k$. The hypothesis of course implies $i > k$. Assume by way of contradiction that not $x_i P x_k$. It follows that $x_i I x_k$. Let x_j be the first element such that $x_i I x_j$; then

$k \geq j$ and $a_k \geq a_j$. If $j = 0$, then $x_i I x_0$ and $x_k I x_0$, because $x_i R x_k$. But then $0 \leq a_i < 1$ and $0 \leq a_k < 1$, which contradicts the inequality $a_i > a_k + 1$. We can conclude that $j > 0$. Now $a_i < a_j + 1$, but $a_k \geq a_j$, and thus $a_i < a_k + 1$, which again is a contradiction. All cases have been covered, and the argument is complete.

Finally define a function f on A such that $f(x_i) = a_i$. We have actually shown that f imbeds $\mathfrak{A}$ in $\langle \mathrm{Re}, \gg \rangle$. Thus it has been proved that S^* is a theory of measurement relative to $\langle \mathrm{Re}, \gg \rangle$, and, by the general remarks on the method of cosets, we conclude that S is also a theory of measurement relative to $\langle \mathrm{Re}, \gg \rangle$.

Notice that the above proof would also work in the infinite case as long as the ordering R is a well-ordering of type ω.

Let us now summarize the steps in establishing the existence of measurement using as examples simple orderings and semiorders. First, after one is given a class, K say, of relational systems, the numerical relational system should be decided upon. The numerical relational system should be suggested naturally by the structure of the systems in K, and as was remarked, it is most practical to consider numerical systems where all the relations can be simply defined in terms of addition and ordering of real numbers. Second, if the proof that K is a theory of measurement is not at once obvious, the cardinality of systems in K should be taken into consideration. The restriction to countable systems would always seem empirically justified, and adequate results are possible with a restriction to finite systems. Third, the proof of the existence of measurement can often be simplified by the reduction of each relational system in K by the method of cosets. Then, instead of trying to find numerical assignments for each member of K, one concentrates only on the reduced systems. This plan was helpful in the case of semiorders. Instead of cosets, it is sometimes feasible to consider imbedding by subsystems. That is to say, one considers some convenient subclass $K' \subseteq K$ such that every element of K is a subsystem of some system in K'. If K' is a theory of measurement, then so is K. In the case of semiorders we could have used either plan: cosets or subsystems.

After the existence of measurement has been established, there is one question which if often of interest: For a given relational system, what is the class of all its numerical assignments? We present an example.

Consider relational systems $\mathfrak{A} = \langle A, D \rangle$ of type $\langle 4 \rangle$. For such systems we introduce the following definitions: xRy *if and only if* $xyDyy$. xyM^1zw *if and only if* $xyDzw$, $zwDxy$, yRz and zRy. $xyM^{n+1}zw$ *if and only if there exist* u, $v \in A$ *such that* xyM^nuv *and* uvM^1zw.

Let H be the class of all such relational systems which satisfy the following axioms for every $x, y, z, u, v, w \in A$:

A1.   *If* $xyDzw$ *and* $zwDuv$, *then* $xyDuv$.

A2. $xyDzw$ *or* $zwDxy$.

A3. *If xyDzw, then xzDyw.*

A4. *If xyDzw, then wzDyx.*

A5. *If xRy and yzDuv, then xzDuv.*

A6. *There is a $z \in A$ such that xzDzy and zyDxy.*

A7. *If not xyDzw and not xRy, then there is a $u \in A$ such that zwDxu, not xRu, and not uRy.*

A8. *If $\dot{x}yDzw$ and not xRy, then there are u, $v \in A$ and an n such that zuM^nvw and zuDxy.*

These axioms imply that for a system $\mathfrak{A}$ in $\boldsymbol{H}$, the relation R is a weak ordering of A, and the intuitive interpretation of $xyDzw$ in case yRx and wRz is that the interval between x and y is not greater than the interval between z and w. Making heavy use of the last three existence axioms, it can be shown that $\boldsymbol{H}$ is a theory of measurement relative to the numerical relational system $\langle \text{Re}, \Delta \rangle$ where Δ is the quaternary relation defined by the condition $xy\Delta zw$ *if and only if* $x-y \leq z-w$ for all x, y, z, $w \in \text{Re}$. It must be stressed that the Archimedean property of the ordering embodied in A8 cannot be formulated in first-order logic, because it implies that all systems in $\boldsymbol{H}^*$ have cardinality not more than the power of the continuum. In addition, it can be shown that, if $\mathfrak{A}$ is in $\boldsymbol{H}$, and f and g are two numerical assignments of $\mathfrak{A}$ relative to $\langle \text{Re}, \Delta \rangle$, then f and g are related by a positive linear transformation; [10] that is, there exist α, $\beta \in \text{Re}$ with $\alpha > 0$ such that, for all $x \in \text{Re}$, $f(x) = \alpha g(x) + \beta$. This gives in a certain sense the answer to the question above: If we know one numerical assignment for $\mathfrak{A}$, we know them all. Except for very special systems in $\boldsymbol{H}$, nothing more specific can really be expected.

Notice that all relational systems in $\boldsymbol{H}$ are necessarily infinite. In the next section we shall consider in detail the theory of measurement $\boldsymbol{F}$ consisting of all finite relational systems imbeddable in $\langle \text{Re}, \Delta \rangle$. Here the situation is quite hopeless. There simply is no apparent general statement that can be made about the relation between assignments. In as much as any function φ which imbeds $\langle \text{Re}, \Delta \rangle$ in itself is necessarily a linear transformation and conversely, it follows that, if $\mathfrak{A}$ is a system in $\boldsymbol{F}$ and f is an assignment for $\mathfrak{A}$, then f composed with a linear transformation is also an assignment. The main difficulty with $\boldsymbol{F}$ is that two assignments for the same system in $\boldsymbol{F}$ need not be related by a linear transformation.

3. Axiomatizability. Given a theory of measurement, it is natural to ask various questions about its axiomatizability, for the axiomatic analysis of any mathematical theory usually throws considerable light on the structure of the theory. In particular, given an extrinsic characteri-

---

[10] The proofs of both these facts about $\boldsymbol{H}$ are very similar to the corresponding proofs in Suppes and Winet [6].

zation of a theory of measurement via a particular numerical relational system, it is quite desirable to have an intrinsic axiomatic characterization of the theory to be able better to recognize when a relational system actually belongs to the theory. In view of the paucity of metamathematical results concerning the axiomatics of higher-order theories, we shall restrict ourselves to the problem of axiomatizing theories of measurement in first-order logic.

It is a well-known result that, if a set of first-order axioms has one infinite model, then it has models of unbounded cardinalities. Since for the most part we are interested in one-one assignments with values in the set of real numbers, unbounded cardinalities are hardly an asset. That is to say, the class of all relational systems that are models of a given set of first-order axioms is usually not a theory of measurement. To remove such difficulties without having to understand them, we simply restrict the cardinalities under consideration. Even a restriction to finite cardinalities is not too strong and leads to some rather difficult questions. Thus for the remainder of this section we shall consider only *finitary theories of measurement*, i.e., theories containing only finite relational systems. Such a theory is called *axiomatizable*, if there exists a set of sentences of first-order logic (the axioms of the theory) such that a finite relational system is in the theory if and only if the system satisfies all the sentences in the set. A theory is *finitely axiomatizable* if it has a finite set of axioms. A theory is *universally axiomatizable* if it has a set of axioms each of which is a universal sentence (i.e., a sentence in prenex normal form with only universal quantifiers).

It should be observed, first, that *any* finitary theory of measurement is axiomatizable. This is no deeper than saying that in first-order logic we can write down a sentence completely describing the isomorphism type of each finite relational system not in the given theory, and clearly the negations of these sentences can serve as the required set of axioms. It is of course quite obvious that we cannot in each instance give an effective method for writing down the axioms, since there are clearly a continuum number of distinct finitary theories of measurement. Notice also that if the theory closed under subsystems then the axioms may be taken as universal sentences, and conversely. In case one considers theories consisting of all finite relational systems imbeddable in a given numerical relational system, then the problem of a recursive or effective axiomatization is simply the problem of whether the class of universal sentences true in the given numerical relational system is recursively enumerable or not. It is not difficult to establish that this last problem is equivalent to the problem of giving a recursive enumeration of all the relation types of finite relational systems *not* imbeddable in the given numerical relational system. For numerical relational systems whose relations are definable in first-order logic in terms of $+$ and $\leq$, these problems do not arise since the first-order theory of $+$ and $\leq$ is decidable, and it is to these relational systems that we shall primarily restrict our further attention.

In the second place, in all domains of mathematics a finite axiomatization of a theory is usually felt to be the most satisfactory result. No doubt the psychological basis for such a feeling rests on the fact that only a finite characterization can in one step explicitly lay bare the full structure of a theory. Of course an extremely complicated axiomatization may be of little practical value, and as regards theories of measurement there is a further complication. Namely, if an axiomatization in first-order logic, no matter how elegant it may be, involves a combination of several universal and existential quantifiers, then the confirmation of this axiom may be highly contingent on the relatively arbitrary selection of the particular domain of objects. From the empirical standpoint, aside from the possible requirement of a fixed minimal number of objects, results ought to be independent of an exact specification of the extent of the domain.

We are thus brought to our third observation: A finite universal axiomatization of a theory of measurement always yields a characterization independent of accidental object selection. To be precise, consider a fixed universal sentence. This formula will obviously contain just a finite number of variables. Hence, to verify the truth of the sentence in a particular relational system, we need consider only subsets of the domain of a uniformly bounded cardinality. Furthermore, verification for each subset is completely independent of any relationships with the complementary set.

Simple orderings and semiorders are examples of this last point. To determine whether a finite relational system of type $\langle 2 \rangle$ is a simple ordering, one has only to consider triples of objects; for semiorders, quadruples. In constructing an experiment, say, on the simple ranking of objects with respect to a certain property, the design is ordinarily such that connectivity and antisymmetry of the relation are satisfied, because for each pair of objects the subject is required to decide the ranking one way or the other, but not in both directions. Analysis of the data then reduces to searching for "intransitive triads".

Vaught [8] has provided a useful criterion for certain classes of relational systems to be axiomatizable by means of a universal sentence. A straightforward analysis of his proof yields immediately the following criterion for finitary theories of measurement.

*A finitary theory of measurement **K** is axiomatizable by a universal sentence, if and only if **K** is closed under subsystems and there is an integer n such that, if any finite relational system $\mathfrak{A}$ has the property that every subsystem of $\mathfrak{A}$ with no more than n elements is in **K**, then $\mathfrak{A}$ is in **K**.*

Though classes of finite simple orderings and finite semiorders are two examples of finitary theories of measurement axiomatizable by a universal sentence, there are interesting examples of finitary theories of measurement closed under subsystems which are *not* axiomatizable by a universal sentence. We now turn to the proof for one such case.

Let F be the class of all finitary relational systems of type $\langle 4 \rangle$ imbeddable in the numerical relational system $\langle \text{Re}, \Delta \rangle$. A wide variety of sets of empirical data are in F. In fact, all sets of psychological data based upon judgments of differences of sensation intensities or of differences in utility qualify as candidates for membership in F. For example, in an experiment concerned with the subjective measurement of loudness of n sounds, the appropriate empirical data would be obtained by asking subjects to compare each of the n sounds with every other and then to compare the difference of loudness in every pair of sounds with every other. More elaborate interpretations are required to obtain appropriate data on utility differences for individuals or social groups (cf. Davidson, Suppes and Siegel [2], Suppes and Winet [6]). It may be of some interest to mention one probabilistic interpretation closely related to the classical scaling method of paired comparisons. Subjects are asked to choose only between objects, but they are asked to make this choice a number of times. There are many situations in which they vacillate in their choice, and the probability p_{xy} that x will be chosen over y may be estimated from the relative frequency with which x is so chosen. From inequalities of the form $p_{xy} \leq p_{zw}$ we may obtain a set of empirical data, that is, a finite relational system of type $\langle 4 \rangle$, which is a candidate for membership in F. The intended interpretation is that, if $p_{xy} \geq \frac{1}{2}$ and $p_{zw} \geq \frac{1}{2}$, then $p_{xy} \leq p_{zw}$ if and only if the difference in sensation intensity or difference in utility between x and y is equal to or less than that between z and w, the idea being, of course, that if x and y are closer together than z and w in the subjective scale, then the relative frequency of choice of x over y is closer to one-half than that of z over w.

Before formally proving that the theory of measurement F is not axiomatizable by a universal sentence, we intuitively indicate for a relational system of ten elements the kind of difficulty which arises in any attempt to axiomatize F. Let the ten elements be $a_1, \ldots, a_{10}$ ordered as shown on the following diagram with atomic intervals given the designations indicated.

α_1	α_2	α_3	α_4	γ	β_1	β_2	β_3	β_4
$a_1 \quad a_2$		$a_3 \quad a_4$		a_5	$a_6 \quad a_7$	a_8	a_9	a_{10}

Let α be the interval (a_1, a_5), let β be the interval (a_6, a_{10}), and let γ be larger than α or β. We suppose further that $\alpha_1, \alpha_2, \alpha_3, \alpha_4$ is equal in size to $\beta_2, \beta_4, \beta_1, \beta_3$, respectively, but α is less than β. [11]

---

[11] Essentially this example was first given in another context by Herman Rubin to show that a particular set of axioms is defective.

The size relationships among the remaining intervals may be so chosen that any subsystem of nine elements is imbeddable in $\langle Re, \Delta \rangle$, whereas the full system of ten elements is clearly not.

Generalizing this example and using the criterion derived from Vaught's theorem we now prove:

THEOREM. *The theory of measurement* F *is not axiomatizable by a universal sentence.*

PROOF. In order to apply the criterion of axiomatizability by a universal sentence, we need to show that for every n there is a finite relational system $\mathfrak{A}$ of type $\langle 4 \rangle$ such that every subsystem of $\mathfrak{A}$ with n elements in its domain is in F but $\mathfrak{A}$ is not.

To this end, for every even integer $n = 2m \geq 10$ we construct a finite relational system $\mathfrak{A}$ of type $\langle 4 \rangle$ such that every subsystem of $2m-1$ elements is in F. (A fortiori every subsystem of $2m-k$ elements for $k < 2m$ is in F.) To make the construction both definite and compact, we take numbers as elements of the domain and disrupt exactly one numerical relationship. Let now m be an even integer equal to or greater than 10. The selection of numbers $a_1, \ldots, a_{2m}$ may be most easily described by specifying the numerical size of the atomic intervals. We define $\alpha_i = a_{i+1} - a_i$ for $i = 1, \ldots, m-1$ and $\beta_i = a_{m+i+1} - a_{m+i}$ for $i = 1, \ldots, m-1$. We then set $a_1 = 1$, $\alpha_i = 2^i$ for $i = 1, \ldots, m-1$, and $a_{m+1} = 2^{2m}$. In fixing the size of β_i, we have two cases to consider depending on the parity of m.

CASE 1. *m is even.* Then $m-1$ is odd, and we set $\beta_i = \alpha_{i/2}$ for $i = 2$, $4, \ldots, m-2$ and $\beta_i = \alpha_{(m+i-1)/2}$ for $i = 1, 3, \ldots, m-1$.

CASE 2. *m is odd.* Then $m-1$ is even, and we set $\beta_i = \alpha_{i/2}$ for $i = 2$, $4, \ldots, m-1$ and $\beta_i = \alpha_{(m+i)/2}$ for $i = 1, 3, \ldots, m-2$. Thus if $n = 2m = 12$, we have $\alpha_1 = \beta_2$, $\alpha_2 = \beta_4$, $\alpha_3 = \beta_1$, $\alpha_4 = \beta_3$, $\alpha_5 = \beta_5$. With the set $A = \{a_1, \ldots, a_{2m}\}$ defined, we now define the relation D as the expected numerical relation except for permutations of a_1, a_m, a_{m+1} and a_{2m}. If $x, y, z, w \in A$ and $\langle x, y, z, w \rangle$ is not some permutation of $\langle a_1, a_m, a_{m+1}, a_{2m} \rangle$, then $\langle x, y, z, w \rangle \in D$ if and only if

(1) $$x - y \leq z - w.$$

Moreover, let $a = a_1$, $b = a_m$, $c = a_{m+1}$, $d = a_{2m}$. Then we put the following nine permutations of $\langle a, b, c, d \rangle$ in D:

$$\langle b, a, d, c \rangle \qquad \langle a, b, d, c \rangle \qquad \langle c, b, d, a \rangle$$
$$\langle b, d, a, c \rangle \qquad \langle a, c, d, b \rangle \qquad \langle c, d, a, b \rangle$$
$$\langle b, d, c, a \rangle \qquad \langle a, d, c, b \rangle \qquad \langle c, d, b, a \rangle$$

(These nine permutations correspond exactly to the strict inequalities following from $b - a < d - c$. All nine are needed to make the subsystems of $\langle A, D \rangle$ have the appropriate properties.)

From the choice of the numbers in A and the definition of D it is obvious that $\langle A, D \rangle$ is not imbeddable in $\langle \mathrm{Re}, \Delta \rangle$, that is, that $\langle A, D \rangle$ is not in F; for the atomic intervals between a_1 and a_m must add up to a length equal to the sum of the atomic intervals between a_{m+1} and a_{2m}, but by hypothesis the interval (a_1, a_m) is less than the interval (a_{m+1}, a_{2m}). It remains to show that every subsystem of $2m-1$ elements is in F. Two cases naturally arise.

CASE 1. The element omitted in the subsystem is a_1, a_m, a_{m+1} or a_{2m}. Then the nine permutations of (2) are not in D restricted to the subsystem, and the subsystem is not merely imbeddable in $\langle \mathrm{Re}, \Delta \rangle$, but by virtue of (1) is a subsystem of it.

CASE 2. The element omitted is neither a_1, a_m, a_{m+1} nor a_{2m}. Let a_i be the element not in the subsystem. There are two cases to consider.

CASE 2a. $a_i < a_m$. For this situation we may use for our numerical assignment the function f defined by $f(a_{i-j}) = a_{i-j}+1$ for $j = 1, \ldots, i-1$, $f(a_{i+j}) = a_{i+j}$ for $j = 1, \ldots, n-i$. It is straightforward but tedious to verify that f is a numerical assignment, that is, that it preserves the relation D as defined by (1) and (2). Only two observations are crucial to this verification. First, regarding atomic intervals (in the full system), if $a_{i-j+1}-a_{i-j} = a_{k+1}-a_k$ for $k > i$, then $f(a_{i-j+1})-f(a_{i-j}) = (a_{i-j+1}-1)-(a_{i-j}-1) = a_{k+1}-a_k = f(a_{k+1})-f(a_k)$. Second, the numbers in A were so chosen that, if $x, y, z, w \in A$, and (z, w) is not an atomic interval, and $(x, y) \neq (z, w)$ and $x-y \leq z-w$, then $x-y+2 \leq z-w$. Then it is clear from the definition of f that $f(x) - f(y) \leq f(z) - f(w)$. (Note that the above implies the weaker result that no two distinct nonatomic intervals have the same size.)

CASE 2b. $a_i > a_m+1$. Here we may use a numerical assignment f defined, as would be expected from the previous case, by $f(a_{i-j}) = a_{i-j}$ for $j = 1, \ldots, i-1$, $f(a_{i+j}) = a_{i+j}+1$ for $j = 1, \ldots, n-i$. This completes the proof of the theorem.

It would be pleasant to report that we could prove a stronger result about the theory of measurement F, namely, that it is not finitely axiomatizable. Unfortunately, there seems to be a paucity of tools available for studying such questions for classes of relational systems. However, we would like to state a conjecture which if true would provide one useful tool for studying the finite axiomatizability of finitary theories of measurement like F which are closed under submodels. We say that two sentences are *finitely equivalent* if and only if they are satisfied by the same finite relational systems, and we conjecture: *If S is a sentence such that if it is satisfied by a finite model it is satisfied by every submodel of the finite model, then there is a universal sentence finitely equivalent to S.* If this conjecture is true, it follows that any finitary theory of measurement closed under submodels is finitely axiomatizable if and only if it is axiomatizable by a universal sentence.

The proof (or disproof) of this conjecture appears difficult. It easily follows from Tarski's results [7] on universal (arithmetical) classes in the wider sense that, if the finitistic restrictions are removed throughout in the conjecture, the thus modified conjecture is true; for the class of relational systems satisfying S, being closed under submodels, is a universal class in the wider sense and is axiomatizable by a denumerable set of universal sentences. Since S is logically equivalent to this set of universal sentences, it is a logical consequence of some finite subset of them; but because it implies the full set, it also implies the finite subset and is thus equivalent to it.

Our conjecture is one concerning the general theory of models and its pertinence is not restricted to theories of measurement. In conclusion we should like to mention an unsolved problem typical of those which arise in the special area of measurement. *Let R be any binary numerical relation definable in an elementary manner in terms of plus and less than. Is the finitary theory of measurement of all systems imbeddable in R finitely axiomatizable?* (If our conjecture about finite models is true, then the theory of measurement F is not finitely axiomatizable and shows that the answer to this problem is negative for quaternary relations definable in terms of plus and less than.)

REFERENCES

[1] G. BIRKHOFF, *Lattice theory,* American Mathematical Society colloquium series, vol. 25, revised ed. (1948), xiv + 283 pp.

[2] D. DAVIDSON, P. SUPPES and S. SIEGEL, *Decision making: An experimental approach,* Stanford, California (Stanford University Press), 1957, 121 pp.

[3] T. HAILPERIN, *Remarks on identity and description in first-order axiom systems,* this JOURNAL, vol. 19 (1954), pp. 14–20.

[4] R. D. LUCE, *Semiorders and a theory of utility discrimination,* **Econometrica,** vol. 24 (1956), pp. 178–191.

[5] W. SIERPINSKI, *Hypothèse du continu,* Warsaw and Lwów 1934, v + 192 pp.

[6] P. SUPPES and M. WINET, *An axiomatization of utility based on the notion of utility differences,* **Management science,** vol. 1 (1955), pp. 259–270.

[7] A. TARSKI, *Contributions to the theory of models, I, II, III,* **Indagationes mathematicae,** vol. 16 (1954), pp. 572–581, 582–588, and vol. 17 (1955), pp. 56–64.

[8] R. VAUGHT, *Remarks on universal classes of relational systems,* **Indagationes mathematicae,** vol. 16 (1954), pp. 589–591.

PRINCETON UNIVERSITY AND STANFORD UNIVERSITY

MODELS FOR CHOICE-REACTION TIME

Mervyn Stone

MEDICAL RESEARCH COUNCIL[*]

In the two-choice situation, the Wald sequential probability ratio decision procedure is applied to relate the mean and variance of the decision times, for each alternative separately, to the error rates and the ratio of the frequencies of presentation of the alternatives. For situations involving more than two choices, a fixed sample decision procedure (selection of the alternative with highest likelihood) is examined, and the relation is found between the decision time (or size of sample), the error rate, and the number of alternatives.

This paper develops to the point of usefulness several mathematical models for choice-reaction time. The working details are confined to appendices and only definitions and results appear in the text. It is hoped that this method of presentation will assist the reader in making a quick "calculated-observed" analysis of the data he may have. The choice of models is made mainly by analogy with statistical decision procedures, but no model is presented which is psychologically unreasonable. Also no comparisons are made with experimental data for several reasons: (i) the paucity of available data means that the field should be kept open to avoid premature rejections; (ii) published data are often summarized in directions orthogonal to our interests; (iii) for the most powerful discrimination, experiments will need to be designed with specific models in mind.

The models are envisaged as applying to the situation in which the subject (S) is given a time-stationary stimulus or signal and is required to identify some attribute of the signal and make an appropriate reaction. The signal remains present until the reaction is made. S is presented with signal after signal and the successive attributes form a random sequence; that is, for a given run of signals, the attributes of different signals are mutually independent and their probabilities of presentation do not change with time. The models assume that S has a settled mode of response. They will be hydrodynamic in the following sense. At the onset of each signal, a stream of information about the signal flows at a uniform rate into S. After a certain time, the input time, the front of this stream reaches S's decision taking mechanism or "computer." After a further time, the decision time, S makes a response. The time taken for the response to be recorded will be called the motor time. Thus the choice-reaction time is made up of three components:

[*]Applied Psychology Research Unit, 15 Chaucer Road, Cambridge, England.

This article appeared in *Psychometrika*, 1960, **25**, 251–260. Reprinted with permission.

the input time, T_i ; the decision time, T_d ; the motor time, T_m . The models apply to T_d , which will be related to the environmental variables (the number of signals and their frequencies of presentation) and the rate at which S makes incorrect responses. By concentrating on T_d in this way, it is not implied that T_i and T_m are necessarily independent of these factors.

Likelihood Ratio Models for the Two-Choice Situation

It is assumed that the subject knows when the signal (either s_0 or s_1 , say) commences; that is, he knows when to start examining the stream of information arriving at the computer. (This stream is "noisy" until the stream from the signal is added to it.) This assumption holds in the self-paced condition and also when some preparatory warning signal is given. It is supposed that there is some overlap in the information; that is, some patterns of information may arise from either s_0 or s_1 . If there is no uncertainty in this sense, there is no need for a statistical computer. The uncertainty may arise from the external situation, from noise added at the input stage, or from both sources. We will suppose that the information on which S's computer operates is equivalent to a series of independent random variables at short time intervals t and that each random variable has the (stationary) distribution of a random variable x (dependent on which signal has occurred) until the response is made.

Signal

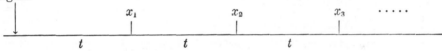

Let $p_0(x)$ and $p_1(x)$ be the probabilities of x when the signal is s_0 and s_1 , respectively. If the x's are instantaneous samples of an almost continuous stream of information then the assumption of independence implies zero auto-correlation between parts of the stream not less than time t apart. If the x's are integrals of the stream over the successive intervals, then the assumption requires zero auto-correlation for all time lags (or at least for those not small compared with t). Suppose the computer transforms each x to a quantity $c(x)$ which is then stored in an adder.

Sequential Case

The computer makes a running total of $c(x_1)$, $c(x_2)$, $\cdots$. Constant log A and log B with $A > B$ are preselected so that S decides for s_0 (and makes the appropriate motor action) as soon as the total falls below log B, provided the total has not previously exceeded log A when the decision would have been made for s_1 . (The odd way of expressing the constants facilitates later

references.) If the decision is made at the nth sample $T_d = nt$. The theory
of the sequential probability ratio test [1] shows that the optimum choice
of the function $c(x)$ is

(1) $$c(x) = \log p_1(x) - \log p_0(x).$$

Such a function implies that S is familiar with the probability distributions
$p_0(x)$ and $p_1(x)$. Such familiarity may be the result of a process of learning,
provided S has performed many trials of the discrimination task and is
given knowledge of results. S's computer may be thought of as exploratory,
trying out different $c(x)$'s until the optimal one is found. However it is con-
ceivable that the distributions can be deduced by S from the structure of
the situation and then imposed on his computer. The optimality of (1) is
stated by Wald [1] in the following terms: let $\bar{n}_0$, $\bar{n}_1$ be the averages of the
number of samples necessary for decision when the signals presented are
s_0 , s_1 , respectively. If $\bar{n}_0^*$, $\bar{n}_1^*$ are the averages for any other decision procedure based on x_1 , x_2 , etc., with equal probabilities of incorrect response
to s_0 and s_1 , then $\bar{n}_0^* \geq \bar{n}_0$ and $\bar{n}_1^* \geq \bar{n}_1$. It is possible that this form of
optimality does not appeal to S, who may have to be trained to use it by
suitable reward.

Before testing the model, it must be remembered that it is T which is
measured and not T_d . Even so, a test is available which requires only the
following assumption. Consider trials leading to a decision for s_0 . The assumption is, given the value of T_d , that the distribution of $T_i + T_m$ is the same
whether the decision is right or wrong. (The same assumption is made for
decisions for s_1 .) This does not exclude the possibility that $T_i + T_m$ and T_d
be correlated. The length of time, T_i , may affect the uncertainty in the
information presented to the computer and therefore may affect T_d ; alternatively, if T_d is long, T_m may be deliberately shortened. However, it does
assume that T_m cannot be influenced by information processed since the
initiation of the motor action. In Appendix 1 it is shown that, with mild
restrictions on $p_0(x)$ and $p_1(x)$, the distribution of the n's, and therefore of
the T_d's, leading to a decision for s_0 (or of those leading to s_1) is the same
whether the decisions are correct or incorrect. With the above assumption,
this implies that the same result should hold for a comparison of the correct
and incorrect T's leading to s_0 (and for a comparison of those leading to s_1).
This provides the basis of a reasonable test of the model. However, a fair
proportion of errors would be needed to give a powerful test.

Without making assumptions about $p_0(x)$ and $p_1(x)$, it is difficult to
think of more ways of examining the validity of the model. Since x is an
intervening variable without operational definition, it would clearly be
unwise to assume much about $p_0(x)$ and $p_1(x)$. However, there is one assumption, called the "condition of symmetry," which in some discrimination

tasks may be reasonable. This is that the distribution of $p_1(x)/p_0(x)$, when x is distributed according to $p_0(x)$, is identical with that of $p_0(x)/p_1(x)$, when x is distributed according to $p_1(x)$. It is shown in Appendix 2 that, if this condition holds,

$$(2) \qquad \bar{n}_1/\bar{n}_0 = J(\beta, \alpha)/J(\alpha, \beta);$$

$$(3) \quad \begin{aligned} J(\alpha, \beta)v_1 &- J(\beta, \alpha)v_0 \\ &= \{J(\beta, \alpha)\alpha(1 - \alpha)[4\bar{n}_1^2 - (\bar{n}_1 - \bar{n}_0)^2] \\ &\quad - J(\alpha, \beta)\beta(1 - \beta)[4\bar{n}_0^2 - (\bar{n}_0 - \bar{n}_1)^2]\}/(1 - \alpha - \beta)^2, \end{aligned}$$

where α and β are the probabilities of incorrect response to a single s_0 and s_1, respectively, v_i is the variance of the sample sizes when s_i is presented, and

$$J(\alpha, \beta) = \alpha \log [\alpha/(1 - \beta)] + (1 - \alpha) \log [(1 - \alpha)/\beta].$$

If it is feasible to estimate T_d directly for each trial by eliminating $T_i + T_m$ from T, then (2) and (3) imply

$$(4) \qquad \bar{T}_{d1}/\bar{T}_{d0} = J(\beta, \alpha)/J(\alpha, \beta),$$

$$(5) \quad \begin{aligned} J(\alpha, \beta) \operatorname{var} T_{d1} &- J(\beta, \alpha) \operatorname{var} T_{d0} \\ &= \{J(\beta, \alpha)\alpha(1 - \alpha)[4\bar{T}_{d1}^2 - (\bar{T}_{d1} - \bar{T}_{d0})^2] \\ &\quad - J(\alpha, \beta)\beta(1 - \beta)[4\bar{T}_{d0}^2 - (\bar{T}_{d0} - \bar{T}_{d1})^2]\}/(1 - \alpha - \beta)^2. \end{aligned}$$

Equations (4) and (5) are most relevant if S can be persuaded to achieve different (α, β) combinations without changing the distributions $p_0(x)$ and $p_1(x)$. When $\alpha = \beta$, then $\bar{n}_0 = \bar{n}_1$ and $v_0 = v_1$; with the assumptions that $T_i + T_m$ is (i) uncorrelated with T_d and (ii) independent of the signal presented, this implies equality of means and variances of reaction times to the signals. So, for the latter special case, it is not necessary to measure T_d.

For the "condition of symmetry" it is sufficient that, with x represented as a number, $p_0(x) = p_1(x - d)$ for some number d with $p_0(x)$ symmetrical about its mean. This might occur when s_0, s_1 are signals which are close together on some scale and the error added to the signals to make x has the same distribution for each signal. Symmetry would not be expected in absolute threshold discriminations or in the discrimination of widely different colors in a color-noisy background. Another sufficient condition is that x be bivariate, $[x(1), x(2)]$, the probabilities under s_0 obtained from those under s_1 by interchanging $x(1)$ and $x(2)$. For instance, $x(1)$ and $x(2)$ may be the inputs on two noisy channels and s_0 consists of stimulation of the first while s_1 consists of stimulation of the second.

A further prediction of the model for the symmetrical case can be made when S is persuaded by a suitable reward to give equal weight to errors to s_0 and s_1, that is to minimize his unconditional error probability, by adjustment of the constants A and B in his computer. If p_0 is the frequency of presentation of s_0 then the error probability is $p_0 \alpha + (1 - p_0)\beta$ or e, say, and the average decision time is $p_0\bar{T}_{d0} + (1 - p_0)\bar{T}_{d1}$ or $\bar{T}_d$, say. It is shown in Appendix 3 that, provided $10e < p_0 < 1 - 10e$, the minimization results in the following relation between $\bar{T}_d$, e and p_0 :

$$\bar{T}_d \propto J(e, e) - J(p_0, p_0).$$

The Non-Sequential Fixed-Sample Case

If S has an incentive to react quickly and correctly, then the advantage of the sequential decision procedure is that those discriminations which by chance happen to be easy are made quickly and time is saved. However it is possible that S may adopt a different, less efficient strategy—which is to fix T_d for all trials at a value which will give a certain accepted error rate. Let the sample size corresponding to this decision time be n. The likelihood ratio procedures are as follows: decide for s_0 if $c(x_1) + \cdots + c(x_n) < \log C$; decide for s_1 if $c(x_1) + \cdots + c(x_n) \geq \log C$; $c(x) = \log p_1(x) - \log p_0(x)$ and $C > 0$. These procedures are optimal in the sense that, if any other procedure based on $x_1, \cdots, x_n$ is used, there exists one of the likelihood ratio procedures with smaller error probabilities. It was remarkable that in the sequential case useful predictions were obtainable under mild restrictions on $p_0(x)$ and $p_1(x)$. Unfortunately this does not hold for the fixed-sample case, making more difficult the problem of testing whether such a model holds.

If there is no input storage, it is possible that the results of the self-imposed strategy just outlined are equivalent to those obtainable when the experimenter himself cuts off the signals after an exposure time T_d. But this is the type of situation considered by Peterson and Birdsall [2]. The emphasis of these authors is mainly on the external parameters (such as energy) rather than on any supposed intervening variable. They define a set of physical situations for auditory discrimination in terms of a parameter d, which is equivalent to the difference between the means of two normal populations with unit variance. (For, in the cases considered, it happens that the logarithm of the likelihood ratio of the actual physical random variables for the two alternatives is normally distributed with equality of variance under the two alternatives.) This parameter sets a limit to the various performances (error probabilities to s_0 and s_1) of any discriminator using the whole of the physical information. It therefore sets an upper bound on the performance of S who can only use less than the whole. In [2] the authors make the assumption that the information on the basis of which S makes his discrimination nevertheless gives normality of logarithm of the likelihood ratio. They examine data to see whether S is producing error frequencies that lie on a curve defined by a d greater than that in the external situation.

More than Two Alternatives

For m alternatives there are m probability distributions for the intervening variable x (which may be multivariate); that is, signal s_i induces an

x with the probability distribution $p_i(x)$ for $i = 1, \cdots, m$. We will consider the consequences of a fixed-sample decision procedure based on $x_1, \cdots, x_n$, where n is fixed.

If the signals are presented independently with probabilities $p_1, \cdots, p_m$ (adding to unity) and if $\alpha_i(\mathfrak{D})$ is the probability of error to signal s_i when the decision procedure $\mathfrak{D}$ (based on $x_1, \cdots, x_n$) is used, then the probability of error to a single presentation is

$$e = \sum_1^m p_i \alpha_i(\mathfrak{D}).$$

It is shown in Appendix 4 that the $\mathfrak{D}$ minimizing e is that which effectively selects the signal with maximum posterior probability. In this section, this minimum e will be related to n (or T_d/t) and m when distributions are normal. However in the validation of the model it might be necessary to supplement T_d with a time $T_{\bar{d}}$, representing the time the computer requires to examine the m posterior probabilities to decide which is the largest. For, although it might be reasonable to suppose that $T_i + T_m$ is independent of m, one would expect $T_{\bar{d}}$ to vary with m. The simplest model for $T_{\bar{d}}$ would be to suppose that $T_{\bar{d}} = (m - 1)t'$, where t' is the time necessary to compare any two of the probabilities and decide which is the larger.

We will state the relation between n and m when e is constant in the following special case (treated by Peterson and Birdsall [3], who stated the relation between e and m when n is held constant by the experimenter): we take $p_1 = p_2 = \cdots = p_m = 1/m$ and x a multivariate random variable $x(1), \cdots, x(m)$. Under s_i, suppose that $x(1), \cdots, x(m)$ are independent and that $x(i)$ is normally distributed with mean $\mu > 0$ and unit variance, while the other components of x are normal with zero means and unit variances. Thus there is all-round symmetry. $x(1), \cdots, x(m)$ can be regarded as the inputs on m similar channels. The ith channel is stimulated under s_i. It is readily seen that the optimal procedure is to choose the signal corresponding to the channel with the largest total. It is shown in Appendix 5 that, with this procedure,

$$n\mu^2 = \{1 + [0.64(m - 1)^{-1/2} + 0.45]^2\}[\Phi^{-1}(1 - e) - \Phi^{-1}(1/m)]^2$$

for those m for which $e < 1 - (1/m)$. Φ^{-1} is the inverse of the normal standardized distribution function. The values of $n\mu^2$ for certain values of e and m have been calculated. If μ is independent of m, then T_d is proportional to $n\mu^2$ and the results are plotted in Figure 1. It can be seen that T_d is very nearly linear against $\log m$, which agrees with some experimental findings in this field.

The question may be raised whether any m-choice task can obey the symmetry condition of the model. Peterson and Birdsall apply the model to the case where an auditory signal is presented in one of four equal periods

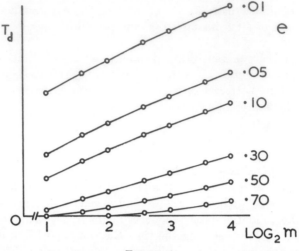

FIGURE 1

The Decision Time (T_d) for Error Rate (e) and Number of Equally Likely Alternatives (m)

of an exposure of S to "white" noise. In this case symmetry is superficially present, but any memory difficulties of S would upset it. We would not expect the model to apply to the case of response to one of m fairly easily discriminable lights arranged in some display, for the noise would be highly positional. However, in the case where the lights are patches of white noise on one of which a low intensity visual signal is superimposed so that response is difficult, the positional effect may not be important and there may be symmetry.

Appendix 1

Let n_{ij} be the sample size for a decision in favor of s_i when s_j is presented. The distribution of n_{ij} is completely determined by its characteristic function, ψ_{ij}. From $A5.1$ of [1], if

$$\phi_i(t) = \sum_x p_i(x)[p_1(x)/p_0(x)]^t,$$

then

(6) $$(1 - \alpha)B^t\psi_{00}[-\log \phi_0(t)] + \alpha A^t\psi_{10}[-\log \phi_0(t)] \equiv 1,$$

(7) $$\beta B^t\psi_{01}[-\log \phi_1(t)] + (1 - \beta)A^t\psi_{11}[-\log \phi_1(t)] \equiv 1,$$

provided the quantities E_i, V_i defined in Appendix 2 are small. If $\alpha < 0.1$ and $\beta < 0.1$ then to a good approximation $A = (1 - \beta)/\alpha$ and $B = \beta/(1 - \alpha)$. Now $\phi_0 (1 + u) = \phi_1(u)$; so, putting $t = 1 + u$ in (6) and (7),

$$\beta B^u\psi_{00}[-\log \phi_1(u)] + (1 - \beta)A^u\psi_{10}[-\log \phi_1(u)] \equiv 1,$$

$$(1 - \alpha)B^u\psi_{01}[-\log \phi_0(u)] + \alpha A^u\psi_{11}[-\log \phi_0(u)] \equiv 1.$$

By comparing these equations with (6) and (7), it is found that $\psi_{00} = \psi^0_1$ and $\psi_{10} = \psi_{11}$. Therefore the distributions of n_{00} and n_{01} (and similarly those of n_{10} and n_{11}) are identical.

Appendix 2

In the case of symmetry,

$$\sum_x p_0(x) \log [p_0(x)/p_1(x)] = \sum_x p_1(x) \log [p_1(x)/p_0(x)] = E,$$

and

$$\text{var } \log [p_0(x)/p_1(x)] \text{ under } p_0(x) = \text{var } \log [p_1(x)/p_0(x)] \text{ under } p_1(x) = V.$$

From $A{:}72$ of [1], if E and V are small,

$$(8) \qquad \bar{n}_0 = J(\alpha, \beta)/E; \qquad \bar{n}_1 = J(\beta, \alpha)/E.$$

Therefore

$$\bar{n}_1/\bar{n}_0 = J(\beta, \alpha)/J(\alpha, \beta).$$

By differentiating (6) twice with respect to t and substituting $t = 0$, using (8) and the fact that ψ_{ij} is the characteristic function of n_{ij},

$$v_0 = \frac{VJ(\alpha, \beta)}{E^3} - \frac{\alpha(1 - \alpha)[4\bar{n}_1^2 - (\bar{n}_1 - \bar{n}_0)^2]}{(1 - \alpha - \beta)^2}.$$

By symmetry

$$v_1 = \frac{VJ(\beta, \alpha)}{E^3} - \frac{\beta(1 - \beta)[4\bar{n}_0^2 - (\bar{n}_0 - \bar{n}_1)^2]}{(1 - \alpha - \beta)^2}.$$

Hence

$$J(\alpha, \beta)v_1 - J(\beta, \alpha)v_0$$
$$= \{J(\beta, \alpha)\alpha(1 - \alpha)[4\bar{n}_1^2 - (\bar{n}_1 - \bar{n}_0)^2]$$
$$- J(\alpha, \beta)\beta(1 - \beta)[4\bar{n}_0^2 - (\bar{n}_0 - \bar{n}_1)^2]\}/(1 - \alpha - \beta)^2.$$

Appendix 3

If $\alpha < 0.1$ and $\beta < 0.1$ then, by (8), $\bar{T}_d \propto p_0 J(\alpha, \beta) + (1 - p_0)J(\beta, \alpha)$. Keeping e [or $p_0 \alpha + (1 - p_0)\beta$] constant at a value in the range given by $10e < p_0 < 1 - 10e$, the condition on α and β will be satisfied. It is found by the usual methods that the minimum $\bar{T}_d$ is proportional to $J(e, e) - J(p_0, p_0)$.

Appendix 4

Let X be the set of all possible values of $x = (x_1, \cdots, x_n)$ and X_i the set of x for which a decision is made for s_i. Then

$$e = \sum_{i=1}^m p_i \sum_{x \epsilon X - X_i} p_i(x).$$

Suppose X_i and X_j have a common boundary; then, for e to be a minimum, it will not be changed by small displacements in this boundary. Hence, on the boundary, $p_i p_i(x) = p_j p_j(x)$; that is, the posterior probability of s_i equals that of s_j . Considering all possible boundaries, the solution is that X_i is the set of x's for which s_i has greater posterior probability than the other signals.

Appendix 5

Write

$$\bar{x}(i) = \sum_{s=1}^{n} x_s(i)/n.$$

Then, under s_1 , $\sqrt{n}\bar{x}(1)$ is $N(\sqrt{n}\mu, 1)$ and $\sqrt{n}\bar{x}(i)$ is $N(0, 1)$ for $i \neq 1$. Therefore,

$$\alpha_1(\mathfrak{D}) = \cdots = \alpha_m(\mathfrak{D})$$

$$= 1 - (2\pi)^{-1/2} \int_{-\infty}^{\infty} [\Phi(u)]^{m-1} \exp\left[-\tfrac{1}{2}(u - \sqrt{n}\,\mu)^2\right] du.$$

On integration by parts,

$$(9) \qquad e = \sum p_i \alpha_i(\mathfrak{D})$$

$$= (m - 1)(2\pi)^{-1/2} \int_{-\infty}^{\infty} \Phi(u)^{m-2} \Phi(u - \sqrt{n}\,\mu) \exp\left(-\tfrac{1}{2}u^2\right) du$$

$$= e_m(\theta),$$

say, where $\theta = \sqrt{n}\mu$. Peterson and Birdsall [3] use this form as the basis of their tabulation. However $e_m(\theta) \to 0$ as $\theta \to \infty$ and $e_m(\theta) \to 1$ as $\theta \to -\infty$; while $e_m'(\theta) \leq 0$. Therefore $|e_m'(\theta)|$ is a "probability density function" for θ. The characteristic function and hence the distribution of θ turns out to be the same as that of $v + w$, where $w = \max(v_1, \cdots, v_{m-1})$ and $v, v_1, \cdots, v_{m-1}$ are m independent standard normal variables. Referring to Graph 4.2.2(7) of [4], it can be seen that, for $m < 20$, the first and second moment quotients of w are not very different from those of a normal distribution. Also the addition of v to w will improve normality. Hence θ is approximately normal, agreeing with the calculations of Peterson and Birdsall. If θ is $N(\nu, \sigma^2)$, we determine ν and σ^2 as follows. From (9), $e_m(0) = 1 - (1/m)$. Also $e_m(0) = 1 - \Phi(-\nu/\sigma)$. Therefore

$$\nu/\sigma = -\Phi^{-1}(1/m).$$

Also $\sigma^2 = \text{var } v + \text{var } w$ and from Graph 4.2.2(6) of [4], var $w = [0.64 (m - 1)^{-\frac{1}{2}} + 0.45]^2$ for $m < 20$, which determines σ^2. Putting $e_m(\theta) = e$, the constant error rate,

$$n\mu^2 = \{1 + [0.64(m - 1)^{-1/2} + 0.45]^2\}[\Phi^{-1}(1 - e) - \Phi^{-1}(1/m)]^2.$$

REFERENCES

[1] Wald, A. *Sequential analysis*, New York: Wiley, 1947.
[2] Peterson, W. W. and Birdsall, T. G. The theory of signal detectability. Tech. Rep. No. 13, Electronic Defense Group, Univ. Michigan, 1953.
[3] Peterson, W. W. and Birdsall, T. G. The probability of a correct decision in a forced choice among M alternatives. Quarterly Prog. Rep. No. 10, Electronic Defense Group, Univ. Michigan, 1954.
[4] Gumbel, E. J. *Statistics of extremes*. New York: Columbia Univ. Press, 1958.

Manuscript received 10/26/59

Revised manuscript received 1/4/60

PART II

LEARNING AND STOCHASTIC PROCESSES

STATISTICAL INFERENCE ABOUT MARKOV CHAINS

T. W. Anderson and Leo A. Goodman[1]

Columbia University and University of Chicago

Summary. Maximum likelihood estimates and their asymptotic distribution are obtained for the transition probabilities in a Markov chain of arbitrary order when there are repeated observations of the chain. Likelihood ratio tests and χ^2-tests of the form used in contingency tables are obtained for testing the following hypotheses: (a) that the transition probabilities of a first order chain are constant, (b) that in case the transition probabilities are constant, they are specified numbers, and (c) that the process is a uth order Markov chain against the alternative it is rth but not uth order. In case $u = 0$ and $r = 1$, case (c) results in tests of the null hypothesis that observations at successive time points are statistically independent against the alternate hypothesis that observations are from a first order Markov chain. Tests of several other hypotheses are also considered. The statistical analysis in the case of a single observation of a long chain is also discussed. There is some discussion of the relation between likelihood ratio criteria and χ^2-tests of the form used in contingency tables.

1. Introduction. A Markov chain is sometimes a suitable probability model for certain time series in which the observation at a given time is the category into which an individual falls. The simplest Markov chain is that in which there are a finite number of states or categories and a finite number of equi-distant time points at which observations are made, the chain is of first-order, and the transition probabilities are the same for each time interval. Such a chain is described by the initial state and the set of transition probabilities; namely, the conditional probability of going into each state, given the immediately preceding state. We shall consider methods of statistical inference for this model when there are many observations in each of the initial states and the same set of transition probabilities operate. For example, one may wish to estimate the transition probabilities or test hypotheses about them. We develop an asymptotic theory for these methods of inference when the number of observations increases. We shall also consider methods of inference for more general models, for example, where the transition probabilities need not be the same for each time interval.

An illustration of the use of some of the statistical methods described herein has been given in detail [2]. The data for this illustration came from a "panel study" on vote intention. Preceding the 1940 presidential election each of a number of potential voters was asked his party or candidate preference each

Received August 29, 1955; revised October 18, 1956.

[1] This work was carried out under the sponsorship of the Social Science Research Council, The RAND Corporation, and the Statistics Branch, Office of Naval Research.

This article appeared in *Ann. Math. Stat.*, 1957, **28**, 89–110. Reprinted with permission.

month from May to October (6 interviews). At each interview each person was classified as Republican, Democrat, or "Don't Know," the latter being a residual category consisting primarily of people who had not decided on a party or candidate. One of the null hypotheses in the study was that the probability of a voter's intention at one interview depended only on his intention at the immediately preceding interview (first-order case), that such a probability was constant over time (stationarity), and that the same probabilities hold for all individuals. It was of interest to see how the data conformed to this null hypothesis, and also in what specific ways the data differed from this hypothesis.

This present paper develops and extends the theory and the methods given in [1] and [2]. It also presents some newer methods, which were first mentioned in [9], that are somewhat different from those given in [1] and [2], and explains how to use both the old and new methods for dealing with more general hypotheses. Some corrections of formulas appearing in [1] and [2] are also given in the present paper. An advantage of some of the new methods presented herein is that, for many users of these methods, their motivation and their application seem to be simpler.

The problem of the estimation of the transition probabilities, and of the testing of goodness of fit and the order of the chain has been studied by Bartlett [3] and Hoel [10] in the situation where only a single sequence of states is observed; they consider the asymptotic theory as the number of time points increases. We shall discuss this situation in Section 5 of the present paper, where a χ^2-test of the form used in contingency tables is given for a hypothesis that is a generalization of a hypothesis that was considered from the likelihood ratio point of view by Hoel [10].

In the present paper, we present both likelihood ratio criteria and χ^2-tests, and it is shown how these methods are related to some ordinary contingency table procedures. A discussion of the relation between likelihood ratio tests and χ^2-tests appears in the final section.

For further discussion of Markov chains, the reader is referred to [2] or [7].

2. Estimation of the parameters of a first-order Markov chain.

2.1. The model. Let the states be $i = 1, 2, \cdots, m$. Though the state i is usually thought of as an integer running from 1 to m, no actual use is made of this ordered arrangement, so that i might be, for example, a political party, a geographical place, a pair of numbers (a, b), etc. Let the times of observation be $t = 0, 1, \cdots, T$. Let $p_{ij}(t)$ $(i, j = 1, \cdots, m; t = 1, \cdots, T)$ be the probability of state j at time t, given state i at time $t - 1$. We shall deal both with (a) stationary transition probabilities (that is, $p_{ij}(t) = p_{ij}$ for $t = 1, \cdots, T$) and with (b) nonstationary transition probabilities (that is, where the transition probabilities need not be the same for each time interval). We assume in this section that there are $n_i(0)$ individuals in state i at $t = 0$. In this section, we treat the $n_i(0)$ as though they were nonrandom, while in Section 4, we shall discuss the case where they are random variables. An observation on a given individual consists of the sequence of states the individual is in at $t = 0, 1, \cdots,$ T, namely $i(0), i(1), i(2), \cdots, i(T)$. Given the initial state $i(0)$, there are m^T possible sequences. These represent mutually exclusive events with probabilities

$$(2.1) \qquad p_{i(0)i(1)} \, p_{i(1)i(2)} \, \cdots \, p_{i(T-1)i(T)}$$

when the transition probabilities are stationary. (When the transition probabilities are not necessarily stationary, symbols of the form $p_{i(t-1)i(t)}$ should be replaced by $p_{i(t-1)i(t)}(t)$ throughout.)

Let $n_{ij}(t)$ denote the number of individuals in state i at $t - 1$ and j at t. We shall show that the set of $n_{ij}(t)$ $(i, j = 1, \cdots, m; t = 1, \cdots, T)$, a set of $m^2 T$ numbers, form a set of sufficient statistics for the observed sequences. Let $n_{i(0)i(1)\cdots i(T)}$ be the number of individuals whose sequence of states is $i(0)$, $i(1), \cdots, i(T)$. Then

$$(2.2) \qquad n_{gj}(t) = \sum n_{i(0)i(1)\cdots i(T)} \,,$$

where the sum is over all values of the i's with $i(t - 1) = g$ and $i(t) = j$. The probability, in the nmT dimensional space describing all sequences for all n individuals (for each initial state there are nT dimensions), of a given ordered set of sequences for the n individuals is

$$
\begin{aligned}
& \prod [p_{i(0)i(1)}(1) \, p_{i(1)i(2)}(2) \, \cdots \, p_{i(T-1)i(T)}(T)]^{n_{i(0)i(1)\cdots i(T)}} \\
& = \left(\prod [p_{i(0)i(1)}(1)]^{n_{i(0)i(1)\cdots i(T)}} \right) \cdots \left(\prod [p_{i(T-1)i(T)}(T)]^{n_{i(0)i(1)\cdots i(T)}} \right) \\
(2.3) \quad & = \left(\prod_{i(0),i(1)} p_{i(0)i(1)}(1)^{n_{i(0)i(1)(1)}} \right) \cdots \left(\prod_{i(T-1),i(T)} p_{i(T-1)i(T)}(T)^{n_{i(T-1)i(T)(T)}} \right) \\
& = \prod_{t=1}^{T} \prod_{g,j} p_{gj}(t)^{n_{gj}(t)} \,,
\end{aligned}
$$

where the products in the first two lines are over all values of the $T + 1$ indices. Thus, the set of numbers $n_{ij}(t)$ form a set of sufficient statistics, as announced.

The actual distribution of the $n_{ij}(t)$ is (2.3) multiplied by an appropriate function of factorials. Let $n_i(t - 1) = \sum_{j=1}^{m} n_{ij}(t)$. Then the conditional distribution of $n_{ij}(t), j = 1, \cdots, m$, given $n_i(t - 1)$ (or given $n_k(s)$, $k = 1, \cdots,$ $m; s = 0, \cdots, t - 1$) is

$$(2.4) \qquad \frac{n_i(t - 1)!}{\prod\limits_{j=1}^{m} n_{ij}(t)!} \prod_{j=1}^{m} p_{ij}(t)^{n_{ij}(t)} .$$

This is the same distribution as one would obtain if one had $n_i(t - 1)$ observations on a multinomial distribution with probabilities $p_{ij}(t)$ and with resulting numbers $n_{ij}(t)$. The distribution of the $n_{ij}(t)$ (conditional on the $n_i(0)$) is

$$(2.5) \qquad \prod_{t=1}^{T} \left\{ \prod_{i=1}^{m} \left[\frac{n_i(t - 1)!}{\prod\limits_{j=1}^{m} n_{ij}(t)!} \prod_{j=1}^{m} p_{ij}(t)^{n_{ij}(t)} \right] \right\}.$$

For a Markov chain with stationary transition probabilities, a stronger result concerning sufficiency follows from (2.3); namely, the set $n_{ij} = \sum_{t=1}^{T} n_{ij}(t)$ form a set of sufficient statistics. This follows from the fact that, when the transition probabilities are stationary, the probability (2.3) can be written in the form

(2.6) $$\prod_{t=1}^{T} \prod_{g,j} p_{gj}^{n_{gj}(t)} = \prod_{i,j} p_{ij}^{n_{ij}}.$$

For not necessarily stationary transition probabilities $p_{ij}(t)$, the $n_{ij}(t)$ are a minimal set of sufficient statistics.

2.2. Maximum likelihood estimates. The stationary transition probabilities p_{ij} can be estimated by maximizing the probability (2.6) with respect to the p_{ij}, subject of course to the restrictions $p_{ij} \geq 0$ and

(2.7) $$\sum_{j=1}^{m} p_{ij} = 1, \qquad\qquad i = 1, 2, \cdots, m,$$

when the n_{ij} are the actual observations. This probability is precisely of the same form, except for a factor that does not depend on p_{ij}, as that obtained for m independent samples, where the ith sample ($i = 1, 2, \cdots, m$) consists of $n_i^* = \sum_j n_{ij}$ multinomial trials with probabilities p_{ij} ($i, j = 1, 2, \cdots, m$). For such samples, it is well-known and easily verified that the maximum likelihood estimates for p_{ij} are

(2.8)
$$\hat{p}_{ij} = n_{ij}/n_i^* = \sum_{t=1}^{T} n_{ij}(t) / \sum_{k=1}^{m} \sum_{t=1}^{T} n_{ik}(t)$$
$$= \sum_{t=1}^{T} n_{ij}(t) / \sum_{t=0}^{T-1} n_i(t),$$

and hence this is also true for any other distribution in which the elementary probability is of the same form except for parameter-free factors, and the restrictions on the p_{ij} are the same. In particular, it applies to the estimation of the parameters p_{ij} in (2.6).

When the transition probabilities are not necessarily stationary, the general approach used in the preceding paragraph can still be applied, and the maximum likelihood estimates for the $p_{ij}(t)$ are found to be

(2.9) $$\hat{p}_{ij}(t) = n_{ij}(t)/n_i(t-1) = n_{ij}(t) \Big/ \sum_{k=1}^{m} n_{ik}(t).$$

The same maximum likelihood estimates for the $p_{ij}(t)$ are obtained when we consider the conditional distribution of $n_{ij}(t)$ given $n_i(t-1)$ as when the joint distribution of the $n_{ij}(1), n_{ij}(2), \cdots, n_{ij}(T)$ is used. Formally these estimates are the same as one would obtain if for each i and t one had $n_i(t-1)$ observations on a multinomial distribution with probabilities $p_{ij}(t)$ and with resulting numbers $n_{ij}(t)$.

The estimates can be described in the following way: Let the entries $n_{ij}(t)$ for given t be entered in a two-way $m \times m$ table. The estimate of $p_{ij}(t)$ is the i, jth entry in the table divided by the sum of the entries in the ith row. In order to estimate p_{ij} for a stationary chain, add the corresponding entries in the two-way tables for $t = 1, \cdots, T$, obtaining a two-way table with entries $n_{ij} = \sum_t n_{ij}(t)$. The estimate of p_{ij} is the i, jth entry of the table of n_{ij}'s divided by the sum of the entries in the ith row.

The covariance structure of the maximum likelihood estimates presented in this section will be given further on.

2.3. Asymptotic behavior of $n_{ij}(t)$. To find the asymptotic behavior of the $\hat{p}_{ij}$, first consider the $n_{ij}(t)$. We shall assume that $n_k(0)/\sum n_j(0) \to \eta_k$ ($\eta_k > 0$, $\sum \eta_k = 1$) as $\sum n_j(0) \to \infty$. For each $i(0)$, the set $n_{i(0)i(1)\cdots i(T)}$ are simply multinomial variables with sample size $n_{i(0)}(0)$ and parameters $p_{i(0)i(1)} \, p_{i(1)i(2)} \cdots p_{i(T-1)i(T)}$, and hence are asymptotically normally distributed as the sample size increases. The $n_{ij}(t)$ are linear combinations of these multinomial variables, and hence are also asymptotically normally distributed.

Let $P = (p_{ij})$ and let $p_{ij}^{[t]}$ be the elements of the matrix P^t. Then $p_{ij}^{[t]}$ is the probability of state j at time t given state i at time 0. Let $n_{k;ij}(t)$ be the number of sequences including state k at time 0, i at time $t - 1$ and j at time t. Then we seek the low order moments of

$$(2.10) \qquad n_{ij}(t) = \sum_{k=1}^{m} n_{k;ij}(t).$$

The probability associated with $n_{k;ij}(t)$ is $p_{ki}^{[t-1]} \, p_{ij}$, with a sample size of $n_k(0)$. Thus

$$(2.11) \qquad \mathcal{E}n_{k;ij}(t) = n_k(0)p_{ki}^{[t-1]}p_{ij} ,$$

$$(2.12) \qquad \text{Var}\{n_{k;ij}(t)\} = n_k(0)p_{ki}^{[t-1]}p_{ij}[1 - p_{ki}^{[t-1]}p_{ij}],$$

$$(2.13) \qquad \text{Cov}\{n_{k;ij}(t), n_{k;gh}(t)\} = -n_k(0)p_{ki}^{[t-1]}p_{ij}p_{kg}^{[t-1]}p_{gh}, \qquad (i, j) \neq (g, h),$$

since the set of $n_{k;ij}(t)$ follows a multinomial distribution. Covariances between other variables were given in [1].

Let us now examine moments of $n_{k;ij}(t) - n_{k;i}(t - 1)p_{ij}$, where $n_{k;i}(t - 1) = \sum_j n_{k;ij}(t)$; they will be needed in obtaining the asymptotic theory for test procedures. The conditional distribution of $n_{k;ij}(t)$ given $n_{k;i}(t - 1)$ is easily seen to be multinomial, with the probabilities p_{ij}. Thus,

$$(2.14) \qquad \mathcal{E}\{n_{k;ij}(t) \mid n_{k;i}(t - 1)\} = p_{ij} n_{k;i}(t - 1),$$

$$(2.15) \qquad \begin{aligned} \mathcal{E}\{n_{k;ij}(t) &- n_{k;i}(t - 1)p_{ij}\} \\ &= \mathcal{E}\mathcal{E}\{[n_{k;ij}(t) - n_{k;i}(t - 1)p_{ij}] \mid n_{k;i}(t - 1)\} = 0. \end{aligned}$$

The variance of this quantity is

$$\mathcal{E}[n_{k;ij}(t) - n_{k;i}(t - 1)\, p_{ij}]^2$$

(2.16)
$$= \mathcal{E}\mathcal{E}\{[n_{k;ij}(t) - n_{k;i}(t - 1)\, p_{ij}]^2 \mid n_{k;i}(t - 1)\}$$

$$= \mathcal{E}n_{k;i}(t - 1)\, p_{ij}(1 - p_{ij})$$

$$= n_k(0)\, p_{ki}^{[t-1]}\, p_{ij}(1 - p_{ij}).$$

The covariances of pairs of such quantities are

$$\mathcal{E}[n_{k;ij}(t) - n_{k;i}(t - 1)\, p_{ij}][n_{k;ih}(t) - n_{k;i}(t - 1)\, p_{ih}]$$

(2.17)
$$= \mathcal{E}\mathcal{E}\{[n_{k;ij}(t) - n_{k;i}(t - 1)p_{ij}][n_{k;ih}(t) - n_{k;i}(t - 1)p_{ih}] \mid n_{k;i}(t - 1)\}$$

$$= \mathcal{E}[-n_{k;i}(t - 1)\, p_{ij}\, p_{ih}] = -n_k(0)\, p_{ki}^{[t-1]}\, p_{ij}p_{ih}\,, \qquad\qquad j \neq h,$$

$$\mathcal{E}[n_{k;ij}(t) - n_{k;i}(t - 1)p_{ij}][n_{k;gh}(t) - n_{k;g}(t - 1)\, p_{gh}]$$

(2.18)
$$= \mathcal{E}\mathcal{E}\{[n_{k;ij}(t) - n_{k;i}(t - 1)p_{ij}][n_{k;gh}(t) - n_{k;g}(t - 1)p_{gh}]$$
$$\mid n_{k;i}(t - 1),\, n_{k;g}(t - 1)\}$$

$$= 0, \qquad\qquad i \neq g.$$

$$\mathcal{E}[n_{k;ij}(t) - n_{k;i}(t - 1)p_{ij}][n_{k;gh}(t + r) - n_{k;g}(t + r - 1)p_{gh}]$$

(2.19)
$$= \mathcal{E}\mathcal{E}\{[n_{k;ij}(t) - n_{k;i}(t - 1)p_{ij}][n_{k;gh}(t + r) - n_{k;g}(t + r - 1)p_{gh}]$$
$$\mid n_{k;g}(t + r - 1),\, n_{k;i}(t - 1),\, n_{k;ij}(t)\}$$

$$= 0, \qquad\qquad r > 0.$$

To summarize, the random variables $n_{k;ij}(t) - n_{k;i}(t - 1)p_{ij}$ for $j = 1, \cdots ,$ m have means 0 and variances and covariances of multinomial variables with probabilities p_{ij} and sample size $n_k(0)p_{ki}^{[t-1]}$. The variables $n_{k;ij}(t) - n_{k;i}(t - 1)p_{ij}$ and $n_{k;g}(s) - n_{k;g}(s - 1)p_{gh}$ are uncorrelated if $t \neq s$ or $i \neq g$.

Since we assume $n_k(0)$ fixed, $n_{k;ij}(t)$ and $n_{l;gh}(t)$ are independent if $k \neq l$. Thus

(2.20)
$$\mathcal{E}[n_{ij}(t) - n_i(t - 1)p_{ij}] = 0,$$

(2.21)
$$\mathcal{E}[n_{ij}(t) - n_i(t - 1)p_{ij}]^2 = \sum_{k=1}^{m} n_k(0)p_{ki}^{[t-1]}\, p_{ij}(1 - p_{ij}),$$

$$\mathcal{E}[n_{ij}(t) - n_i(t - 1)p_{ij}][n_{ih}(t) - n_i(t - 1)p_{ih}]$$

(2.22)
$$= - \sum_{k=1}^{m} n_k(0)p_{ki}^{[t-1]}\, p_{ij}\, p_{ih}\,, \quad j \neq h,$$

(2.23)
$$\mathcal{E}[n_{ij}(t) - n_i(t - 1)p_{ij}][n_{gh}(s) - n_g(s - 1)p_{gh}] = 0, \qquad t \neq s \text{ or } i \neq g.$$

2.4. The asymptotic distribution of the estimates. It will now be shown that when $n \to \infty$,

$$
\sqrt{n}(\hat{p}_{ij} - p_{ij}) = \sqrt{n} \left[\frac{\sum_{t=1}^{T} n_{ij}(t)}{\sum_{t=1}^{T} n_i(t-1)} - p_{ij} \right]
$$

$$(2.24) \qquad = \sqrt{n} \left[\frac{\sum_{t=1}^{T} [n_{ij}(t) - p_{ij} n_i(t-1)]}{\sum_{t=1}^{T} n_i(t-1)} \right]$$

$$
= \sqrt{n} \left[\frac{\sum_{k=1}^{m} \sum_{t=1}^{T} [n_{k;ij}(t) - p_{ij} n_{k;i}(t-1)]}{\sum_{t=1}^{T} n_i(t-1)} \right]
$$

has a limiting normal distribution, and the means, variances and covariances of the limiting distribution will be found. Because $n_{k;ij}(t)$ is a multinomial variable, we know that

$$(2.25) \qquad n_{k;ij}(t)/n \approx [n_{k;ij}(t)/n_k(0)]\eta_k$$

converges in probability to its expected value when $n_k(0)/n \to \eta_k$. Thus

$$
\text{p} \lim_{n \to \infty} \frac{1}{n} \sum_{t=1}^{T} n_i(t-1) = \lim_{n \to \infty} \frac{1}{n} \mathcal{E} \sum_{t=1}^{T} n_i(t-1)
$$

$$(2.26)$$

$$
- \sum_{k=1}^{m} \eta_k \sum_{t=1}^{T} p_{ki}^{[t-1]}.
$$

Therefore $n^{1/2}(\hat{p}_{ij} - p_{ij})$ has the same limit distribution as

$$(2.27) \qquad \frac{\sum_{t=1}^{T} [n_{ij}(t) - p_{ij} n_i(t-1)]/n^{1/2}}{\sum_{k=1}^{m} \sum_{t=1}^{T} \eta_k p_{kj}^{[t-1]}}$$

(see p. 254 in [6]).

From the conclusions in Section 2.3, the numerator of (2.27) has mean 0 and variance

$$(2.28) \qquad \mathcal{E} \left[\sum_{t=1}^{T} n_{ij}(t) - p_{ij} n_i(t-1) \right]^2 \Big/ n = \sum_{k=1}^{m} \sum_{t=1}^{T} n_k(0) p_{ki}^{[t-1]} p_{ij}(1 - p_{ij})/n.$$

The covariance between two different numerators is

$$
\mathcal{E} \left[\sum_{t=1}^{T} n_{ij}(t) - p_{ij} n_i(t-1) \right] \left[\sum_{t=1}^{T} n_{gh}(t) - p_{gh} n_g(t-1) \right] \Big/ n
$$

$$(2.29)$$

$$
= -\delta_{ig} \sum_{k=1}^{m} \sum_{t=1}^{T} n_k(0) p_{ki}^{[t-1]} p_{ij} p_{gh}/n,
$$

where $\delta_{ig} = 0$ if $i \neq g$ and $\delta_{ii} = 1$.

Let

$$(2.30) \qquad \sum_{k=1}^{m} \sum_{t=1}^{T} \eta_k \, p_{ki}^{[t-1]} = \phi_i \, .$$

Then the limiting variance of the numerator of (2.27) is $\phi_i \, p_{ij}(1 - p_{ij})$, and the limiting covariance between two different numerators is $-\delta_{ig} \, \phi_i \, p_{ij} \, p_{gh}$. Because the numerators of (2.27) are linear combinations of normalized multinomial variables, with fixed probabilities and increasing sample size, they have a limiting normal distribution and the variances and covariances of this limit distribution are the limits of the respective variances and covariances (see, e.g., Theorem 2, p. 5 in [4]).

Since $n^{1/2} \, (\hat{p}_{ij} - p_{ij})$ has the same limit distribution as (2.27), the variables $n^{1/2} \, (\hat{p}_{ij} - p_{ij})$ have a limiting joint normal distribution with means 0, variances $p_{ij}(1 - p_{ij})/\phi_i$ and the covariances $-\delta_{ig} \, p_{ij} p_{gh}/\phi_i$. The variables $(n\phi_i)^{1/2}(\hat{p}_{ij} - p_{ij})$ have a limiting joint normal distribution with means 0, variances $p_{ij}(1 - p_{ij})$ and covariances $-\delta_{ig} p_{ij} p_{gh}$. Also, the set $(n_i^*)^{1/2} \, (\hat{p}_{ij} - p_{ij})$ has a limiting joint normal distribution with means 0, variances $p_{ij}(1 - p_{ij})$ and covariances $-\delta_{ig} p_{ij} p_{gh}$, where $n_i^* = \sum_{t=0}^{T-1} n_i(t)$.

In other terms, the set $(n\phi_i)^{1/2} \, (\hat{p}_{ij} - p_{ij})$ for a given i has the same limiting distribution as the estimates of multinomial probabilities p_{ij} with sample size $n\phi_i$, which is the expected total number of observations n_i^* in the ith state for $t = 0, \cdots , T - 1$. The variables $(n\phi_i)^{1/2} \, (\hat{p}_{ij} - p_{ij})$ for m different values of i $(i = 1, 2, \cdots , m)$ are asymptotically independent (i.e., the limiting joint distribution factors), and hence have the same limiting joint distribution as obtained from similar functions of the estimates of multinomial probabilities p_{ij} from m independent samples with sample sizes $n\phi_i$ $(i = 1, 2, \cdots , m)$. It will often be possible to reformulate hypotheses about the p_{ij} in terms of m independent samples consisting of multinomial trials.

We shall also make use of the fact that the variables $\hat{p}_{ij}(t) = n_{ij}(t)/n_i(t - 1)$ for a given i and t have the same asymptotic distribution as the estimates of multinomial probabilities with sample sizes $\mathcal{E}n_i(t - 1)$, and the variables $\hat{p}_{ij}(t)$ for two different values of i or two different values of t are asymptotically independent. This fact can be proved by methods similar to those used earlier in this section. Hence, in testing hypotheses concerning the $p_{ij}(t)$ it will sometimes be possible to reformulate the hypotheses in terms of $m \times T$ independent samples consisting of multinomial trials, and standard test procedures may then be applied.

3. Tests of hypotheses and confidence regions.

3.1. Tests of hypotheses about specific probabilities and confidence regions. On the basis of the asymptotic distribution theory in the preceding section, we can derive certain methods of statistical inference. Here we shall assume that every $p_{ij} > 0$.

First we consider testing the hypothesis that certain transition probabilities

p_{ij} have specified values p_{ij}^0. We make use of the fact that under the null hypothesis the $(n_i^*)^{1/2} (\hat{p}_{ij} - p_{ij}^0)$ have a limiting normal distribution with means zero, and variances and covariances depending on p_{ij}^0 in the same way as obtains for multinomial estimates. We can use standard asymptotic theory for multinomial or normal distributions to test a hypothesis about one or more p_{ij}, or determine a confidence region for one or more p_{ij}.

As a specific example consider testing the hypothesis that $p_{ij} = p_{ij}^0, j = 1, \cdots, m$, for a given i. Under the null hypothesis,

$$(3.1) \qquad \sum_{j=1}^{m} n_i^* \frac{(\hat{p}_{ij} - p_{ij}^0)^2}{p_{ij}^0}$$

has an asymptotic χ^2-distribution with $m - 1$ degrees of freedom (according to the usual asymptotic theory of multinomial variables). Thus the critical region of one test of this hypothesis at significance level α consists of the set $\hat{p}_{ij}$ for which (3.1) is greater than the α significance point of the χ^2-distribution with $m - 1$ degrees of freedom. A confidence region of confidence coefficient α consists of the set p_{ij}^0 for which (3.1) is less than the α significance point. (The p_{ij}^0 in the denominator can be replaced by $\hat{p}_{ij}$.) Since the variables $n_i^*(\hat{p}_{ij} - p_{ij})^2$ for different i are asymptotically independent, the forms (3.1) for different i are asymptotically independent, and hence can be added to obtain other χ^2-variables. For instance a test for all p_{ij} $(i, j = 1, 2, \cdots, m)$ can be obtained by adding (3.1) over all i, resulting in a χ^2-variable with $m(m - 1)$ degrees of freedom.

The use of the χ^2-test of goodness of fit is discussed in [5]. We believe that there is as good reason for adopting the tests, which are analogous to χ^2-tests of goodness of fit, described in this section as in the situation from which they were borrowed (see [5]).

3.2. Testing the hypothesis that the transition probabilities are constant. In the stationary Markov chain, p_{ij} is the probability that an individual in state i at time $t - 1$ moves to state j at t. A general alternative to this assumption is that the transition probability depends on t; let us say it is $p_{ij}(t)$. We test the null hypothesis $H: p_{ij}(t) = p_{ij}$ $(t = 1, \cdots, T)$. Under the alternate hypothesis, the estimates of the transition probabilities for time t are

$$(3.2) \qquad \hat{p}_{ij}(t) = \frac{n_{ij}(t)}{n_i(t - 1)}.$$

The likelihood function maximized under the null hypothesis is

$$(3.3) \qquad \prod_{t=1}^{T} \prod_{i,j} \hat{p}_{ij}^{n_{ij}(t)}.$$

The likelihood function maximized under the alternative is

$$(3.4) \qquad \prod_{t} \prod_{i,j} \hat{p}_{ij}(t)^{n_{ij}(t)}.$$

The ratio is the likelihood ratio criterion

$$(3.5) \qquad \lambda = \prod_t \prod_{i,j} \left[\frac{\hat{p}_{ij}}{\hat{p}_{ij}(t)} \right]^{n_{ij}(t)}$$

A slight extension of a theorem of Cramér [6] or of Neyman [11] shows that $-2 \log \lambda$ is distributed as χ^2 with $(T - 1)[m(m - 1)]$ degrees of freedom when the null hypothesis is true.

The likelihood ratio (3.5) resembles likelihood ratios obtained for standard tests of homogeneity in contingency tables (see [6], p. 445). We shall now develop further this similarity to usual procedures for contingency tables. A proof that the results obtained by this contingency table approach are asymptotically equivalent to those presented earlier in this section will be given in Section 6.

For a given i, the set $\hat{p}_{ij}(t)$ has the same asymptotic distribution as the estimates of multinomial probabilities $p_{ij}(t)$ for T independent samples. An $m \times T$ table, which has the same formal appearance as a contingency table, can be used to represent the joint estimates $\hat{p}_{ij}(t)$ for a given i and for $j = 1, 2, \cdots, m$ and $t = 1, 2, \cdots, T$.

t \ j	1	2	$\cdots$	m
1	$\hat{p}_{i1}(1)$	$\hat{p}_{i2}(1)$	$\cdots$	$\hat{p}_{im}(1)$
2	$\hat{p}_{i1}(2)$	$\hat{p}_{i2}(2)$	$\cdots$	$\hat{p}_{im}(2)$
$\vdots$	$\vdots$	$\vdots$	$\vdots$	$\vdots$
T	$\hat{p}_{i1}(T)$	$\hat{p}_{i2}(T)$	$\cdots$	$\hat{p}_{im}(T)$

The hypothesis of interest is that the random variables represented by the T rows have the same distribution, so that the data are homogeneous in this respect. This is equivalent to the hypothesis that there are m constants p_{i1}, $p_{i2}, \cdots, p_{im}$, with $\sum_j p_{ij} = 1$, such that the probability associated with the jth column is equal to p_{ij} in all T rows; that is, $p_{ij}(t) = p_{ij}$ for $t = 1, 2, \cdots, T$. The χ^2-test of homogeneity seems appropriate here ([6], p. 445); that is, in order to test this hypothesis, we calculate

$$(3.6) \qquad \chi_i^2 = \sum_{t,j} n_i(t - 1)[\hat{p}_{ij}(t) - \hat{p}_{ij}]^2 / \hat{p}_{ij} ;$$

if the null hypothesis is true, χ_i^2 has the usual limiting distribution with $(m - 1)$ $(T - 1)$ degrees of freedom.

Another test of the hypothesis of homogeneity for T independent samples from multinomial trials can be obtained by use of the likelihood ratio criterion; that is, in order to test this hypothesis for the data given in the $m \times T$ table, calculate

$$(3.7) \qquad \lambda_i = \prod_{t,j} [\hat{p}_{ij} / \hat{p}_{ij}(t)]^{n_{ij}(t)}.$$

which is formally similar to the likelihood ratio criterion. The asymptotic distribution of $-2 \log \lambda_i$ is χ^2 with $(m - 1)(T - 1)$ degrees of freedom.

The preceding remarks relating to the contingency table approach dealt with a given value of i. Hence, the hypothesis can be tested separately for each value of i.

Let us now consider the joint hypothesis that $p_{ij}(t) = p_{ij}$ for all $i = 1, 2, \cdots ,$ $m, j = 1, 2, \cdots , m, t = 1, \cdots , T$. A test of this joint null hypothesis follows directly from the fact that the random variables $\hat{p}_{ij}(t)$ and $\hat{p}_{ij}$ for two different values of i are asymptotically independent. Hence, under the null hypothesis, the set of χ_i^2 calculated for each $i = 1, 2, \cdots , m$ are asymptotically independent, and the sum

$$(3.8) \qquad \chi^2 = \sum_{i=1}^{m} \chi_i^2 = \sum_i \sum_{t,j} n_i(t-1)[\hat{p}_{ij}(t) - \hat{p}_{ij}]^2 / \hat{p}_{ij}$$

has the usual limiting distribution with $m(m-1)(T-1)$ degrees of freedom. Similarly, the test criterion based on (3.5) can be written

$$(3.9) \qquad \sum_{i=1}^{m} -2 \log \lambda_i = -2 \log \lambda.$$

3.3. Test of the hypothesis that the chain is of a given order.

Consider first a second-order Markov chain. Given that an individual is in state i at $t - 2$ and in j at $t - 1$, let $p_{ijk}(t)$ $(i, j, k = 1, \cdots , m; t = 2, 3, \cdots , T)$ be the probability of being in state k at t. When the second-order chain is stationary, $p_{ijk}(t) = p_{ijk}$ for $t = 2, \cdots , T$. A first-order stationary chain is a special second-order chain, one for which $p_{ijk}(t)$ does not depend on i. On the other hand, as is well-known, the second-order chain can be represented as a more complicated first-order chain (see, e.g. [2]). To do this, let the pair of successive states i and j define a composite state (i, j). Then the probability of the composite state (j, k) at t given the composite state (i, j) at $t - 1$ is $p_{ijk}(t)$. Of course, the probability of state (h, k), $h \neq j$, given (i, j), is zero. The composite states are easily seen to form a chain with m^2 states and with certain transition probabilities 0. This representation is useful because some of the results for first-order Markov chains can be carried over from Section 2.

Now let $n_{ijk}(t)$ be the number of individuals in state i at $t - 2$, in j at $t - 1$, and in k at t, and let $n_{ij}(t-1) = \sum_k n_{ijk}(t)$. We assume in this section that the $n_i(0)$ and $n_{ij}(1)$ are nonrandom, extending the idea of the earlier sections where the $n_i(0)$ were nonrandom and the $n_{ij}(1)$ were random variables. The $n_{ijk}(t)$ $(i, j, k = 1, \cdots , m; t = 2, \cdots , T)$ is a set of sufficient statistics for the different sequences of states. The conditional distribution of $n_{ijk}(t)$, given $n_{ij}(t-1)$, is

$$(3.10) \qquad \frac{n_{ij}(t-1)!}{\prod_k n_{ijk}(t)!} \prod_{k=1}^{m} p_{ijk}^{n_{ijk}(t)}.$$

(When the transition probabilities need not be the same for each time interval, the symbols p_{ijk} should, of course, be replaced by the appropriate $p_{ijk}(t)$ throughout). The joint distribution of $n_{ijk}(t)$ for $i, j, k = 1, \cdots, m$ and $t = 2, \cdots, T$, when the set of $n_{ij}(1)$ is given, is the product of (3.10) over i, j and t.

For chains with stationary transition probabilities, a stronger result concerning sufficiency can be obtained as it was for first-order chains; namely, the numbers $n_{ijk} = \sum_{t=2}^{T} n_{ijk}(t)$ form a set of sufficient statistics. The maximum likelihood estimate of p_{ijk} for stationary chains is

$$(3.11) \qquad \hat{p}_{ijk} = n_{ijk} \Big/ \sum_{l=1}^{m} n_{ijl} = \sum_{t=2}^{T} n_{ijk}(t) \Big/ \sum_{t=2}^{T} n_{ij}(t-1).$$

Now let us consider testing the null hypothesis that the chain is first-order against the alternative that it is second-order. The null hypothesis is that $p_{1jk} = p_{2jk} = \cdots = p_{mjk} = p_{jk}$, say, for $j, k = 1, \cdots, m$. The likelihood ratio criterion for testing this hypothesis is[2]

$$(3.12) \qquad \lambda = \prod_{i,j,k=1}^{m} (\hat{p}_{jk} / \hat{p}_{ijk})^{n_{ijk}},$$

where

$$(3.13) \qquad \hat{p}_{jk} = \sum_{i=1}^{m} n_{ijk} \Big/ \sum_{i=1}^{m} \sum_{l=1}^{m} n_{ijl} = \sum_{t=2}^{T} n_{jk}(t) \Big/ \sum_{t=1}^{T-1} n_j(t)$$

is the maximum likelihood estimate of $\hat{p}_{jk}$. We see here that $\hat{p}_{jk}$ differs somewhat from (2.8). This difference is due to the fact that in the earlier section the $n_{ij}(1)$ were random variables while in this section we assumed that the $n_{ij}(1)$ were nonrandom. Under the null hypothesis, $-2 \log \lambda$ has an asymptotic χ^2-distribution with $m^2(m-1) - m(m-1) = m(m-1)^2$ degrees of freedom.

We observe that the likelihood ratio (3.12) resembles likelihood ratios obtained for problems relating to contingency tables. We shall now develop further this similarity to standard procedures for contingency tables.

For a given j, the $n^{1/2}(\hat{p}_{ijk} - p_{ijk})$ have the same asymptotic distribution as the estimates of multinomial probabilities for m independent samples ($i = 1, 2, \cdots, m$). An $m \times m$ table, which has the same formal appearance as a contingency table, can be used to represent the estimates $\hat{p}_{ijk}$ for a given j and for $i, k = 1, 2, \cdots, m$. The null hypothesis is that $p_{ijk} = p_{jk}$ for $i = 1, 2, \cdots, m$, and the χ^2-test of homogeneity seems appropriate. To test this hypothesis, calculate

$$(3.14) \qquad \chi_j^2 = \sum_{i,k} n_{ij}^*(\hat{p}_{ijk} - \hat{p}_{jk})^2/\hat{p}_{jk},$$

where

$$(3.15) \qquad n_{ij}^* = \sum_{k} n_{ijk} = \sum_{k} \sum_{t=2}^{T} n_{ijk}(t) = \sum_{t=2}^{T} n_{ij}(t-1) = \sum_{t=1}^{T-1} n_{ij}(t).$$

If the hypothesis is true, χ_j^2 has the usual limiting distribution with $(m-1)^2$ degrees of freedom.

---

[2] The criterion (3.12) was written incorrectly in (6.35) of [1] and (4.10) of [2].

In continued analogy with Section 3.2, another test of the hypothesis of homogeneity for m independent samples from multinomial trials can be obtained by use of the likelihood ratio criterion. We calculate

$$(3.16) \qquad \lambda_j = \prod_{i,k} (\hat{p}_{jk} / \hat{p}_{ijk})^{n_{ijk}},$$

which is formally similar to the likelihood ratio criterion. The asymptotic distribution of $-2 \log \lambda_j$ is χ^2 with $(m - 1)^2$ degrees of freedom.

The preceding remarks relating to the contingency table approach dealt with a given value of j. Hence, the hypothesis can be tested separately for each value of j.

Let us now consider the joint hypothesis that $p_{ijk} = p_{jk}$ for all $i, j, k = 1, 2, \cdots, m$. A test of this joint hypothesis can be obtained by computing the sum

$$(3.17) \qquad \chi^2 = \sum_{j=1}^{m} \chi_j^2 = \sum_{j,i,k} n_{ij}^*(\hat{p}_{ijk} - \hat{p}_{jk})^2 / \hat{p}_{jk},$$

which has the usual limiting distribution with $m(m - 1)^2$ degrees of freedom. Similarly the test criterion based on (3.12) can be written

$$(3.18) \qquad \begin{aligned} \sum_{j=1}^{m} -2 \log \lambda_j = -2 \log \lambda &= 2 \sum_{ijk} n_{ijk} \log [\hat{p}_{ijk} / \hat{p}_{jk}] \\ &= 2 \sum_{ijk} n_{ijk} [\log \hat{p}_{ijk} - \log \hat{p}_{jk}]. \end{aligned}$$

The preceding remarks can be directly generalized for a chain of order r. Let $p_{ij\ldots kl}$ ($i, j, \cdots, k, l = 1, 2, \cdots, m$) denote the transition probability of state l at time t, given state k at time $t - 1 \cdots$ and state j at time $t - r + 1$ and state i at time $t - r$ ($t = r, r + 1, \cdots, T$). We shall test the null hypothesis that the process is a chain of order $r - 1$ (that is, $p_{ij\ldots kl} = p_{j\ldots kl}$ for $i = 1, 2, \cdots, m$) against the alternate hypothesis that it is not an $r - 1$ but an r-order chain.

Let $n_{ij\ldots kl}(t)$ denote the observed frequency of the states $i, j, \cdots, k, l$ at the respective times $t - r, t - r + 1, \cdots, t - 1, t$, and let $n_{ij\ldots k}(t - 1) = \sum_{l=1}^{m} n_{ij\ldots kl}(t)$. We assume here that the $n_{ij\ldots k}(r - 1)$ are nonrandom. The maximum likelihood estimate of $p_{ij\ldots kl}$ is

$$(3.19) \qquad \hat{p}_{ij\ldots kl} = n_{ij\ldots kl}/n_{ij\ldots k}^*,$$

where $n_{ij\ldots kl} = \sum_{t=r}^{T} n_{ij\ldots kl}(t)$ and

$$(3.20) \qquad n_{ij\ldots k}^* = \sum_{l} n_{ij\ldots kl} = \sum_{t=r}^{T} n_{ij\ldots k}(t - 1) = \sum_{t=r-1}^{T-1} n_{ij\ldots k}(t).$$

For a given set $j, \cdots, k$, the set $\hat{p}_{ij\ldots kl}$ will have the same asymptotic distribution as estimates of multinomial probabilities for m independent samples ($i = 2, \cdots, m$), and may be represented by an $m \times m$ table. If the null hypothesis

$(p_{ij...kl} = p_{j...kl}$ for $i = 1, 2, \cdots, m)$ is true, then the χ^2-test of homogeneity seems appropriate, and

$$(3.21) \qquad \chi^2_{j...k} = \sum_{i,l} n^*_{ij...k}(\hat{p}_{ij...kl} - \hat{p}_{j...kl})^2 / \hat{p}_{j...kl},$$

where

$$(3.22) \qquad \hat{p}_{j...kl} = \sum_i n_{ij...kl} / \sum_i n^*_{ij...k} = \sum_{t=r}^{T} n_{j...kl}(t) \Big/ \sum_{t=r-1}^{T-1} n_{j...k}(t),$$

has the usual limiting distribution with $(m-1)^2$ degrees of freedom. We see here that $\hat{p}_{j...kl}$ differs somewhat from the maximum likelihood estimate for $p_{j...kl}$ for an $(r-1)$-order chain (viz., $\sum_{t=r-1}^{T} n_{j...kl}(t)/\sum_{t=r-2}^{T-1} n_{j...k}(t)$). This difference is due to the fact that the $n_{j...kl}(r-1)$, for an $(r-1)$-order chain, are assumed to be multinomial random variables with parameters $p_{j...kl}$ while in this paragraph we have assumed that the $n_{j...kl}(r-1)$ are fixed.

Since there are m^{r-1} sets $j, \cdots, k$ $(j = 1, 2, \cdots, m; \cdots; k = 1, 2, \cdots, m)$, the sum $\sum_{j,...,k} \chi^2_{j...k}$ will have the usual limiting distribution with $m^{r-1}(m-1)^2$ degrees of freedom under the joint null hypothesis $(p_{ij...kl} = p_{j...kl}$ for $i = 1, 2, \cdots, m$ and all values from 1 to m of $j, \cdots, k)$ is true.

Another test of the null hypothesis can be obtained by use of the likelihood ratio criterion

$$(3.23) \qquad \lambda_{j...k} = \prod_{i,l} (\hat{p}_{j...kl}/\hat{p}_{ij...l})^{n_{ij\cdots kl}},$$

where $-2 \log \lambda_{j...k}$ is distributed asymptotically as χ^2 with $(m-1)^2$ degrees of freedom. Also,

$$(3.24) \qquad \sum_{j,\cdots,k} \{-2 \log \lambda_{j...k}\} = 2 \sum_{i,j,\cdots,k,l} n_{ij...kl} \log(\hat{p}_{ij...kl}/\hat{p}_{j...kl})$$

has a limiting χ^2-distribution with $m^{r-1}(m-1)^2$ degrees of freedom when the joint null hypothesis is true (see [10]).

In the special case where $r = 1$, the test is of the null hypothesis that observations at successive time points are statistically independent against the alternate hypothesis that observations are from a first-order chain.

The reader will note that the method used to test the null hypothesis that the process is a chain of order $r - 1$ against the alternate hypothesis that it is of order r can be generalized to test the null hypothesis that the process is of order u against the alternate hypothesis that it is of order r $(u < r)$. By an approach similar to that presented earlier in this section, we can compute the χ^2-criterion or -2 times the logarithm of the likelihood ratio and observe that these statistics are distributed asymptotically as χ^2 with $[m^r - m^u](m-1)$ degrees of freedom when the null hypothesis is true.

In this section, we have assumed that the transition probabilities are the same for each time interval, that is, stationary. It is possible to test the null hypothesis that the rth order chain has stationary transition probabilities using methods that are straightforward generalizations of the tests presented in the previous section for the special case of a first-order chain.

3.4. Test of the hypothesis that several samples are from the same Markov chain of a given order. The general approach presented in the previous sections can be used to test the null hypothesis that s ($s \geqq 2$) samples are from the same rth order Markov chain; that is, that the s processes are identical.

Let $\hat{p}_{ij\cdots kl}^{(h)} = n_{ij\cdots kl}^{(h)}/n_{ij\cdots k}^{*(h)}$ denote the maximum likelihood estimate of the rth order transition probability $p_{ij\cdots kl}^{(h)}$ for the process from which sample h ($h = 1, 2, \cdots, s$) was obtained. We wish to test the null hypothesis that $p_{ij\cdots kl}^{(h)} = p_{ij\cdots kl}$ for $h = 1, 2, \cdots, s$. Using the approach presented herein, it follows that

$$(3.25) \qquad \chi_{ij\cdots k}^{2} = \sum_{h,l} n_{ij\cdots k}^{*(h)} (\hat{p}_{ij\cdots kl}^{(h)} - \hat{p}_{ij\cdots kl}^{(\cdot)})^{2}/\hat{p}_{ij\cdots kl}^{(\cdot)},$$

where $n_{ij\cdots kl}^{(\cdot)} = \sum_{h} n_{ij\cdots kl}^{(h)}$ and $\hat{p}_{ij\cdots kl}^{(\cdot)} = n_{ij\cdots kl}^{(\cdot)}/\sum_{v=1}^{m} n_{ij\cdots kv}^{(\cdot)}$, has the usual limiting distribution with $(s - 1)(m - 1)$ degrees of freedom. Also, $\sum_{i,j,\cdots,k} \chi_{ij\cdots k}^{2}$ has a limiting χ^{2}-distribution with $m^{r}(s - 1)(m - 1)$ degrees of freedom.

When $s = 2$, $\chi_{ij\cdots k}^{2}$ can be rewritten in the form

$$(3.26) \qquad \chi_{ij\cdots k}^{2} = \sum_{l} C_{ij\cdots k} (\hat{p}_{ij\cdots kl}^{(1)} - \hat{p}_{ij\cdots kl}^{(2)})^{2}/\hat{p}_{ij\cdots kl}^{(\cdot)},$$

where $\hat{p}_{ij\cdots kl}^{(\cdot)}$ is the estimate of $p_{ij\cdots kl}$ obtained by pooling the data in the two samples, and $C_{ij\cdots k}^{-1} = (1/n_{ij\cdots k}^{*(1)}) + (1/n_{ij\cdots k}^{*(2)})$. Also, $\sum_{i,j,\cdots,k} \chi_{ij\cdots k}^{2}$ has the usual limiting distribution with $m^{r}(m - 1)$ degrees of freedom in the two sample case.

Analogous results can also be obtained using the likelihood-ratio criterion.

3.5. A test involving two sets of states. In the case of panel studies, a person is usually asked several questions. We might classify each individual according to his opinion on two different questions. In an example in [2], one classification indicated whether a person saw the advertisement of a certain product and the other whether he bought the product in a certain time interval. Let the state be denoted (α, β), $\alpha = 1, \cdots, A$ and $\beta = 1, \cdots, B$ where α denotes the first opinion or class and β the second. We assume that the sequence of states satisfies a first-order Markov chain with transition probabilities $p_{\alpha\beta,\mu\nu}$. We ask whether the sequence of changes in one classification is independent of that in the second. For example, if a person notices an advertisement, is he more likely to buy the product? The null hypothesis of independence of changes is

$$(3.27) \qquad p_{\alpha\beta,\mu\nu} = q_{\alpha\mu} r_{\beta\nu} \; \alpha, \mu = 1, \cdots, A; \beta, \nu = 1, \cdots, B,$$

where $q_{\alpha\mu}$ is a transition probability for the first classification and $r_{\beta\nu}$ is for the second. We shall find the likelihood ratio criterion for testing this null hypothesis.

Let $n_{\alpha\beta,\mu\nu}(t)$ be the number of individuals in state (α, β) at $t - 1$ and (μ, ν) at t. From the previous results, the maximum likelihood estimate of $p_{\alpha\beta,\mu\nu}$, when the null hypothesis is not assumed, is

$$(3.28) \qquad \hat{p}_{\alpha\beta,\mu\nu} = \frac{n_{\alpha\beta,\mu\nu}}{\sum_{s=1}^{A} \sum_{h=1}^{B} n_{\alpha\beta,sh}}$$

where $n_{\alpha\beta,\mu\nu} = \sum_{t=1}^{T} n_{\alpha\beta,\mu\nu}(t)$. When the null hypothesis is assumed, the maximum likelihood estimate of $p_{\alpha\beta,\mu\nu}$ is $\hat{q}_{\alpha\mu} \hat{r}_{\beta\nu}$, where

(3.29)
$$\hat{q}_{\alpha\mu} = \frac{\sum\limits_{\beta,\nu=1}^{B} n_{\alpha\beta,\mu\nu}}{\sum\limits_{\beta,\nu=1}^{B} \sum\limits_{s=1}^{A} n_{\alpha\beta,s\nu}},$$

(3.30)
$$\hat{r}_{\beta\nu} = \frac{\sum\limits_{\alpha,\mu=1}^{A} n_{\alpha\beta,\mu\nu}}{\sum\limits_{\alpha,\mu=1}^{A} \sum\limits_{s=1}^{B} n_{\alpha\beta,\mu s}}.$$

The likelihood ratio criterion is

(3.31)
$$\lambda = \prod_{t=1}^{T} \prod_{\alpha,\mu=1}^{A} \prod_{\beta,\nu=1}^{B} \left(\frac{\hat{q}_{\alpha\mu} \hat{r}_{\beta\nu}}{\hat{p}_{\alpha\beta,\mu\nu}}\right)^{n_{\alpha\beta,\mu\nu}(t)}.$$

Under the null hypothesis, $-2 \log \lambda$ has an asymptotic χ^2-distribution, and the number of degrees of freedom is $AB(AB - 1) - A(A - 1) - B(B - 1) = (A - 1)(B - 1)(AB + A + B)$.

4. A modified model. In the preceding sections, we assumed that the $n_i(0)$ were nonrandom. An alternative is that the $n_i(0)$ are distributed multinomially with probability η_i and sample size n. Then the distribution of the set $n_{ij}(t)$ is (2.5) multiplied by the marginal distribution of the set $n_i(0)$ which is

(4.1)
$$\frac{n!}{\prod\limits_{i=1}^{m} n_i(0)!} \prod_{i=1}^{m} \eta_i^{n_i(0)}.$$

In this model, the maximum likelihood estimate of p_{ij} is again (2.8), and the maximum likelihood estimate of η_i is

(4.2)
$$\hat{\eta}_i = \frac{n_i(0)}{n}.$$

The means, variances, and covariances of $n_{ij}(t) - n_i(t - 1)p_{ij}$ are found by taking the expected values of (2.20) to (2.23); the same formulas apply with $n_k(0)$ replaced by $n\eta_k$. Also $n_{ij}(t) - n_i(t - 1)p_{ij}$ are uncorrelated with $n_i(0)$. Since $n_k(0)/n$ estimates η_k consistently, the asymptotic variances and covariances of $n^{1/2}(\hat{p}_{ij} - p_{ij})$ are as in Section 2.4. It follows from these facts that the asymptotic theory of the tests given in Section 3 hold for this modified model.

The asymptotic variances and covariances simplify somewhat if the chain starts from a stationary state; that is, if

(4.3)
$$\sum_{k=1}^{m} \eta_k p_{ki} = \eta_i.$$

For then $\sum \eta_k \, p_{ki}^{[t-1]} = \eta_i$ and $\phi_i = T\eta_i$. If it is known that the chain starts from a stationary state, equations (4.3) should be of some additional use in the estimation of p_{ki} when knowledge of the η_i, or even estimates of the η_i, are available. We have dealt in this paper with the more general case where it is not known whether (4.3) holds, and have used the maximum likelihood estimates for this case. The estimates obtained for the more general case are not efficient in the special case of a chain in a stationary state because relevant information is ignored. In the special case, the maximum likelihood estimates for the η_i and p_{ij} are obtained by maximizing $\log L = \sum n_{ij} \log p_{ij} + \sum n_i(0) \log \eta_i$ subject to the restrictions $\sum_j p_{ij} = 1$, $\sum_i \eta_i p_{ij} = \eta_j$, $\sum_j \eta_j = 1$, $p_{ij} \geqq 0$, $\eta_i \geqq 0$. In the case of a chain in a stationary state where the η_i are known, the maximum likelihood estimates for the p_{ij} are obtained by maximizing $\sum n_{ij} \log p_{ij}$ subject to the restrictions $\sum_j p_{ij} = 1$, $\sum_i \eta_i p_{ij} = \eta_j$, $p_{ij} \geqq 0$. Lagrange multipliers can be used to obtain the equations for the maximum hood estimates.

5. One observation on a chain of great length. In the previous sections, asymptotic results were presented for $n_i(0) \to \infty$, and hence $\sum_{i=1}^{m} n_i(0) = n \to \infty$, while T was fixed. The case of one observed sequence of states ($n = 1$) has been studied by Bartlett [3] and Hoel [10], and they consider the asymptotic theory when the number of times of observation increases ($T \to \infty$). Bartlett has shown that the number n_{ij} of times that the observed sequence was in state i at time $t - 1$ and in state j at time t, for $t = 1, \cdots, T$, is asymptotically normally distributed in the 'positively regular' situation (see [3], p. 91). He also has shown ([3], p. 93) that the maximum likelihood estimates $\hat{p}_{ij} = n_{ij}/n_i^*$ ($n_i^* = \sum_{j=1}^{m} n_{ij}$) have asymptotic variances and covariances given by the usual multinomial formulas appropriate to $\varepsilon \, n_i^*$ independent observations ($i = 1, 2, \cdots, m$) from multinomial probabilities p_{ij} ($j = 1, 2, \cdots, m$), and that the asymptotic covariances for two different values of i are 0. An argument like that of Section 2.4 shows that the variables $(n_i^*)^{1/2} \, (\hat{p}_{ij} - p_{ij})$ have a limiting normal distribution with means 0 and the variances and covariances given in Section 2.4. This result was proved in a different way by L. A. Gardner [8].

Thus we see that the asymptotic theory for $T \to \infty$ and $n = 1$ is essentially the same as for T fixed and $n_i(0) \to \infty$. Hence, the same test procedures are valid except for such tests as on possibly nonstationary chains. For example, Hoel's likelihood ratio criterion [10] to test the null hypothesis that the order of the chain is $r - 1$ against the alternate hypothesis that it is r is parallel to the likelihood ratio criterion for this test given in Section 3.3. The χ^2-test for this hypothesis, and the generalizations of the tests to the case where the null hypothesis is that the process is of order u and the alternate hypothesis is that the process is of order $r(u < r)$, which are presented in Section 3.3, are also applicable for large T. Also, the χ^2-test presented in Section 3.1 can be generalized to provide an alternative to Bartlett's likelihood ratio criterion [3] for testing the null hypothesis that $p_{ij\ldots kl} = p_{ij\ldots kl}^0$ (specified).

6. χ^2-tests and likelihood ratio criteria. The χ^2-tests presented in this paper are asymptotically equivalent, in a certain sense, to the corresponding likelihood ratio tests, as will be proved in this section. This fact does not seem to follow from the general theory of χ^2-tests; the χ^2-tests presented herein are different from those χ^2-tests that can be obtained directly by considering the number of individuals in each of the m^T possible mutually exclusive sequences (see Section 2.1) as the multinomial variables of interest. The χ^2-tests based on m^T categories need not consider the data as having been obtained from a Markov chain and the alternate hypothesis may be extremely general, while the χ^2-tests presented herein are based on a Markov chain model.

For small samples, not enough data has been accumulated to decide which tests are to be preferred (see comments in [5]). The relative rate of approach to the asymptotic distributions and the relative power of the tests for small samples is not known. In this section, a method somewhat related to the relative power will be tentatively suggested for deciding which tests are to be preferred when the sample size is moderately large and there is a specific alternate hypothesis. An advantage of the χ^2-tests, which are of the form used in contingency tables, is that, for many users of these methods, their motivation and their application seem to be simpler.

We shall now prove that the likelihood ratio and the χ^2-tests (tests of homogeneity) presented in Section 3.2 are asymptotically equivalent in a certain sense. First, we shall show that the χ^2-statistic has an asymptotic χ^2-distribution under the null hypothesis. The method of proof can be used whenever the relevant $\hat{p}$'s have the appropriate limiting normal distribution. In particular, this will be true for statistics of the form χ_i^2 (see (3.6)). In order to prove that statistics of the form λ_i (see (3.7)), which are formally similar to the likelihood ratio criterion but are not actually likelihood ratios, have the appropriate asymptotic distribution, we shall then show that $-2 \log \lambda_i$ is asymptotically equivalent to the χ_i^2-statistic, and therefore it has an asymptotic χ^2-distribution under the null hypothesis. Then we shall discuss the question of the equivalence of the tests under the alternate hypothesis. The method of proof presented here can be applied to the appropriate statistics given in the other sections herein, and also where $T \to \infty$ as well as where $n \to \infty$.

Let us consider the distribution of the χ^2-statistic (3.8) under the null hypothesis. From Section 2.4, we see that $n^{1/2} (\hat{p}_{ij}(t) - p_{ij})$ are asymptotically normally distributed with means 0 and variances $p_{ij}(1 - p_{ij})/m_i(t - 1)$, etc., where $m_i(t) = \mathcal{E}n_i(t)/n$. For different t or different i, they are asymptotically independent. Then the $[nm_i(t - 1)]^{1/2} [\hat{p}_{ij}(t) - p_{ij}]$ have asymptotically variances $p_{ij}(1 - p_{ij})$, etc. Let $\hat{p}_{ij}^* = \sum_t m_i(t - 1) \hat{p}_{ij}(t)/\sum_t m_i(t - 1)$. Then by the usual χ^2-theory, $\sum nm_i (t - 1)[\hat{p}_{ij}(t) - \hat{p}_{ij}^*]^2/\hat{p}_{ij}^*$ has an asymptotic χ^2-distribution under the null hypothesis. But

(6.1) $$\text{p lim } (\hat{p}_{ij}^* - \hat{p}_{ij}) = 0$$

because

(6.2) $$\operatorname{p\,lim} \left(\frac{n_i(t)}{n} - m_i(t) \right) = 0.$$

From the convergence in probability of $(\hat{p}_{ij}^* - \hat{p}_{ij})$ and $(m_i(t) - n_i(t)/n)$, and the fact that $n^{1/2}(\hat{p}_{ij}(t) - p_{ij})$ has a limiting distribution, it follows that

(6.3) $$\operatorname{p\,lim} \left[n\sum \frac{m_i(t-1)(\hat{p}_{ij}(t) - \hat{p}_{ij}^*)^2}{\hat{p}_{ij}^*} - \sum \frac{n_i(t-1)(\hat{p}_{ij}(t) - \hat{p}_{ij})^2}{\hat{p}_{ij}} \right] = 0.$$

Hence, the χ^2-statistic has the same asymptotic distribution as $\sum n m_i(t-1)$ $[\hat{p}_{ij}(t) - \hat{p}_{ij}^*]^2/\hat{p}_{ij}^*$; that is, a χ^2-distribution. This proof also indicates that the χ_i^2-statistics (3.6) also have a limiting χ^2-distribution. We shall now show that $-2 \log \lambda_i$ (see (3.7)) is asymptotically equivalent to χ_i^2 under the null hypothesis; and hence will also have a limiting χ^2-distribution.

We first note that for $|x| < \frac{1}{2}$

(6.4) $$(1 + x) \log (1 + x) = (1 + x)(x - x^2/2 + x^3/3 - x^4/4 + \cdots)$$
$$= x + x^2/2 - (x^3/6)(1 - x/2 + \cdots),$$

and

(6.5) $$| (1 + x) \log (1 + x) - x - x^2/2 | = | (x^3/6)(1 - x/2 + \cdots)| \leqq |x^3|$$

(see p. 217 in [6]). We see also that

(6.6) $$-2 \log \lambda_i = -2 \sum_{j,t} n_{ij}(t) \log [\hat{p}_{ij}/\hat{p}_{ij}(t)]$$
$$= 2 \sum_{j,t} n_i(t-1) \hat{p}_{ij}(t) \log [\hat{p}_{ij}(t)/\hat{p}_{ij}]$$
$$= 2 \sum_{j,t} n_i(t-1) \hat{p}_{ij}[1 + x_{ij}(t)] \log [1 + x_{ij}(t)],$$

where $x_{ij}(t) = [\hat{p}_{ij}(t) - \hat{p}_{ij}]/\hat{p}_{ij}$. The difference Δ between $-2 \log \lambda_i$ and the χ_i^2-statistic is

(6.7) $$\Delta = -2 \log \lambda_i - \chi_i^2$$
$$= 2 \sum_{j,t} n_i(t-1)\hat{p}_{ij}\{[1 + x_{ij}(t)] \log [1 + x_{ij}(t)] - [x_{ij}(t)]^2/2\}.$$

Since $\sum_{j=1}^m \hat{p}_{ij}x_{ij}(t) = 0$,

(6.8) $$\Delta = 2 \sum_{j,t} n_i(t-1)\hat{p}_{ij}\{[1 + x_{ij}(t)] \log [1 + x_{ij}(t)] - x_{ij}(t) - [x_{ij}(t)]^2/2\}.$$

We shall show that Δ converges to 0 in probability; i.e. for any $\epsilon > 0$, the probability of the relation $|\Delta| < \epsilon$, under the null hypothesis, tends to unity as $n = \sum_i n_i(t) \to \infty$. The probability satisfies the relation

(6.9) $$Pr\{ |\Delta| < \epsilon\} \geqq Pr\{ |\Delta| < \epsilon \text{ and } |x_{ij}(t)| < \tfrac{1}{2}\}$$
$$\geqq Pr\{ |2 \sum_{j,t} n_i(t-1)\hat{p}_{ij}[x_{ij}(t)]^3| < \epsilon \text{ and } |x_{ij}(t)| < \tfrac{1}{2}\}$$
$$\geqq Pr\{2n \sum_{j,t} |x_{ij}(t)|^3 < \epsilon \text{ and } |x_{ij}(t)| < \tfrac{1}{2}\}.$$

It is therefore necessary only to prove that $n[x_{ij}(t)]^3$ converges to 0 in probability. Since $x_{ij}(t) = [\hat{p}_{ij}(t) - \hat{p}_{ij}]/\hat{p}_{ij}$ converges to zero in probability under the null hypothesis, and

$$(6.10) \qquad \sqrt{x_{ij}(t)n}\, x_{ij}(t) = \sqrt{x_{ij}(t)n}\left\{\left[\frac{\hat{p}_{ij}(t) - p_{ij}}{\hat{p}_{ij}}\right] - \left[\frac{\hat{p}_{ij} - p_{ij}}{\hat{p}_{ij}}\right]\right\},$$

it follows that

$$(6.11) \qquad n[x_{ij}(t)]^3 = [(x_{ij}(t)n)^{1/2}\, x_{ij}(t)]^2$$

converges to zero in probability when the null hypothesis is true. Q.E.D.

Since the χ^2-statistic has a limiting χ^2-distribution under the null hypothesis, and $\Delta = -2\log\lambda_i - \chi_i^2$ converges in probability to zero, $-2\log\lambda_i = \chi_i^2 + \Delta$ has a limiting χ^2-distribution under the null hypothesis.

The method presented herein for showing the asymptotic equivalence of $-2\log\lambda_i$ and χ_i^2 could also be used to show the asymptotic equivalence of statistics of the form $-2\log\lambda$ and χ^2. It was proved in Section 3.2 that, under the null hypothesis, $-2\log\lambda$ has a limiting χ^2-distribution with $m(m-1)$ $(T-1)$ degrees of freedom. (The proof in Section 3.2 applied to λ, a likelihood ratio criterion, but would not apply to λ_i since they are not actually likelihood ratios.) Hence, we have another proof that the χ^2-statistic has the same limiting distribution as the likelihood ratio criterion under the null hypothesis.

The previous remarks refer to the case where the null hypothesis is true. Now suppose the alternate hypothesis is true; that is, $p_{ij}(t) \neq p_{ij}(s)$ for some t, s, i, j. It is easy to see that both the χ^2-test and the likelihood ratio test are consistent under any alternate hypothesis. In other words, if the values of $p_{ij}(t)$ for the alternate hypothesis and the significance level are kept fixed, then as n increases, the power of each test tends to 1 (see [5] and [11]).

In order to examine the situation in which the power is not close to 1 in large samples and also to make comparisons between tests, the alternate hypothesis may be moved closer to the null hypothesis as n increases. If the values of $p_{ij}(t)$ for the alternate hypothesis are not fixed but move closer to the null hypothesis, it can be seen that the two tests are again asymptotically equivalent. This can be deduced by a slight modification of the proof of asymptotic equivalence under the null hypothesis given in this section (see also [5], p. 323).

We shall now suggest another approach to the comparison of these tests when the alternate hypothesis is kept fixed. Since the null hypothesis is rejected when an appropriate statistic (χ^2 or $-2\log\lambda$) exceeds a specified critical value, we might decide that the χ^2-test is to be preferred to the likelihood ratio test if the statistic χ^2 is in some sense (stochastically) larger than $-2\log\lambda$ under the alternate hypothesis.

Since $n_i(t)$ is a linear combination of multinomial variables, we see that $n_i(t)/n$ converges in probability to its expected value $\mathcal{E}[n_i(t)/n] = m_i(t)$. Hence, χ^2/n converges in probability to

$$(6.12) \qquad \sum_{i,j,t} m_i(t-1)[p_{ij}(t) - \bar{p}_{ij}]^2/\bar{p}_{ij},$$

and $(-2 \log \lambda)/n$ converges in probability to

$$(6.13) \qquad 2 \sum_{i,j,t} m_i(t-1)p_{ij}(t) \log [p_{ij}(t)/\bar{p}_{ij}],$$

where

$$(6.14) \qquad \bar{p}_{ij} = \sum_t p_{ij}(t) \, m_i(t-1)/ \sum_t m_i(t-1) = \operatorname*{p\,lim}_{n\to\infty} \hat{p}_{ij}.$$

The difference between (6.12) and (6.13) is approximately

$$(6.15) \qquad \sum m_i\,(t-1)[p_{ij}(t) - \bar{p}_{ij}]^3/(3\bar{p}_{ij}^2).$$

Under the alternate hypothesis, these two stochastic limits differ from 0, and computation of them suggests which test is better. If $(p_{ij}(t) - \bar{p}_{ij})/\bar{p}_{ij}$ is small, then there will be only a small difference between the two limits. When the alternative is some composite hypothesis, as is usually the case when χ^2-tests are applied, then these stochastic limits can be computed and compared for the simple alternatives that are included in the alternate hypothesis.

This method for comparing tests is somewhat related to Cochran's comment (see p. 323 in [5]) that either (a) the significance probability can be made to decrease as n increases, thus reducing the chance of an error of type I, or (b) the alternate hypothesis can be moved steadily closer to the null hypothesis. Method (b) was discussed in [3]. If method (a) is used, then the critical value of the statistic (χ^2 or $-\log \lambda$) will increase as n increases. When the critical value has the form cn, where c is a constant (there may be some question as to whether this form for the critical value is really suitable), we see from the remarks in the preceding paragraph that the power of a test will tend to 1 if c is less than the stochastic limit and it will tend to 0 if c is greater than the stochastic limit. Hence, by this approach we find that the power of the χ^2-test can be quite different from the power of the likelihood ratio test, and some approximate computations can suggest which test is to be preferred.

However, a more appealing approach is to vary the significance level so the ratio of significance level to the probability of some particular Type II error approaches a limit (or at least it seems that desirable sequences of significance points lie between c' and cn). While the usual asymptotic theory does not give enough information to handle this problem, the comparison of stochastic limits may suggest a comparison of powers.

The methods of comparison discussed herein can also be used in the study of the χ^2 and likelihood ratio methods for ordinary contingency tables. We have seen that, in a certain sense, the χ^2 and likelihood ratio methods are not equivalent when the alternate hypothesis is true and fixed, and we have suggested a method for determining which test is to be preferred.

REFERENCES

[1] T. W. Anderson, "Probability models for analyzing time changes in attitudes," RAND Research Memorandum No. 455, 1951.

[2] T. W. ANDERSON, "Probability models for analyzing time changes in attitudes," *Mathematical Thinking in the Social Sciences*, edited by Paul F. Lazarsfeld, The Free Press, Glencoe, Illinois, 1954.

[3] M. S. BARTLETT, "The frequency goodness of fit test for probability chains," *Proc. Cambridge Philos. Soc.*, Vol. 47 (1951), pp. 86–95.

[4] H. CHERNOFF, "Large-sample theory: parametric case," *Ann. Math. Stat.* Vol. 27 (1956), pp. 1–22.

[5] W. G. COCHRAN, "The χ^2-test of goodness of fit," *Ann. Math. Stat.*, Vol. 23 (1952), pp. 315–345.

[6] H. CRAMÈR, *Mathematical Methods of Statistics*, Princeton University Press, Princeton, 1946.

[7] W. FELLER, *An Introduction to Probability Theory and Its Applications*, Vol. 1, John Wiley and Sons, New York, 1950.

[8] L. A. GARDNER, JR., "Some estimation and distribution problems in information theory," Master's Essay, Columbia University Library, 1954.

[9] L. A. GOODMAN, "On the statistical analysis of Markov chains" (abstract), *Ann. Math. Stat.*, Vol. 26 (1955), p. 771.

[10] P. G. HOEL, "A test for Markoff chains," *Biometrika*, Vol. 41 (1954), pp. 430–433.

[11] J. NEYMAN, "Contribution to the theory of the χ^2-test," *Proceedings of the Berkeley Symposium on Mathematical Statistics and Probability*, University of California Press, Berkeley, 1949, pp. 239–274.

A STOCHASTIC MODEL FOR INDIVIDUAL
CHOICE BEHAVIOR [1]

R. J. AUDLEY

University College, London

This paper presents a stochastic model which is concerned with the interrelations of the response variables observed in choice situations. The model is not a complete theory, because it involves no assumptions about the relations between stimulus and response variables. However, for given stimulus conditions, the parameters of the stochastic process do provide a convenient summary of many aspects of behaviour in a choice situation. Furthermore, the most elementary assumptions about the way in which these parameters might vary with changed stimulus conditions lead to predictions which are in qualitative agreement with experimental findings. In a sense, therefore, the stochastic model can be regarded as a rudimentary theory of certain aspects of choice behaviour.

Descriptors of Choice Behavior

A wide variety of experiments require the use of a situation involving a choice between two or more alternatives. There are several variables which may be employed in a descriptive summary of the behavior which

[1] The writer is grateful to A. R. Jonckheere for his generous criticisms during the preparation of the manuscript. He and G. C. Drew were also kind enough to comment upon an earlier draft.

appears in these situations. These variables can be of two kinds. Firstly, there are descriptors of the primary response to the situation, and, secondly, there are descriptors of the responses which the S makes to his primary choices. Those of the first kind are most commonly used and the three principal ones are: (*a*) Response time —the time taken for a definite choice to be made. (*b*) Relative response frequency—the proportion of occasions on which a particular choice response is made. (*c*) The number of vicarious trial and error responses (VTEs)—the number of vacillations between the various alternatives before a definite choice occurs. In the second group, where the descriptor is usually a verbal statement by the S, there are such variables as: (*a*) confidence in the correctness of a given choice and (*b*) an assessment of the subjective difficulty of the choice task.

Clearly, the extent to which these various descriptors can be employed will depend upon the specific details of an experiment. But, for many choice situations, all three descriptors of the first kind can be employed. Also in most studies with human Ss the second kind are also available. In fact, this paper will be mainly concerned with the first kind of descriptor, but some suggestions will be advanced

This article appeared in *Psychol. Rev.,* 1960, **67**, 1–15. Reprinted with permission.

which permit those of the second kind to be also included in a unitary stochastic description of choice behavior.

Particular Choice Situations Which Are Considered

It is believed that the underlying hypotheses upon which the stochastic description is based are applicable to most choice situations. However, the derivation of a mathematical model from these hypotheses which can be readily applied to experimental data without additional assumptions is more conveniently achieved for a certain class of situations. This class consists of experiments where knowledge of the outcome or correctness of a response is not available to the S until after the choice has been made. Thus, for example, most ordinary disjunctive reaction time studies are *not* considered because the S in these experiments can *match* his response with a known requirement. Nevertheless, the class of situations which can be considered is not a trivial one. It includes among others (*a*) Discrimination experiments, including most conventional psychophysical procedures in this category. (*b*) Studies of preference and conflict. (*c*) Investigations of learning in choice situations.

The next section of the paper is mainly concerned with the events supposed to be taking place during a single experimental trial.

THE STOCHASTIC MODEL

The notions upon which the model is based are very simple and involve only two assumptions:

Assumption 1. It is first assumed that, *for given stimulus and organismic conditions, there is associated with each possible choice response a single parameter. This parameter determines the probability that in a small interval of time* (t, t + Δt), *there will occur an "implicit" response of the kind with which the parameter is associated.*

No specific interpretation is given to the term "implicit response." It may, in certain circumstances, be taken to be equivalent to the partial response usually classified as a VTE. But there are some situations in which VTEs are not observed and would seem unlikely to be present. In these cases the "implicit" response may be regarded as a tendency to make a given response, or might perhaps be given some physiological interpretation.

The probabilities of the various kinds of "implicit" responses occurring are considered to be independent of one another. So that for given conditions, implicit responses of each kind are appearing at random intervals unaffected by the appearance of other implicit responses. It follows from the first assumption that the distribution of the intervals between successive implicit responses *of a given kind* is exponential and is determined entirely by the response parameter [e.g., see Feller, 1950, p. 220].

Assumption 2. It is assumed that *a final choice response is made when a run of K implicit responses of a given kind appears, this run being uninterrupted by occurrences of implicit responses of other kinds. K* may either be assumed to take a particular value or can be regarded as a further parameter, which can be estimated from experimental data.

Assumption 1 has been employed before. Mueller (1950) has used this approach to describe the intervals between bar-presses in an operant conditioning experiment where only one response is involved. For the same situation, Estes (1950) and Bush & Mosteller (1951) have used an assumption which is very similar, the only difference being that their models used a discontinuous rather than a continuous distribution of responses in time. Christie (1952) in discussing the determination of response probabilities in a discrimination experiment, has used the same assumption for situations where two responses are competing. Finally, the author of the present paper (Audley: 1957, 1958) has previously used the same notions to combine response times and response probabilities in a stochastic description of individual learning behavior. However, in all these examples, it has been assumed that $K = 1$. Bush and Mosteller (1955), in an analysis of response times in a runway situation, have considered a continuous model with $K > 1$, but this generalization does not appear to have been previously employed in a situation involving choice.

There are several reasons which can be advanced for assuming that $K > 1$. Firstly, when $K = 1$, but not if $K > 1$, the distributions of response times for all alternatives can be shown to be identically the same, and are exponential (e.g., see Audley, 1958). Neither of these properties is in agreement with experimental findings. Secondly, when $K > 1$, the sequence of "implicit" responses occurring before a final choice is made offer a possible means of including VTE's within the description of choice behavior. Thirdly, classification of the various sequences of "implicit" choice suggests an approach to descriptors of the second kind. For example, "perfect confidence" in a choice might be identified with sequences consisting of "implicit" responses of one kind only.

Derivation of the Stochastic Model

No further assumptions are required in the derivation of the model, which can be applied to situations involving any number, m, of choices. However,

in order to keep the exposition as brief as possible, consideration in this paper will be limited to situations involving a choice between only two alternatives, i.e., $m = 2$. Furthermore, the mathematical problem is relatively simple when $K = 2$, so that only this special case will be presented. Results for the more general case have been derived and will be elaborated elsewhere.

The two-choice situation with $K = 2$. The two possible responses will be called A and B, and implicit responses of the two kinds will be labelled a and b respectively. Let the parameters associated with the two responses be α and β. Assumption 1 means that $p(a)$, the probability of an a occurring in a small time interval $(t, t + \Delta t)$ is given by:

$$p(a) = \alpha \Delta t \qquad [1a]$$

Similarly

$$p(b) = \beta \Delta t \qquad [1b]$$

The probability $p(a \text{ or } b)$, of an implicit response of either kind but not both, occurring in the small time interval is

$$p(a \text{ or } b) = p(a) + p(b) - 2p(a)p(b)$$
$$= (\alpha + \beta)\Delta t - 2\alpha\beta(\Delta t)^2$$

Hence

$$p(a \text{ or } b) = (\alpha + \beta)\Delta t \qquad [1c]$$

if terms of order $(\Delta t)^2$ are ignored. This becomes possible if a transition is made to the continuous case when the distribution in time of implicit responses follows that of a Poisson process (e.g., see Feller, 1950, p. 220). Therefore the probability, $p(n, t)$, of obtaining n implicit responses in the time interval (o, t) is (e.g., again see Feller, 1950, p. 221):

$$p(n, t) = \frac{(\alpha + \beta)^n t^n e^{-(\alpha+\beta)t}}{n!} \qquad [2]$$

In particular the probability, $p(o, t)$, of obtaining no implicit response of either kind in time t is given by:

$$p(o, t) = e^{-(\alpha+\beta)t} \qquad [3]$$

The probability: P_a, that the first implicit response to occur is an a is

$$P_a = \int_{t=o}^{\infty} p(o, t)\alpha dt$$

$$= \int_{t=o}^{\infty} e^{-(\alpha+\beta)t}\alpha dt = \frac{\alpha}{\alpha + \beta} \qquad [4a]$$

$$= \text{say}, p$$

Similarly, for implicit b responses

$$P_b = \frac{\beta}{\alpha + \beta} = \text{say}, q = 1 - p \qquad [4b]$$

Since occurrences of implicit responses follow a Poisson process, Equations 4a and 4b also give the probability that, starting at any given moment, the next implicit response to occur will be an a or b respectively. Therefore, ignoring for the moment questions concerning the time intervals between successive implicit responses, the sequence of events leading to a final choice can be treated as a sequence of independent binomial trials, with the probabilities, P_a and P_b, of the two types of event given by Equations 4a and 4b.

The Probability, P_A, That the Final Choice is an A Response

The possible sequences which terminate with the occurrence of an A can be easily classified when $K = 2$. For they must all be simple alternations between a and b, until two successive a's occur. The early members of this class of sequences are: aa, baa, $abaa$, $babaa$, etc. The respective probabilities of these various sequences is clearly: p^2, p^2q, p^3q, p^3q^2 etc. The over-all probability, P_A, that the final choice is an A, is the sum of this infi-

nite series of sequence probabilities. Thus,

$$P_A = p^2 + p^2q + p^3q + p^3q^2 + \cdots \qquad [5]$$

Whence, simplifying, and substituting for p and q from Equations 4a and 4b

$$P_A = \frac{\alpha^2[\alpha + 2\beta]}{[\alpha + \beta][(\alpha + \beta)^2 - \alpha\beta]} \qquad [6a]$$

Similarly

$$P_B = \frac{\beta^2[2\alpha + \beta]}{[\alpha + \beta][(\alpha + \beta)^2 - \alpha\beta]} \qquad [6b]$$

Equation 6a may be written in the following form:

$$P_A = \frac{\alpha}{\alpha + \beta} \cdot \frac{[(\alpha + \beta)^2 - \beta^2]}{[(\alpha + \beta)^2 - \alpha\beta]}$$

so that when $\alpha > \beta$, $P_A > \dfrac{\alpha}{\alpha + \beta}$ and

$$P_B < \frac{\beta}{\alpha + \beta}$$

Thus the difference between the probabilities of the various implicit responses occurring is accentuated in the expressions for the probabilities of overt choice responses. The accentuation increases with K and implies that there is more certainty in the overt choices than in the underlying processes which determine them. This is believed to be a property which many organisms exhibit.

Vicarious Trial and Error

If we identify alternating appearances of the "implicit" responses, a and b, with VTEs, the moments of the distribution of VTEs can readily be obtained. Attention here will be confined to the mean number of VTEs preceding (a) any choice (b) a particular choice.

The Mean Number of VTEs Preceding Any Choice, $\bar{V}$

There are no VTEs if the sequence of implicit responses is aa or bb.

There is 1 VTE if the sequence is *baa* or *abb*.

There are 2 VTEs if the sequence is *abaa* or *babb*, and so on.

Dividing the sequences of implicit responses into those with an odd number and those with an even number of VTEs, the following probabilities are found (letting $P(V = n)$ be the probability of obtaining n VTEs):

$$p(V = 0) = p^2 + q^2$$
$$P(V = 2) = p^3q + pq^3$$
$$P(V = 4) = p^4q^2 + p^2q^4$$
etc.

$$P(V = 1) = p^2q + pq^2$$
$$P(V = 3) = p^3q^2 + p^2q^3$$
$$P(V = 5) = p^4q^3 + p^3q^4$$
etc.

Now

$$\bar{V} = P(V = 1) + 2P(V = 2) + 3P(V = 3) + \cdots$$

and after some algebraic manipulation and again substituting for p and q from Equation 4a and 4b.

$$\bar{V} = \frac{3\alpha\beta}{(\alpha + \beta)^2 - \alpha\beta} \qquad [7]$$

If $\gamma = \dfrac{\beta}{\alpha}$, then Equation 7 may be re-written as

$$\bar{V} = \frac{3\gamma}{(1 + \gamma)^2 - \gamma}$$

Thus $\bar{V}$ is dependent only on the ratio of β to α, and becomes a maximum when $\gamma = 1$, i.e., $\alpha = \beta$. Therefore the number of VTEs would be a maximum when $P_A = P_B = \frac{1}{2}$.

The Mean Number of VTEs Preceding A and B Responses, $\bar{V}_A$ and $\bar{V}_B$

Separate consideration of the mean number of VTEs preceding an A and B choice yields the following results:

$$\bar{V}_A = \frac{2\alpha\beta}{(\alpha + \beta)^2 - \alpha\beta} + \frac{\beta}{\alpha + 2\beta} \qquad [8a]$$

$$\bar{V}_B = \frac{2\alpha\beta}{(\alpha + \beta)^2 - \alpha\beta} + \frac{\alpha}{2\alpha + \beta} \qquad [8b]$$

Since $\dfrac{\beta}{\alpha + 2\beta}$ and $\dfrac{\alpha}{2\alpha + \beta}$ may be re-written as $\dfrac{1}{\dfrac{\alpha}{\beta} + 2}$ and $\dfrac{1}{\dfrac{\beta}{\alpha} + 2}$ respec-tively, it can be seen that on the average there would be fewer VTEs preceding the response which is domi-nant at any given moment, i.e., if $P_A > P_B$, $\bar{V}_A < \bar{V}_B$.

The Time Distribution of Final Choice

It is possible to determine all the moments of the time distribution of final responses. Here, however, con-sideration will be limited to the mean latency, $\bar{L}$, of all responses and the mean latencies for A and B re-sponses taken separately, $\bar{L}_A$ and $\bar{L}_B$ respectively.

The Mean Latencies for A and B Re-sponses, $\bar{L}_A$ and $\bar{L}_B$

Let $P(a, t)$ be the probability that, at time t, no two consecutive a's or b's have appeared, and that the last implicit response was an a. Let $P(a, t; n)$ be the probability that, at Line t, no two consecutive a's or b's have appeared, and that the last im-plicit response was an a, and also that there have been exactly n implicit responses. Thus

$$P(a, t) = \sum_{n=1}^{\infty} P(a, t; n)$$

To determine $P(a, t; n)$, Equation 2 and the method employed to find P_A are combined.

Let $P(a; n)$ be the probability that a sequence of n events ends with an a, no two consecutive a's or b's having occurred. Clearly,

$$P(a;1) = \frac{\alpha}{\alpha + \beta},$$

$$P(a;2) = \frac{\alpha\beta}{(\alpha + \beta)^2},$$

$$P(a;3) = \frac{\alpha^2\beta}{(\alpha + \beta)^3}, \text{ etc.}$$

these probabilities being respectively associated with the sequences; a, ba, aba, etc.

Now $P(a, t; n) = P(n, t) \cdot P(a; n)$, and Equation 2 gives $P(n, t)$, so that

$$P(a, t; 1)$$
$$= P(1, t) \cdot P(a; 1)$$
$$= (\alpha + \beta)te^{-(\alpha+\beta)t} \cdot \frac{\alpha}{\alpha + \beta}$$
$$= \frac{\alpha t e^{-(\alpha+\beta)t}}{1!}$$

$$P(a, t; 2)$$
$$= \frac{(\alpha + \beta)^2 t^2 e^{-(\alpha+\beta)t}}{2!} \cdot \frac{\alpha\beta}{(\alpha + \beta)^2}$$
$$= \frac{\alpha\beta t^2 e^{-(\alpha+\beta)t}}{2!}$$

Similarly

$$P(a, t; 3) = \frac{\alpha^2\beta t^3 e^{-(\alpha+\beta)t}}{3!}$$

etc. Hence

$$P(a, t) = \sum_{n=1}^{\infty} P(a, t; n)$$
$$= \frac{\alpha t e^{-(\alpha+\beta)t}}{1!} + \frac{\alpha\beta t^2 e^{-(\alpha+\beta)t}}{2!}$$
$$+ \frac{\alpha^2\beta t^3 e^{-(\alpha+\beta)t}}{3!} + \cdots$$

which, upon simplification, gives

$$P(a, t) = e^{-(\alpha+\beta)t}\left[\left(\frac{e^{t\sqrt{\alpha\beta}} + e^{-t\sqrt{\alpha\beta}}}{2} - 1\right)\right.$$
$$\left. + \sqrt{\frac{\alpha}{\beta}}\left(\frac{e^{t\sqrt{\alpha\beta}} - e^{-t\sqrt{\alpha\beta}}}{2}\right)\right] \quad [9a]$$

Similarly it may be determined that

$$P(b, t) = e^{-(\alpha+\beta)t}\left[\left(\frac{e^{t\sqrt{\alpha\beta}} + e^{-t\sqrt{\alpha\beta}}}{2} - 1\right)\right.$$
$$\left. + \sqrt{\frac{\beta}{\alpha}}\left(\frac{e^{t\sqrt{\alpha\beta}} - e^{-t\sqrt{\alpha\beta}}}{2}\right)\right] \quad [9b]$$

Now

$$\bar{L}_A = \int_{t=o}^{\infty} P(a, t)\alpha t dt \bigg/ \int_{t=o}^{\infty} P(a, t)\alpha dt$$
$$= \frac{2(\alpha + \beta)}{(\alpha + \beta)^2 - \alpha\beta}$$
$$+ \frac{\beta}{(\alpha + \beta)(\alpha + 2\beta)} \quad [10a]$$

and similarly

$$\bar{L}_B = \frac{2(\alpha + \beta)}{(\alpha + \beta)^2 - \alpha\beta}$$
$$+ \frac{\alpha}{(\alpha + \beta)(2\alpha + \beta)} \quad [10b]$$

By the same kind of argument it may be demonstrated that the mean latency for all responses, $\bar{L}$, is given by

$$\bar{L} = \frac{2(\alpha+\beta)^2 + \alpha\beta}{[\alpha+\beta][(\alpha+\beta)^2 - \alpha\beta]} = \frac{2}{\alpha+\beta}$$
$$+ \frac{3\alpha\beta}{[\alpha+\beta][(\alpha+\beta)^2 - \alpha\beta]} \quad [11]$$

Returning to Equations 10a and 10b it can be seen that $\dfrac{\beta}{(\alpha+\beta)(\alpha+2\beta)}$ and $\dfrac{\alpha}{(\alpha+\beta)(2\alpha+\beta)}$ may be written as

$$\frac{1}{(\alpha+\beta)\left(\frac{\alpha}{\beta}+2\right)} \text{ and } \frac{1}{(\alpha+\beta)\left(\frac{\beta}{\alpha}+2\right)} \text{ re-}$$

spectively. Thus the dominant response will, on the average, have a shorter choice time than the other, i.e., if $P_A > P_B$, $\bar{L}_A < \bar{L}_B$.

In order to compare the theoretical response time distribution to observed data, the probability $P(0, t)$ of no final response having occurred by time t is also given. This is clearly

$$P(0, t) = P(o, t) + P(a, t) + P(b, t)$$

$P(o, t)$ is given by Equation 3 and $P(a, t)$ and $P(b, t)$ by Equations 9a and 9b so that, upon some simplification,

$$P(0, t) = e^{-(\alpha+\beta)t}\left[(e^{\sqrt{\alpha\beta}t}+e^{-\sqrt{\alpha\beta}t}-1) \right.$$
$$\left. +\frac{\alpha+\beta}{2\sqrt{\alpha\beta}} (e^{\sqrt{\alpha\beta}t}-e^{-\sqrt{\alpha\beta}t}) \right] \quad [12]$$

The Model and Descriptors of the Second Kind

At present, it is only possible to advance some speculations concerning variables such as "degree of confidence" in the correctness of a given choice. Nevertheless, it seems worth considering these since there appears to be a definite relation between the second kind of descriptor and the more conventional indices of choice behavior. Henmon (1911), whose paper will be considered in more detail later, showed that choices regarded by an S with confidence are generally quicker and more accurate than others. This result was demonstrated in a psychophysical discrimination situation where a definite correct choice existed.

There seem to be two possible ways in which "confidence" might be attributed to a particular choice. The first of these involves some classification of the various sequences of implicit responses preceding a final choice. For example, sequences which involve no vacillation at all, such as *aa*, or *bb*, might be regarded as "more confident" than sequences involving a large number of vacillations, such as *abababaa*. It will be shown that this kind of "confident" sequence has the properties required by Henmon's data.

For, suppose A be the correct and B the incorrect choice in a psychophys-

ical situation, then generally speaking one would expect $\alpha > \beta$. The probability of the sequence *aa* would be $\dfrac{\alpha^2}{(\alpha + \beta)^2}$ and the probability of *bb*, $\dfrac{\beta^2}{(\alpha + \beta)^2}$. Hence, the probability, P_c, of being correct for this type of confident "choice," i.e., choosing A, is given by

$$P_C = \frac{\alpha^2}{\alpha^2 + \beta^2} \quad [13]$$

Comparing this probability with the overall probability of an A response, P_A given by Equation 6a,

$$P_C - P_A$$
$$= \frac{\alpha^2}{\alpha^2+\beta^2} - \frac{\alpha^2(\alpha+2\beta)}{[\alpha+\beta][(\alpha+\beta)^2-\alpha\beta]}$$
$$= \frac{\alpha^2\beta^2(\alpha-\beta)}{[\alpha^2+\beta^2][\alpha+\beta][(\alpha+\beta)^2-\alpha\beta]}$$
$$[14]$$

Clearly, Equation 14 is positive when $\alpha > \beta$ and hence $P_C > P_A$.

Since for these "confident" responses only two implicit responses occur before a final choice, it is clear that their mean response time is shorter than the over-all average response time. This approach consists essentially in equating "degree of confidence" with some function of the reciprocal of the number of VTEs preceding the final choice.

The second suggested approach to judgmental confidence is based upon the fact that these appraisals of a response, under normal instructions, follow after the response itself. Degree of confidence, therefore, might be associated with implicit responses continuing to occur after an overt choice response has occurred. If, after an A response has been made, a further a occurs in the time before the statement of confidence is produced, this might be taken to lead to greater confidence than if nothing or a *b* appeared. Indeed, it might be possible to develop a model for the distribution of the times between making the primary choice response and giving an estimate for degree of confidence from this kind of assumption.

Other approaches to the second kind of descriptor are undoubtedly possible within the present scheme. The important point is that it is possible to test these various hypotheses quite easily. They each predict how often a given level of confidence would be employed. Also the expected distribution of descriptors of the first kind associated with each level of confidence can be determined.

The Agreement between the Properties of the Model and Empirical Data

The principal aim of this paper is to show that a set of very simple assumptions can be used to derive relations which might be expected among the variables observed in a choice situation. In an exposition of this kind it is not possible to examine, in any detail, the success of the model in describing the results of experiments which are relevant. For one thing, only the particular case arising when $K = 2$ has been presented, whereas in practice it may be more profitable to treat K as a parameter. Also, the argument so far presented is concerned with the events supposed to occur at a single experimental trial. The manner in which the model is applied to experimental data based upon a number of trials will depend very much upon the way in which separate trials resemble one another. There may be actual variations in stimulus conditions from trial to trial, or there may be a direct dependence of later upon earlier trials, as in learning experiments. For this reason, considera-

tion of quantitative evidence will be mainly confined to an experiment by Henmon (1911), in which the conditions under which individual trials were conducted closely resemble one another and where it can reasonably be assumed that there are no systematic changes in an S's behavior. This data can therefore be regarded as appropriate for testing the model without there being any need to make further special assumptions. However, before examining Henmon's results, it seems worthwhile to exhibit the manner in which the model seems to match empirical evidence about choice behavior in general.

In effecting a general appraisal of the model, one is hindered by the general lack of individual results in the experimental literature. For reasons which cannot be examined here it seems preferable to test hypotheses about functional relations upon *individual* data. A brief argument for this point of view has been presented by Bakan (1955) and for the study of learning behavior by Audley and Jonckheere (1956). The reader is referred to these papers for further details. However, irrespective of the stand taken on this question, it is clear that the present model is concerned with *individual* results and that such results are not generally available. For this reason, the following comparison of the model with experimental evidence is largely qualitative, although, given appropriate data, quantitative comparisons would have been possible.

Psychophysical Discrimination Situations

In considering results from psychophysical experiments, say using the constant method, it is necessary to consider separately the comparison of each variable with the standard. This is so because no assumptions have thus far been made about the relation between stimulus and response variables. In spite of this, some general predictions can be made.

Consider the results obtained from the comparison of the standard with a particular variable stimulus. In this comparison, it can be supposed that the responses A and B refer to the respective statements "the variable is greater than the standard" and "the variable is smaller than the standard." α will clearly be a monotonically increasing function of the magnitude of the variable, and β a monotonically decreasing function of the same magnitude. At the PSE, $\alpha = \beta$. Within limits, and certainly for a range of stimuli close to the PSE, $(\alpha + \beta)$ can be assumed to be approximately constant. This supposition is not crucial, but simplifies the ensuing argument.

Relation of Judgment Time to the Perceived Distance between Stimuli

Equation 11 gives the mean choice time as a function of α and β. This can be rewritten in the following way:

$$\bar{L} = \frac{2}{\alpha+\beta} + \frac{3}{[\alpha+\beta]\left[\frac{(\alpha+\beta)^2}{\alpha\beta} - 1\right]} \quad [15]$$

If $(\alpha+\beta)$ is approximately constant, $\bar{L}$ will depend principally upon the product of the parameters, $\alpha\beta$. Thus $\bar{L}$ will have a maximum when $\alpha = \beta$. From Equation 6a it can be seen that the point, $\alpha = \beta$, also defines the PSE, since for these parameter values $P_A = P_B = 0.5$. It can be seen that decision time will therefore rise monotonically up to the PSE and then decrease monotonically beyond the PSE. For the range and distribution of stimuli employed in most psychophysical studies, the decrease in decision time upon either side of the PSE will be, according to the model,

approximately symmetrical. These properties are in agreement with empirical data, as for example summarized by Guilford (1954).

Even where the S is allowed three categories of response, it is the boundaries between these categories which show peak decision times (Cartwright, 1941). This would be expected if a further parameter be used to characterize "equal" or "doubtful" responses. It would be of great interest to determine whether, in fact, a further response parameter is required when a third response category is permitted. Almost by definition, the response "doubtful" implies that no decision has been reached by a certain time. Such responses would then appear to be best described by the time which the S is willing to spend in attempting to come to a decision. This would make the range of stimuli over which judgments of "doubtful" are made depend only indirectly upon differential sensitivity. The readiness of the S to continue attempting to arrive at a definite answer would also play an important role. This is in accord with the generally accepted view of the use of a third category, e.g., Woodworth (1938), Guilford (1954). On the other hand, a parameter to specify judgments of "equality" may still be required. This would allow for a time determined "doubtful" judgment of the kind discussed above, but would also introduce a true "equals" category. This would enable an analysis of the third category to be carried out in accordance with the suggestions of Cartwright (1941) and George (1917).

The Relation between Confidence, Decision Time and Perceived Distance between Stimuli

The exact nature of the relations between the variables considered in this section, will depend upon whether stimulus conditions are the same for all trials. Nevertheless, some general predictions can be advanced.

Here, "degree of confidence" will be equated with some function of the reciprocal of the number of VTEs preceding a final choice. The number of VTEs can, of course, range from zero to infinity. Generally speaking, confidence is rated upon some scale from zero to unity. Let C, be the degree of confidence associated with a given choice, and, V, the number of VTEs preceding this choice act. Determining a suitable relation between C and V would, in fact, be one of the experimental problems suggested by the present approach. For the moment, however, it will be assumed that,

$$C = \frac{1}{V + 1} \qquad [16]$$

so that when $V = 0$, $C = 1$; and when $V = \infty$, $C = 0$.

It will be recalled from the section concerned with VTEs that the mean number of these will, when $K = 2$, be two less than the number of implicit responses preceding a final choice. Now it can easily be demonstrated, using Equation 1c, that the mean choice time when n implicit responses occur, T_n, is given by

$$T_n = \frac{n}{\alpha + \beta} \qquad [17]$$

Whence, since $V = n - 2$, and because n is eliminated from Equation 17, it is possible to express the mean choice time $\bar{T}$, as a function of V, given by

$$\bar{T} = \frac{V + 2}{\alpha + \beta} \qquad [18]$$

Substituting for V from Equation 16 and adding an arbitrary constant, T_0, for the minimum choice time possible,

$$\bar{T} = \frac{1}{(\alpha + \beta)C} + \frac{1}{\alpha + \beta} + T_0. \qquad [19]$$

This hyperbolic function is in agreement with experimental determinations of the relation between confidence and judgment time, e.g., see again Guilford (1954).

If the stimulus conditions are varied between different sets of trials, as for example in the constant method discussed in the previous section, general conclusions are again possible. For in discussing Equation 7, it was shown that the mean number of VTEs depends only upon the ratio of α to β. Again assuming that $(\alpha + \beta)$ is approximately constant, V would be a roughly symmetrical function of the magnitude of the variable, having a maximum at the PSE. Thus the average degree of confidence, $\bar{C}$, would be a roughly **U** shaped function having a minimum at the PSE. Since choice time has been shown to have a maximum at the PSE and to decrease upon either side of this point, $\bar{C}$ and $\bar{T}$ would again vary inversely. This agrees with experimental data (see Guilford, 1954).

Preference and Conflict Situations

In this kind of situation, a number of objects are paired and the subject makes a choice indicating the preferred object of each pair. For any given pair of objects, say A and B, the parameters α and β can be taken to represent some measure of preference for A and B. Because there are a number of objects, it is more convenient to label the r objects presented to the subject as X_i, and to let the parameter associated with a kind of "absolute preference" for each, be α_i $(i = 1, 2, \cdots r)$. The α and β of the equations will now be replaced by, say α_j and α_k, for the comparison of the ith and jth objects, X_j and X_k. This, of course, is to make the very strong assumption that the α_i's are independent of the particular comparison in which they are involved. This assumption could be readily tested by using the model appropriately, and is accepted here only in order to simplify notation. The results of the following argument would be qualitatively the same, even if there were in fact, contextual effects peculiar to each comparison.

Variation in choice time among different comparisons. The set of r objects, on the basis of a paired comparison technique, can usually be ranked. Let i be an individual's ranking of an object, so that we may write $X_1 > X_2 > \cdots > X_i > X_{i+1} > \cdots > X_r$, meaning X_i is preferred to X_2 and so on. This means that $\alpha_1 > \alpha_2 > \cdots > \alpha_i > \alpha_{i+1} > \cdots > \alpha_r$. Consider any pair of parameters, say α_j and α_k, and let these be the α and β of the earlier equations. Then the mean choice time is given by Equation 11, and this can now be rewritten as

$$\bar{L}_{(j,k)} = \frac{2}{\alpha_j + \alpha_k}$$
$$+ \frac{3\alpha_j\alpha_k}{[\alpha_j + \alpha_k][(\alpha_j + \alpha_k)^2 - \alpha_j\alpha_k]} \quad [20]$$

Clearly $\bar{L}_{(j,k)}$ depends upon two things; the sum of the parameters $(\alpha_j + \alpha_k)$ and, secondly, the product of the parameters, $\alpha_j\alpha_k$. Other things being equal, the choice time will decrease as $(\alpha_j + \alpha_k)$ increases. Again, with $(\alpha_j + \alpha_k)$ constant, $\bar{L}_{(j,k)}$ will increase with the product, reaching a maximum when $\alpha_j = \alpha_k$. Choice time will therefore (a) depend upon the general level of preference for objects, being quicker for preferred objects, (b) will be quicker the greater the difference in preference for the two paired objects. This in agreement with experimental finding, e.g., for children choosing among liquids to drink, Barker (1942), for aesthetic preferences, Dashiell (1937).

It will be interesting to determine how far the assumption of an absence of contextual effects can be maintained. If the assumption turns out to be approximately true, then the parameters, α_i, would provide a means of scaling the stimulus objects for a given individual. In essence, such an approach would resemble that adopted by Bradley and Terry (1952), but would have the added advantage that the scale values would have an absolute rather than a relative basis, so that the scale values should be unaffected by the inclusion of new comparisons.

Number of VTEs for different comparisons. It was shown, in discussing Equation 7, that the mean number of VTEs in a given situation, depends entirely upon the ratio of α to β. Using the present notation this would be the ratio of α_j to α_k, for objects X_j and X_k. The number of VTEs has a maximum when $\alpha_j = \alpha_k$, and decreases as the values of the parameter become more disparate. Thus the number of VTEs should depend entirely upon the differences in preference and not upon the general level of preference for the two paired objects. Thus for adjacent objects, X_i and X_{i+1}, the number of VTEs before a final choice will not rise with choice time as one proceeds from preferred to nonpreferred objects. This is slightly complicated by differences in "preference distance" between adjacent objects, but the prediction is again found to be in agreement with experimental evidence, e.g., see Barker (1942).

Learning in choice situations. It is in considering learning behavior that the need for individual results is greatest (Audley & Jonckheere, 1956). The full advantages of the present approach to response variables can only be gained by incorporating the assumption in a stochastic model for learning. The way in which this might be contrived, when $K = 1$, has already been outlined and illustrated elsewhere (Audley: 1957, 1958). On the whole, therefore, the experimental literature does not provide results in a way which enable the predictions of the model to be falsified, even at a qualitative level. The most that can be done here is to show that the predictions might well be good approximations to the properties of learning data.

Given a particular theory of learning it would, of course, be possible to anchor the theory more closely to response variables by identifying the parameter of the choice model with an appropriate theoretical construction.

The properties of the model and simple learning behavior. Consider, for example, learning in a simple two-choice situation. Let α be associated with A, the correct response, and β with B, the incorrect response. The way in which α and β vary with reward and punishment is naturally a matter for investigation and would certainly condition the form of the prediction which would be made. Nevertheless, it is not unreasonable to assume that α will be some monotonic increasing function, and β some monotonic decreasing function of practice and of punishments and rewards.

Let it be supposed that the S has at first a strong tendency to produce the incorrect choice, i.e., α is small relative to β. Consider, firstly, what might be expected to happen to the over-all latency $\bar{L}$, and the latencies of A and B, $\bar{L}_A$ and $\bar{L}_B$ respectively. In discussing Equations 10a and 10b it was shown that the dominant response, on the average, will have the shorter choice time. Thus in the first place it will be expected that $\bar{L}_A$ will be greater than $\bar{L}\cdot$ until the probability of making the correct choice,

P_A, reaches and exceeds 0.5, when $\bar{L}_A$ will be generally shorter than $\bar{L}_B$.

All of the latencies are dependent upon two factors, the sum $(\alpha + \beta)$ and the ratio of α to β. The over-all latency, $\bar{L}$, if $(\alpha + \beta)$ remains constant, will rise to a maximum until $P_A = P_B = 0.5$ (i.e., $\alpha = \beta$) and then fall again. Superimposed upon this rise and fall will be the influence of $(\alpha + \beta)$, and if the levels of, say punishment and reward, are such as to disturb the constancy of this quantity, then there will be an accentuation or flattening of the curve of latency as a function of practice. The monotonic decline in response latencies observed when an S is introduced into a learning situation for the first time does not counter this prediction. For, then, it is to be expected that $(\alpha + \beta)$ will be initially small and the effect of increasing α, and, hence, $(\alpha + \beta)$ will be reinforced by the growing difference in magnitude between α and β. In original learning, therefore, the two factors work together and produce the monotonic decrease in latency.

The number of VTEs, from Equation 7, is seen to be a function only of the ratio of α to β. Thus VTEs would be expected to rise to a maximum until $\alpha = \beta$, i.e., $P_A = P_B = 0.5$, and the decline.

These predictions are probably only applicable to the very simple two-choice situations so far considered. For discrimination studies, the problem is complicated by the way in which the relevant cues are being utilized by the organism and there is no point in reviewing the controversy over this matter. It does however seem worthwhile pointing out that, in discrimination behavior, it is very probable that there appears something like the problem of the use of the third category in psychophysical procedures. That is, a distinction seems to be necessary between, on the one hand, a definite act of choice and, on the other hand, behavior which occurs simply because something has to be done in the situation. This speculative point is raised because the size of the parameters may exert an influence upon behavior in two ways. Firstly, by determining the probability of making a particular response when a "true" choice is made and, secondly, by determining the probability that a "true" choice is made.

Henmon's experiment. The experiment conducted by Henmon (1911) is of particular interest, because it provides data from individual Ss, in a situation where stimulus conditions can be assumed to be fairly constant from trial to trial. The observations, therefore, are important for any model concerned with the properties of choice behavior.

Henmon required Ss, in each of 1,000 trials, to decide whether one of two horizontal lines was longer or shorter than the other. The lengths of the lines were always 20 mm and 20.3 mm respectively. In addition, Ss were instructed to indicate their confidence in each judgment.

The model is qualitatively in agreement with Henmon's data, except in two things. Firstly, although average choice time for wrong responses is larger than that for correct choices, as predicted by the model, the wrong responses are relatively quicker in each category of confidence. The second qualitative difference appears in examining accuracy as a function of time. There is some indication for some Ss that although there is a general decline in accuracy with longer choice times, again predicted by the model, there is also a slight rise in accuracy in going from very short to moderately short choice times. It is

possible that both of these differences may be accounted for by a suitable analysis of judgments of confidence about which only a few speculations have been advanced in the present paper. The important point, it seems to the author, is that the general stochastic model is capable of dealing with this kind of issue, rather than that it succeeds in all details at the present time.

Henmon gives the distribution of all choice times for each individual. Since this can also be derived from the model, a comparison of the two distributions should give further indications as to the adequacy of the present approach to choice behavior. In testing the goodness of fit of the model in this matter, it would be usual to estimate the parameters from the distribution of choice times alone. However, it was decided that perhaps a stronger case could be made out if the only time datum used to estimate the parameters was the mean latency. Two equations are of course required if values of α and β are to be determined, and P_A, the probability of a correct response, was chosen for the second. Accordingly the present estimates are based upon Equations 6a and 11.

There must, of course, be some minimum response time before which no response can occur. This is not easy to determine from Henmon's tables of results, because the data are already grouped in intervals of 200 milliseconds. For this reason, the minimum possible time was estimated in the following way. For various assumed minimum times, estimates of α and β were determined, and the theoretical distribution of choice times computed. The value leading to the best fit was then adopted. This is not entirely a satisfactory procedure, but with K assumed to be 2, and with no

TABLE 1

Subject Bl			Subject Br		
Time interval in milliseconds	Observed Frequency	Expected Frequency	Time interval in milliseconds	Observed Frequency	Expected Frequency
100–	(2)[a]	—	100–299	(2)[a]	—
300–	57	53	300–	350	352
500–	214	229	500–	381	398
700–	220	229	700–	170	165
900–	159	168	900–	65	57
1100–	113	111	1100–	26	19
1300–	85	83	1300–	5	6
1500–	74	48	Above 1500	1	3
1700–	32	30			
1900–	18	20		1000	1000
2100–	11	10			
2300–	8	8			
Above 2500–	7	11			
	1000	1000			

[a] These observations ignored in calculations.

direct indication of the minimum time, it seemed the best available in the circumstances. The results for Henmon's (1911, Table 2, p. 194) Ss Bl and Br are considered below.

For Bl, the minimum possible time was taken to be about 0.40 sec. On this basis $\alpha = 3.19$ and $\beta = 1.28$, these values referring to a time scale measured in seconds. For Br, the minimum time was taken to be 0.34 sec. giving $\alpha = 6.68$ and $\beta = 4.28$. A comparison of the observed and expected distributions of response times is given in Table 1. The agreement between model and data seems to be reasonably good.

CONCLUDING REMARKS

On the whole, there is a certain looseness in the way in which many contemporary theories and even local hypotheses are linked to observed response variables. It seems worthwhile, therefore, to try to determine whether these variables might not be related to one another by relatively simple laws which operate in most choice situations. In this way, not only are descriptions of choice behavior considerably simplified, but better ways of formulating and testing theories are suggested. The model itself is naturally also a theory about a certain aspect of behavior, and as such needs to be tested.

In this presentation of the general stochastic model the intention is to indicate the potentialities of the approach, rather than to make specific tests of the case arising when $K = 2$. It is not to be expected that the two simple assumptions will alone account for the relations existing between response variables in a wide diversity of situations. Each situation will undoubtedly have certain unique conditions which have to be taken into account. But the model does seem to share certain important properties with choice behavior and therefore it appears to be a reasonable initial working hypothesis. It can be tested in great detail against data, and the parameters are of a kind which could be identified with either psychological or physiological constructs.

Methods of estimating parameters and statistical tests of goodness of fit will be discussed elsewhere. For the present model, neither of these procedures involves any novel problems. For example, given the probability of occurrence of one of the alternative responses and the over-all mean response time, Equations 6 and 11 may be easily solved to give the appropriate parameter values.

REFERENCES

AUDLEY, R. J. A stochastic description of the learning behaviour of an individual subject. *Quart. J. exp. Psychol.*, 1957, 9, 12–20.

AUDLEY, R. J. The inclusion of response times within a stochastic description of the learning behaviour of individual subjects. *Psychometrika*, 1958, 23, 25–31.

AUDLEY, R. J., & JONCKHEERE, A. R. Stochastic processes for learning. *Brit. J. statist. Psychol.*, 1956, 9, 87–94.

BAKAN, D. The general and the aggregate: A methodological distinction. *Perceptual & Motor Skills*, 1955, 5, 211–212.

BARKER, R. G. An experimental study of the resolution of conflict by children. In Q. McNemar & M. A. Merrill (Eds.), *Studies in personality*. New York: McGraw Hill, 1942.

BRADLEY, R. A., & TERRY, H. E. The rank analysis of incomplete block designs. I. The method of paired comparisons. *Biometrika*, 1952, 39, 324–345.

BUSH, R. R., & MOSTELLER, F. A mathematical model for simple learning. *Psychol. Rev.*, 1951, 58, 313–323.

BUSH, R. R., & MOSTELLER, F. *Stochastic models for learning*. New York: Wiley, 1955.

CARTWRIGHT, D. Relation of decision-time to the categories of response. *Amer. J. Psychol.*, 1941, 54, 174–196.

CHRISTIE, L. S. The measurement of discriminative behaviour. *Psychol. Rev.*, 1952, 59, 443–452.

DASHIELL, J. F. Affective value-distances as a determinant of esthetic judgments. *Amer. J. Psychol.*, 1937, 50, 57–67.

ESTES, W. K. Toward a statistical theory of learning. *Psychol. Rev.*, 1950, 57, 94–107.

FELLER, W. *An introduction to probability theory and its applications*. New York: Wiley, 1950.

GEORGE, S. S. Attitude in relation to psychophysical judgment. *Amer. J. Psychol.*, 1917, 28, 1–37.

GUILFORD, J. P. *Psychometric Methods*. New York: McGraw Hill, 1954.

HENMON, V. A. C. The relation of the time of a judgment to its accuracy. *Psychol. Rev.*, 1911, 18, 186–201.

MUELLER, C. G. Theoretical relationships among some measures of conditioning. *Proc. Nat. Acad. Sci.*, 1950, 36, 123–130.

WOODWORTH, R. S. *Experimental psychology*. New York: Henry Holt, 1938.

A MATHEMATICAL MODEL FOR SIMPLE LEARNING

BY ROBERT R. BUSH [1] AND FREDERICK MOSTELLER

Harvard University [2]

Introduction

Mathematical models for empirical phenomena aid the development of a science when a sufficient body of quantitative information has been accumulated. This accumulation can be used to point the direction in which models should be constructed and to test the adequacy of such models in their interim states. Models, in turn, frequently are useful in organizing and interpreting experimental data and in suggesting new directions for experimental research. Among the branches of psychology, few are as rich as learning in quantity and variety of available data necessary for model building. Evidence of this fact is provided by the numerous attempts to construct quantitative models for learning phenomena. The most recent contribution is that of Estes (2).

In this paper we shall present the basic structure of a new mathematical model designed to describe some simple learning situations. We shall focus attention on acquisition and extinction

[1] SSRC-NRC Post-doctoral Fellow in the Natural and Social Sciences.

[2] This research was supported by the Laboratory of Social Relations, Harvard University, as part of a program of the Laboratory's Project on Mathematical Models.

The authors are grateful to many persons for helpful advice and constant encouragement, but especially to Drs. W. O. Jenkins, R. R. Sears, and R. L. Solomon.

in experimental arrangements using straight runways and Skinner boxes, though we believe the model is more general; we plan to extend the model in order to describe multiple-choice problems and experiments in generalization and discrimination in later papers. Wherever possible we shall discuss the correspondence between our model and the one being developed by Estes (2), since striking parallels do exist even though many of the basic premises differ. Our model is discussed and developed primarily in terms of reinforcement concepts while Estes' model stems from an attempt to formalize association theory. Both models, however, may be re-interpreted in terms of other sets of concepts. This state of affairs is a common feature of most mathematical models. An example is the particle and wave interpretations of modern atomic theory.

We are concerned with the type of learning which has been called "instrumental conditioning" (5), "operant behavior" or "type R conditioning" (10), and not with "classical conditioning" (5), "Pavlovian conditioning" or "type S conditioning" (10). We shall follow Sears (9) in dividing up the chain of events as follows: (1) perception of a stimulus, (2) performance of a response or instrumental act, (3) occurrence of an environmental event,

This article appeared in *Psychol. Rev.*, 1951, **58**, 313–323. Reprinted with permission.

and (4) execution of a goal response. Examples of instrumental responses are the traversing of a runway, pressing of a lever, etc. By environmental events we mean the presentation of a "reinforcing stimulus" (10) such as food or water, but we wish to include in this category electric shocks and other forms of punishment, removal of the animal from the apparatus, the sounding of a buzzer, etc. Hence any change in the stimulus situation which follows an instrumental response is called an environmental event. A goal response, such as eating food or drinking water, is not necessarily involved in the chain. It is implied, however, that the organism has a motivation or drive which corresponds to some goal response. Operationally speaking, we infer a state of motivation from observing a goal response.

Probabilities and How They Change

As a measure of behavior, we have chosen the probability, p, that the instrumental response will occur during a specified time, h. This probability will change during conditioning and extinction and will be related to experimental variables such as latent time, rate, and frequency of choices. The choice of the time interval, h, will be discussed later. We conceive that the probability, p, is increased or decreased a small amount after each occurrence of the response and that the determinants of the amount of change in p are the environmental events and the work or effort expended in making the response. In addition, of course, the magnitude of the change depends upon the properties of the organism and upon the value of the probability before the response occurred. For example, if the probability was already unity, it could not be increased further.

Our task, then, is to describe the change in probability which occurs after each performance of the response being studied. We wish to express this change in terms of the probability immediately prior to the occurrence of the response and so we explicitly assume that the change is independent of the still earlier values of the probability. For convenience in describing the step-wise change in probability, we introduce the concept of a mathematical operator. The notion is elementary and in no way mysterious: an operator Q when applied to an operand p yields a new quantity Qp (read Q operating on p). Ordinary mathematical operations of addition, multiplication, differentiation, etc., may be defined in terms of operators. For the present purpose, we are interested in a class of operators Q which when applied to our probability p will give a new value of probability Qp. As mentioned above, we are assuming that this new probability, Qp, can be expressed in terms of the old value, p. Supposing Qp to be a well-behaved function, we can expand it as a power series in p:

$$Qp = a_0 + a_1 p + a_2 p^2 + \cdots \quad (1)$$

where $a_0, a_1, a_2, \cdots$ are constants independent of p. In order to simplify the mathematical analysis which follows, we shall retain only the first two terms in this expansion. Thus, we are assuming that we can employ operators which represent a linear transformation on p. If the change is small, one would expect that this assumption would provide an adequate first approximation. Our operator Q is then completely defined as soon as we specify the constants a_0 and a_1; this is the major problem at hand. For reasons that will soon be apparent, we choose to let $a_0 = a$ and $a_1 = 1 - a - b$. This choice of parameters permits us to write our operator in the form

$$Qp = p + a(1 - p) - bp. \quad (2)$$

This is our basic operator and equation (2) will be used as the cornerstone for our theoretical development. To maintain the probability between 0 and 1, the parameters a and b must also lie between 0 and 1. Since a is positive, we see that the term, $a(1 - p)$, of equation (2) corresponds to an increment in p which is proportional to the maximum possible increment, $(1 - p)$. Moreover, since b is positive, the term, $-bp$, corresponds to a decrement in p which is proportional to the maximum possible decrement, $-p$. Therefore, we can associate with the parameter a those factors which always increase the probability and with the parameter b those factors which always decrease the probability. It is for these reasons that we rewrote our operator in the form given in equation (2).

We associate the event of presenting a reward or other reinforcing stimulus with the parameter a, and we assume that $a = 0$ when no reward is given as in experimental extinction. With the parameter b, we associate events such as punishment and the work required in making the response. (See the review by Solomon [11] of the influence of work on behavior.) In many respects, our term, $a(1 - p)$, corresponds to an increment in "excitatory potential" in Hull's theory (6) and our term, $-bp$, corresponds to an increment in Hull's "inhibitory potential."

In this paper, we make no further attempt to relate our parameters, a and b, to experimental variables such as amount of reward, amount of work, strength of motivation, etc. In comparing our theoretical results with experimental data, we will choose values of a and b which give the best fit. In other words, our model at the present time is concerned only with the form of conditioning and extinction curves, not with the precise values of parameters for particular conditions and particular organisms.

Continuous Reinforcement and Extinction

Up to this point, we have discussed only the effect of the occurrence of a response upon the probability of that response. Since probability must be conserved, *i.e.*, since in a time interval h an organism will make some response or no response, we must investigate the effect of the occurrence of one response upon the probability of another response. In a later paper, we shall discuss this problem in detail, but for the present purpose we must include the following assumption. We conceive that there are two general kinds of responses, overt and non-overt. The overt responses are subdivided into classes A, B, C, etc. If an overt response A occurs and is neither rewarded nor punished, then the probability of any mutually exclusive overt response B is not changed. Nevertheless, the probability of that response A is changed after an occurrence on which it is neither rewarded nor punished. Since the total probability of all responses must be unity, it follows that the probability gained or lost by response A must be compensated by a corresponding loss or gain in probability of the non-overt responses. This assumption is important in the analysis of experiments which use a runway or Skinner box, for example. In such experiments a single class of responses is singled out for study, but other overt responses can and do occur. We defer until a later paper the discussion of experiments in which two or more responses are reinforced differentially.

With the aid of our mathematical

operator of equation (2) we may now describe the progressive change in the probability of a response in an experiment such as the Graham-Gagné runway (3) or Skinner box (10) in which the same environmental events follow each occurrence of the response. We need only apply our operator Q repeatedly to some initial value of the probability p. Each application of the operator corresponds to one occurrence of the response and the subsequent environmental events. The algebra involved in these manipulations is straightforward. For example, if we apply Q to p twice, we have

$$Q^2 p = Q(Qp) = a + (1 - a - b)Qp$$
$$= a + (1 - a - b)$$
$$\times [a + (1 - a - b)p]. \quad (3)$$

Moreover, it may be readily shown that if we apply Q to p successively n times, we have

$$Q^n p = \frac{a}{a + b} - \left(\frac{a}{a + b} - p\right)$$
$$\times (1 - a - b)^n. \quad (4)$$

Provided a and b are not both zero or both unity, the quantity $(1 - a - b)^n$ tends to an asymptotic value of zero as n increases. Therefore, $Q^n p$ approaches a limiting value of $a/(a + b)$ as n becomes large. Equation (4) then describes a curve of acquisition.

It should be noticed that the asymptotic value of the probability is not necessarily either zero or unity. For example, if $a = b$ (speaking roughly this implies that the measures of reward and work are equal), the ultimate probability of occurrence in time h of the response being studied is 0.5.

Since we have assumed that $a = 0$ when no reward is given after the response occurs, we may describe an extinction trial by a special operator E which is equivalent to our operator

Q of equation (2) with a set equal to zero:

$$Ep = p - bp = (1 - b)p. \quad (5)$$

It follows directly that if we apply this operator E to p successively for n times we have

$$E^n p = (1 - b)^n p. \quad (6)$$

This equation then describes a curve of experimental extinction.

Probability, Latent Time, and Rate

Before the above results on continuous reinforcement and extinction can be compared with empirical results, we must first establish relationships between our probability, p, and experimental measures such as latent time and rate of responding. In order to do this, we must have a model. A simple and useful model is the one described by Estes (2). Let the activity of an organism be described by a sequence of responses which are independent of one another. (For this purpose, we consider doing "nothing" to be a response.) The probability that the response or class of responses being studied will occur first is p. Since we have already assumed that non-reinforced occurrences of other responses do not affect p, one may easily calculate the mean number of responses which will occur before the response being studied takes place. Estes (2) has presented this calculation and shown that the mean number of responses which will occur, including the one being studied, is simply $1/p$. In that derivation it was assumed that the responses were all independent of one another, i.e., that transition probabilities between pairs of responses are the same for all pairs. This assumption is a bold one indeed (it is easy to think of overt responses that *cannot* follow one another), but it appears to us that any other assumption would require a detailed specification of the many possible responses in each experimental arrangement being considered. (Miller and Frick [8] have attempted such an analysis for a particular experiment.) It is further assumed that every response requires the same amount of time, h, for its performance. The mean latent time, then, is simply h times the mean number of responses which occur on a "trial":

$$L = \frac{h}{p}. \qquad (7)$$

The time, h, required for each response will depend, of course, on the organism involved and very likely upon its strength of drive or motivation.

The mean latent time, L, is expressed in terms of the probability, p, by equation (7), while this probability is given in terms of the number of trials, n, by equation (4). Hence we may obtain an expression for the mean latent time as a function of the number of trials. It turns out that this expression is identical to equation (4) of Estes' paper (2) except for differences in notation. (Estes uses T in place of our n; our use of a difference equation rather than of a differential equation gives us the term $(1 - a - b)$ instead of Estes' e^{-q}.) Estes fitted his equation to the data of Graham and Gagné (3). Our results differ from Estes' in one respect, however: the asymptotic mean latent time in Estes' model is simply h, while we obtain

$$L_\infty = h\left(\frac{a + b}{a}\right). \qquad (8)$$

This equation suggests that the final mean latent time depends on the amount of reward and on the amount of required work, since we have assumed that a and b depend on those two variables, respectively. This conclusion seems to agree with the data

of Grindley (4) on chicks and the data of Crespi (1) on white rats.

Since equation (7) is an expression for the mean time between the end of one response of the type being studied and the end of the next response of the type being studied, we may now calculate the mean rate of responding in a Skinner-box arrangement. If t represents the mean time required for the occurrence of n responses, measured from some arbitrary starting point, then each occurrence of the response being studied adds an increment in t as follows:

$$\frac{\Delta t}{\Delta n} = \frac{h}{p}. \qquad (9)$$

If the increments are sufficiently small, we may write them as differentials and obtain for the mean rate of responding

$$\frac{dn}{dt} = \frac{p}{h} = \omega p, \qquad (10)$$

where $\omega = 1/h$. We shall call ω the "activity level" and by definition ω is the maximum rate of responding which occurs when $p = 1$ obtains.

The Free-Responding Situation

In free-responding situations, such as that in Skinner box experiments, one usually measures rate of responding or the cumulative number of responses versus time. To obtain theoretical expressions for these relations, we first obtain an expression for the probability p as a function of time. From equation (2), we see that if the response being studied occurs, the change in probability is $\Delta p = a(1 - p) - bp$. We have already assumed that if other responses occur and are not reinforced, no change in the probability of occurrence of the response being studied will ensue. Hence the expected change in probability during a time interval h is merely the change in probability times the probability p that the response being studied occurs in that time interval:

Expected (Δp)

$$= p\{a(1 - p) - bp\}. \quad (11)$$

The expected rate of change of probability with time is then this expression divided by the time h. Writing this rate as a derivative we have

$$\frac{dp}{dt} = \omega p\{a(1 - p) - bp\} \quad (12)$$

where, as already defined, $\omega = 1/h$ is the activity level. This equation is easily integrated to give p as an explicit function of time t. Since equation (10) states that the mean rate of responding, dn/dt, is ω times the probability p, we obtain after the integration

$$\frac{dn}{dt} = \frac{\omega p_0}{p_0(1+u)+[1 - p_0(1+u)]e^{-a\omega t}} = V \quad (13)$$

where we have let $u = b/a$. The initial rate of responding at $t = 0$ is $V_0 = \omega p_0$, and the final rate after a very long time t is

$$V_\infty = \left[\frac{dn}{dt}\right]_{t=\infty} = \frac{\omega}{1+u} = \frac{\omega}{1+b/a}. \quad (14)$$

Equation (13) is quite similar to the expression obtained by Estes except for our inclusion of the ratio $u = b/a$. The final rate of responding according to equation (14), increases with a and hence with the amount of reward given per response, and decreases with b and hence with the amount of work per response. These conclusions do not follow from Estes' results (2).

An expression for the cumulative number of responses during continuous reinforcement is obtained by integrating equation (13) with respect to

time t. The result is

$$n = \frac{1}{1+u}\left\{\omega t + \frac{1}{a}\log\left[p_0(1 + u)\right.\right.$$
$$\times (1 - e^{-a\omega t}) + e^{-a\omega t}\Big]\Big\}. \quad (15)$$

As the time t becomes very large, the exponentials in equation (15) approach zero and n becomes a linear function of time. This agrees with equation (14) which says that the asymptotic rate is a constant. Both equations (13) and (15) for rate of responding and cumulative number of responses, respectively, have the same form as the analogous equations derived by Estes (2) which were fitted by him to data on a bar-pressing habit of rats. The essential difference between Estes' results and ours is the dependence, discussed above, of the final rate upon amount of work and amount of reward per trial.

We may extend our analysis to give expressions for rates and cumulative responses during extinction. Since we have assumed that $a = 0$ during extinction, we have in place of equation (12)

$$\frac{dp}{dt} = -\omega b p^2 \quad (16)$$

which when integrated for p and multiplied by ω gives

$$\frac{dm}{dt} = \frac{\omega p_e}{1 + \omega b p_e t} \quad (17)$$

where p_e is the probability at the beginning of extinction. The rate at the beginning of extinction is $V_e = \omega p_e$. Hence we may write equation (17) in the form

$$V = \frac{dm}{dt} = \frac{V_e}{1 + V_e bt}. \quad (18)$$

An integration of this equation gives for the cumulative number of extinction responses

$$m = \frac{1}{b} \log [1 + V_e bt]$$

$$= \frac{1}{b} \log \left(\frac{V_e}{V} \right). \quad (19)$$

This result is similar to the empirical equation $m = K \log t$, used by Skinner in fitting experimental response curves (**10**). Our equation has the additional advantage of passing through the origin as it must.

It may be noted that the logarithmic character of equation (19) implies that the total number of extinction responses, m, has no upper limit. Thus, if our result is correct, and indeed if Skinner's empirical equation is correct, then there is no upper limit to the size of the "reserve" of extinction responses. For all practical purposes, however, the logarithmic variation is so slow for large values of the time t, it is justified to use some arbitrary criterion for the "completion" of extinction. We shall consider extinction to be "complete" when the mean rate of responding V has fallen to some specified value, V_f. Thus, the "total" number of extinction responses from this criterion is

$$m_T = \frac{1}{b} \log \frac{V_e}{V_f}. \quad (20)$$

We now wish to express this "total" number of extinction responses, m_T, as an explicit function of the number of preceding reinforcements, n. The only quantity in equation (20) which depends upon n is the rate, V_e, at the beginning of extinction. If we assume that this rate is equal to the rate at the end of acquisition, we have from equations (4) and (10)

$$V_e = \frac{dn}{dt} = \omega p_n = V_{max}$$

$$- (V_{max} - V_0)(1 - a - b)^n \quad (21)$$

where we have let

$$V_{max} = \omega \frac{a}{a + b}, \quad (22)$$

and where $V_0 = \omega p_0$ is the rate at the beginning of acquisition. If we now substitute equation (21) into equation (20), we obtain

$$m_T = \frac{1}{b} \log \left\{ \frac{V_{max}}{V_f} - \left[\frac{V_{max}}{V_f} - \frac{V_0}{V_f} \right] \right.$$

$$\left. \times (1 - a - b)^n \right\}. \quad (23)$$

This result may be compared with the data of Williams (**12**) obtained by measuring the "total" number of extinction responses after 5, 10, 30 and 90 reinforcements. From the data, the ratio V_{max}/V_f was estimated to be about 5, and the ratio V_0/V_f was assumed to be about unity. Values of $a = 0.014$ and $b = 0.026$ were chosen in fitting equation (23) to the data. The result is shown in the figure.

Fixed Ratio and Random Ratio Reinforcement

In present day psychological language, the term "fixed ratio" (**7**) refers to the procedure of rewarding every kth response in a free-responding situation ($k = 2, 3, \cdots$). In a "random ratio" schedule, an animal is rewarded on the average after k responses but the actual number of responses per reward varies over some specified range. We shall now derive expressions for mean rates of responding and cumulative numbers of responses for these two types of reinforcement schedules. If we apply our operator Q, of equation (2), to a probability p, and then apply our operator E, of equation (5), to Qp repeatedly for $(k - 1)$ times, we obtain

$$(E^{k-1}Q)p = (1-b)^{k-1}[p+a(1-p)-bp]$$

$$= p + a'(1-p) - b'p \quad (24)$$

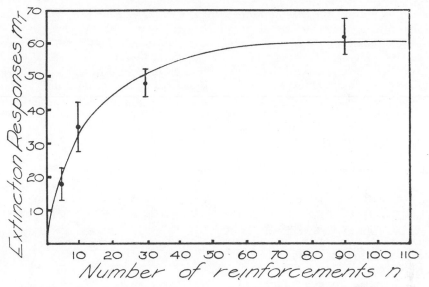

"Total" number of extinction responses as a function of the number of reinforcements. Curve plotted from equation (23) with $b = 0.026$, $a = 0.014$, $V_{max} = 5V_0$, $V_f = V_0$. Data from Williams (12).

where

$$a' = a(1-b)^{k-1}$$
$$= a\{1 - (k-1)b + \cdots\} \cong a \quad (25)$$

and

$$b' = 1 - (1-b)^k$$
$$= kb\left\{1 - \frac{k-1}{2}b + \cdots\right\} \cong kb. \quad (26)$$

The symbol $\cong$ means "approximately equal to." In the present case the exact approach would be to retain the primes on a and b throughout; however the approximations provide a link with the previous discussion. The approximations on the right of these two equations are justified if kb is small compared to unity. Now the mean change in p *per response* will be the second and third terms of equation (24) divided by k:

$$\Delta p = \frac{a'}{k}(1-p) - \frac{b'}{k}p$$
$$\cong \frac{a}{k}(1-p) - bp. \quad (27)$$

This equation is identical to our result for continuous reinforcement, except that a'/k replaces a and b'/k replaces b.

We may obtain a similar result for the "random ratio" schedule as follows: After any response, the probability that Q operates on p is $1/k$ and the probability that E operates on p is $(1 - 1/k)$. Hence the expected change in p per response is

$$\text{Expected }(\Delta p) = \frac{1}{k}Qp$$
$$+ (1 - 1/k)Ep - p. \quad (28)$$

After equations (2) and (5) are inserted and the result simplified, we obtain from equation (28)

$$\text{Expected }(\Delta p)$$
$$= \frac{a}{k}(1-p) - bp. \quad (29)$$

This result is identical to the approximate result shown in equation (27) for the fixed ratio case. Since both equations (27) and (29) have the same form as our result for the continuous reinforcement case, we may at once write for the mean rate of responding an equation identical to equation (13), except that a is replaced by a'/k. Similarly, we obtain an expression for the final rate of responding identical to equation (14) except that a is replaced by a'/k. This result is meant to apply to both fixed ratio and random ratio schedules of reinforcement.

In comparing the above result for the asymptotic rates with equation (14) for continuous reinforcement, we must be careful about equating the activity level, ω, for the three cases (continuous, fixed ratio and random ratio reinforcements). Since $1/\omega$ represents the minimum mean time between successive responses, it includes both the eating time and a "recovery time." By the latter we mean the time necessary for the animal to reorganize itself after eating and get in a position to make another bar press or key peck. In the fixed ratio case, presumably the animal learns to look for food not after each press or peck, as in the continuous case, but ideally only after every k response. Therefore both the mean eating time and the mean recovery time *per response* are less for the fixed ratio case than for the continuous case. In the random ratio case, one would expect a similar but smaller difference to occur. Hence, it seems reasonable to conclude that the activity level, ω, would be smaller for continuous reinforcement than for either fixed ratio or random ratio, and that ω would be lower for random ratio than for fixed ratio when the mean number of responses per reward was the same. Moreover, we should expect that ω would increase with the number of responses per reward, k. Even if eating time were subtracted out in all cases we should expect these arguments to apply. Without a quantitative estimate of the mean recovery time, we see no meaningful way of comparing rates of responding under continuous reinforcement with those under fixed ratio and random ratio, nor of comparing rates under different ratios (unless both ratios are large). The difficulty of comparing rates under various reinforcement schedules does not seem to be a weakness of our model, but rather a natural consequence of the experimental procedure. However, the importance of these considerations hinges upon the orders of magnitude involved, and such questions are empirical ones.

Aperiodic and Periodic Reinforcement

Many experiments of recent years were designed so that an animal was reinforced at a rate aperiodic or periodic in time (7). The usual procedure is to choose a set of time intervals, $T_1, \cdots, T_n$, which have a mean value T. Some arrangement of this set is used as the actual sequence of time intervals between rewards. The first response which occurs after one of these time intervals has elapsed is rewarded.

To analyze this situation we may consider k, the mean number of responses per reward, to be equal to the mean time interval T multiplied by the mean rate of responding:

$$k = T \frac{dn}{dt} = T\omega p. \qquad (30)$$

Equation (29) for the expected change in probability per response is still valid if we now consider k to be a variable as expressed by equation (30). Thus, the time rate of change of p is

$$\frac{dp}{dt} = \frac{a}{T}(1 - p) - \omega b p^2. \qquad (31)$$

With a little effort, this differential equation may be integrated from 0 to

t to give

$$\frac{dn}{dt} = \omega p$$

$$= \frac{\omega}{z} \frac{(s-1) + (s+1)Ke^{-sat/T}}{1 - Ke^{-sat/T}} \quad (32)$$

where

$$z = 2\omega Tb/a, \quad (33)$$

$$s = \sqrt{1 + 2z}, \quad (34)$$

$$K = (1 + zp_0 - s)/(1 + zp_0 + s). \quad (35)$$

For arbitrarily large times t, the final rate is

$$\left(\frac{dn}{dt}\right)_{t=\infty} = \frac{\omega}{z}(s-1). \quad (36)$$

For sufficiently large values of T, z becomes large compared to unity and we may write approximately

$$\left(\frac{dn}{dt}\right)_{t=\infty} = \omega\sqrt{2/z} = \omega\sqrt{a/b\omega T}. \quad (37)$$

Thus, for large values of T, the final rate varies inversely as the square root of T.

Periodic reinforcement is a special case of aperiodic reinforcement in which the set of time intervals, $T_1, \cdots, T_n$, discussed above, consists of a single time interval, T. Thus, all the above equations apply to both periodic and aperiodic schedules. One essential difference is known, however. In the periodic case the animal can learn a time discrimination, or as is sometimes said, eating becomes a cue for not responding for a while. This seems to be an example of stimulus discrimination which we will discuss in a later paper.

Extinction After Partial Reinforcement Schedules

In the discussion of extinction in earlier sections, it may be noted that the equations for mean rates and cumulative responses depended on the previous reward training only through V_e, the mean rate at the beginning of extinction. Hence, we conclude that equations (18) and (19) apply to extinction after any type of reinforcement schedule. However, the quantities V_e and b in our equations may depend very much on the previous training. Indeed, if our model makes any sense at all, this must be the case, for "resistance" to extinction is known to be much greater after partial reinforcement training than after a continuous reinforcement schedule (7).

Since the rate at the start of extinction, V_e, is nearly equal to the rate at the end of acquisition, it will certainly depend on the type and amount of previous training. However, the logarithmic variation in equations (19) and (20) is so slow, it seems clear that empirical results demand a dependence of b on the type of reinforcement schedule which preceded extinction. We have argued that b increases with the amount of work required per response. We will now try to indicate how the required work might depend upon the type of reinforcement schedule, even though the lever pressure or key tension is the same. For continuous reinforcement, the response pattern which is learned by a pigeon, for example, involves pecking the key once, lowering its head to the food magazine, eating, raising its head, and readjusting its body in preparation for the next peck. This response pattern demands a certain amount of effort. On the other hand, the response pattern which is learned for other types of reinforcement schedules is quite different; the bird makes several key pecks before executing the rest of the pattern just described. Thus we would expect that the average work required per *key peck* is considerably less than for continuous reinforcement. This would imply that b is larger and thus "resistance" to extinction is less for continuous reinforcement than for all other schedules. This deduction is consistent with experimental results (7). However, this is just part of the story. For one thing, it seems clear that it is easier for the organism to discriminate between continuous reinforcement and extinction; we have not handled this effect here.

Summary

A mathematical model for simple learning is presented. Changes in the probability of occurrence of a response in a small time h are described with the aid of mathematical operators. The parameters which appear in the operator equations are related to experimental variables such as the amount of reward and work. Relations between the probability and empirical measures of rate of responding and latent time are defined. Acquisition and extinction of behavior habits are discussed for the simple runway and for the Skinner box. Equations of mean latent time as a function of trial number are derived for the runway problem; equations for the mean rate of responding and cumulative numbers of responses versus time are derived for the Skinner box experiments. An attempt is made to analyze the learning process with various schedules of partial reinforcement in the Skinner type experiment. Wherever possible, the correspondence between the present model and the work of Estes (2) is pointed out.

REFERENCES

1. CRESPI, L. P. Quantitative variation of incentive and performance in the white rat. *Amer. J. Psychol.*, 1942, 55, 467–517.
2. ESTES, W. K. Toward a statistical theory of learning. PSYCHOL. REV., 1950, 57, 94–107.
3. GRAHAM, C., AND GAGNÉ, R. M. The acquisition, extinction, and spontaneous recovery of a conditioned operant response. *J. exp. Psychol.*, 1940, 26, 251–280.
4. GRINDLEY, C. C. Experiments on the influence of the amount of reward on learning in young chickens. *Brit. J. Psychol.*, 1929–30, 20, 173–180.
5. HILGARD, E. R., AND MARQUIS, D. G. *Conditioning and learning.* New York: D. Appleton-Century Co., 1940.
6. HULL, C. L. *Principles of behavior.* New York: Appleton-Century-Crofts, 1943.
7. JENKINS, W. O., AND STANLEY, J. C. Partial reinforcement: a review and critique. *Psychol. Bull.*, 1950, 47, 193–234.
8. MILLER, G. A., AND FRICK, F. C. Statistical behavioristics and sequences of responses. PSYCHOL. REV., 1949, 56, 311–324.
9. SEARS, R. R. Lectures at Harvard University, Summer, 1949.
10. SKINNER, B. F. *The behavior of organisms.* New York: Appleton-Century-Crofts, 1938.
11. SOLOMON, R. L. The influence of work on behavior. *Psychol. Bull.*, 1948, 45, 1–40.
12. WILLIAMS, S. B. Resistance to extinction as a function of the number of reinforcements. *J. exp. Psychol.*, 1938, 23, 506–521.

[MS. Received September 21, 1950]

A MODEL FOR STIMULUS GENERALIZATION
AND DISCRIMINATION

BY ROBERT R. BUSH[1] AND FREDERICK MOSTELLER

Harvard University[2]

INTRODUCTION

The processes of stimulus generalization and discrimination seem as fundamental to behavior theory as the simple mechanisms of reinforcement and extinction are to learning theory. Whether or not this distinction between learning and behavior is a useful one, there can be little doubt that few if any applications of behavior theory to practical problems can be made without a clear exposition of the phenomena of generalization and discrimination. It is our impression that few crucial experiments in this area have been reported compared with the number of important experiments on simple conditioning and extinction. Perhaps part of the reason for this is that there are too few theoretical formulations available. That is to say, we conceive that explicit and quantitative theoretical structures are useful in guiding the direction of experimental research and in suggesting the type of data which are needed.

In this paper we describe a model, based upon elementary concepts of mathematical set theory. This model provides one possible framework for analyzing problems in stimulus generalization and discrimination. Further, we shall show how this model generates the basic postulates of our previous work on acquisition and extinction (1), where the stimulus situation as defined by the experimenter was assumed constant.

Stated in the simplest terms, generalization is the phenomenon in which an increase in strength of a response learned in one stimulus situation implies an increase in strength of response in a somewhat different stimulus situation. When this occurs, the two situations are said to be similar. Although there are several intuitive notions as to what is meant by "similarity," one usually means the properties which give rise to generalization. We see no alternative to using the amount of generalization as an operational definition of degree of "similarity." In the model, however, we shall give another definition of the degree of similarity, but this definition will be entirely consistent with the above-mentioned operational definition.

We also wish to clarify what we mean by stimulus discrimination. In one sense of the term, all learning is a process of discrimination. Our usage of the term is a more restricted one, however. We refer specifically to the process by which an animal learns to make response A in one stimulus situation and response B (or response A with different "strength") in a different stimulus situation. We are not at the moment concerned with, for example, the process by which an animal learns to discriminate between

[1] SSRC-NRC Post-doctoral Fellow in the Natural and Social Sciences.

[2] This research was supported by the Laboratory of Social Relations, Harvard University, as part of a program of the Laboratory's Project on Mathematical Models.

We are indebted to many persons for assistance and encouragement, but in particular to F. R. Brush, C. I. Hovland, K. C. Montgomery, F. D. Sheffield, and R. L. Solomon. We are also grateful to W. K. Estes for sending us a pre-publication copy of his paper(2).

This article appeared in *Psychol. Rev.*, 1951, **58**, 413–423. Reprinted with permission.

various possible responses in a fixed stimulus situation.

As prototypes of the more general problems of stimulus generalization and discrimination, we shall consider the following two kinds of experiments:

(i) An animal is trained to make a particular response, by the usual reinforcement procedure, in an experimentally defined stimulus situation. At the end of training, the response has a certain strength or probability of occurrence. The animal is then "tested" in a new stimulus situation similar to the training one and in which the same response, insofar as it is experimentally defined, is possible. One then asks about the strength or probability of occurrence of the response in this new stimulus situation and how it depends on the degree of similarity of the new situation to the old stimulus situation.

(ii) An animal is presented alternately with two stimulus situations which are similar. In one, an experimentally defined response is rewarded, and in the other that response is either not rewarded or rewarded less than in the first. Through the process of generalization, the effects of rewards and non-rewards in one stimulus situation influence the response strength in the other, but eventually the animal learns to respond in one but not in the other, or at least to respond with different probabilities (rates or strengths). One then asks how the probability of the response in each situation varies with the number of training trials, with the degree of similarity of the two situations, and with the amount of reward.

We do not consider that these two kinds of experiments come close to exhausting the problems classified under the heading of generalization and discrimination, but we do believe that they are fundamental. Thus, the model to be described has been designed to permit analysis of these experiments. In the next section we will present the major features of the model, and in later sections we shall apply it to the above described experiments.

THE MODEL

We shall employ some of the elementary notions of mathematical set theory to define our model. A particular stimulus situation, such as an experimental box with specific properties (geometrical, optical, acoustical, etc.) is regarded as separate and distinct from the rest of the universe. Thus, we shall denote this situation by a set of stimuli which is part of the entire universe of stimuli. The elements of this set are undefined and we place no restriction on their number. This lack of definition of the stimulus elements does not give rise to any serious difficulties since our final results involve neither properties of individual elements nor numbers of such elements. We next introduce the notion of the *measure* of a set. If the set consists of a finite number of elements, we may associate with each element a positive number to denote its "weight"; the measure of such a set is the sum of all these numbers. Intuitively, the weight associated with an element is the measure of the potential importance of that element in influencing the organism's behavior. More generally, we can define a density function over the set; the measure is the integral of that function over the set.

To bridge the gap between stimuli and responses, we shall borrow some of the basic notions of Estes (2). (The concept of reinforcement will play an integral role, however.) It is assumed that stimulus elements exist in one of two states as far as the organism involved is concerned; since the elements are undefined, these states do not require definition but merely need labelling. However, we shall speak of elements which are in one state as being "conditioned" to the response, and of elements in the other state as being "non-conditioned."

On a particular trial or occurrence of a response in the learning process, it is conceived that an organism perceives a sub-set of the total stimuli available. It is postulated that the probability of occurrence of the response in a given time interval is equal to the measure of the elements in the sub-set which had been previously conditioned, divided by the measure of the entire sub-set. Speaking roughly, the probability is the ratio of the importance of the conditioned elements perceived to the importance of all the elements perceived. It is further assumed that the sub-set perceived is conditioned to the response if that response is rewarded.

The situation is illustrated in Fig. 1. It would be wrong to suppose that the conditioned and non-conditioned elements are spatially separated in the actual situation as Fig. 1 might suggest; the conditioned elements are spread out smoothly among the non-conditioned ones. In set-theoretic notation, we then have for the probability of occurrence of the response

$$p = \frac{m(X \cap C)}{m(X)}, \qquad (1)$$

where $m(\ )$ denotes the measure of any set or sub-set named between the parentheses, and where $X \cap C$ indicates the intersection of X and C (also called set-product, meet, or overlap of X and C). We then make an assumption of equal proportions in the measures so that

$$p = \frac{m(X \cap C)}{m(X)} = \frac{m(C)}{m(S)}. \qquad (2)$$

Heuristically, this assumption of equal proportions can arise from a fluid model. Suppose that the total situation is represented by a vessel containing an ideal fluid which is a

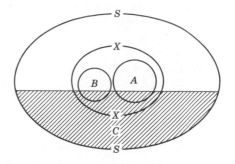

FIG. 1. Set diagram of the single stimulus situation S with the various sub-sets involved in a particular trial. C is the sub-set of elements previously conditioned, X the sub-set of S perceived on the trial. The sub-sets A and B are defined in the text.

mixture of two substances which do not chemically interact but are completely miscible. For discussion let the substances be water and alcohol and assume, contrary to fact, that the volume of the mixture is equal to the sum of the partial volumes. The volume of the water corresponds to the measure of the sub-set of non-conditioned stimuli, $S - C$ (total set minus the conditioned set), and the volume of the alcohol corresponds to the measure of the sub-set C of conditioned stimuli. The sub-set X corresponds to a thimbleful of the mixture and of course if the fluids are well mixed, the volumetric fraction of alcohol in a thimbleful will be much the same as that in the whole vessel. Thus the fraction of measure of conditioned stimuli in X will be equal to the fraction in the whole set S, as expressed by equation (2). Our definition of p is essentially that of Estes (2) except that where he speaks of number of elements, we speak of the measure of the elements.

We next consider another stimulus situation which we denote by a set S'. In general this new set S' will not be disjunct from the set S, i.e., S and S'

will intersect or overlap as shown in Fig. 2. We denote the intersection by

$$I = S \cap S'. \qquad (3)$$

We can now define an index of similarity of S' to S by

$$\eta(S' \text{ to } S) = \frac{m(I)}{m(S')}. \qquad (4)$$

In words this definition says that the index of similarity of S' to S is the measure of their intersection divided by the measure of the set S'. (Our notation makes clear that we have made a tacit assumption that the measure of an element or set of elements is independent of the set in which it is measured.) Definition (4) also gives the index of similarity of S to S' as

$$\eta(S \text{ to } S') = \frac{m(I)}{m(S)}$$

$$= \frac{m(S')}{m(S)} \eta(S' \text{ to } S). \qquad (5)$$

From this last equation it is clear that the similarity of S' to S may not be the same as the similarity of S to S'. In fact, if the measure of the intersection is not zero, the two indices are equal only if the measures of S and S' are equal. It seems regrettable that similarity, by our definition, is non-symmetric. However, we do not care to make the general assumption that (a) the measures of all situations are equal and at the same time make the assumption that (b) measures of an element or set of elements is the same in each situation in which it appears. For then the importance of a set of elements, say a light bulb, would have to be the same in a small situation, say a $2' \times 2' \times 2'$ box, as in a large situation, say a ballroom. Further this pair of assumptions, (a) and (b), leads to conceptual difficulties.

THE GENERALIZATION PROBLEM

We are now in a position to say something about the first experimental problem described in the Introduction. An animal is trained to make a response in one stimulus situation and then his response strength is measured in a similar situation. After the animal has been trained in the first situation whose elements form the set S, a sub-set C of S will have been conditioned to the response as shown in Fig. 2. But part of the sub-set C is also contained in the second situation whose elements form the set S'; we denote this part by $C \cap S'$.

From the discussion preceding equations (1) and (2), we can easily see that the probability of the response occurring in S' is

$$p' = \frac{m(C \cap S')}{m(S')}. \qquad (6)$$

We now use the assumption of equal proportions so that

$$\frac{m(C \cap S')}{m(I)} = \frac{m(C \cap I)}{m(I)} = \frac{m(C)}{m(S)}. \qquad (7)$$

The first equality in this equation follows from the fact that the only part of C which is in S' is in the inter-

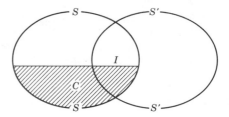

FIG. 2. Diagram of two similar stimulus situations after conditioning in one of them. The situation in which training occurred is denoted by the set S; the sub-set C of S represents the portion of S which was conditioned to the response. The new stimulus situation in which the response strength is to be measured is represented by the set S', and the intersection of S' and S is denoted by I.

section I as shown in Fig. 2. The second equality in equation (7) is an application of our assumption that the measure of C is uniformly distributed over S and so the intersection contains the same fraction of measure of C as does the entire set S.

If now we combine equations (6) and (7), we obtain

$$p' = \frac{m(I)}{m(S')} \cdot \frac{m(C)}{m(S)}. \qquad (8)$$

From equation (4) we note that the first ratio in equation (8) is the index of similarity of S' to S, while from equation (2) we observe that the second ratio in equation (8) is merely the probability p of the response in S. Hence

$$p' = \eta(S' \text{ to } S)p. \qquad (9)$$

Equation (9) now provides us with the necessary operational definition of the index of similarity, $\eta(S' \text{ to } S)$, of the set S' to the set S. The probabilities p and p' of the response in S and S', respectively, can be measured either directly or through measurements of latent time or rate of responding (1). Therefore, with equation (9), we have an operational way of determining the index of similarity.

As a direct consequence of our assumption of equal proportions, we can draw the following general conclusion. *Any change made in a stimulus situation where a response was conditioned will reduce the probability of occurrence of that response, provided the change does not introduce stimuli which had been previously conditioned to that response.* This conclusion follows from equation (9) and the fact that we have defined our similarity index in such a way that it is never greater than unity.

A word needs to be said about the correspondence between our result and the experimental results such as those of Hovland (3). Our model predicts nothing about the relation of the index

of similarity defined above to such physical dimensions as light or sound intensity, frequency, etc. In fact, our model suggests that no such general relation is possible, *i.e.*, that any sensible measure of similarity is very much organism determined. Therefore, from the point of view of our model, experiments such as those of Hovland serve only as a clear demonstration that stimulus generalization exists. In addition, of course, such experiments provide empirical relations, characteristic of the organism studied, between the proposed index of similarity and various physical dimensions, but these relations are outside the scope of our model.

We conclude, therefore, that our model up to this point has made no quantitative predictions about the shape of generalization gradients which can be compared with experiment. Nevertheless, the preceding analysis of generalization does provide us with a framework to discuss experiments on stimulus discrimination. In the following sections we shall extend our model so as to permit analysis of such experiments.

THE REINFORCEMENT AND EXTINCTION OPERATORS

In this section we develop some results that will be used later and show that the model of the present paper generates postulates used in our previous paper (1). We shall examine the step-wise change in probability of a response in a single stimulus situation S. We generalize the notions already presented as follows: Previous to a particular trial or occurrence of the response, a sub-set C of S will have been conditioned. On the trial in question a sub-set X of S will be perceived as shown in Fig. 1. According to our previous assumptions, the probability of the response is

$$p = \frac{m(X \cap C)}{m(X)} = \frac{m(C)}{m(S)}. \quad (10)$$

We now assume that a sub-set A of X will be conditioned to the response as a result of the reward given and that the measure of A will depend on the amount of reward, on the strength of motivation, etc. We further assume that another sub-set B of X will become non-conditioned as a result of the work required in making the response. For simplicity we assume that A and B are disjunct. (The error resulting from this last assumption can be shown to be small if the measures of A and B are small compared to that of S.)

We extend our assumption of equal proportions so that we have

$$\frac{m(A \cap C)}{m(A)} = \frac{m(B \cap C)}{m(B)} = \frac{m(C)}{m(S)}. \quad (11)$$

Now at the end of the trial being considered, sub-set A is part of the new conditional sub-set while sub-set B is part of the new non-conditioned sub-set. Thus, the change in the measure of C is

$$\Delta m(C) = [m(A) - m(A \cap C)]$$
$$- m(B \cap C) \quad (12)$$
$$= m(A)(1 - p) - m(B)p.$$

This last form of writing equation (12) results from the equalities given in equations (10) and (11). If we then let

$$a = \frac{m(A)}{m(S)}, \quad b = \frac{m(B)}{m(S)}, \quad (13)$$

and divide equation (12) through by $m(S)$, we have finally for the change in probability:

$$\Delta p = \frac{\Delta m(C)}{m(S)} = a(1 - p) - bp. \quad (14)$$

We thus define a mathematical operator Q which when applied to p gives

a new value of probability Qp effective at the start of the next trial:

$$Qp = p + a(1 - p) - bp. \quad (15)$$

This operator is identical to the general operator postulated in our model for acquisition and extinction in a fixed stimulus situation (1). Hence, the set-theoretic model we have presented generates the basic postulates of our previous model which we applied to other types of learning problems (1). When the operator Q is applied n times to an initial probability p_0, we obtain

$$Q^n p_0 = p_n = p_\infty - (p_\infty - p_0)g^n, \quad (16)$$

where $p_\infty = a/(a+b)$ and $g = 1 - a - b$.

In the next section we shall apply these results to the experiment on stimulus discrimination described in the Introduction.

The Discrimination Problem

We are now in a position to treat the second experimental problem described in the Introduction. An animal is presented alternately with two stimulus situations S and S' which are similar, i.e., which have a non-zero

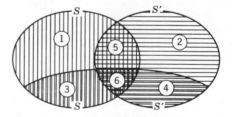

FIG. 3. Set diagram for discrimination training in two similar stimulus situations, S and S'. The various disjunct sub-sets are numbered. Set S includes 1, 3, 5, and 6; S' includes 2, 4, 5, and 6. The intersection I is denoted by 5 and 6. T, the complement of I in S, is shown by 1 and 3; T', the complement of I in S', is shown by 2 and 4. C, the conditioned sub-set in S, is represented by 3 and 6, while the conditioned sub-set in S', is represented by 4 and 6. T_c is denoted by 3, T_c' by 4, and I_c by 6.

intersection. The rewards which follow occurrences of the response are different for the two situations, and we are interested in how the response strengths vary with training. At any point in the process, sub-sets of S and S' will be conditioned to the response as shown in Fig. 3. We shall distinguish between that part of S which is also in S' and that part which is not by letting $I = S \cap S'$ and $T = S - (S \cap S') = S - I$. We also distinguish between the part of the conditioned sub-set C of S which is in I and that which is in T, by letting $I_c = C \cap I$ and $T_c = C - (C \cap I) = T \cap C$. The probability of the response in S is

$$p = \frac{m(C)}{m(S)} = \frac{m(T_c) + m(I_c)}{m(S)}. \quad (17)$$

Then we let

$$\alpha = \frac{m(T_c)}{m(T)}, \quad (18) \quad \beta = \frac{m(I_c)}{m(I)}, \quad (19)$$

and, abbreviating $\eta(S \text{ to } S')$ with η, we may write (17) in the form

$$p = \alpha(1 - \eta) + \beta\eta. \quad (20)$$

We write the probability of the response in this form because we shall soon argue that the index η varies during discrimination training. First, however, we shall investigate the variation of α and β with the number of training trials. From the definitions of α and β, equations (18) and (19), we see that these variables are very much like our probability p of equation (17) except that they refer to sub-sets of S rather than to the entire set. By strict analogy with the arguments in the last section, we conclude that

$$\alpha_n = Q^n\alpha_0 = \alpha_\infty - (\alpha_\infty - \alpha_0)g^n, \quad (21)$$

where $\alpha_\infty = a/(a+b)$ and $g = 1 - a - b$. Now, β, the fraction of conditioned stimuli in the intersection I, changes with each presentation of S' as well as

of S. Thus, for each presentation of S, we must operate on β twice, once by our operator Q which describes the effect of the environmental events in S, and once by an analogous operator Q' which describes the effect of the events in S'. Hence, it may be shown that

$$\beta_n = (Q'Q)^n\beta_0 = \beta_\infty - (\beta_\infty - \beta_0)f^n, \quad (22)$$

where

$$\beta_\infty = \frac{a' + a(1 - a' - b')}{\{a' + a(1 - a' - b') + b' + b(1 - a' - b')\}}, \quad (23)$$

and where $f = (1 - a' - b')(1 - a - b)$.

It should be stressed that we are assuming that the response occurs and is rewarded to the same degree on every presentation of S. The same statement, mutatis mutandis, applies to S'. Without this assumption, we are not justified in applying the operators Q and Q' for each presentation. The probability is then the probability that the response will occur in an interval of time, h. The operational measure of this probability is the mean latent time, which according to the response model discussed earlier varies inversely as the probability (1).

We now have cleared the way for discussing the central feature of our model for discrimination problems. We conceive that *the measure of the intersection I of the two sets S and S' decreases as discrimination learning progresses.* This concept seems to make sense intuitively since the measure of any sub-set of stimuli indicates the importance of that sub-set in influencing behavior. If an animal is rewarded for a response in S but not rewarded for it in S', then the stimuli in I are unreliable for deciding whether or not to make the response. And it is just this ambiguity which causes the measure of the intersection to decrease with training. We shall describe this change by introducing a "discrimination operator," denoted by D, which operates on the similarity index η each time the environmental event following the response changes from one type of event to another, e.g., from reward to non-reward. In the present problem, we are considering alternate presentations of S and S' and thus alternate occurrences of the events associated with the operators Q and Q'. So if η_i is the ratio of the measure of I to that of S after the ith presentation of S, the ratio after the $(i + 1)$th presentation is

$$\eta_{i+1} = D\eta_i. \tag{24}$$

Our next task is to postulate the form of the operator D.

We find that neither experimental data nor our intuition is of much help in guiding our choice of such a postulate. For mathematical simplicity we choose an operator which represents a linear transformation on η. Moreover, we wish to have an operator which always decreases η (or holds it fixed), but which will never lead to negative values of η. Therefore, we postulate that

$$D\eta = k\eta, \tag{25}$$

where k is a new parameter which is in the range between zero and 1. We then have

$$\eta_n = D^n\eta_0 = k^n\eta_0. \tag{26}$$

Combining equations (20), (21), (22), and (26), we have

$$p_n = Q^n\alpha_0(1 - D^n\eta_0) + (Q'Q)^n\beta_0 D^n\eta_0$$
$$= [\alpha_\infty - (\alpha_\infty - \alpha_0)g^n](1 - k^n\eta_0)$$
$$+ [\beta_\infty - (\beta_\infty - \beta_0)f^n]k^n\eta_0. \tag{27}$$

This is our final expression for the variation of p_n, the probability of the response in situation S, as a function of the trial number n. This equation is composed of two major terms. The first term corresponds to the relative measures of the stimulus elements of

S which are not in S' (the measure of T_c divided by the measure of S). The second term corresponds to the relative measure of the elements in the intersection of S and S' (the measure of I_c divided by the measure of S).

Because of the symmetry between S and S', we may write for the probability in S':

$$p_n' = [\alpha_\infty' - (\alpha_\infty' - \alpha_0')g'^n](1 - k^n\eta_0')$$
$$+ [\beta_\infty - (\beta_\infty - \beta_0)f^n]k^n\eta_0', \tag{28}$$

where $\alpha_\infty' = a'/(a' + b')$, and $g' = 1 - a' - b'$, and where η_0' is the initial value of

$$\eta' \equiv \eta(S' \text{ to } S)$$
$$= \frac{m(I)}{m(S')} = \frac{m(S)}{m(S')}\eta. \tag{29}$$

We shall now consider some special examples for which certain simplifying assumptions can be made.

(a) *No conditioning before discrimination training.* If no previous conditioning took place in either S or S', it seems reasonable to assume that the "operant" levels of performance in the two situations are the same. Moreover, in view of our assumptions of equal proportions, we may assume that *initially:*

$$\frac{m(C)}{m(S)} = \frac{m(T_c)}{m(T)} = \frac{m(I_c)}{m(I)}$$
$$= \frac{m(T_c')}{m(T')} = \frac{m(C')}{m(S')}. \tag{30}$$

Hence, from equations (17), (18), and (19), we have $p_0 = \alpha_0 = \alpha_0' = \beta_0$. Moreover, inspection of equation (27) shows that, except when $k = 1$, we have $p_\infty = \alpha_\infty$, and in like manner from equation (28) for $k \neq 1$, we have $p_\infty' = \alpha_\infty'$. In Fig. 4 we have plotted equations (27) and (28) with the above assumptions. The values $a = 0.12$, $b = 0.03$, $p_0 = 0.05$, $\eta_0 = \eta_0' = 0.50$, $k = 0.95$ were chosen for these calculations. As can be seen, the proba-

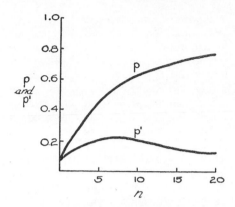

FIG. 4. Curves of probability, p (in S), and p' (in S'), versus trial number, n, for discrimination training without previous conditioning. It was assumed that the response was rewarded in S but not rewarded in S'. Equation (27), equation (28), and the values $p_0 = p_0' = 0.05$, $a = 0.12$, $a' = 0$, $b = b' = 0.03$, $\eta_0 = \eta_0' = 0.50$, and $k = 0.95$ were used.

bility of the response in S is a monotonically increasing, negatively accelerated function of the trial number, while the probability in S' first increases due to generalization, but then decreases to zero as the discrimination

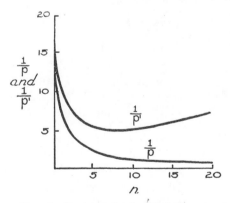

FIG. 5. Reciprocals of probability, p, of the response in S, and p', of the response in S', versus trial number, n, for discrimination training without previous conditioning. In the model described earlier (1), mean latent time is proportional to the reciprocal of probability. The curves were plotted from the values of probability shown in Fig. 4.

is learned. These curves describe the general sort of result obtained by Woodbury for auditory discrimination in dogs (4).

We have argued (1) that the mean latent time varies inversely as the probability. Thus in Fig. 5 we have plotted the reciprocals of p_n and p_n' given in Fig. 4. These curves exhibit the same general property of the experimental curves on running time of rats obtained by Raben (5).

(b) *Complete conditioning in S before discrimination training.* Another spe-

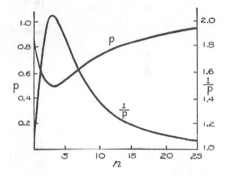

FIG. 6. Curves of probability, p, and its reciprocal versus trial number, n, for the case of complete conditioning in S before the discrimination training. Equation (27) with the values $p_\infty = 1$, $\beta_\infty = 0$, $\eta_0 = 0.80$, $k = 0.90$, and $f = 0.50$ were used.

cial case of interest is that in which the set S is completely conditioned to the response before the discrimination experiment is performed. In this case, $\alpha_0 = \beta_0 = p_0 = p_\infty$. In Fig. 6 we have plotted p_n and $1/p_n$ with these conditions and the values $p_\infty = 1$, $\beta_\infty = 0$, $\eta_0 = 0.80$, $k = 0.90$, and $f = 0.50$. The curve of $1/p$ versus n is similar in shape to the experimental latency curve obtained by Solomon (6) from a jumping experiment with rats.

(c) *Limiting case of S and S' identical.* Another limiting case of the kind of discrimination experiment being considered here obtains when we make the two stimulus situations S and S' identical. The problem degenerates into one type of partial reinforcement where, for example, an animal is rewarded on every second trial in a fixed stimulus situation. The intersection I of S and S' is of course identical to both S and S'. Thus the measure of I must equal the measure of S. From equation (5), we have

$$\eta = \frac{m(I)}{m(S)} = 1, \qquad (31)$$

while according to our postulate about the operator D, equation (26), the similarity index varies from trial to trial:

$$\eta_n = k^n \eta_0. \qquad (32)$$

For S and S' identical, the above two equations are incompatible, unless we take $k = 1$. Thus, we are forced to assume that k depends on how many cues are *available* for discrimination in such a way that $k = 1$ when none are available. Moreover, since I and S are identical, the measure of T, the complement of I in S, must be zero. Since T_e is a sub-set of T, the measure of T_e must also be zero. Therefore, equations (17) and (19) give in place of equation (20)

$$p = \beta \eta. \qquad (33)$$

But we have just argued that for S and S' identical, we have $\eta = 1$. Thus

$$p = \beta. \qquad (34)$$

Equation (22) gives us then

$$p_n = (Q'Q)^n p_0 = p_\infty - (p_\infty - p_0)f^n. \qquad (35)$$

This equation agrees with our previous result on partial reinforcement (1).

(d) *Irregular presentations of S and S'.* In most experiments, S and S' are not presented alternately, but in an irregular sequence so that the animal cannot learn to discriminate on the basis of temporal order. A simple generalization of the above analysis will handle the problem. The usual procedure is to select a block of $(j + j')$ trials during which S is presented j times and S' presented j' times. The actual sequence is determined by drawing "S balls" and "S' balls" at random from an urn containing j "S balls" and j' "S' balls." This sequence is then repeated throughout training. In our model, we can describe the effects on the probability of a known sequence by an appropriate application of our operators Q, Q', and D for presentations of S, presentations of S', and shifts from one to the other, respectively. A less cumbersome method provides a reasonable approximation: for each block of $(j + j')$ trials we describe an effective or expected new value of probability by applying Q to its operand j times, Q' to its operand j' times, and D to the index η a number of times determined by the mean number of shifts from S to S'. For the special case of $j = j'$, the mean number of shifts is j. Since previously, we applied D to η for each *pair* of shifts, we write for the $(i+1)$th block of $(2j)$ trials

$$\overline{p_{i+1}} = Q^i \alpha_i (1 - D^{i/2} \eta_i) \\ + (Q'Q)^i \beta_i D^{i/2} \eta_i. \qquad (36)$$

The rest of the analysis exactly parallels that given above for the case of alternate presentations of S and S'. The results will be identical except for the value of k involved in the operator D.

SUMMARY

A mathematical model for stimulus generalization and discrimination is described in terms of simple set-theoretic concepts. An index of similarity is defined in terms of the model but is related to measurements in generalization experiments. The mathematical operators for acquisition and extinction, discussed in an earlier paper (1), are derived from the set-theoretic model presented here. The model is finally applied to the analysis of experiments on stimulus discrimination.

[MS. received October 13, 1950]

REFERENCES

1. BUSH, R. R., & MOSTELLER, F. A mathematical model for simple learning. PSYCHOL. REV., 1951, **58**, 313–323
2. ESTES, W. K. Toward a statistical theory of learning. PSYCHOL. REV., 1950, **57**, 94–107.
3. HOVLAND, C. I. The generalization of conditioned responses: I. *J. gen. Psychol.*, 1937, **17**, 125–148; The generalization of conditioned responses: II. *J. genet. Psychol.*, 1937, **51**, 279–291.
4. WOODBURY, C. B. The learning of stimulus patterns by dogs. *J. comp. Psychol.*, 1943, **35**, 29–40.
5. RABEN, M. W. The white rat's discrimination of differences in intensity of illumination measured by a running response. *J. comp. & physiol. Psychol.*, 1949, **42**, 254–272.
6. SOLOMON, R. L. Latency of response as a measure of learning in a 'single door' discrimination. *Amer. J. Psychol.*, 1943, **56**, 422–432.

TWO-CHOICE BEHAVIOR OF PARADISE FISH

ROBERT R. BUSH AND THURLOW R. WILSON

Harvard University [1]

Our problem stems principally from two experiments. Brunswik (1) observed the acquisition of a position discrimination by rats when food was placed more frequently in one box. Research by Humphreys (9) was comparable in that S had two choices with partial reinforcement of both. He required college students to guess on every trial whether or not a light would flash, and then in accordance with a predetermined schedule, the light did or did not flash. The Humphreys study exemplifies a noncontingent procedure for two-choice learning since the flash of the light did not depend upon the choice made by S. Brunswik's rats faced a contingent situation since the environmental change, presentation of food, was contingent in part on S's response. A contingent two-choice research on humans has been performed by Goodnow (2, pp. 294–296). Her Ss decided on every trial which of two buttons to press. If the choice was correct, they earned a poker chip, otherwise not. Human two-choice learning with partial reinforcement has been further observed under contingent procedure (3) and under noncontingent procedure (3, 4, 5, 6, 7, 8, 10).

Bush and Mosteller (2) suggest that these two types of procedures are associated with different forms of asymptotic choice distribution (choice distribution after learning) for the individual Ss. In general, most Ss in a contingent experiment are found to have an asymptotic choice distribution of 100% selection of the favorable alternative. Noncontingent situations give rise to other kinds of choice distributions; in such experiments, the asymptotic proportion of choices of the favorable alternative has been observed to match the proportion of reinforcements scheduled for the alternative. [2]

We attempted to obtain the noncontingent results with nonhuman Ss. Red paradise fish were confronted by a position discrimination with partial reinforcement in which one side was correct a random 75% and the other side correct for the remaining 25%. The apparatus was a discrimination box with adjacent goal compartments. For the experimental Ss, E placed the food in the correct compartment regardless of whether S had entered the correct goal box; the division between the two goal boxes was transparent for the experimental group so that these Ss were able to see the food in the correct compartment when they had chosen incorrectly. The control group was run with an opaque divider separating the goal compartments in order to produce conditions comparable to those used by Brunswik.

THEORY

We attempt to describe the experimental data within the framework of the

[1] This research was supported by the Laboratory of Social Relations, Harvard University. We are indebted to W. S. Verplanck for suggesting that we use fish in learning experiments and to F. Mosteller for numerous suggestions and criticisms.

[2] Besides contingent and noncontingent procedure, other kinds of factors, such as a gambling versus a problem-solving orientation, have been related to asymptotic choice distribution (6) We shall not deal with these other factors.

This article appeared in *J. exp. Psychol.,* 1956, **51**, 315–322. Reprinted with permission.

stochastic model given by Bush and Mosteller (2). On trial n (where $n = 0$, 1, 2, . . .) there exists a probability p_n that S will choose the more favorable side. One of four events occurs on this trial and each leads to a different value of p_{n+1}. As in similar analyses, we assume that the effect of feeding is symmetrical for the two goal boxes; we make a similar assumption for non-feeding. In addition, we assume that a long sequence of feedings on one side would tend to make the probability of going there unity. These special assumptions reduce the general model to the following statements about p_{n+1}.

Event	p_{n+1}	Probability of occurrence
favorable side, food	$\alpha_1 p_n + (1 - \alpha_1)$	$.75 p_n$
favorable side, no food	$\alpha_2 p_n + (1 - \alpha_2)\lambda$	$.25 p_n$
unfavorable side, food	$\alpha_1 p_n$	$.25(1 - p_n)$
unfavorable side, no food	$\alpha_2 p_n + (1 - \alpha_2)(1 - \lambda)$	$.75(1 - p_n)$

The model previously used for analyzing two-choice experiments using the contingent procedure is obtained from the above table by imposing the further restriction that $\alpha_2 = 1$. This assumption implies that nonfeeding is an event which does not alter the response probabilities. It was expected that this model would describe learning by the control group in the present experiment. Given this specific model, it can be shown that the asymptotic p for each S will be either 1.0 or 0; for the 75:25 schedule it is predicted that a high percentage of Ss will tend towards 1.0. The exact percentage depends upon the value of α_1.

We propose two specific models for the experimental group of the present experiment. These models are obtained from the foregoing table by imposing two different sets of additional restrictions which in turn are suggested by two different theories of learning. The first specific model, herein called the *information model*, is obtained by taking $\alpha_1 = \alpha_2$ and $\lambda = 0$. As a result, the first and fourth listed events in the foregoing table have the same effect on p_n; they correspond to food being placed on the favorable side. Similarly, the second and third listed events have the same effect; they correspond to food being placed on the unfavorable side. These restrictions appear to arise most readily from a cognitive learning point of view, because each trial may be described as providing information about the payoff schedules. This information model is equivalent to the models used by Bush and Mosteller (2) and by Estes (4) for describing human experiments with the non-contingent procedure.

The other specific model for the experimental group, herein called the *secondary reinforcement model*, is obtained from the additional restrictions, $\lambda = 1$ and $\alpha_2 > \alpha_1$. This model assumes that when S enters one goal box and sees food in the other goal box it is secondarily reinforced for the response just made. It has been shown that this model predicts that each S will have an asymptotic p of 1 or 0 and that more Ss will tend towards 1 than 0. The precise proportion that tend towards 1 depends on the values of α_1 and α_2.

We are chiefly concerned with predictions about the forms of the asymptotic distributions of choices of the favorable side. These predictions could be tested experimentally by running many trials in the experiment and obtaining a proportion of choices for each S during, say, the last 100 trials. The proportions thus obtained would form a distribution which could be compared with the predicted ones. Unfortunately, the mathematical analysis presented by Karlin (11) suggests that the convergence of the distributions of these models is very slow. Therefore, a great many trials would be required in the experiment to obtain the desired distribution. In view of these considerations, we are forced to examine the "near-asymptotic" distributions. The information model predicts that such a distribution will be clustered around a point just below .75, whereas the secondary reinforcement model predicts that it will be U-shaped with a peak near 1 and a somewhat smaller peak near 0. The model for the control group ($\alpha_2 = 1$) also predicts a U-shaped near-asymptotic distribution, but the peak near 0 should be very small compared to that for the secondary reinforcement model. These predictions are compared with data below.

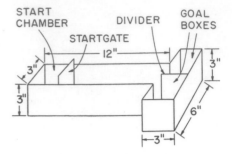

Fig. 1. Sketch of the discrimination apparatus.

METHOD

Subjects.—The Ss were 49 red paradise fish, 27 in the control group and 22 in the experimental group. The red paradise fish (*Macropodus opercularis*) is a hardy tropical fish about 2 in. in length selected because of its small demands for care. The Ss were housed separately in tanks with a water temperature of $80° \pm 1°F$. This was the temperature indicated by our feeding studies for maximum appetite. Lighting was by fluorescent fixtures which were automatically turned on for a standard 12-hr. period each day to control the activity cycle. (This fish has a diurnal rhythm of activity.)

Apparatus.—The apparatus was a discrimination box as shown in Fig. 1. The maze was constructed of $\frac{1}{8}$-in. opaque white Plexiglas, except for parts of the goal boxes. The control group had a white opaque divider, whereas for the experimental group this divider was transparent. For one goal box the side opposite the entrance to the box was formed from a piece of opaque light yellow plastic; the corresponding side of the other box was white opaque. These sides could be interchanged. (Exploratory studies indicated that a position discrimination with identical goal boxes is learned very slowly by these fish.)

The apparatus was placed in a 10-gal. tank shielded from room lights. Lighting came largely from a 75-w. spotlight 2 ft. above the maze and focused on the start chamber. Care was taken to ensure that water conditions of this experimental tank were as close as possible to those of the home tanks of Ss.

Feeding.—The experimental food was prepared fish eggs from an inexpensive (10 cents an ounce) caviar ("Lumpfish caviar" packed by Hansen Caviar Co., New York, N. Y.). These eggs were found to be a highly preferred food of the paradise fish and were convenient to obtain and store. The eggs were presented singly; the egg was held on the end of a medicine dropper

by suction (the egg was 1 mm. to 2 mm. in diameter and larger than the opening of the dropper). To secure the egg, the fish was obliged to pull it from the dropper. A fish was required to earn all of its food by solving the discrimination problem.

Pretraining.—The pretraining took two or three days. On the first day the fish was fed eggs (10 or 20) by eye dropper in its home tank. For the next one or two days the fish underwent forced trials (10 or 20) in the maze. Half of the forced trials were to the right-side goal box. About one-third of the fish were rejected from the experiment at the end of pretraining or after one or two days of discrimination training leaving 49 Ss. (Fish were rejected because they would not eat in the apparatus or because E made an error in procedure.)

Procedure.—All Ss received a total of 140 trials, 20 trials a day or less. One goal box (the favorable side) was scheduled for reinforcement on 75% of the trials while the other goal was scheduled for reinforcement on the remaining trials. On a given trial only one goal box was correct. The trials for which the favorable side was incorrect were selected by restricted randomization within blocks of 20. The restriction was that runs of incorrect could not be longer than two. All fish had the same schedule.

The right, yellow side was favorable for about one-fourth of the Ss; right, white for one-fourth; left and yellow for one-fourth, and left and white for one-fourth.

The procedure for the control group was as follows. The fish was released from the start chamber, and it swam down to the goal boxes. If the fish poked its nose into the goal box which was correct for that trial, E lowered a medicine dropper with a fish egg into the compartment (the dropper was secured to an arm) to allow the fish to feed. If the fish entered the incorrect goal box, no food was placed in the goal box. In either case, the fish was chased back into the start chamber after 3–4 sec. in the goal box. This was accomplished with a piece of plastic of width slightly less than the width of the maze; the fish quickly developed avoidance tendencies to this "paddle." As soon as it was lowered into the tank, the fish promptly returned to the start chamber. The interval between trials was 12 sec. No retracing was permitted. Except for the transparent rather than opaque piece dividing the two goal boxes, the procedure for the experimental group differed only in one detail: after the fish had entered a compartment E placed the medicine dropper with a fish egg in the correct goal box. If the fish had entered the correct goal box, it secured the egg. Otherwise the fish could see the egg through the transparent divider but could not obtain it. Observations indicated that they did in fact see the egg on most of these trials.

Results and Discussion

Initial preferences.—Position and color preferences may strongly influence the results of a discrimination study. For this reason the balanced design described in the preceding section was used. This technique, however, tends to eliminate a *group*

TABLE 1

Observed Distribution of Choices of the Favorable Side During the First Ten Trials for the Two Groups of Fish Combined, and the Theoretical Distributions for the Binomial Model ($P = .5$) and for the Symmetric Beta Distribution with $s = .7$

Number Choices	Observed Number Fish	Predicted	
		Binomial	Beta
0	2	0.05	2.34
1	3	0.48	3.71
2	5	2.16	4.66
3	7	5.75	5.28
4	4	10.06	5.64
5	8	12.07	5.76
6	8	10.06	5.64
7	1	5.75	5.28
8	5	2.16	4.66
9	2	0.48	3.71
10	4	0.05	2.34
	49	49.07	49.02

preference only. From an analysis of variance of the responses on the first 10 trials, we concluded that there were no group color or position preferences but that there were individual preferences. The stochastic models used in analyzing the data are sensitive to the entire distribution of initial probabilities, not only its mean. Therefore, it is necessary to consider the actual distribution.

One binomial observation for each initial probability is insufficient to determine anything about the initial distribution except the mean. Thus we must look at the number of successes (choices of the favorable side) by each fish during the first several trials and assume that the probability for each fish does not appreciably change during these trials. For this purpose the two groups of Ss were combined, giving an N of 49, and the first 10 trials of the data were used. In Table 1 we show the frequencies of choice observed as well as those predicted by two models which are now briefly discussed.

The mean number of observed successes during the first 10 trials is .496 and so the balanced design accomplished its purpose. But, if we assume that each of the 49 fish had a binomial probability of .5, the predicted frequencies of choices are those shown in the third column of Table 1. The discrepancies are highly significant. The likelihood ratio test (**12**, p. 257) (this is essentially the chi-square test) leads to $P < .005$. Therefore we consider an alternative assumption: that the initial distribution is a symmetric beta distribution (**12**, p. 115) with a mean of .5. It may be written in the form

$$f(p) = C[p(1 - p)]^s,$$

where C is a constant chosen so that the total density is unity, and where

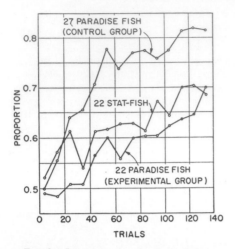

Fig. 2. Learning curve for each of the two groups of fish and for the 22 stat-fish which parallel the experimental group. Mean proportion of choices of the favorable side is plotted for each block of 10 trials.

s is a parameter which determines the spread of the distribution. The method of maximum likelihood (**12,** pp. 152–160) was used to estimate s from the data, giving .7 as the estimate. The distribution of successes during 10 trials can then be computed. The results are shown in the last column of Table 1 and the likelihood ratio test gives $P = .4$. This fit was considered satisfactory.

Learning curves.—In Fig. 2 we show the proportion of successes in blocks of 10 trials for each of the two groups of fish. It is clear that the control group learned more rapidly than the experimental group, but little more can be inferred from this figure. One can conjecture, of course, that the sight of food in the opposite goal box when food was not obtained slowed down the learning process. Just how this comes about can be determined only by a more detailed analysis of the data.

We hasten to note at this point that the models described above do not predict the relative rates of learning of groups of Ss run under different experimental conditions. Within the framework of the models, rates of learning are determined by the values of parameters which must be estimated from data. The models do predict, however, other properties of the data considered in the following sections.

The near-asymptotic distributions.— The two specific models for the experimental group—the information model and the secondary reinforcement model—make very different predictions about the shape of the distributions of successes after learning is nearly complete. In the second column of Table 2 we show the frequencies of successes during the last 49 trials (the number of successes varies from 0 through 49). The observed **U**-shaped near-asymptotic distribution is not determined by initial preferences alone; the rank-order correlation coefficient between the number of favorable choices on the first and last 10 trials is .22. The information model predicts a clustering

TABLE 2

DISTRIBUTION OF SUCCESSES (CHOICES OF THE FAVORABLE SIDE) DURING THE LAST 49 TRIALS FOR THE TWO GROUPS OF FISH AND FOR THE 22 STAT-FISH WHICH PARALLEL THE EXPERIMENTAL GROUP OF REAL FISH

Number Successes	Experimental Group	Stat-Fish	Control Group
0–4	4	4	1
5–9	1	2	0
10–14	2	0	0
15–19	0	0	1
20–24	0	0	2
25–29	0	1	0
30–34	1	0	2
35–39	2	2	3
40–44	2	3	7
45–49	10	10	11
	22	22	27

around 37 but this prediction is clearly *not* confirmed by the experimental group data. The secondary reinforcement model, on the other hand, predicts a U-shaped distribution with greater density at the high end than at the low end. This prediction *is* confirmed. On this basis alone we can choose the secondary reinforcement model in favor of the information model. Detailed questions of goodness of fit are considered in the following sections.

The model proposed for the control group involves the assumption that nonreward has no effect ($\alpha_2 = 1$) and it predicts that the near-asymptotic distribution of successes will also be U-shaped but with very small density at the low end. This indeed agrees with the data shown in the last column of Table 2; one out of 27 fish stabilized at the unfavorable side—it chose that side 46 times during the last 49 trials. The other 26 fish either stabilized on the favorable side or did not yet stabilize during the trials run. In the next section we consider the basic assumption that $\alpha_2 - 1$ made in the model for the control group.

Parameter estimates.—Having chosen the secondary reinforcement model for the experimental group, we need to estimate the primary reward parameter, α_1, and the secondary reward parameter, α_2. These estimates are required for two reasons: (*a*) we wish to measure the relative effects of primary and secondary reinforcement in this experiment (the smaller the value of α, the

greater the effect), and (*b*) the estimates are used in measuring goodness of fit of the model to the data in a detailed way. For the control group, we assume that the same model applies and then estimate both parameters and determine whether or not the assumption that $\alpha_2 = 1$ is tenable.

The procedure used to estimate the two reward parameters cannot be described in detail here. It uses the first three moments of the observed distributions of successes in each block of 10 trials; these are used in conjunction with formulas for moments of the p-value distributions derived by Bush and Mosteller (2, p. 98). The results, however, are shown in Table 3. It can be noted that the secondary reward parameter, α_2, is larger for both groups than the corresponding primary reward parameter, α_1. This confirms the expectation that primary reward is more effective. (A small value of α implies a more effective event than does a large value.) For the control group, the value of α_2 is near 1.0 as assumed in the model for the control group, but the fact that it is not quite 1.0 suggests that nonreward is slightly reinforcing even for the control group. The result that α_1 is less for the experimental group than for the control group (primary reward more effective) is not predicted by any of the models.

The relative effects of primary and secondary reward for each group can be estimated as follows. We note that $(.916)^{.59} = .942$ and this means that secondary reward is about 60% as effective as primary reward for the experimental group. Similarly, $(.956)^{.31} = .986$, and so secondary reward is about 30% effective for the control group. These percentages may be in error appreciably because of the sampling errors in the parameter estimates, but they do indicate roughly the effects.

Stat-fish.—A convenient way of comparing model predictions with data is to run Monte Carlo computations or "stat-fish" as described elsewhere (2, pp. 129–131, 251–252). One hundred runs of 140 trials each were carried out on IBM

TABLE 3

Estimates of the Two Parameters Obtained for Each of the Two Groups of Fish

Parameters	Experimental Group	Control Group
Primary reward, α_1	0.916	0.956
Secondary reward, α_2	0.942	0.986

machines[3] using the parameter values given in Table 3 for the experimental group. From these 100 runs, a stratified sample of 22 runs was drawn such that the initial distribution of probabilities would approximate the symmetric beta distribution with the parameter $s = .7$. These 22 stat-fish can then be compared directly with the 22 paradise fish in the experimental group.

The "learning curve" of the stat-fish is shown in Fig. 2 along with those of the real fish. It can be seen that the stat-fish curve is slightly above the curve for the experimental group. This should not be interpreted as a discrepancy between the model and the data. Rather it is some indication of how well the model parameters were estimated from the data. Loosely speaking, the estimates were obtained by requiring that the learning rates of the model population and of the experimental sample be equal. To measure goodness of fit we must look at other properties of the data.

The near-asymptotic distribution of successes of the 22 stat-fish was obtained in the same manner as for the real fish. The results are shown in the third column of Table 2 and are sufficiently close to the corresponding frequencies of the experimental group that we consider formal tests for goodness of fit would be superfluous.

Many sequential properties of the data can be compared to the corresponding properties of the stat-fish "data" in order to obtain further measures of goodness of fit. Thus we have tabulated the distribution of runs (of successes and failures) for the experimental group and for the stat-fish. In Table 4 we show the mean and SD of the total number of runs, of the number of runs of various lengths, as well as the number of successes per S. It can be seen that all but one of the tabulated means are slightly smaller for the real fish than for the stat-fish, and that the variability of these measures is less for the real fish.

[3] We are indebted to B. P. Cohen and P. D. Seymour for making these computations.

TABLE 4

COMPARISON OF STATISTICS COMPUTED FROM THE DATA FOR THE EXPERIMENTAL GROUP OF 22 FISH AND FROM THE SEQUENCES OBTAINED FROM THE 22 STAT-FISH

Statistic	Experimental Group		Stat-Fish	
	Mean	SD	Mean	SD
Total number runs	27.3	13.7	29.8	20.2
Runs of length 1	12.9	6.7	14.2	10.1
Runs of length 2	4.4	3.8	5.3	6.3
Runs of length 3	2.0	1.8	3.0	2.6
Runs of length 4	1.5	1.6	2.2	2.2
Runs of length 5	1.1	1.3	1.0	1.4
Number successes	81.3	48.0	87.6	48.2

All these discrepancies are a result of the fact that two of the stat-fish never chose the unfavorable side and two others chose it only once each. These four stat-fish had initial success probabilities of .95, .95, .85, and .85, respectively. The smallest number of failures by the real fish is five. This suggests that better agreement would have been found if the initial distribution of probabilities had had less density in the extremes; the symmetric beta distribution was used only as an approximation to the true initial distribution. Furthermore, learning during the first 10 trials tends to spread out the distribution of response probabilities and so the true initial distribution probably had less variance than the symmetric beta distribution used in the stat-fish computations.

The distributions of the statistics given in Table 4 for the real fish and stat-fish can be compared in the same manner as used to compare two groups of Ss. The distributions are not normal and so we used the Mann-Whitney test (13). Comparison of each of the seven statistics listed in Table 4 led to P values greater than .3. Thus, we conclude that the model adequately describes much of the fine-grain character of the data.

SUMMARY

A two-choice experiment designed to provide *Ss* with complete information about the outcomes of each choice on each trial is described. The *Ss* were 49 red paradise fish divided into two groups; the control *Ss* were run with the conventional procedure whereas the experimental *Ss* were given an opportunity to observe the presence or absence of food on both sides of the maze. Both groups were rewarded on one side 75% of the time and on the other side the remaining 25% of the time.

Two stochastic models for predicting the behavior of the experimental group are discussed. The "information model" assumed an increment in the probability of a fish choosing on a particular trial the side on which food was placed on the preceding trial. This model predicts that the distribution of choices approaches about .75 for all fish. The "secondary reinforcement model," on the other hand, assumes that sight of food in the opposite goal box reinforces the response just made and predicts that individual fish will approach 100% choice of one side or the other.

The data obtained support the secondary reinforcement model. Parameters which measure the effectiveness of primary and secondary reward are estimated from the data and then detailed comparisons between model predictions and experimental results are made. It is concluded that the secondary reinforcement model adequately describes much of the fine-grain structure of the data.

REFERENCES

1. BRUNSWIK, E. Probability as a determiner of rat behavior. *J. exp. Psychol.*, 1939, **25**, 175–197.
2. BUSH, R. R., & MOSTELLER, F. *Stochastic models for learning.* New York: Wiley, 1955.
3. DETAMBEL, M. H. A test of a model for multiple-choice behavior. *J. exp. Psychol.*, 1955, **49**, 97–104.
4. ESTES, W. K. Individual behavior in uncertain situations: an interpretation in terms of statistical association theory. In R. M. Thrall, C. H. Coombs, & R. L. Davis (Eds.), *Decision processes.* New York: Wiley, 1954.
5. ESTES, W. K., & STRAUGHAN, J. H. Analysis of a verbal conditioning situation in terms of statistical learning theory. *J. exp. Psychol.*, 1954, **47**, 225–234.
6. GOODNOW, J. J., & POSTMAN, L. Probability learning in a problem-solving situation. *J. exp. Psychol.*, 1955, **49**, 16–22.
7. GRANT, D. A., HAKE, H. W., & HORNSETH, J. P. Acquisition and extinction of a verbal conditioned response with differing percentages of reinforcement. *J. exp. Psychol.*, 1951, **42**, 1–5.
8. HAKE, H. W., & HYMAN, R. Perception of the statistical structure of a random series of binary symbols. *J. exp. Psychol.*, 1953, **45**, 64–74.
9. HUMPHREYS, L. G. Acquisition and extinction of verbal expectations in a situation analogous to conditioning. *J. exp. Psychol.*, 1939, **25**, 294–301.
10. JARVIK, M. E. Probability learning and a negative recency effect in the serial anticipation of alternative symbols. *J. exp. Psychol.*, 1951, **41**, 291–297.
11. KARLIN, S. Some random walks arising in learning models I. *Pacific J. Math.*, 1953, **3**, 725–756.
12. MOOD, A. M. *Introduction to the theory of statistics.* New York: McGraw-Hill, 1950.
13. MOSTELLER, F., & BUSH, R. R. Selected quantitative techniques. In G. Lindzey (Ed.), *Handbook of social psychology.* Cambridge, Mass.: Addison-Wesley, 1954.

(Received May 26, 1955)

TOWARD A STATISTICAL THEORY OF LEARNING *

BY WILLIAM K. ESTES

Indiana University

Improved experimental techniques for the study of conditioning and simple discrimination learning enable the present day investigator to obtain data which are sufficiently orderly and reproducible to support exact quantitative predictions of behavior. Analogy with other sciences suggests that full utilization of these techniques in the analysis of learning processes will depend to some extent upon a comparable refinement of theoretical concepts and methods. The necessary interplay between theory and experiment has been hindered, however, by the fact that none of the many current theories of learning commands general agreement among researchers. It seems likely that progress toward a common frame of reference will be slow so long as most theories are built around verbally defined hypothetical constructs which are not susceptible to unequivocal verification. While awaiting resolution of the many apparent disparities among competing theories, it may be advantageous to systematize well established empirical relationships at a peripheral, statistical level of analysis. The possibility of agreement on a theoretical framework, at least in certain intensively studied areas, may be maximized by defining concepts in terms of experimentally manipulable variables, and developing the consequences of assumptions by strict mathematical reasoning. This essay will introduce a series of

* For continual reinforcement of his efforts at theory construction, as well as for many specific criticisms and suggestions, the writer is indebted to his colleagues at Indiana University, especially Cletus J. Burke, Douglas G. Ellson, Norman Guttman, and William S. Verplanck.

studies developing a statistical theory of elementary learning processes. From the definitions and assumptions which appear necessary for this kind of formulation, we shall attempt to derive relations among commonly used measures of behavior and quantitative expressions describing various simple learning phenomena.

PRELIMINARY CONSIDERATIONS

Since propositions concerning psychological events are verifiable only to the extent that they are reducible to predictions of behavior under specified environmental conditions, it appears likely that greatest economy and consistency in theoretical structure will result from the statement of all fundamental laws in the form

$$R = f(S),$$

where R and S represent behavioral and environmental variables respectively. Response-inferred laws, as for example those of differential psychology, should be derivable from relationships of this form. The reasoning underlying this position has been developed in a recent paper by Spence (8). Although developed within this general framework, the present formulation departs to some extent from traditional definitions of S and R variables.

Many apparent differences among contemporary learning theories seem to be due in part to an oversimplified definition of stimulus and response. The view of stimulus and response as elementary, reproducible units has always had considerable appeal because of its simplicity. This simplicity is deceptive, however, since it entails the postulation of various hypothetical processes to ac-

This article appeared in *Psychol. Rev.*, 1950, **57**, 94–107. Reprinted with permission.

count for observed variability in behavior. In the present formulation, we shall follow the alternative approach of including the notion of variability in the definitions of stimulus and response, and investigating the theoretical consequences of these definitions.

It will also be necessary to modify the traditional practice of stating laws of learning in terms of relations between isolated stimuli and responses. Attempts at a quantitative description of learning and extinction of operant behavior have led the writer to believe that a self-consistent theory based upon the classical *S-R* model may be difficult, if not impossible, to extend over any very wide range of learning phenomena without the continual addition of *ad hoc* hypotheses to handle every new situation. A recurrent difficulty might be described as follows. In most formulations of simple learning, the organism is said originally to "do nothing" in the presence of some stimulus; during learning, the organism comes to make some predesignated response in the presence of the stimulus; then during extinction, the response gradually gives way to a state of "not responding" again. But this type of formulation does not define a closed or conservative system in any sense. In order to derive properties of conditioning and extinction from the same set of general laws, it is necessary to assign specific properties to the state of not responding which is the alternative to occurrence of the designated response. One solution is to assign properties as needed by special hypotheses, as has been done, for example, in the Pavlovian conception of inhibition. In the interest of simplicity of theoretical structure, we shall avoid this procedure so far as possible.

The role of competing reactions has been emphasized by some writers, but usually neglected in formal theorizing.

The point of view to be developed here will adopt as a standard conceptual model a closed system of behavioral and environmental variables. In any specific behavior-system, the environmental component may include either the entire population of stimuli available in the situation or some specified portion of that population. The behavioral component will consist in mutually exclusive classes of responses, defined in terms of objective criteria; these classes will be exhaustive in the sense that they will include all behaviors which may be evoked by that stimulus situation. Given the initial probabilities of the various responses available to an organism in a given situation, we shall expect the laws of the theory to enable predictions of changes in those probabilities as a function of changes in values of independent variables.

DEFINITIONS AND ASSUMPTIONS

1. *R-variables.* It will be assumed that any movement or sequence of movements may be analyzed out of an organism's repertory of behavior and treated as a "response," various properties of which can be treated as dependent variables subject to all the laws of the theory. (Hereafter we shall abbreviate the word response as *R*, with appropriate subscripts where necessary.) In order to avoid a common source of confusion, it will be necessary to make a clear distinction between the terms *R*-class and *R*-occurrence.

The term *R*-class will always refer to a class of behaviors which produce environmental effects within a specified range of values. This definition is not without objection (*cf.* 4) but has the advantage of following the actual practice of most experimenters. It may be possible eventually to coordinate *R*-classes defined in terms of environmental effects with *R*-classes defined in terms of effector activities.

By *R*-occurrence we shall mean a particular, unrepeatable behavioral event. All occurrences which meet the defining criteria of an *R*-class are counted as instances of that class, and as such are experimentally interchangeable. In fact, various instances of an *R*-class are ordinarily indistinguishable in the record of an experiment even though they may actually vary with respect to properties which are not picked up by the recording mechanism.

Indices of tendency to respond, *e.g.*, probability as defined below, always refer to *R*-classes.

These distinctions may be clarified by an illustration. In the Skinner-type conditioning apparatus, bar-pressing is usually treated as an *R*-class. Any movement of the organism which results in sufficient depression of the bar to actuate the recording mechanism is counted as an instance of the class. The *R*-class may be subdivided into finer classes by the same kind of criteria. We could, if desired, treat depression of a bar by the rat's right forepaw and depression of the bar by the left forepaw as instances of two different classes provided that we have a recording mechanism which will be affected differently by the two kinds of movements and mediate different relations to stimulus input (as for example the presentation of discriminative stimuli or reinforcing stimuli). If probability is increased by reinforcement, then reinforcement of a right-forepaw-bar-depression will increase the probability that instances of that subclass will occur, and will also increase the probability that instances of the broader class, bar-pressing, will occur.

2. *S-variables.* For analytic purposes it is assumed that all behavior is conditional upon appropriate stimulation. It is not implied, however, that responses can be predicted only when eliciting stimuli can be identified. Ac-

cording to the present point of view, laws of learning enable predictions of changes in probability of response as a function of time under given environmental conditions.

A stimulus, or stimulating situation, will be regarded as a finite population of relatively small, independent, environmental events, of which only a sample is effective at any given time. In the following sections we shall designate the total number of elements associated with a given source of stimulation as S (with appropriate subscripts where more than one source of stimulation must be considered in an experiment), and the number of elements effective at any given time as s. It is assumed that when experimental conditions involve the repeated stimulation of an organism by the "same stimulus," that is by successive samples of elements from an S-population, each sample may be treated as an independent random sample from S. It is to be expected that sample size will fluctuate somewhat from one moment to the next, in which case s will be treated as the average number of elements per sample over a given period.

In applying the theory, any portion of the environment to which the organism is exposed under uniform conditions may be considered an S-population. The number of different S's said to be present in a situation will depend upon the number of independent experimental operations, and the degree of specificity with which predictions of behavior are to be made. If the experimenter attempts to hold the stimulating situation constant during the course of an experiment, then the entire situation will be treated as a single S. If in a conditioning experiment, a light and shock are to be independently manipulated as the *CS* and *US*, then each of these sources of stimulation will be treated as a separate S-population, and so on.

It should be emphasized that the division of environment and behavior into elements is merely an analytic device adopted to enable the application of the finite-frequency theory of probability to behavioral phenomena. In applying the theory to learning experiments we shall expect to evaluate the ratio s/S for any specific situation from experimental evidence, but for the present at least no operational meaning can be given to a numerical value for either S or s taken separately.

3. *Probability of response.* Probability will be operationally defined as the average frequency of occurrence of instances of an R-class relative to the maximum possible frequency, under a specified set of experimental conditions, over a period of time during which the conditions remain constant. In accordance with customary usage the term probability, although defined as a relative frequency, will also be used to express the likelihood that a response will occur at a given time.

4. *Conditional relation.* This relation may obtain between an R-class and any number of the elements in an S-population, and has the following implications.

(a) If a set of x elements from an S are conditioned to (*i.e.*, have the conditional relation to) some R-class, R_1, at a given time, the probability that the next response to occur will be an instance of R_1 is x/S.

(b) If at a given time in an S-population, x_1 elements are conditioned to some R-class, R_1, and x_2 elements are conditioned to another class, R_2, then x_1 and x_2 have no common elements.

(c) If all behaviors which may be evoked from an organism in a given situation have been categorized into mutually exclusive classes, then the probabilities attaching to the various classes must sum to unity at all times.

We consider the organism to be always "doing something." If any arbitrarily defined class of activities may be selected as the dependent variable of a given experiment, it follows that the activity of the organism at any time must be considered as subject to the same laws as the class under consideration. Any increase in probability of one R-class during learning will, then, necessarily involve the reduction in probability of other classes; similarly, while the probability of one R decreases during extinction, the probabilities of others must increase. In other words, learning and unlearning will be considered as transfers of probability relations between R-classes.

5. *Conditioning.* It is assumed that on each occurrence of a response, R_1, all new elements (*i.e.*, elements not already conditioned to R_1) in the momentarily effective sample of stimulus elements, s, become conditioned to R_1.

An important implication of these definitions is that the conditioning of a stimulus element to one R automatically involves the breaking of any pre-existing conditional relations with other R's.

6. *Motivation.* Experimental operations which in the usual terminology are said to produce motives (*e.g.*, food-deprivation) may affect either the composition of an S or the magnitude of the s/S ratio. Detailed discussion of these relations is beyond the scope of the present paper. In all derivations presented here we shall assume motivating conditions constant throughout an experiment.

7. *Reinforcement.* This term will be applied to any experimental condition which ensures that successive occurrences of a given R will each be contiguous with a new random sample of elements from some specified S-population. Various ways of realizing this definition experimentally will be discussed in the following sections.

SIMPLE CONDITIONING: REINFORCEMENT BY CONTROLLED ELICITATION

Let us consider first the simplest type of conditioning experiment. The system to be described consists of a subpopulation of stimulus elements, S_o, which may be manipulated independently of the remainder of the situation, S, and a class, R, of behaviors defined by certain measurable properties. By means of a controlled original stimulus, that is, one which has initially a high probability of evoking R, it is ensured that an instance of R will occur on every trial contiguously with the sample of stimulus elements which is present. In the familiar buzz-shock conditioning experiment, for example, S_o would represent the population of stimulus elements emanating from the sound source and R would include all movements of a limb meeting certain specifications of direction and amplitude; typically, the R to be conditioned is a flexion response which may be evoked on each training trial by administration of an electric shock.

Designating the mean number of elements from S_o effective on any one trial as s_o, and the number of elements from S_c which are conditioned to R at any time as x, the expected number of new elements conditioned on any trial will be

$$\Delta x = s_c \frac{(S_c - x)}{S_c}. \qquad (1)$$

If the change in x per trial is relatively small, and the process is assumed continuous, the right hand portion of (1) may be taken as the average rate of change of x with respect to number of trials, T, at any moment, giving

$$\frac{dx}{dT} = s_c \frac{(S_c - x)}{S_c}. \qquad (2)$$

This differential equation may be integrated to yield

$$x = S_c - (S_c - x_0)e^{-qT}, \qquad (3)$$

where x_0 is the initial value of x, and q represents the ratio s_c/S_c. Thus x will increase from its initial value to approach the limiting value, S_c, in a negatively accelerated curve. A method of evaluating x in these equations from empirical measures of response latency, or reaction time, will be developed in a later section.

If the remainder of the situation has been experimentally neutralized, the probability of R in the presence of a sample from S_c will be given by the ratio x/S_c. Representing this ratio by the single letter p, and making appropriate substitutions in (3), we have the following expression for probability of R as a function of the number of reinforced trials.

$$p = 1 - (1 - p_0)e^{-qT}. \qquad (3')$$

Since we have not assumed any special properties for the original (or unconditioned) stimulus other than that of regularly evoking the response to be conditioned, it is to be expected that the equations developed in this section will describe the accumulation of conditional relations in other situations than classical conditioning, provided that other experimental operations function to ensure that the response to be learned will occur in the presence of every sample drawn from the S-population.

OPERANT CONDITIONING: REINFORCEMENT BY CONTINGENT STIMULATION

In the more common type of experimental arrangement, various termed operant, instrumental, trial and error, etc. by different investigators, the response to be learned is not elicited by a controlled original stimulus, but has some initial strength in the experimental situation and occurs originally as part of so-called "random activity." Here the response cannot be evoked concurrently with the presentation of each new stimulus sample, but some of the same effects can be secured by making changes in the stimulating situation contingent upon occurrences of the response. Let us consider a situation of this sort, assuming that the activities of the organism have been catalogued and classified into two categories, all movement sequences characterized by a certain set of properties being assigned to class R and all others to the class R_e, and that members of class R are to be learned.

If changes in the stimulus sample are independent of the organism's behavior, we should expect instances of the two response classes to occur, on the average, at rates proportional to their initial probabilities. For if x elements from the S-population are originally conditioned to R, then the probability of R will be x/S; the number of new elements conditioned to R if an instance occurs will be $s[(S - x)/S]$, s again representing the number of stimulus elements in a sample; and the mathematically expected increase in x will be the product of these quantities, $sx[(S - x)/S^2]$. At the same time, the probability of R_e will be $(S - x)/S$, and the number of new elements conditioned to R_e if an instance occurs will be $sx/S;$ multiplying these quantities, we have $sx[(S - x)/S^2]$ as the mathematically expected decrease in x. Thus we should predict no average change in x under these conditions.

In the acquisition phase of a learning experiment two important restrictions imposed by the experimenter tend to force a correlation between changes in the stimulus sample and occurrences of R. The organism is usually introduced into the experimental situation at the beginning of a trial, and the trial lasts until the pre-designated response, R, occurs. For example, in a common discrimination apparatus the animal is placed on a jumping stand at the beginning of each trial and the trial continues until the animal leaves the stand; a trial in a runway experiment lasts until the animal reaches the end box, and so on. Typically the stimulating situation present at the beginning of a trial is radically changed, if not completely terminated, by the occurrence of the response in question; and a new trial begins under the same conditions, except for sampling variations, after some pre-designated interval. The pattern of movement-produced stimuli present during a trial may be changed after occurrences of R by the evocation of some uniform bit of behavior such as eating or drinking; in some cases the behavior utilized for this purpose must be established by special training prior to a learning experiment. In the Skinner box, for example, the animal is trained to respond to the sound of the magazine by approaching it and eating or drinking. Then when operation of the magazine follows the occurrence of a bar-pressing response during conditioning of the latter, the animal's response to the magazine will remove it from the stimuli in the vicinity of the bar and ensure that for an interval of time thereafter the animal will not be exposed to most of the S-population; therefore the sample of elements to which the animal will next respond may be considered very nearly a new random sample from S.

In the simplest operant conditioning experiments it may be possible to change almost the entire stimulus sample after each occurrence of R (complete reinforcement), while in other cases the sampling of only some restricted portion of the S-population is correlated with R (partial reinforcement). We shall consider the former case in some detail in the remainder of this section.

By our definition of the conditional relation, we shall expect all R-classes from which instances actually occur on any trial to be conditioned to stimulus elements present on that trial. The first movement to occur will be conditioned to the environmental cues present at the beginning of the trial; the next movement will be conditioned to some external cues, if the situation is not completely constant during a trial, and to proprioceptive cues from the first movement, and so on, until the predesignated response, R, occurs and terminates the trial. If complete constancy of the stimulating situation could be maintained, the most probable course of events on the next trial would be the recurrence of the same sequence of movements. In practice, however, the sample of effective stimulus elements will change somewhat in composition, and some responses which occur on one trial may fail to occur on the next. The only response which may never be omitted is R, since the trial continues until R occurs. This argument has been developed in greater detail by Guthrie (4). In order to verify the line of reasoning involved, we need now to set these ideas down in mathematical form and investigate the possibility of deriving functions which will describe empirical curves of learning.

Since each trial lasts until R occurs, we need an expression for the probable duration of a trial in terms of the strength of R. Suppose that we have categorized all movement sequences which are to be counted as "responses" in a given situation, and that the minimum time needed for completion of a response-occurrence is, on the average, h. For convenience in the following development, we shall assume that the mean duration of instances of class R is ap-

proximately equal to that of class R_e. Let the total number of stimulus elements available in the experimental situation be represented by S, the sample effective on any one trial by s, and the ratio s/S by q. The probability, p, of class R at the beginning of any trial will have the value x/S; if this value varies little within a trial, we can readily compute the probable number of responses (of all classes) that will occur before the trial is terminated. The probability that an instance of R will be the first response to occur on the trial in question is p; the probability that it will be the second is $p(1-p)$; the probability that it will be the third is $p(1-p)^2$; etc. If we imagine an indefinitely large number of trials run under identical conditions, and represent the number of response occurrences on any trial by n, we may weight each possible value of n by its probability (*i.e.*, expected relative frequency) and obtain a mean expected value of n. In symbolic notation we have

$$\bar{n} = \Sigma n p (1 - p)^{n-1} = p \Sigma n (1 - p)^{n-1}.$$

The expression inside the summation sign will be recognized as the general term of a well-known infinite series with the sum $1/(1 - (1 - p))^2$. Then we have, by substitution,

$$\bar{n} = p/(1 - (1 - p))^2 = 1/p.$$

Then $\bar{L}$, the average time per trial, will be the product of the expected number of responses and the mean time per response.

$$\bar{L} = \bar{n}h = h/p = Sh/x.$$

Since R will be conditioned to all new stimulus elements present on each trial, we may substitute for x its equivalent from equation (3), dropping the subscripts from S_o and s_o, and obtaining

$$\bar{L} = \frac{Sh}{S - (S - x_0)e^{-qT}}$$

$$= \frac{h}{1 - \dfrac{(\bar{L}_0 - h)e^{-qT}}{\bar{L}_0}}. \quad (4)$$

Thus, $\bar{L}$ will decline from an initial value of $\bar{L}_0$ (equal to Sh/x_0) and approach the asymptotic minimum value h over a series of trials.

A preliminary test of the validity of this development may be obtained by applying equation (4) to learning data from a runway experiment in which the conditions assumed in the derivation are realized to a fair degree of approximation. In Fig. 1 we have plotted acquisition data reported by Graham and Gagné (3). Each empirical point represents the geometric mean latency for a group of 21 rats which were reinforced with food for traversing a simple elevated runway. The theoretical curve

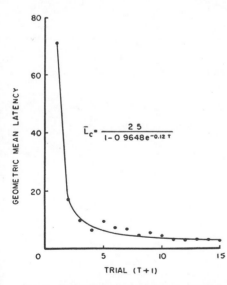

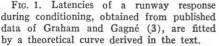

FIG. 1. Latencies of a runway response during conditioning, obtained from published data of Graham and Gagné (3), are fitted by a theoretical curve derived in the text.

in the figure represents the equation

$$\bar{L} = \frac{2.5}{1 - .9648e^{-.12T}},$$

where values of $\bar{L}_0$, h, and q have been estimated from the data. This curve appears to give a satisfactory graduation of the obtained points and, it might be noted, is very similar in form to the theoretical acquisition curve developed by Graham and Gagné. The present formulation differs from theirs chiefly in including the time of the first response as an integral part of the learning process. The quantitative description of extinction in this situation will be presented in a forthcoming paper.

In order to apply the present theory to experimental situations such as the Skinner box, in which the learning period is not divided into discrete trials, we shall have to assume that the intervals between reinforcements in those situations may be treated as "trials" for analytical purposes. Making this assumption, we may derive an expression for rate of change of conditioned response strength as a function of time in the experimental situation, during a period in which all responses of class R are reinforced.

$\bar{L}$, as defined above, will represent the time between any two occurrences of R. Then if we let t represent time elapsed from the beginning of the learning period to a given occurrence of R, and T the number of occurrences (and therefore reinforcements) of R, we have from the preceding development

$$\bar{L} = Sh/x.$$

Since $\bar{L}$ may be considered as the increment in time during a trial, we can write the identity

$$\frac{\Delta x}{\Delta t} = \frac{\Delta x}{\Delta T} \cdot \frac{\Delta T}{\Delta t}.$$

Substituting for $\Delta x/\Delta T$ its equivalent from (1), without subscripts, and for

$\Delta T/\Delta t$ its equivalent from the preceding equation, we have

$$\frac{\Delta x}{\Delta t} = \frac{s(S-x)}{S} \cdot \frac{x}{hS} = \frac{s(S-x)x}{hS^2} . \quad (5)$$

If the change in x per reinforcement is small and the process is assumed continuous, the right hand portion of equation (5) may be taken as the value of the derivative dx/dt and integrated with respect to time—

$$x = \frac{S}{1 + \dfrac{(S-x_0)}{x_0}e^{-Bt}} , \quad (6)$$

where $B = s/Sh$. In general, this equation defines a logistic curve with the amount of initial acceleration depending upon the value of x_0. Curves of probability (x/S) vs. time for $S = 100$, $B = 0.25$, and several different values of x_0 are illustrated in Fig. 2.

Since we are considering a situation in which a reinforcement is administered (or a new "trial" is begun) after each occurrence of R, we are now in a position to express the expected rate of occurrence of R as a function of time. Representing rate of occurrence of R by $r = dR/dt$, and the ratio $1/h$ by w, we have

$$r = \frac{dR}{dt} = \frac{dT}{dt} = \frac{wx}{S} = \frac{w}{1 + \dfrac{(S-x_0)}{x_0}e^{-Bt}}$$

and if we take the rate of R at the beginning of the experimental period as $r_0 = wx_0/S$ this relation becomes

$$r = \frac{w}{1 + \dfrac{(w-r_0)}{r_0}e^{-Bt}} . \quad (7)$$

To illustrate this function, we have plotted in Fig. 3 measures of rate of

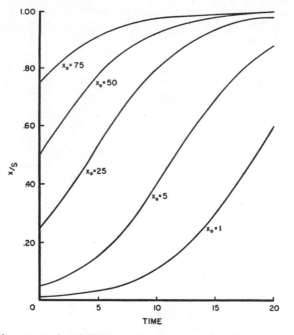

FIG. 2. Illustrative curves of probability vs. time during conditioning; parameters of the curves are the same except for the initial x-values.

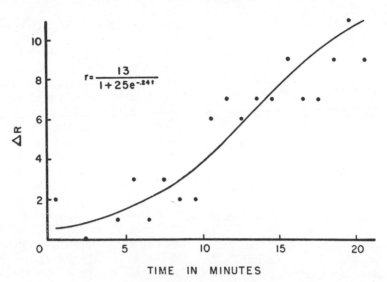

FIG. 3. Number of responses per minute during conditioning of a bar-pressing habit in a single rat; the theoretical curve is derived in the text.

responding during conditioning of a bar-pressing response by a single rat. The apparatus was a Skinner box; motivation was 24 hours thirst; the animal had previously been trained to drink out of the magazine, and during the period illustrated was reinforced with water for all bar-pressing responses. Measures of rate at various times were obtained by counting the number of responses made during the half-minute before and the half-minute after the point being considered, and taking that value as an estimate of the rate in terms of responses per minute at the midpoint. The theoretical curve in the figure represents the equation

$$r = \frac{13}{1 + 25e^{-.24t}}.$$

A considerable part of the variability of the empirical points in the figure is due to the inaccuracy of the method of estimating rates. In order to avoid this loss of precision, the writer has adopted the practice of using cumulative curves of responses *vs.* time for most purposes, and fitting the cumulative records with the integral of equation (7):

$$R = wt + \frac{w}{B} \log \left(\frac{r_0}{w} + \frac{(w - r_0)}{w} e^{-Bt} \right), \quad (8)$$

where R represents the number of responses made after any interval of time, t, from the beginning of the learning period. The original record of responses *vs.* time, from which the data of Fig. 3 were obtained, is reproduced in Fig. 4. Integration of the rate equation for this animal yields

$$R = 13t + 125 \log_{10} (.038 + .962e^{-.24t}).$$

Magnitudes of R computed from this equation for several values of t have been plotted in Fig. 4 to indicate the goodness of fit; the theoretical curve has not been drawn in the figure since it would completely obscure most of the empirical record. In an experimental report now in press (2), equation (8) is fitted to several mean conditioning curves for groups of four rats; in all cases, the theoretical curve accounts for

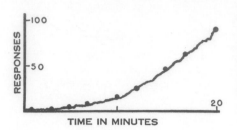

FIG. 4. Reproduction of the original cumulative record from which the points of Fig. 3 were obtained. Solid circles are computed from an equation given in the text.

more than 99 per cent of the variance of the observed R values. Further verification of the present formulation has been derived from that study by comparing the acquisition curves of successively learned bar-pressing habits, obtained in a Skinner-type conditioning apparatus which included two bars differing only in position. It has been found that the parameters w and s/S can be evaluated from the conditioning curve of one bar response, and then used to predict the detailed course of conditioning of a second learned response.

The overall accuracy of these equations in describing the rate of conditioning of bar-pressing and runway responses should not be allowed to obscure the fact that a small but systematic error is present in the initial portion of most of the curves. It is believed that these disparities are due to the fact that experimental conditions do not usually fully realize the assumption that only one R-class receives any reinforcement during the learning period. A more general formulation of the theory, which does not require this assumption, will be discussed in the next section.

Partial Reinforcement

It can be shown that a given response may be "learned" in a trial and error situation provided that some sub-population of stimulus elements is so controlled by experimental conditions that each sample of elements drawn from it is contiguous with an occurrence of the response. The sort of derivation needed to handle this kind of partial reinforcement will be sketched briefly in this section. A more detailed treatment will be given, together with relevant experimental evidence, in a paper now in preparation. It should be emphasized that we are using the term "partial" to refer to incomplete change of the stimulus sample on each occurrence of a given response, and not to periodic, or intermittent reinforcement.

Consider a behavior system involving two classes of competing behaviors, R and R_e, which may occur in a situation, S, composed of two independently manipulable sub-populations, S_r and S_e. Experimental conditions are to ensure that of the sample, s, of elements stimulating the organism at any time, elements from S_r remain effective until terminated by the occurrence of R, while elements from S_e remain effective until terminated by the occurrence of R_e. This kind of system might be illustrated by a Skinner box in which the entire stimulus sample is not terminated by occurrence of the bar-pressing response; for example, if the box is illuminated, the visual stimulation will be relatively unaffected by bar-pressing but will be terminated if the animal closes its eyes (the latter behavior being, then, an instance of R_e).

Let x represent the total number of elements from S conditioned to R at a given time, x_r the number of elements from S_r conditioned to R, T_r and T_e the numbers of occurrences of R and R_e prior to the time in question, and q the ratio s/S. By reasoning similar to that utilized in deriving equations (2) and (5), we may obtain for the average rate of change of x_r with respect to

T_r at any time

$$\frac{dx_r}{dT_r} = s \cdot \frac{S_r}{S} \cdot \frac{(S_r - x_r)}{S_r}$$

$$= q(S_r - x_r). \qquad (9)$$

This may be integrated to yield

$$x_r = S_r - (S_r - x_{r0})e^{-qT_r}, \qquad (10)$$

which is identical in form with equation (2).

The other component of x, $(x - x_r)$, will decrease as these elements become conditioned to the competing response class, R_e, according to the following relations.

$$\frac{d(x - x_r)}{dT_e} = \frac{-s(S - S_r)}{S} \cdot \frac{(x - x_r)}{(S - S_r)}$$

$$= - q(x - x_r) \qquad (11)$$

and the integral,

$$x - x_r = (x_0 - x_{r0})e^{-qT_e}. \qquad (12)$$

It will be observed that an analogous set of equations could be written for changes in the number of elements conditioned to R_e, and that the argument could be extended to any number of mutually exclusive classes of responses. From these relations it is not difficult to deduce differential equations which may be at least numerically integrated to yield curves giving probability of occurrence of each response class as a function of number of reinforcements. We shall not carry out the derivations here, but shall point out a number of properties of the curves obtained which will be evident from inspection of equations (10) and (12).

1. Regardless of the initial probabilities, the behavior system will tend to a state of equilibrium in which the final mean probability of R will be S_r/S and the final mean probability of R_e will be $(S - S_r)/S$.

2. If the number of elements from S conditioned to R at the start of an experiment is greater than S_r, the probability of R will decrease until the equilibrium is reached. (Of course all statements made here about R have analogues for R_e.)

3. If the number of elements from S conditioned to R at the start of an experiment is less than S_r, the probability of R will increase until the equilibrium value is reached.

4. If all elements originally conditioned to R belong to the sub-population S_r, then the curve relating probability to number of reinforcements will be identical with equation (3′) except for the asymptote, which will be S_r/S rather than unity.

5. If some of the elements originally conditioned to R do not belong to S_r, but x_0 is less than S_r, then the curve relating probability to number of reinforcements will rise less steeply at first than equation (3′), and may even have an initial positively accelerated limb.

It will be noted that from the present point of view, conditioning and extinction are regarded simply as two aspects of a single process. In practice we categorize a given experiment as a study of conditioning or a study of extinction depending upon which behaviors are being recorded. It seems quite possible that both conditioning and extinction always occur concurrently in any behavior system, and that the common practice of regarding them as separate processes is based more on tradition and the limitations of recording apparatus than upon rational considerations. In the present formulation, reinforcement is treated as a quantitatively graded variable with "pure extinction" at one end of a continuum. Any portion of an S-population may be related to an R-class by experimental conditions which produce a correlation between stimulus sampling and R-occurrences. Under given conditions of reinforcement an R-class may increase or decrease in probability of occurrence over a series of trials depending upon whether the momentary probability is less than or greater than the equilibrium value for those conditions.

DISCUSSION

The foregoing sections will suffice to illustrate the manner in which problems of learning may be handled within the framework of a statistical theory. The extent to which the formal system developed here may be fruitfully applied to interpret experimental phenomena can only be answered by a considerable program of research. A study of concurrent conditioning and extinction of simple skeletal responses which realizes quite closely the simplified conditions assumed in the derivations of the present paper has been completed, and a report is now in press. Other papers in preparation will apply this formulation to extinction, spontaneous recovery, discrimination, and related phenomena.

The relation of this program to contemporary theories of learning requires little comment. No attempt has been made to present a "new" theory. It is the purpose of our investigation to clarify some of the conceptions of learning and discrimination by stating important concepts in quantitative form and investigating their interrelationships by mathematical analysis. Many similarities will be noted between functions developed here and "homologous" expressions in the quantitative formulations of Graham and Gagné (3) and of Hull (6). A thorough study of those theories has influenced the writer's thinking in many respects. Rather than build directly on either of those formulations, I have felt it desirable to explore an alternative point of view based on a statistical definition of environment and behavior and doing greater justice to the theoretical views of Skinner and Guthrie. A statistical

theory seems to be an inevitable development at the present stage of the science of behavior; agreement on this point may be found among writers of otherwise widely diverse viewpoints, e.g., Brunswik (1), Hoagland (5), Skinner (7), and Wiener (9). It is to be expected that with increasing rigor of definition and continued interplay between theory and experiment, the various formulations of learning will tend to converge upon a common set of concepts.

It may be helpful to outline briefly the point of view on certain controversial issues implied by the present analysis.

Stimulus-response terminology. An attempt has been made to overcome some of the rigidity and oversimplification of traditional stimulus-response theory without abandoning its principal advantages. We have adopted a definition of stimulus and response similar to Skinner's (7) concept of generic classes, and have given it a statistical interpretation. Laws of learning developed within this framework refer to behavior systems (as defined in the introductory section of this paper) rather than to relations between isolated stimulus-response correlations.

The learning curve. This investigation is not intended to be another search for "the learning function." The writer does not believe that any simple function will be found to account for learning independently of particular experimental conditions. On the other hand, it does seem quite possible that from a relatively small set of definitions and assumptions we may be able to derive expressions describing learning under various specific experimental arrangements.

Measures of behavior. Likelihood of responding has been taken as the primary dependent variable. Analyses presented above indicate that simple relations can be derived between probability and such common experimentally obtained measures as rate of responding and latency.

Laws of contiguity and effect. Available experimental evidence on simple learning has seemed to the writer to require the assumption that temporal contiguity of stimuli and behavior is a necessary condition for the formation of conditional relations. At the level of differential analysis, that is of laws relating momentary changes in behavior to changes in independent variables, no other assumption has proved necessary at the present stage of the investigation. In order to account for the accumulation of conditional relations in favor of one *R*-class at the expense of others in any situation, we have appealed to a group of experimental operations which are usually subsumed under the term "reinforcement" in current experimental literature. Both Guthrie's (4) verbal analyses and the writer's mathematical investigations indicate that an essential property of reinforcement is that it ensures that successive occurrences of a given *R* will be contiguous with different samples from the available population of stimuli. We have made no assumptions concerning the role of special properties of certain after-effects of responses, such as drive-reduction, changes in affective tone, etc. Thus the quantitative relations developed here may prove useful to investigators of learning phenomena regardless of the investigators' beliefs as to the nature of underlying processes.

Summary

An attempt has been made to clarify some issues in current learning theory by giving a statistical interpretation to the concepts of stimulus and response and by deriving quantitative laws that govern simple behavior systems. Dependent variables, in this formulation, are classes of behavior samples with common quantitative properties; independent variables are statistical distributions of environmental events. Laws of the theory state probability relations between momentary changes in behavioral and environmental variables.

From this point of view it has been possible to derive simple relations between probability of response and several commonly used measures of learning, and to develop mathematical expressions describing learning in both classical conditioning and instrumental learning situations under simplified conditions.

No effort has been made to defend the assumptions underlying this formulation by verbal analyses of what "really" happens inside the organism or similar arguments. It is proposed that the theory be evaluated solely by its fruitfulness in generating quantitative functions relating various phenomena of learning and discrimination.

REFERENCES

1. BRUNSWIK, E. Probability as a determiner of rat behavior. *J. exp. Psychol.*, 1939, 25, 175–197.

2. ESTES, W. K. Effects of competing reactions on the conditioning curve for bar-pressing. *J. exp. Psychol.* (in press).

3. GRAHAM, C. H., & GAGNÉ, R. The acquisition, extinction, and spontaneous recovery of a conditioned operant response. *J. exp. Psychol.*, 1940, 26, 251–280.

4. GUTHRIE, E. R. Psychological facts and psychological theory. *Psychol Bull.*, 1946, 43, 1–20.

5. HOAGLAND, H. The Weber-Fechner law and the all-or-none theory. *J. gen. Psychol.*, 1930, 3, 351–373.

6. HULL, C. L. *Principles of behavior.* New York: Appleton-Century, 1943.

7. SKINNER, B. F. *The behavior of organisms.* New York: Appleton-Century, 1938.

8. SPENCE, K. W. The nature of theory construction in contemporary psychology. PSYCHOL. REV., 1944, 51, 47–68.

9. WIENER, N. *Cybernetics.* New York: Wiley, 1948.

[MS. received July 15, 1949]

STATISTICAL THEORY OF SPONTANEOUS RECOVERY AND REGRESSION

W. K. ESTES [1]

Indiana University

From the viewpoint of one interested in constructing a learning theory, it would be convenient if an organism's habits of responding with respect to any given situation were modifiable only during periods of exposure to the situation. In that case, it would not be unreasonable, prima facie, to hope that all of the empirical laws of learning could be stated in terms of relations between behavioral and environmental variables. Nothing in psychology is much more certain, however, than that orderly changes in response tendencies—e.g., spontaneous recovery, forgetting—do occur during intervals when the organism and the situation are well separated.

How are these "spontaneous" changes to be accounted for? It is easy enough to construct a law expressing some behavioral measure as a function of time, but an unfilled temporal interval never remains permanently satisfying as an explanatory variable. The temporal gap has to be filled with events of some sort, observed or inferred, in the environment or in the organism. The favorite candidate for the intervening position has usually been a postulated state or process, either neural or purely hypothetical, which varies spontane-

ously during rest intervals in whatever manner is required to account for the behavioral changes. The difficulty with this type of construct is that it is always much easier to postulate than to unpostulate. Few hypothetical entities are so ill-favored that once having secured a foothold they cannot face out each new turn of empirical events with the aid of a few *ad hoc* assumptions.

The approach to time-dependent learning phenomena which will be illustrated in this paper attempts to shift the burden of explanation from hypothesized processes in the organism to statistical properties of environmental events. The very extensiveness of the array of hypothetical constructs—e.g., set, reactive inhibition, memory trace—which now compete for attention in this area suggests that postulates of this type have entered the scene prematurely. Until more parsimonious explanatory variables have been fully explored, it will scarcely be possible either to define clearly the class of problems which require explanation or to evaluate the various special hypotheses that have been proposed.

By "more parsimonious" sources of explanation, I refer to the variables, ordinarily stimulus variables, which are intrinsic to a given type of behavioral situation and thus must be expected to play a role in any interpretive schema.

[1] This paper was prepared during the author's tenure as a faculty research fellow of the Social Science Research Council.

This article appeared in *Psychol. Rev.,* 1955, **62**, 145–154. Reprinted with permission.

In the present instance we are interested specifically in the way learned response tendencies change during rest intervals following experimental periods. And we note that there are two principal ways in which stimulus variables could lead to modification in response tendencies during rest intervals. The first is the direct effect that changes in the stimulus characteristics of experimental situations from trial to trial or period to period may have upon response probability. The second is the learning that may occur between periods if the stimulating situations obtaining within and between periods have elements in common. The former category can again be subdivided according as the environmental variation is systematic or random.

The random component has been selected as our first subject of investigation for several reasons. One is that it has received little attention heretofore in learning theory. Another is that in other sciences apparently spontaneous changes in observables have frequently turned out to be attributable to random processes at a more molecular level. Perhaps not surprisingly, considerable analysis has been needed in order to ascertain how random environmental fluctuations during intervals of rest following learning periods would be expected to influence response probabilities. It will require the remainder of this paper to summarize the methods and results of this one phase of the over-all investigation.

General Theory of Stimulus Fluctuation

Even prior to a detailed analysis, we can anticipate that whenever environmental fluctuation occurs, the probability of a response at the end of one experimental period will not be the same as the probability at the beginning of the next. If conditioning is carried out during a given period, some of the newly conditioned stimulus elements [2] will be replaced before the next period by elements which have not previously been available for conditioning. Similarly, during the interval following an extinction period, random fluctuation will lead to the replacement of some of the just extinguished stimulus elements by others which were sampled during conditioning but have not been available during extinction. In either case, the result will be a progressive change in response probability as a function of duration of the rest interval.

In order to make these ideas testable, we must state more formally and explicitly the concepts and assumptions involved. Once this is done, we will have in effect a fragmentary theory, or model, which may account for certain apparently spontaneous changes in response tendencies. At a minimum, this formal model will enable us to derive the logical consequences of the concept of random environmental fluctuation so that they may be tested against experimental data. If the correspondence turns out to be good, we may wish to incorporate this model into the conceptual structure of S-R learning theory, viewing it as a limited theory which accounts for a specific class of time-dependent phenomena.

Most of the assumptions we shall require have been discussed elsewhere (8) and need only be restated briefly for our present purposes.

a. Any environmental situation, as constituted at a given time, determines for a given organism a population of

---

[2] For reasons of mathematical simplicity and convenience I shall develop these ideas in terms of the concepts of statistical learning theory. It will be apparent, however, that within the Hullian system a similar argument could be worked out in terms of the fluctuation of stimuli along generalization continua.

stimulus events from which a sample affects the organism's behavior at any instant; in statistical learning theories the population is conceptualized as a set of stimulus elements from which a random sample is drawn on each trial.

b. Conditioning and extinction occur only with respect to the elements sampled on a trial.

c. The behaviors available to an organism in a given situation may be categorized into mutually exclusive and exhaustive response classes.

d. At any time, each stimulus element in the population is conditioned to exactly one of these response classes.

On the basis of these assumptions, functions have been derived by various investigators (2, 5, 8, 16, 21) to describe the course of learning predicted for an idealized situation in which the physical environment is perfectly constant and the organism samples the stimulus population on each trial. No idealized situations are available for testing purposes, but the theory seems to give good approximations to empirical learning functions obtained in short experimental periods under well-controlled conditions.

In the present paper we turn our attention from behavioral changes that occur within experimental periods to the changes that occur as a function of the intervals between periods. Correspondingly, we replace the simplifying assumption of a perfectly constant situation with the assumption of a randomly fluctuating situation.[3] Specifically, it will be assumed that the availability of stimulus elements during a given learning period depends upon a large number of independently variable components or aspects of the environ-

[3] It is possible now to go back and "correct" the functions derived earlier to allow for this random variation, but we will not be able to go into this point in the present paper.

mental situation, all of which undergo constant random fluctuation.

Now let us consider the type of experiment in which an organism is run for more than one period in the same apparatus. In dealing with the behavior that occurs during any given experimental period, the total population S_* of stimulus elements available in the situation at any time during the experiment can be partitioned into two portions: the subset S of elements which are available during that period and the subset S' of elements which are not. Under the conditions considered in this paper, the probability of a response at any given time during the period is equal to the proportion of elements in the available set S that are conditioned to that response. Owing to environmental fluctuation, there is some probability j that an element in the available set S will become unavailable, i.e., go into S', during any given interval Δt, and a probability j' that an element in S' will enter S. These ideas are illustrated in Fig. 1 for a hypothetical situation.

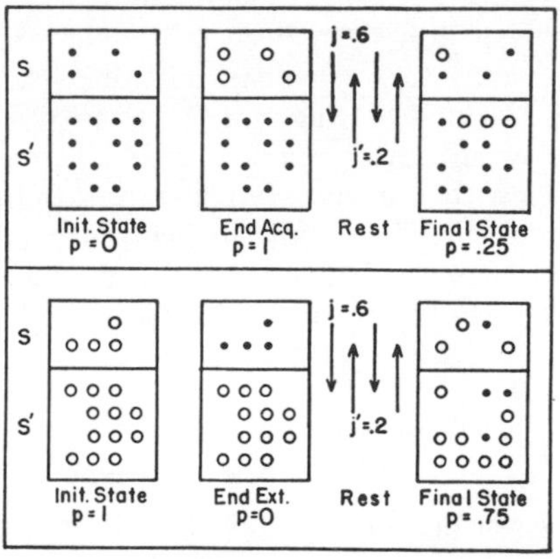

FIG. 1. Fluctuations in stimulus sets during spontaneous regression (upper panel) and spontaneous recovery from extinction (lower panel). Circles represent elements connected to response A. Values of p represent probabilities of response A in the available set S.

The relevance of the scheme for learning phenomena arises from the fact that both conditioned and unconditioned elements will constantly be fluctuating in and out of the available set S. During an experimental period in which conditioning or extinction occurs, the proportion of conditioned elements in S will increase or decrease relative to the proportion in S'. But during a subsequent rest interval, these proportions will tend toward equality as a result of the fluctuation process.

Interpretation of Spontaneous Recovery and Regression [4]

The essentials of our treatment of spontaneous recovery and regression will be clear from an inspection of Fig. 1. The upper panel illustrates a case in which, starting from a zero level, conditioning of a given response A is carried out during one period until the probability of A in the available situation represented by the set S is unity. At the end of the conditioning period we will have, neglecting any fluctuation that may have occurred during the period, all of the elements in S conditioned to A and all of the temporarily unavailable elements in S' unconditioned. During the first interval Δt of the ensuing rest interval, the proportion $j = .6$ of the conditioned elements will escape from S, being replaced by the proportion $j' = .2$ of the unconditioned elements from S'. During further intervals the interchange will continue, at a progressively decreasing rate, until the system arrives at the final state of statistical equilib-

[4] The term *spontaneous regression* will be used here to refer to any decrease in response probability which is attributable solely to stimulus fluctuation. It is assumed that over short time intervals, the empirical phenomenon of forgetting may be virtually identified with regression, but that over longer intervals forgetting is influenced to an increasing extent by effects of interpolated learning.

rium in which the densities of conditioned elements in S and S' are equal. The predicted course of spontaneous regression in terms of the proportion of conditioned elements that will be in S at any time following the conditioning period is given by the topmost curve in the upper panel of Fig. 2. The equation of the curve will be derived in a later section.

In an analogous fashion the essentials of the spontaneous recovery process are schematized in the lower panel of Fig. 1. We begin at the left with a situation following maximal conditioning so that all elements are conditioned to response A. During a single period of extinction, all elements in the available set S are conditioned to the class of competing responses $\bar{A}$ and the probability of A goes temporarily to zero. Then during a recovery interval, the random interchange of conditioned and unconditioned elements between S and S' results in a gradual increase in the proportion of conditioned elements in S until the final equilibrium state is reached. The predicted course of spontaneous recovery as a function of time is given by the topmost curve in the lower panel of Fig. 3.

According to this analysis, spontaneous regression and recovery are to be regarded as two aspects of the same process. In each case the form of the process is given by a negatively accelerated curve with the relative rate of change depending solely upon the characteristics of the physical situation embodied in the parameters j and j'. Rates of regression and recovery should, then, vary together whenever the variability of the stimulating situation is modified.

It cannot be assumed, however, that amounts of regression and recovery should be equal and opposite in all experiments. The illustrative example of Fig. 1 meets two special conditions that do not always hold: (a) the condition-

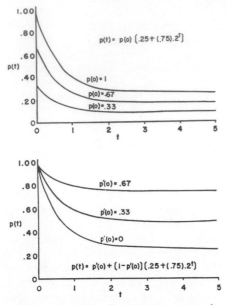

FIG. 2. Families of spontaneous regression curves. In the upper panel the proportion of conditioned elements in S' at the end of conditioning is zero and the proportion in S is the parameter. In the lower panel the proportion of conditioned elements in S at the end of conditioning is unity and the proportion in S' is the parameter.

ing and extinction series start from initial response probabilities of zero and unity, respectively; and (*b*) conditioning and extinction are carried to comparable criteria within the experimental period preceding the rest interval.

PREDICTIONS CONCERNING EFFECTS OF EXPERIMENTAL VARIABLES

Terminal level of conditioning or extinction. If other conditions remain fixed, the level of response probability attained at the end of a single learning period will determine both the initial value and the asymptote of the curve of regression or recovery. For the situation represented by the upper panel of Fig. 1, the curve of conditioning goes to unity, and the predicted course of spontaneous regression is

given by the top curve in the upper panel of Fig. 2. If in the same situation, conditioning has been carried only to a probability level of, say, .67, then the total number of conditioned elements will be smaller and the curve of regression will not only start at a lower value, but will run to a lower asymptote, and so on. Similarly, if in the situation represented by the lower panel of Fig. 1, response probability goes to zero during the extinction period, the predicted course of spontaneous recovery is given by the lowest curve in the upper panel of Fig. 3; if extinction terminates at higher probability levels, we obtain the successively higher recovery curves shown in the figure.

Number of preceding learning periods. Increasing the number of preceding acquisition periods would tend to increase the total number of condi-

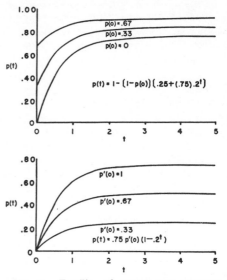

FIG. 3. Families of spontaneous recovery curves. In the upper panel the proportion of conditioned elements in S' at the end of extinction is unity and the proportion of conditioned elements in S at the end of extinction is the parameter. In the lower panel, the proportion of conditioned elements in S' at the end of extinction is the parameter and the proportion in S is zero.

tioned elements in S_* and therefore the asymptote of the curve of regression. If level of response probability at the end of the last acquisition period is fixed at some one value, say unity, then variation in the proportion of conditioned elements in S' yields the family of regression curves illustrated in the lower panel of Fig. 2, all curves starting at the same point but diverging to different asymptotes. This curve family will be recognized as corresponding to the well-known relationship between retention and amount of overlearning, where overlearning is defined in terms of additional training beyond the point at which response probability in the temporarily available situation reaches unity.

Analogous considerations apply in the case of spontaneous recovery. Increasing the number of preceding extinction periods would tend to decrease the proportion of conditioned elements remaining in S' at the end of extinction and thus the asymptote of the curve of spontaneous recovery, as illustrated in the lower panel of Fig. 3. On the other hand, increasing the number of conditioning periods prior to extinction would tend to increase the density of conditioned elements in S' and thus the asymptote of the curve of recovery following a period of extinction.

The experimental phenomenon of "extinction below zero" corresponds to a case in which additional extinction trials are given beyond the point at which temporary response probability first reaches zero. The results of this procedure will clearly depend upon the conditioning history. Consider, for example, the situation illustrated in the top row of Fig. 1. If extinction were begun immediately following the conditioning period, then we would expect extinction below zero to have little effect, for at the end of the first extinction period the set S would be ex-

hausted of conditioned elements and there would be few or none in S' to fluctuate back into S during further periods of extinction. If, however, extinction began long enough after the end of the acquisition period so that an appreciable number of conditioned elements were in S' during the first extinction period, the additional extinction would further reduce the total number of conditioned elements and thus increase the amount of training that would be required for reconditioning. If conditioning extended over more than one period, then there would be conditioned elements in S' at the end of conditioning, and similar effects of extinction below zero would be expected even if extinction began immediately after the last conditioning period.

Distribution of practice. In general, amount of spontaneous regression should vary inversely with duration of the intertrial interval during conditioning, and spontaneous recovery should vary inversely with duration of the intertrial interval during extinction. In each case, the length of the intertrial interval will determine the extent to which the stimulating situation can change between trials, and thus the proportion of the elements in the stimulus population S_* which will be sampled during a given number of trials. These relationships will be treated in more detail in a forthcoming paper (7).

MATHEMATICAL DEVELOPMENT OF FLUCTUATION THEORY

Stimulus fluctuation model. Let the probability that any given element of a total set S_* is in the available set S at time t be represented by $f(t)$, the probability that an element in S escapes into the unavailable set S' during a time interval Δt by j, and the probability that an element in S' enters S during an interval Δt by j'. Then by elementary probability theory we have for the probability that an element is in S at the end of the $(t+1)$st interval Δt following an experimental period:

$$f(t+1) = [1-f(t)]j' + f(t)(1-j).$$

This difference equation can be solved by standard methods (2, 12) to yield a formula for $f(t)$ in terms of t and the parameters:

$$f(t) = \frac{j'}{j+j'}$$

$$- \left[\frac{j'}{j+j'} - f(0)\right](1-j-j')^t$$

$$= J - [J-f(0)]a^t \qquad [1]$$

where $f(0)$ is the initial value of $f(t)$; J represents the fraction $j'/j + j'$; and a represents the quantity $(1-j-j')$. Since a is bounded between -1 and $+1$ by the definition of j and j', the probability that any element [5] is in S will settle down to the constant value J after a sufficiently long interval of time, and the total numbers of elements in S and S' will stabilize at mean values N and N', respectively, which satisfy the relation.

$$N = J(N+N'). \qquad [2]$$

Spontaneous recovery and regression. Curves of spontaneous recovery and regression can now be obtained by appropriate application of Equation 1.

[5] For simplicity, it has been assumed in this paper that all of the elements in S_* have the same values of j and j'. In dealing with some situations it might be more reasonable to assume that different parameter values are associated with different elements. For example, data obtained by Homme (11) suggest that in the Skinner box a portion of the elements should be regarded as fixed and always available while the remainder fluctuate. Application of an analytic method described elsewhere (8) shows that conclusions in the general case will differ only quantitatively from those given in this paper.

Let us designate by $p(t)$ and $p'(t)$ the proportions of conditioned elements, and therefore the response probabilities, in S and S' respectively at time t following an experimental period. The set of conditioned elements in S at time t will come in part from the conditioned elements, $p(0)N$ in number, that were in S at the end of the experimental period, and in part from the conditioned elements, $p'(0)N'$ in number, that were in S'. The probabilities of finding elements from these two sources in S at time t are obtained from Equation 1 by setting $f(0)$ equal to 1 and 0 respectively. With these relations at hand we are ready to write the general expression for spontaneous recovery and regression:

$$p(t) = \frac{1}{N}[p(0)\{J - (J-1)a^t\}N$$

$$+ p'(0)J(1-a^t)N']$$

$$= p(0)[J - (J-1)a^t]$$

$$+ p'(0)(1-a^t)(1-J), \qquad [3]$$

the parameters N and N' having been eliminated by means of Equation 2.

The functions illustrated by the curve families of Fig. 2 and 3 are all special cases of Equation 3. In the upper panel of Fig. 2, $p'(0)$ has been set equal to 0; in the lower panel, $p(0)$ has been set equal to 1. In the upper panel of Fig. 3, $p'(0)$ has been set equal to 1; in the lower panel, $p(0)$ has been set equal to 0.

EMPIRICAL RELEVANCE AND ADEQUACY

General considerations. The theoretical developments of the preceding sections present two aspects, one general and one specific, which are by no means on the same footing with regard to testability. It will be necessary to discuss separately the general concept of stimulus fluctuation and the specific mathematical model utilized for purposes of deriving its testable consequences.

The reason why the fluctuation concept had to be incorporated into a formal theory in order to be tested was, of course, the difficulty of direct observational check. Thus for the present this concept must be treated with the same reserve and even suspicion as any interpretation which appeals to unobservable events. This remoteness from direct observation may, however, represent only a transitory stage in the development of the theory. Relatively direct attacks upon certain aspects of the stimulus element concept are provided by recent experiments (1, 21) in which the sampling of stimulus populations has been modified experimentally and the outcome compared with theoretical expectation. Further, it should be noted that the idea of stimulus fluctuation is well grounded in physical considerations. Surely no one would deny that stimulus fluctuation must occur continuously; the only question is whether fluctuations are large enough under ordinary experimental conditions to yield detectable effects upon behavior. The surmise that they are is not a new one; the idea of fluctuating environmental components has been used in an explanatory sense by a number of investigators in connection with particular problems: e.g., by Pavlov (19) and Skinner (22) in accounting for perturbations in curves of conditioning or extinction, by Guthrie (10) in accounting for the effects of repetition, and recently by Saltz (20) in accounting for disinhibition and reminiscence.

Considered in isolation, the concept of stimulus fluctuation is not even indirectly testable; it must be incorporated into some broader body of theory before empirical consequences can be derived. In the present paper we have found that when this concept is taken in conjunction with other concepts and assumptions common to contemporary statistical learning theories (2, 5, 8, 16), the result of the union is a mathematical model which yields a large number of predictions concerning changes in response probability during rest intervals. Once formulated, this model is readily subject to experimental test. Its adequacy as a descriptive theory of spontaneous recovery and regression can be evaluated quite independently of the merits of the underlying idea of stimulus fluctuation.

Spontaneous recovery. Space does not permit the detailed discussion of experimental studies, and we shall have to limit ourselves to a brief summary of empirical relationships derivable from the theory, together with appropriate references to the experimental literature. To the best of my knowledge, the references cited include all studies which provide quantitative data suitable for comparison with predicted functions.

a. The curve of recovery is exponential in form (3, 9, 17) with the slope independent of the initial value (3).

b. The asymptote of recovery is inversely related to the degree of extinction (3, 11).

c. The asymptote of recovery is directly related to the number of conditioning periods given prior to extinction (11).

d. The asymptote of recovery is directly related to the spacing of preceding conditioning periods (11).

e. Amount of recovery progressively decreases during a series of successive extinction periods (4; 13; 19, p. 61).

It may be noted that items *c* and *d* represent empirical findings growing out of a study conducted expressly to test certain aspects of the theory. Many additional predictions derivable from the theory must remain unevaluated until appropriate experimental evidence becomes available, e.g., the inverse relation between asymptote of recovery and spacing of extinction trials or periods, and the predictions concerning "extinction below zero" mentioned in a previous section.

Spontaneous regression. Predictions concerning functional relationships between spontaneous regression and such experimental variables as trial spacing or degree of learning parallel those given above for spontaneous recovery, but in the case of regression there are fewer data available for purposes of verification. The predicted exponential decrease in amount of regression as a function of number of preceding learning periods has been observed in several studies (6, 11, 13, 14). Predictions concerning regression in relation to spacing of learning periods have not been tested in conditioning situations, but they seem to be in agreement with rather widely established empirical relationships between spacing and retention in human learning (15, pp. 156–158; 18, p. 508).

Finally, the question may be raised whether there are no experimental facts that would embarrass the present theory. If a claim of comprehensiveness had been made for the theory, then negative instances would be abundantly available. Under some conditions, for example, recovery or regression fails to appear at all following extinction or conditioning, respectively. Since, however, we are dealing with a theory that is limited to effects of a single independent variable, stimulus fluctuation, instances of that sort are of no special significance. Like any limited theory, this one can be tested only in situations where suitable measures are taken and where the effects of variables not represented in the model are either negligible or else quantitatively predictable. And subject to these qualifications, available evidence seems to be uniformly confirmatory. The danger of continually evading negative evidence by *ad hoc* appeals to other variables cannot be entirely obviated, but it may be progressively reduced if we are successful in bringing other relevant independent variables into the theoretical fold by further applications of the analytical method illustrated here.

SUMMARY

In this paper we have investigated the possibility that certain apparently spontaneous behavioral changes, e.g., recovery from extinction, may be accounted for in terms of random fluctuation in stimulus conditions. Taken in isolation, the concept of random stimulus fluctuation has proved untestable, but when incorporated into a model it has led to quantitative descriptions of a variety of already established empirical relationships concerning spontaneous recovery and regression and to the determination of some new ones. A forthcoming paper in which the same model is applied to the problem of distribution of practice will provide further evaluation of its scope and usefulness in the interpretation of learning phenomena.

REFERENCES

1. BURKE, C. J., ESTES, W. K., & HELLYER, S. Rate of verbal conditioning in relation to stimulus variability. *J. exp. Psychol.*, 1954, **48**, 153–161.
2. BUSH, R. R., & MOSTELLER, F. *Stochastic models for learning.* New York: Wiley, in press.
3. ELLSON, D. G. Quantitative studies of the interaction of simple habits: I. Recovery from specific and generalized effects of extinction. *J. exp. Psychol.*, 1938, **23**, 339–358.
4. ELLSON, D. G. Successive extinctions of a bar-pressing response in rats. *J. gen. Psychol.*, 1940, **23**, 283–288.
5. ESTES, W. K. Toward a statistical theory of learning. *Psychol. Rev.*, 1950, **57**, 94–107.
6. ESTES, W. K. Effects of competing reactions on the conditioning curve for bar pressing. *J. exp. Psychol.*, 1950, **40**, 200–205.
7. ESTES, W. K. Statistical theory of distributional phenomena in learning. *Psychol. Rev.*, in press.

8. ESTES, W. K., & BURKE, C. J. A theory of stimulus variability in learning. *Psychol. Rev.,* 1953, **60**, 276–286.

9. GRAHAM, C. H., & GAGNÉ, R. M. The acquisition, extinction, and spontaneous recovery of a conditioned operant response. *J. exp. Psychol.,* 1940, **26**, 251–280.

10. GUTHRIE, E. R. *The psychology of learning.* New York: Harper, 1952.

11. HOMME, L. E. Spontaneous recovery from extinction in relation to number of reinforcements, spacing of acquisition, and duration of initial extinction period. Unpublished Ph.D. thesis, Indiana Univer., 1953.

12. JORDAN, C. *Calculus of finite differences.* New York: Chelsea, 1950.

13. LAUER, D. W., & ESTES, W. K. Successive acquisitions and extinctions of a jumping habit in relation to schedule of reinforcements. *J. comp. physiol. Psychol.,* 1955, **48**, 8–13.

14. LAUER, D. W., & ESTES, W. K. Rate of learning successive discrimination reversals in relation to trial spacing. *Amer. Psychologist,* 1953, **8**, 384. (Abstract)

15. McGEOCH, J. A., & IRION, A. L. *The psychology of human learning.* New York: Longmans, Green, 1952.

16. MILLER, G. A., & McGILL, W. J. A statistical description of verbal learning. *Psychometrika,* 1952, **17**, 369–396.

17. MILLER, N. E., & STEVENSON, S. S. Agitated behavior of rats during experimental extinction and a curve of spontaneous recovery. *J. comp. Psychol.,* 1936, **21**, 205–231.

18. OSGOOD, C. E. *Method and theory in experimental psychology.* New York: Oxford Univer. Press, 1953.

19. PAVLOV, I. P. *Conditioned reflexes.* (Trans. by G. V. Anrep.) London: Oxford Univer. Press, 1927.

20. SALTZ, E. A single theory for reminiscence, act regression, and other phenomena. *Psychol. Rev.,* 1953, **60**, 159–171.

21. SCHOEFFLER, M. S. Probability of response to compounds of discriminated stimuli. *J. exp. Psychol.,* 1954, **48**, 323–329.

22. SKINNER, B. F. *The behavior of organisms.* New York: Appleton-Century-Crofts, 1938.

(Received April 18, 1954)

A THEORY OF STIMULUS VARIABILITY IN LEARNING [1]

W. K. ESTES AND C. J. BURKE

Indiana University

There are a number of aspects of the stimulating situation in learning experiments that are recognized as important by theorists of otherwise diverse viewpoints but which require explicit representation in a formal model for effective utilization. One may find, for example, in the writings of Skinner, Hull, and Guthrie clear recognition of the statistical character of the stimulus concept. All conceive a stimulating situation as made up of many components which vary more or less independently. From this locus of agreement, strategies diverge. Skinner (17) incorporates the notion of variability into his stimulus-class concept, but makes little use of it in treating data. Hull states the concept of multiple components explicitly (13) but proceeds to write postulates concerning the conditions of learning in terms of single components, leaving a gap between the formal theory and experimentally defined variables. Guthrie (11) gives verbal interpretations of various phenomena, e.g., effects of repetition, in terms of stimulus variability; these interpretations generally appear plausible but they have not gained wide acceptance among investigators of learning, possibly because Guthrie's assumptions have not been formalized in a way that would make them easily used

by others. Statistical theories of learning differ from Hull in making stimulus variability a central concept to be used for explanatory purposes rather than treating it as a source of error, and they go beyond Skinner and Guthrie in attempting to construct a formalism that will permit unambiguous statements of assumptions about stimulus variables and rigorous derivation of the consequences of these assumptions.

It has been shown in a previous paper (7) that several quantitative aspects of learning, for example the exponential curve of habit growth regularly obtained in certain conditioning experiments, follow as consequences of statistical assumptions and need not be accounted for by independent postulates. All of the derivations were carried out, however, under the simplifying assumption that all components of a stimulating situation are equally likely to occur on any trial. By removing that restriction, we are now in a position to generalize and extend the theory in several respects. It will be possible to show that regardless of whether assumptions as to the necessary conditions for learning are drawn from contiguity theories or from reinforcement theories, certain characteristics of the learning process are invariant with respect to stimulus properties while other characteristics depend in specific ways upon the nature of the stimulating situation.

THE GENERALIZED SET MODEL: ASSUMPTIONS AND NOTATION

The exposure of an organism to a stimulating situation determines a set

[1] This paper is based upon a paper reported by the writers at the Boston meetings of the Institute of Mathematical Statistics in December 1951. The writers' thinking along these and related lines has been stimulated and their research has been facilitated by participation in an interuniversity seminar in mathematical models for behavior theory which met at Tufts College during the summer of 1951 and was sponsored by SSRC.

This article appeared in *Psychol. Rev.*, 1953, **60**, 276–286. Reprinted with permission.

of events referred to collectively as stimulation. These events constitute the data of the various special disciplines concerned with vision, audition, etc. We wish to formulate our model of the stimulus situation so that information from these special disciplines can be fed into the theory, although utilization of that information will depend upon the demands of learning experiments.

For the present we shall make only the following very general assumptions about the stimulating situation: (*a*) The effect of a stimulus situation upon an organism may be regarded as made up of many component events. (*b*) When a situation is repeated on a series of trials, any one of these component stimulus events may occur on some trials and fail to occur on others; as a first approximation, at least, the relative frequencies of the various stimulus events when the same situation (as defined experimentally) occurs on a series of trials, may be represented by independent probabilities. We formulate these assumptions conceptually as follows:

(*a*) With any given organism we associate a set S^* of N^* elements.[2] The N^* elements of S^* are to represent all of the stimulus events that can occur in that organism in any situation whatever with each of these possible events corresponding to an element of the set. (*b*) For any reproducible stimulating situation we assume a distribution of values of the parameter θ; we represent by θ_i the probability that the stimulus event corresponding to the ith element of S^* occurs on any given trial.

[2] In the sequel, various sets will be designated by the letter S, accompanied by appropriate subscripts and superscripts. The letter N, with the same arrangement of subscripts and superscripts, always denotes the size of the set.

It is assumed that any change in the situation (and we shall attempt to deal only with controlled changes corresponding to manipulations of experimental variables) determines a new distribution of values of the θ_i. By repeating the "same" situation, we mean the same as described in physical terms, and we recognize that, strictly speaking, repetition of the same situation refers to an idealized state of affairs which can be approached by increasing experimental control but possibly never completely realized.

It is recognized that some sources of stimulation are internal to the organism. This means that in order to have a reproducible situation in a learning experiment it is necessary to control the maintenance schedule of the organism and also activities immediately preceding the trial. In the present paper we shall not use the term "trial" in a sufficiently extended sense to necessitate including in the θ distribution movement-produced-stimulation arising from the responses occurring on the trial.

We have noted that the behavior on a given trial is assumed to be a function of the stimulus elements which are sampled on that trial. If in a given situation certain elements of S^* have a probability $\theta = 0$ of being sampled, those elements have a negligible effect upon the behavior in that situation. For this reason we often represent a specific situation by means of a reduced set S. An element of S^* is in S if and only if it has a non-zero value of θ in the given situation. These sets are represented in Fig. 1. In this connection, we must note that a probability of zero for a given event does not mean that the event can never occur "accidentally"; this probability has the weaker meaning that the relative frequency of occurrence of the event is zero in the long run. For a

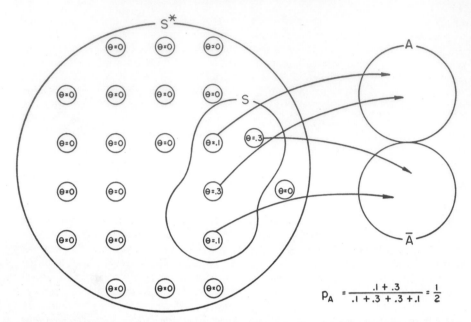

FIG. 1. A schematic representation of stimulus elements, the stimulus space S^*, the reduced set S containing elements with non-zero θ values for a given stimulating situation, and the response classes A and $\bar{A}$. The arrows joining elements of S to the response classes represent the partition of S into S_A and $S_{\bar{A}}$

more detailed explication of this point the reader is referred to Cramér (5).

It should be clearly understood that the probability, θ, that a given stimulus event occurs on a trial may depend upon many different environmental events. For example, a stimulus event associated with visual stimulation may depend for its probability upon several different light sources in the environment. Suppose that for a given stimulus element, the associated probability θ in a given situation depends only upon two separately manipulable components of the environment, a and b, and that the probabilities of the element's being drawn if only a or b alone were present are θ_a and θ_b, respectively. Then the probability attached to this element in the situation with both components present will be

$$\theta = \theta_a + \theta_b - \theta_a\theta_b.$$

THE RESPONSE MODEL

The response model formulated in a previous paper (7) will be used here without any important modification. We shall deal only with the simple case of two mutually exclusive and exhaustive response classes. The response class being recorded in a given situation will be designated A and the complementary class, $\bar{A}$. The dependent variable of the theory is the probability that the response occurring on a given trial is a member of class A. It is recognized that in a learning experiment the behaviors available to the organism may be classified in many different ways, depending upon the interests of the experimenter. The response class selected for investigation may be anything from the simplest reflex to a complex chain of behaviors involving many different groups of effectors. Adequate treatment of all levels of response specification would require the formulation of a model for the response space and will not be attempted in the present paper. Preliminary investigation of this problem leads us to believe that when a response model is elaborated, the theory developed in this paper will be found to hold rigorously for the most elementary response components and to a first approximation for simple response classes that do not involve chaining. For experimental verification of the present theory we shall look to experiments involving response classes no more complex than flexing a limb, depressing a bar, or moving a key.

Conditional Relations and Response Probability

We assume that the behavior of an organism on any trial is a function, not of the entire population of possible stimulus events, but only of those stimulus events which occur on that trial; further, when learning takes place, it involves a change in the dependency of the response upon the stimulus events which have occurred on the given trial.

Conditional relations, or for brevity, connections, between response classes and stimulus elements are defined as in other papers on statistical learning theory (3, 7). The response classes A and $\bar{A}$ define a partition of S^* into two subsets S_A^* and $S_{\bar{A}}^*$. Elements in S_A^* are said to be "connected to" or "conditioned to" response $A;$ those in $S_{\bar{A}}^*$ to response $\bar{A}$. The concept of a partition implies specifically that every element of S^* must be connected either to A or to $\bar{A}$ but that no element may be connected to both simultaneously.[3] Various features of the model are illustrated in Fig. 1.

[3] The argument of this section could as well be given in terms of the set S as of S^*, defin-

For each element in S^* we define a quantity $F_i(n)$ representing the probability that the element in question is connected to response A, i.e., is in the subset S_A^*, at the end of trial n. The mean value of $F_i(n)$ over S^* is, then, simply the expected proportion of elements connected to A, and if all of the θ_i were equal, it would be natural to define this proportion as the probability, $p(n)$, that response A occurs on trial $n + 1$. In the general case, however, not all of the θ_i are equal and the contribution of each element should be weighted by its probability of occurrence, giving

$$(1) \quad p(n) = \frac{\sum_i \theta_i F_i(n)}{\sum_i \theta_i} = \frac{1}{N^*\bar{\theta}} \sum_i \theta_i F_i(n).$$

It will be seen that in the equal θ case, expression (1) reduces to

$$(2) \quad p(n) = \frac{\theta}{N^*\theta} \sum_i F_i(n) = E(F_i(n))$$

which, except for changes in notation, is the definition used in previous papers (6, 7).

The quantity p is, then, another of the principal constructs of the theory. It is referred to as a probability, firstly because we assume explicitly that quantities p are to be manipulated mathematically in accordance with the axioms of probability theory, and secondly because in some situations p can be given a frequency interpretation. In any situation where a sequence of responses can be obtained under conditions of negligible learning and independent trials (as at the asymptote of a simple learning experiment carried out with discrete, well-spaced trials) the numerical value of p is taken as the average relative frequency of response A. For all situations the construct p is assumed to

ing S_A and $S_{\bar{A}}$ as the partition of S imposed by the response classes A and $\bar{A}$.

correspond to a parameter of the behavior system, and we do not cease to speak of this as a probability in the case of a situation where it cannot be evaluated as a relative frequency. It has been shown in a previous paper (7) that p can be related in a simple manner to rate or latency of responding in many situations; thus in all applications of the theory, p is evaluated in accordance with the rules prescribed by the theory, either from frequency data or from other appropriate data, and once evaluated is treated for all mathematical purposes as a probability.

REPRESENTATION OF LEARNING PROCESSES

In order to account for the gradual course of learning in most situations, a number of the earlier quantitative theories, e.g., those of Hull (13), Gulliksen and Wolfle (10), Thurstone (18) have assumed that individual connections are formed gradually over a series of learning trials. Once we adopt a statistical view of the stimulating situation, however, it can be shown rigorously that not only the gradual course of learning but the form of the typical learning curve can be accounted for in terms of probability considerations even if we assume that connections are formed on an all-or-none basis. This being the case, there seems to be no evidence whatsoever that would require a postulate of gradual formation of individual connections. Psychologically an all-or-none assumption has the advantage of enabling us to account readily for the fact that learning is sudden in some situations and gradual in others; mathematically, it has the advantage of great simplicity. For these reasons, recent statistical theories of learning have adopted some form of the all-or-none assumption (3, 7, 15).

Under an all-or-none theory, we must specify the probabilities that any stimulus element that is sampled on a given trial will become connected to A or to $\bar{A}$. For convenience in exposition, we shall limit ourselves in this paper to the simplest special case, i.e., a homogeneous series of discrete trials with probability equal to one that all elements occurring on a trial become connected to response A.

We begin by asking what can be said about the course of learning during a sequence of trials regardless of the distribution of stimulus events. It will be shown that our general assumptions define a family of mathematical operators describing learning during any prescribed sequence of trials, the member of the family applicable in a given situation depending upon the θ distribution. We shall first inquire into the characteristics common to all members of a family, and then into the conditions under which the operators can be approximated adequately by the relatively simple functions that have been found convenient for representing learning data in previous work.

Let us consider the course of learning during a sequence of trials in the simplified situation. Each trial in the series is to begin with the presentation of a certain stimulus complex. This situation defines a distribution of θ over S^* so that each element in S^* has some probability, θ_i, of occurring on any trial, and we represent by S the subset of elements with non-zero θ values; any element that occurs on a trial becomes connected to A (or remains connected to A if it has been drawn on a previous trial). For concreteness the reader might think of a simple conditioning experiment with the CS preceding the US by an optimal interval, and with conditions arranged so that the UR is evoked on each trial and decremental factors are negligible; the situation represented by S is that obtaining from the onset of the CS to the onset of the US, and the response probability p will refer to the probability of A in this situation. The number of elements in S will be designated by N. For simplicity we shall suppose in the following derivations that none of the elements in S are connected to A at the beginning of the experiment. This means that the learning curves obtained all begin with N_A and p equal to zero. No loss of generality is involved in this simplification; our results may easily be extended to the case of any arbitrary initial condition.

The ith element in S will still remain in $S_{\bar{A}}$ after the nth trial if and only if it is not sampled on any of the first n trials; the likelihood that this occurs is $(1 - \theta_i)^n$. Hence, if $F_i(n)$ represents the expected probability that this element is connected to A after the nth trial, we obtain:

$$(3) \qquad F_i(n) = 1 - (1 - \theta_i)^n.$$

The expected number of elements in S connected to A after the nth trial, $E[N_A(n)]$, will be the sum of these expected contributions from individual elements:

$$(4) \quad E[N_A(n)] = \sum_i F_i(n)$$
$$= \sum_i \left[1 - (1 - \theta_i)^n\right]$$
$$= N - \sum_i (1 - \theta_i)^n.$$

We are now in a position to express p, the probability of response A, as a function of the number of trials in this situation. By substituting for the term $F_i(n)$ of equation (1) its equivalent from equation (3), we obtain the relation

$$(5) \quad p(n) = \frac{1}{N\bar{\theta}} \sum_i \theta_i \left[1 - (1 - \theta_i)^n\right]$$
$$= 1 - \frac{1}{N\bar{\theta}} \sum_i \theta_i (1 - \theta_i)^n.$$

Equation (5) defines a family of learning curves, one for each possible θ distribution, and it has a number of simple properties that are independent of the distribution of the θ_i. It can easily be verified by substitution that there is a fixed point at $p = 1$, and this will be the asymptote approached by the curve of $p(n)$ vs. n as n increases over all bounds. Members of the family will be monotonically increasing, negatively accelerated curves, approaching a simple negative growth function as the θ_i tend toward equality. If all of the θ_i are equal to $\bar{\theta}$, equation (5) reduces to

$$(6) \qquad p(n) = 1 - (1 - \bar{\theta})^n$$

which, except for a change in notation, is the same function derived previously (7) for the equal θ case [4] and corresponds to the linear operator used by Bush and Mosteller (2) for situations where no decremental factor is involved. In mathematical form, equation (6) is the same as Hull's well-known expression for growth of habit strength, but the function does not have the same relation to observed probability of responding in Hull's theory as in the present formulation.

Except where the distribution function of the θ_i either is known, or can be assumed on theoretical grounds to be approximated by some simple expression, equation (5) will not be convenient to work with. In practice we are apt to assume equal θ_i and utilize equation (6) to describe experimental data. The nature of the error of approximation involved in doing this can be stated generally. Immediately after the first trial, the curve for the general case must lie above the curve for the

[4] This is essentially the same function developed for the equal θ case in a previous paper (7); the terms $\bar{\theta}$ and n of equation (6) correspond to the terms $q = s/S$, and T of that paper.

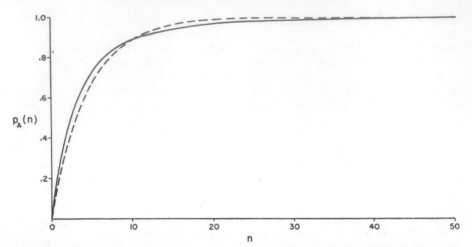

FIG. 2. Response probability, in S, as a function of number of trials for the numerical examples presented in the text. The solid curve is the exact solution for a population of elements, half of which have $\theta = 0.1$ and half $\theta = 0.3$. The dashed curve describes the equal θ approximation with $\bar{\theta} = 0.2$. Initially no elements of S are conditioned to A.

equal θ case; the difference between the two curves increases for a few trials, then decreases until they cross (in constructing hypothetical θ distributions of diverse forms we have usually found this crossing in the neighborhood of the fourth to eighth trial); after crossing, the curves diverge to a smaller extent than before, then come together as both go to the same asymptote at $p = 1$. It can be proved that the curves for the general and special case cross exactly once as n goes from one to infinity. We cannot make any general statement about the maximum error involved in approximating expression (5) with expression (6), but after studying a number of special cases, we are inclined to believe that the error introduced by the approximation will be too small to be readily detectable experimentally for most simple learning situations that do not involve compounding of stimuli.

The development of equations (5) and (6) has necessarily been given in rather general terms, and it may be helpful to illustrate some of the considerations involved by means of a simple numerical example. Imagine that we are dealing with some particular conditioning experiment in which the CS can be represented by a set S, composed of two subsets of stimulus elements, S_1 and S_2, of the sizes $N_1 = N_2 = N/2$, where N is the number of elements in S. Assume that for all elements in S_1 the probability of being drawn on any trial is $\theta_1 = 0.3$ and for those in S_2, $\theta_2 = 0.1$. Now we wish to compute the predicted learning curve during a series of trials on which A responses are reinforced, assuming that we begin with all elements connected to $\bar{A}$. Equation (5) becomes

$$p(n) = 1 - \frac{1}{0.2N}[N_1(0.3)$$
$$\times (1-0.3)^n + N_2(0.1)(1-0.1)^n]$$
$$= 1 - \frac{1}{0.4}[0.3(0.7)^n + 0.1(0.9)^n].$$

Plotting numerical values computed from this equation, we obtain the solid curve given in Fig. 2.

Now let us approach the same problem, but supposing this time that we know nothing about the different θ values in the subsets S_1 and S_2 and are given only that $\bar{\theta} = 0.2$. We now obtain predicted learning curves under the equal θ approximation. Equation (6) becomes:

$$p(n) = 1 - (1 - 0.2)^n$$

and numerical values computed from this yield the dashed curve of Fig. 2.

Inspection of Fig. 2 shows that the exact treatment leads to higher values of $p(n)$ on the early trials but to lower values on the later trials, the difference becoming negligible for large n. The reason, in brief, for the steeper curvature of the exact curve is that elements with high θ values are likely to be drawn, and therefore conditioned to A, earlier in the learning process than elements with low θ values, and then because they will tend to recur frequently in successive samples, to lead to relatively high values of p. During the late stages of learning, elements with low θ values that have not been drawn on the early trials will contribute more unconnected elements per trial than would be appearing at the same stage with an equal θ distribution and will depress the value of p below the curve for the equal θ approximation.

It should be emphasized that the generality of the present approach to learning theory lies in the concepts introduced and the methods developed for operating with them, not in the particular equations derived. Equation (5), for example, can be expected to apply only to an extremely narrow class of learning experiments. On the other hand, the methods utilized in deriving equation (5) are applicable to a wide variety of situations. For the interest of the experimentally oriented reader, we will indicate briefly a few of the most obvious extensions of the theory developed above, limiting ourselves to the equal θ case.

As written, equation (6) represents the predicted course of conditioning for a single organism with an initial response probability of zero. We can allow for the possibility that an experiment may begin at some value of $p(0)$ other than zero by rewriting (6) in the more general form

$$(7) \quad p(n) = 1 - [1 - p(0)](1 - \bar{\theta})^n$$

which has the same form as (6) except for the initial value.

If we wish to consider the mean course of conditioning in a group of m organisms with like values of $\bar{\theta}$ but varying initial response probabilities, we need simply sum equation (7) over the group and divide by m, obtaining

$$(8) \quad \bar{p}(n) = \frac{1}{m} \sum p(n)$$
$$= 1 - [1 - \bar{p}(0)](1 - \bar{\theta})^n.$$

The standard deviation of $p(n)$ under these circumstances is simply

$$(9) \quad \sigma_p(n) = \sqrt{\frac{1}{m} \sum p^2(n) - \bar{p}^2(n)}$$
$$= (1 - \bar{\theta})^n \sigma_p(0)$$

where $\sigma_p(0)$ is the dispersion of the initial p values for the group. Variability around the mean learning curve decreases to zero in a simple manner as learning progresses.

The treatment of counter-conditioning, i.e., extinguishing one response by giving uniform reinforcement to a competing response, follows automatically from our account of the acquisition process. Returning to equation (6) and recalling that the probabilities of A and $\bar{A}$ must always sum to unity, we note that while response A undergoes conditioning in accordance with (6), response $\bar{A}$ must undergo extinction in accordance with the function

$$p_{\bar{A}}(n) = 1 - p_A(n) = (1 - \bar{\theta})^n.$$

If, then, we begin with any arbitrary $p(0)$ and arrange conditions so that $\bar{A}$ is evoked and conditioned to all elements drawn on each trial, the extinction of response A will be given by the simple decay function

$$(10) \qquad p(n) = p(0)(1 - \bar{\theta})^n.$$

Again the mean and standard deviation of $p(n)$ can easily be computed for a group of organisms with like values of $\bar{\theta}$ but varying values of $p(0)$:

$$(11) \qquad \bar{p}(n) = \bar{p}(0)(1 - \bar{\theta})^n$$

$$(12) \qquad \sigma_p(n) = (1 - \bar{\theta})^n \sigma_p(0).$$

As in the case of acquisition, variability around the mean curve decreases to zero in a simple manner over a series of trials.

Since variability due to variation in $p(0)$ is reduced during both conditioning and counter-conditioning, it will be seen that in general we should expect less variability around a curve of re-learning than around a curve of original learning for a given group of subjects.

APPLICATION OF THE STATISTICAL MODEL TO LEARNING EXPERIMENTS

Since our concern in this paper has been with the development of a stimulus model of considerable generality, it has been necessary in the interests of clear exposition to omit reference to most of the empirical material upon which our theoretical assumptions are based. The evaluation of the model must rest upon detailed interpretation of specific experimental situations. It is clear, however, that the statistical model developed here cannot be tested in isolation; only when it is taken together with assumptions as to how learning occurs and with rules of cor-respondence between terms of the theory and experimental variables, will experimental evaluation be possible. Limitations of space preclude a detailed theoretical analysis of individual learning situations in this paper. In order to indicate how the model will be utilized and to suggest some of its explanatory potentialities we shall conclude with a few general remarks concerning the interpretation of learning phenomena within the theoretical framework we have developed.

Application of the model to any one isolated experiment will always involve an element of circularity, for information about a given θ distribution must be obtained from behavioral data. This circularity disappears as soon as data are available from a number of related experiments. The utility of the concept is expected to lie in the possibility of predicting a variety of facts once the parameters of the θ distribution have been evaluated for a situation. The methodology involved has been illustrated on a small scale by an experiment (6) in which the mean θ value for an operant conditioning situation was estimated from the acquisition curve of a bar-pressing habit and then utilized in predicting the course of acquisition of a second bar-pressing habit by the same animals under slightly modified conditions.

When the statistical model is taken together with an assumption of association by contiguity, we have the essentials of a theory of simple learning. The learning functions (5), (6), and (10) derived above should be expected to provide a description of the course of learning in certain elementary experiments in the areas of conditioning and verbal association. It must be emphasized, however, that these functions alone will not constitute an adequate theory of conditioning, for a number of relevant variables, especially those controlling response decrement, have not been taken into account in our derivations. In conditioning experiments where decremental factors are minimized, there is considerable evidence (1, 4, 9, 14, 16) that the curve of conditioning has the principal properties of our equation (5) and can be well approximated by the equal θ case (7). The fact that functions derived from the model can be fitted to certain empirical curves is a desirable outcome, of course, but cannot be regarded as providing a very exacting test of the theory; probably any contemporary quantitative theory will manage to accomplish this much. On the other hand, the fact that the properties of our learning functions follow from the statistical nature of the stimulating situation is of some interest; in this respect the structure of the present theory is simpler than certain others, e.g., that of Hull (13), which require an independent postulate to account for the form of the conditioning curve.

It should also be noted that deviations from the exponential curve form may be as significant as instances of good fit. From the present model we must predict a specific kind of deviation when the stimulating situation contains elements of widely varying θ values. If, for example, curves of conditioning to two stimuli taken separately yield significantly different values of $\bar{\theta}$, then the curve of conditioning to a compound of the two stimuli should be expected to deviate further than either of the separate curves from a simple growth function. The only relevant experiment we have discovered in the literature is one reported by Miller (16); Miller's results appear to be in line with this analysis, but we would hesitate to regard this aspect of the theory as substantiated until additional relevant data become available.

Although we shall not develop the

argument in mathematical detail in the present paper, it may be noted that the statistical association theory yields certain specific predictions concerning the effects of past learning upon the course of learning in a new situation. In general, the increment or decrement in p during any trial depends to a certain extent upon the immediately preceding sequence of trials. Suppose that we have two identical animals each of which has $p(n)$ equal, say, to 0.5 at the end of trial n of an experiment, and suppose that for each animal response A is reinforced on trial $n + 1$. The histories of the two animals are presumed to differ in that the first animal has arrived at $p(n) = 0.5$ via a sequence of reinforced trials while the second animal has arrived at this value via a sequence of unreinforced trials. On trial $n + 1$, the second animal will receive the greater increment to p (except in the equal θ case); the reason is, in brief, that for both animals the stimulus elements most likely to occur on trial $n + 1$ are those with high θ values; for the first animal these elements will have occurred frequently during the immediately preceding sequence of trials and thus will tend to be preponderantly connected to A prior to trial $n + 1$; in the case of the second animal, the high θ elements will have been connected to $\bar{A}$ during the immediately preceding sequence and thus when A is reinforced on trial $n + 1$, the second animal will receive the greater increment in weight of connected elements. From this analysis it follows that, other things equal, a curve of reconditioning will approach its asymptote more rapidly than the curve of original conditioning unless extinction has actually been carried to zero. How important the role of the unequal θ distribution will prove to be in accounting for empirical phenomena of relearning cannot be adequately judged until further research has provided means for estimating the orders of magnitude of the effects we have mentioned here.

SUMMARY

Earlier statistical treatments of simple associative learning have been refined and generalized by analyzing the stimulus concept in greater detail than heretofore and by taking account of the fact that different components of a stimulating situation may have different probabilities of affecting behavior.

The population of stimulus events corresponding to an independent experimental variable is represented in the statistical model by a mathematical set. The relative frequencies with which various aspects of the stimulus variable affect behavior in a given experiment are represented by set operations and functions.

The statistical model, taken together with an assumption of association by contiguity, provides a limited theory of certain conditioning phenomena. Within this theory it has been possible to distinguish aspects of the learning process that depend upon properties of the stimulating situation from those that do not. Certain general predictions from the theory concerning acquisition, extinction, and relearning, are compared with experimental findings.

Salient characteristics of the model elaborated here are compared with other quantitative formulations of learning.

REFERENCES

1. BROGDEN, W. J. Animal studies of learning. In S. S. Stevens (Ed.), *Handbook of experimental psychology*. New York: Wiley, 1951.

2. BUSH, R. R., & MOSTELLER, F. A mathematical model for simple learning. *Psychol. Rev.*, 1951, **58**, 313–323.

3. BUSH, R. R., & MOSTELLER, F. A model for stimulus generalization and discrimination. *Psychol. Rev.*, 1951, **58**, 413–423.

4. CALVIN, J. S. Decremental factors in conditioned-response learning. Unpublished Ph.D. thesis, Yale Univer., 1939.

5. CRAMÉR, H. *Mathematical methods of statistics*. Princeton: Princeton Univer. Press, 1946.

6. ESTES, W. K. Effects of competing reactions on the conditioning curve for bar pressing. *J. exp. Psychol.*, 1950, **40**, 200–205.

7. ESTES, W. K. Toward a statistical theory of learning. *Psychol. Rev.*, 1950, **57**, 94–107.

8. FELLER, W. *An introduction to probability theory and its applications*. New York: Wiley, 1950.

9. GRANT, D. A., & HAKE, H. W. Dark adaption and the Humphreys random reinforcement phenomenon in human eyelid conditioning. *J. exp. Psychol.*, 1951, **42**, 417–423.

10. GULLIKSEN, H., & WOLFLE, D. L. A theory of learning and transfer. *Psychometrika*, 1938, **3**, 127–149.

11. GUTHRIE, E. R. Psychological facts and psychological theory. *Psychol. Bull.*, 1946, **43**, 1–20.

12. HILGARD, E. R., & MARQUIS, D. G. *Conditioning and learning*. New York: Appleton-Century, 1940.

13. HULL, C. L. *Principles of behavior*. New York: D. Appleton-Century, 1943.

14. HUMPHREYS, L. G. Acquisition and extinction of verbal expectations in a situation analogous to conditioning. *J. exp. Psychol.*, 1939, **25**, 294–301.

15. MILLER, G. A., & McGILL, W. J. A statistical description of verbal learning. *Psychometrika*, in press.

16. MILLER, J. The rate of conditioning of human subjects to single and multiple conditioned stimuli. *J. gen. Psychol.*, 1939, **20**, 399–408.

17. SKINNER, B. F. *The behavior of organisms*. New York: Appleton-Century-Crofts, 1938.

18. THURSTONE, L. L. The learning function. *J. gen. Psychol.*, 1930, **3**, 469–493.

[MS. received November 12, 1952]

ANALYSIS OF A VERBAL CONDITIONING SITUATION IN TERMS OF STATISTICAL LEARNING THEORY[1]

W. K. ESTES AND J. H. STRAUGHAN

Indiana University

It is the purpose of this study to investigate the theoretical significance of a rather striking coincidence between an experimental fact and a mathematical fact. The experimental fact has been established in the Humphreys-type "verbal conditioning" situation. In this situation S is asked to predict on each of a series of trials whether some designated event, e.g., the flash of a light, will occur; this event, the analogue of the US in a conditioning experiment, is presented in accordance with a predetermined schedule, usually random with some fixed probability. Several recent investigators (3, 5) have noted that S tends to match his response rate to the rate of occurrence of the predicted event so that if the probability of the latter is, say, .75, the mean response curve for a group of Ss tends over a series of trials toward an apparently stable final level at which the event is predicted on approximately 75% of the trials. This behavior has seemed puzzling to most investigators since it does not maximize the proportion of successful predictions and thus does

not conform to conventional law of effect doctrine. The mathematical fact which will concern us appeared in the course of developing the formal consequences of statistical association theory (1, 2); in a simple associative learning situation satisfying certain conditions of symmetry, the theoretical asymptote of response probability turns out to be equal to the probability of reinforcement. The reasoning involved may be sketched briefly as follows.

We consider a situation in which each trial begins with presentation of a signal, or CS; following the signal, one or the other of two reinforcing stimuli, E_1 or E_2, occurs, the probability of E_1 and E_2 during a given series being π and $1 - \pi$, respectively. The behaviors available to S are categorized into two classes, A_1 and A_2, by experimental criteria. In the verbal conditioning situation, A_1 is a prediction that E_1 will occur, and A_2 a prediction that E_2 will occur on the given trial. We assume that the CS determines a population, S_c, of stimulus elements which is sampled by S on each trial, the proportion θ of the elements in this population constituting the effective sample on any one

[1] This research was facilitated by the senior author's tenure as a faculty research fellow of the Social Science Research Council.

This article appeared in *J. exp. Psychol.*, 1954, **47**, 225–234. Reprinted with permission.

trial. The dependence of S's responses upon the stimulating situation is expressed in the theory by defining a conditional relationship such that each element in S_c is conditioned to (tends to evoke) either A_1 or A_2. In order to interpret the formal model in terms of a verbal conditioning experiment, we assume that when an E_1 occurs it evokes from S a response belonging to class A_1, i.e., one which is compatible with the response of predicting E_1 but which interferes with the response of predicting E_2, and that when an E_2 occurs it evokes a response of class A_2. Then on a trial on which E_1 occurs we expect on the basis of association principles (1) that all elements sampled from S_c on the trial will become conditioned to A_1 while on an E_2 trial the sample will be conditioned to A_2. Now if successive trials are sufficiently discrete so that samples from S_c are statistically independent, the probability of an A_1 after Trial n, abbreviated $p(n)$, is defined in the model as the proportion of elements in S_c that are conditioned to A_1, and similarly for the probability of an A_2, $[1-p(n)]$. With these definitions the rule for calculating the change in response probability on an E_1 trial may be stated formally as

$$p(n + 1) = (1-\theta)p(n) + \theta \quad (1)$$

and on an E_2 trial as

$$p(n + 1) = (1-\theta)p(n). \quad (2)$$

The genesis of these equations will be fairly obvious. The proportion $(1-\theta)$ of stimulus elements is not sampled, and the status of elements that are not sampled on a trial does not change; the proportion θ is sampled and these elements are all conditioned either to A_1 or to A_2 accordingly as an E_1 or an E_2 occurs.[2] Now in a random rein-

forcement situation, Equation 1 will be applicable on the proportion π of trials and Equation 2 on the proportion $(1-\pi)$; then the average probability of A_1 after Trial $n + 1$ will be given by the relation

$$\bar{p}(n + 1) = \pi[(1-\theta)\bar{p}(n) + \theta]$$
$$+ (1 - \pi)(1 - \theta)\bar{p}(n) \quad (3)$$
$$= (1 - \theta)\bar{p}(n) + \theta\pi.$$

If a group of Ss begins an experiment with the value $\bar{p}(0)$, then at the end of Trial 1 we would have

$$\bar{p}(1) = (1 - \theta)\bar{p}(0) + \theta\pi,$$

at the end of Trial 2

$$\bar{p}(2) = (1 - \theta)[(1 - \theta)\bar{p}(0)$$
$$+ \theta\pi] + \theta\pi$$
$$= \pi - [\pi - \bar{p}(0)](1 - \theta)^2,$$

and so on for successive trials; in general it can be shown by induction that at the end of the nth trial

$$\bar{p}(n) = \pi - [\pi - \bar{p}(0)](1 - \theta)^n. \quad (4)$$

Since $(1 - \theta)$ must be a fraction between zero and one, it will be seen that Equation 4 must be a negatively accelerated curve running from the initial value $\bar{p}(0)$ to the asymptotic value π.

This outcome of the statistical learning model is rather surprising at first since it makes asymptotic response probability depend solely upon the probability of reinforcement. It seems, however, to be in excellent agreement with the experimental results of Grant, Hake, and Hornseth (3) and Jarvik (5). The question that interests us

---

[2] Consequently the functions derived in this paper should be expected to apply only to learning situations which are symmetrical in the following sense. To each response class there must correspond a reinforcing condition which, if present on any trial, ensures that a response belonging to the class will terminate the trial. These functions should, for example, be applicable to learning of a simple left-right discrimination with correction; but not to a left-right discrimination without correction, to free responding in the Skinner box, or to Pavlovian conditioning.

now is whether this agreement is to be regarded as a remarkable coincidence or as a confirmation of the theory. We cannot estimate a confidence level for the latter conclusion since the experiments were not conducted specifically to test the theory, and we cannot guarantee that we would be as alert to notice results contrary to the theory which might appear in the literature as we have been in the case of these decidedly positive instances. It has seemed to us that the least objectionable way out of this impasse is to carry out some new experiments, making use of one of the convenient features of a mathematical theory, namely, that if it will generate one testable prediction for a given experimental situation, it can generally be made to yield many more. In the experiment to be reported we have tried to set up a situation similar in essentials to that used by Humphreys, Grant, and others with an experimental design which would permit testing of a variety of consequences of the theory. Each S was run through two successive series of 120 trials in an individualized modification of the Humphreys situation with the schedule of π values shown in Table 1. Within the first series we will be able to compare learning rates and asymptotes of groups starting from similar initial values but exposed to different probabilities of reinforcement; within the second series we will be able to compare groups starting at different initial values but exposed to the same probabilities of reinforcement. Comparison of Group I with the other groups over both series will permit evaluation of the stability of learning rate (θ value) from series to series when the π value does or does not change. Series I_A and series II_B will provide a comparison in which initial response probabilities and π values are the same but the amount of

TABLE 1

EXPERIMENTAL DESIGN IN TERMS OF PROBABILITY OF REINFORCEMENT (π VALUE) DURING EACH SERIES

Group	N	Trials 1–120 Series A	Trials 121–240 Series B
I	16	.30	.30
II	16	.50	.30
III	16	.85	.30

preceding reinforcement differs. In order to separate the effect of over-all π value from that of particular orders of event occurrences, each of the three groups indicated in Table 1 has been subdivided into four subgroups of four Ss each; within a treatment group, say Group I, all subgroups have the same π value but each receives a separate randomly drawn sequence of E_1's and E_2's.

METHOD

Apparatus.—The experiment was run in a room containing a 2-ft. square signal board and four booths. Upon the signal board were mounted 12 12-v., .25-amp. light bulbs spaced evenly in a circle 18 in. in diameter. The bulbs occupied the half-hour positions of a clock face. Only the top two lights on the board were used as signals in this experiment. The signal board was mounted vertically on a table 40 in. high and was about 5 ft. in front of Ss' booths.

The booths were made from two 30 × 60 in. tables, 30 in. high, placed end to end but meeting at an angle so that Ss sitting behind them would be facing almost directly toward the signal board, about 7 ft. in front of Ss' eyes. Two Ss sat at each table. The four Ss were separated from one another by panels 2 ft. high and 32 in. wide. These panels were mounted vertically on the table tops so as to extend 14½ in. beyond the edge of the table between the seated Ss.

In each booth, 18 in. back from S's edge of the table, was a wooden panel 12 in. high mounted vertically on the table top and extending across the width of the booth. On the side of this panel facing S were two reinforcing lights of the same size as those on the signal board but covered by white, translucent lenses. These lights were directly in front of S, 4 in. apart and 8 in. above the table top. On the table below each reinforcing light was a telegraph key.

The orders of presentation and the durations of the signal lights and reinforcing lights were controlled by a modified Esterline-Angus recorder using a punched tape and a system of electrical pick-up brushes. The recorder was placed on the table behind the signal board. Recorder pens which were activated by depression of the telegraph keys in Ss' booths were mounted between the brushes. Thus, the presentations of the lights and Ss' responses were recorded on the same tape. A panel light was mounted above the Esterline-Angus recorder so that E, seated behind the signal board, could watch the operation of brushes and pens during the experiment.

Windows in the experimental room were covered with opaque material and the experiment was run in darkness except for light that came from the apparatus.

Subjects.—The Ss were 48 students obtained from beginning lecture courses in psychology during the fall semester of 1952 and assigned at random to experimental groups.

Procedure.—At the beginning of a session, Ss were brought into the room, asked to be seated, and read the following instructions:

"Be sure you are seated comfortably; it will be necessary to keep one hand resting lightly beside each of the telegraph keys throughout the experiment and to watch both the large board in the front of the room and the two small lights in your own compartment. Your task in this experiment will be to outguess the experimenter on each trial, or at least as often as you can. The ready signal on each trial will be a flash from the two top lights on the big board. About a second later either the left or the right lamp in your compartment will light for a moment. As soon as the ready signal flashes you are to guess whether the left or the right lamp will light on that trial and indicate your choice by pressing the proper key. If you expect the left lamp to light, press the left key; if you expect the right lamp to light, press the right key; if you are not sure, guess. Be sure to make your choice as soon as the ready signal appears, press the proper key down firmly, then release the key before the ready signal goes off. It is important that you press either the left or the right key, never both, on each trial, and that you make your decision and indicate your choice while the signal light is on.

"Now we will give you four practice trials."

At this point the overhead lights were extinguished and the recorder started. If any obvious mistakes were made by S during the four practice trials, they were pointed out by E. During the four practice trials the reinforcing lights were always given in the order: E_1, E_1, E_2, E_2. After the practice trials the following instructions were read:

"Are you sure you understand all of the instructions so far? The rest of the trials will have to be run off without any conversation or other interruptions. Please make a choice on every trial even if it seems difficult. Make a guess on the first trial, then try to improve your guesses as you go along and make as many correct choices as possible."

Questions were answered by rereading or paraphrasing the appropriate part of the instructions. If there were any questions about tricks the following additional paragraph was read.

"We have told you everything that will happen. There are no tricks or catches in this experiment. We simply want to see how well you can profit from experience in a rather difficult problem-solving situation while working under time pressure."

The recorder was now started again and the 240 experimental trials were run off in a continuous sequence with no break or other indication to S at the transition from Series A to Series B. On each trial, the signal lamps were lighted for approximately 2 sec.; 1 sec. later the appropriate reinforcing light in each S's booth lighted for .8 sec.; then after an interval of .4 sec. the next ready signal appeared; and so on. The high rate of stimulus presentation was used in order to minimize verbalization on the part of Ss.

RESULTS AND DISCUSSION

Terminal response probabilities.—It will be clear from our discussion of Equation 4 that the predicted asymptote for each series will be the value of π obtaining during the series. We have taken the mean proportion of A_1 responses during the last 40 trials of each series as an estimate of terminal response probability, and these values are summarized for all groups and both series in Table 2.

TABLE 2

TERMINAL MEAN RESPONSE PROBABILITIES
FOR EACH SERIES

Group	Series A			Series B		
	$\bar{P}$	π	t	$\bar{P}$	π	t
I	.37	.30	2.35	.28	.30	0.77
II	.48	.50	0.55	.37	.30	2.56
III	.87	.85	0.55	.30	.30	0.05
F	69.31			2.98		

For the first series a simple analysis of variance yields an F significant beyond the .001 level for differences among means. From the within-groups variance estimate we obtain a value for the standard error of a group mean, and this is used in the t test between each group mean and the appropriate theoretical mean. For the second series the between-groups F has a probability between the .05 and .10 levels. In neither series were differences among subgroup means significant at the .05 level.

The interpretation seems straightforward. Group III approximates the theoretical asymptote in both series. Group I falls significantly short of the theoretical asymptote in the first series but approximates it in the second series. Group II falls significantly short of the theoretical asymptote in the second series, but reaches the same probability level as had Group I in the first series. Of the t tests computed for differences between the last two blocks of 20 trials in each series, all yielded probabilities greater than .10 except the t for Series II$_B$ which was significant at the .02 level. Evidently the predictions concerning mean asymptotic values are correct, but the rate of approach to asymptote is faster with Group III than under the other conditions.

According to theory, not only group means, but also individual curves should approach π asymptotically. To obtain evidence as to the tenability of this aspect of the theory we have examined the distributions of individual A$_1$ response proportions for the last 40 trials of Series III$_A$, III$_B$, and ^{r}.$_B$. If all individual p values approximate the theoretical asymptotes over these trials, then for each of the series the individual response proportions should cluster around the mean value, π, with an approximately binomial

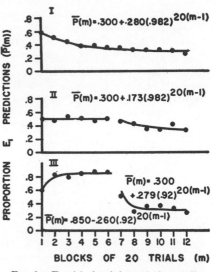

FIG. 1. Empirical and theoretical curves representing mean proportion of E$_1$ predictions (A$_1$ responses) per 20-trial block for each series

distribution. Taking the theoretical σ equal to $\sqrt{40\pi(1-\pi)}$, which is actually a slight underestimate of the true value, we find that approximately half of the scores in each series fall within one σ of the theoretical asymptote and only one score in each series deviates by more than three σ. It appears, then, that except for a few widely deviant cases the p values of individual Ss approach the theoretical asymptote.

One might raise a question as to just what is meant by the asymptote of an empirical curve in a situation of this kind. Naturally one would not expect the Ss to perform at constant rates indefinitely. It does not seem that any sort of breaking point was approached in the present study, however; one subgroup of Group I was run for an additional 60 trials beyond Trial 240 and maintained an average proportion of .304 A$_1$ responses over these trials.

Mean learning curves.—In Fig. 1 mean data are plotted in terms of the proportion of A$_1$ responses per block of

20 trials. The theoretical function which should describe these empirical curves is readily obtained from Equation 4. Letting m be the ordinal number of a block of 20 trials running from Trial $n + 1$ to Trial $n + 20$ inclusive, and $\bar{P}(m)$ the expected proportion of A_1 responses in the block, we can write

$$\bar{P}(m) = \pi$$
$$- \frac{[\pi - \bar{p}(0)](1 - \theta)^{20(m-1)}}{20\,\theta}$$
$$[1 - (1 - \theta)^{20}] \qquad (5)$$

this expression being simply the mean value of $p(n)$ over the mth block of 20 trials. According to theory, Equation 5 should describe each of the mean curves of Fig. 1 once numerical values are substituted for the parameters π, $\bar{p}(0)$, and θ; furthermore, the value of θ required should not differ among groups within either series and should be constant from series to series for each group. The values of π are of course fixed by the experimental procedure. The values of $\bar{p}(0)$ in the first series should be in the neighborhood of .50, but for groups of size 16 sampling deviations could be quite large so it will be best to get rid of $\bar{p}(0)$ in favor of $\bar{P}(1)$ which can be measured more accurately. To do this we write Equation 5 for $m = 1$

$$\bar{P}(1) = \pi$$
$$- \frac{[\pi - \bar{p}(0)]}{20\,\theta} [1 - (1 - \theta)^{20}]$$

then solve for $[\pi - \bar{p}(0)]$

$$[\pi - \bar{p}(0)] = \frac{20\,\theta\,[\pi - \bar{P}(1)]}{1 - (1 - \theta)^{20}}$$

and substitute this result into Equation 5 giving

$$\bar{P}(m) = \pi$$
$$- [\pi - \bar{P}(1)](1 - \theta)^{20(m-1)}. \qquad (6)$$

Observed values of $\bar{P}(1)$ turn out to be .58 and .59 for Series I_A and III_A,

respectively. Now we lack only empirical estimates of θ and these can be obtained by a simple statistical procedure. The method we have used is to sum Equation 6 over all values of m, obtaining for K blocks of trials

$$\sum_{m=1}^{K} \pi - [\pi - \bar{P}(1)](1 - \theta)^{20(m-1)}$$
$$= K\,\pi - [\pi - \bar{P}(1)]$$
$$\frac{[1 - (1 - \theta)^{20K}]}{1 - (1 - \theta)^{20}} \qquad (7)$$

then equate Equation 7 to the sum of the observed proportions for a given series and solve for θ. For Group I we obtain the estimate $\theta = .018$ and for III_A, $\theta = .08$. Using these parameter values we have computed the theoretical curves for Group I and for the first series of Group III, which may be seen in Fig. 1. In this analysis we find agreement between data and theory in one respect but not in another. The theoretical curves provide reasonably good descriptions of the observed points, especially in the case of Group I, but the θ values for the two groups are by no means equal. The latter finding does not come as a surprise inasmuch as we had found in the previous section that Group I was significantly short of its theoretical asymptote in the first series, while Group III was not.

We did not try to estimate a θ value for the first series of Group II since the empirical curve is virtually horizontal and closely approximates the line $\bar{P}(m) = \pi = .50$. We could proceed to estimate θ values for Series II_B and III_B by the method used above, but it will be of more interest to construct predicted curves for these series without using any additional information from the data. According to the theory, it should be possible to compute those curves from information already at our disposal. The $\bar{p}(0)$ values in the second series should be

TABLE 3

PREDICTED AND OBSERVED MEAN FREQUENCIES
OF THE A_1 RESPONSE IN THE
SECOND SERIES

Group	Observed	Predicted	t
I	37.19	37.74	0.22
II	46.00	45.94	0.02
III	42.75	42.86	0.04
F	3.16 $(p > .05)$		

the theoretical asymptotes of the first series, or .50 and .85 for Groups II and III, respectively. The only procedural difference between I_A and II_B lies in the number of preceding reinforcements; according to the statistical model, however, this variable will be expected to have no effect except insofar as it leads to a change in $\bar{p}(0)$, so except for sampling error the θ value estimated for Group I should be applicable to II_B. Using .50, .30, and .018 as the values of $\bar{p}(0)$, π, and θ, respectively, we have computed a theoretical curve for Series II_B, and this is plotted in Fig. 1. Similarly, the θ value estimated for Series III_A should apply also to III_B, and we have used this value, .08, together with .30 for π and .85 for $\bar{p}(0)$ to compute the predicted curve for III_B shown in Fig. 1. Considering that no degrees of freedom in the Series B data have been utilized in curve fitting, the correspondence between the theoretical and

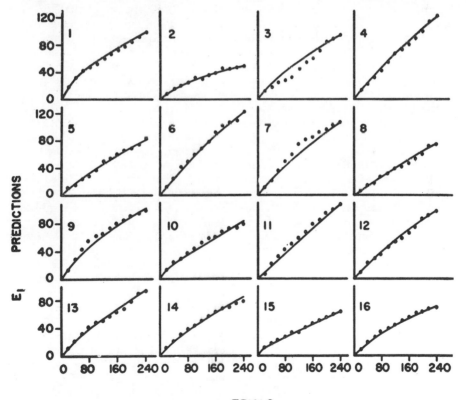

TRIALS

FIG. 2. Empirical and theoretical cumulative response curves for individual Ss of Group I

empirical curves does not seem bad. The reason for some of the irregularities will be brought out in the next section. A statistical test of one aspect of the correspondence can be obtained by calculating for each theoretical curve a predicted mean total of A_1 responses in the second series, by means of Equation 5, and comparing these values with the observed mean totals. This has been done and the comparison is given in Table 3. The t values for differences between observed and theoretical values seem satisfactorily low.

In order to give an idea of the extent to which the behavior of individual Ss conforms to the theoretical function, we have plotted in Fig. 2 the individual cumulative response curves for all Ss of Group I. The cumulative form was chosen for the smoothing effect, some of the noncumulative curves being too irregular for curve-fitting purposes. The theoretical curves in Fig. 2 represent Equation 7 with θ values obtained by a method of approximation. Ten of the curves are fitted quite well by this function with $\pi = .30$ as the asymptote parameter. Four curves, Numbers 2, 11, 15, 16, require other values for this parameter, viz., .075, .45, .24, and .18, respectively. Curves 3 and 4 deviate considerably from the theoretical form. In general, it appears that the empirical curves for most individual Ss can be described quite satisfactorily by the theoretical function, and this fact gives us some basis for inferring that in this situation mean learning curves for groups of Ss reflect the trend of individual learning uncomplicated by any gross artifacts of averaging.

The effect of 120 reinforcements at a π value of .50 may be evaluated by comparing curve forms and mean A_1 response totals for Series I_A and II_B. We find that the reinforcements lead to no increase in resistance to change. Slopes of the two curves are very similar and the response totals do not differ significantly. This result is in line with predictions from the statistical model, but a little surprising, perhaps, from the viewpoint of Thorndikian or Hullian reinforcement theory since partial reinforcement has generally (6) been held to increase resistance to extinction in this situation.

The conclusions from our study of the mean learning curves would seem to be (a) that under some circumstances at least it is possible to evaluate theoretical parameters from the data of one series of learning trials and then to predict the course of learning in a new series; and (b) that the rate at which the mean learning curve approaches its asymptote depends, in an as yet incompletely specified manner, upon the difference between initial response probability and the probability of reinforcement obtaining during the series.

Sequence effects.—The mean curves studied in the preceding section may not reflect adequately all of the learning that went on during the experiment. The irregularities in some of the mean curves of Fig. 1 might be accounted for if there is a significant tendency for Ss' response sequences to follow the vagaries of the sequences of E_1's and E_2's. To check on this possibility we have plotted in Fig. 3 the mean proportions of A_1 responses vs. frequencies of E_1 occurrences per 10-trial block for all groups in Series B. In preparing this graph, the 120 trials of Series B were divided into 12 successive blocks of 10. Since there were 48 Ss, there were 576 of these trial blocks and they were classified according to the number of E_1 occurrences in a block. Then for the set of all blocks in which no E_1's occurred, the mean proportion of A_1 responses was computed and entered as the first point in Fig. 3, and so on for the remaining points. It seems clear that Ss were responding to the particular sequences of E_1's and E_2's, and not simply to the over-all rate. Corresponding graphs for the three groups in the first series had somewhat shallower slopes; they have not been reported since some of the individual points were based on too few cases to be reliable and the groups could not be averaged together in the first series owing to the different π values.

In order to deal statistically with this apparent dependence of response tendency upon the density of E_1 occurrences in the immediately preceding sequence, we have computed for each series the average probability, $\bar{p}_{A_1|E_1}$, that an A_1 occurs on Trial n given that an E_1 occurs on Trial $n - 1$ and the average probability, $\bar{p}_{A_1|E_2}$, that an A_1 occurs on Trial n given that an E_2 occurs on Trial $n - 1$. The difference between these two quantities can be shown to be proportional to the point correlation (7) between $A(n)$ and $E(n - 1)$ for a given series. Furthermore our Equations 1 and 2 may be regarded as theoretical expressions for the two conditional proba-

TABLE 4
Mean Differences between Observed Values of $\bar{p}_{A_1E_1}$ and $\bar{p}_{A_1E_2}$ for Each Series

Series	Group I	Group II	Group III
A	.128	.199	.153
B	.214	.294	.231

bilities, $p_{A_1|E_1}$ and $p_{A_1|E_2}$, respectively, and it will be seen that if these expressions are averaged over all values of n in a series and the second subtracted from the first, the difference is equal to the parameter θ, i.e.,

$$(1 - \theta)\bar{p}(n) + \theta - (1 - \theta)\bar{p}(n) = \theta.$$

Thus from the statistical model we must predict that the difference between empirical estimates of these conditional probabilities for any series should be positive and, if successive trials are independent, this difference should be equal to the value of θ estimated from the mean response curve. The conditional probabilities have been computed from the data for each S and mean differences by groups are summarized in Table 4.

All of the differences are positive and significant at better than the .001 level of confidence. The differences among group means are insignificant for both series (F's equal to .45 and .73, respectively) as are differences among subgroup means. The increases from the first series to the second are, however, significant beyond the .005 level. The latter effect was not anticipated on theoretical grounds; the most plausible explanation that has occurred to us is that alternation tendencies associated with previously established guessing habits extinguished during the early part of the experiment. This hypothesis would also account for the high $\bar{P}(1)$ value observed for Group I in Fig. 1.

Although all of the quantities in Table 4 are positive and apparently

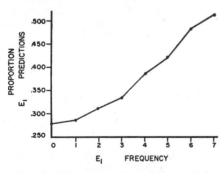

Fig. 3. Mean proportion of E_1 predictions (A_1 responses) in a block of ten trials plotted against the actual number of E_1 occurrences in the block; data averaged for all groups in Series B

independent of π, as required by the theory, the numerical values are all larger than the θ estimates obtained from mean response curves. The most straightforward interpretation of this disparity would be that, owing to the short intertrial interval, successive trials are not independent in the sense required by the theoretical model. Nonindependence would have at least two immediate consequences in so far as the present experiment is concerned. First, stimulus samples drawn on successive trials would overlap, and the learning that occurred on one trial would affect behavior on the next to a greater extent than random sampling would allow for, thus increasing $\bar{p}_{A_1E_1}$, and decreasing $\bar{p}_{A_1E_2}$. Second, the reinforcing stimulus of one trial, E_1 or E_2, would be part of the stimulus complex effective at the beginning of the next trial. If this interpretation is correct, then more widely spaced trials should result in better agreement between the alternative estimates of θ and also in reduction of the dependence of mean learning rate upon probability of reinforcement.

SUMMARY

Learning rates, asymptotic behavior, and sequential properties of response in a verbal conditioning situation were studied in relation to predictions from statistical learning theory.

Forty-eight college students were run in an individualized modification of the "verbal conditioning" experiment originated by Humphreys (4). Each trial consisted in presentation of a signal followed by a left-hand or right-hand "reinforcing" light; S operated an appropriate key to indicate his prediction as to which light would appear on each trial. For each S one of the lights, selected randomly, was designated as E_1, the other as E_2. On the first series of 120 trials, E_1 occurred with probability .30, .50, and .85 for Groups I, II, and III, respectively. On the second 120 trials, E_1 occurred with probability .30 for all groups.

Theoretical predictions were that mean probability of predicting E_1 should tend asymptotically to the actual probability of E_1, both during original learning and following a shift in probability of reinforcement; and that response probabilities should change in accordance with exponential functions, learning rates (as measured by slope parameters) being independent of both initial condition and probability of reinforcement.

The statistical criterion for approach to theoretical asymptote was met by Group I by the end of the second series and by Group III in both first and second series. In the second series, Group II was short of theoretical asymptote but reached the same response probability as had Group I during the first series.

Learning rates were virtually identical for Group I, first series, and Group II, second series, indicating that resistance of response probability to change is not altered by 50% random reinforcement in this situation. Learning rates differed significantly among groups within both series. In general, learning rate was directly related to difference between initial response probability and probability of reinforcement during a series. It was suggested that this relationship may depend upon temporal massing of trials. Not only group means, but individual learning curves could be described satisfactorily by theoretical functions.

No tendency was observed for Ss to respond to a series as a whole. On the contrary, sensitivity to effects of individual reinforcements and nonreinforcements (E_1 and E_2 occurrences) increased significantly as a function of trials.

REFERENCES

1. ESTES, W. K. Toward a statistical theory of learning. *Psychol. Rev.*, 1950, **57**, 94–107.
2. ESTES, W. K., & BURKE, C. J. A theory of stimulus variability in learning. *Psychol. Rev.*, 1953, **60**, 276–286.
3. GRANT, D. A., HAKE, H. W., & HORNSETH, J. P. Acquisition and extinction of a verbal conditioned response with differing percentages of reinforcement. *J. exp. Psychol.*, 1951, **42**, 1–5.
4. HUMPHREYS, L. G. Acquisition and extinction of verbal expectations in a situation analogous to conditioning. *J. exp. Psychol.*, 1939, **25**, 294–301.
5. JARVIK, M. E. Probability learning and a negative recency effect in the serial anticipation of alternative symbols. *J. exp. Psychol.*, 1951, **41**, 291–297.
6. JENKINS, W. O., & STANLEY, J. C. Partial reinforcement: a review and critique. *Psychol. Bull.*, 1950, **47**, 193–234.
7. McNEMAR, Q. *Psychological statistics.* New York: Wiley, 1949.

(Received July 10, 1953)

AN INVESTIGATION OF SOME MATHEMATICAL MODELS FOR LEARNING [1]

CURT F. FEY [2]

University of Pennsylvania

In this study an attempt is made to determine whether the results of two different learning experiments can be described by stochastic models proposed by Bush and Mosteller (1955) and Luce (1959) without changing the model parameters.

The merit of a model lies in its ability to describe and predict data successfully with the aid of a minimum of free parameters. For any one experiment this can be done with several models. Consequently a more stringent test of a model is its ability to predict the fine structure of the data with one invariant set of parameters in such a way that once the values of the parameters are determined in one experiment these same parameters can be used to predict the outcome of another experiment.

Galanter and Bush (1959) previously studied parameter invariance in the linear model of Bush and Mosteller (1955). Their analysis showed an apparent lack of parameter invariance in a T-maze situation, but it is not clear whether the lack of parameter invariance was attributable to a basic mechanism in the model or was a consequence of sampling errors and difficulties in estimating parameters.

The purpose of the present study is to investigate this question of parameter invariance in greater detail. The experimental design was improved over that of Galanter and Bush (1959) by running only one rather than three trials per day, and it was extended to provide a comparison between 100% reinforcement and 75% random reinforcement.

THE MODELS

The two models used in this paper may be designated as the alpha model (Bush & Mosteller, 1955) and the beta model (Luce, 1959). Each of them uses linear transformations. In the alpha model the linear transformation is applied to the response probability p; in the beta model it is applied to the quantity $p/(1 - p)$.

Both of these models are stochastic, i.e., they deal with probabilities of making responses. The models are path-independent: the response probability on a given trial depends only on the response probability and the outcome on the previous trial.

An animal in a T maze can turn either to the left or to the right on any given trial. The models state that if on one trial S makes a response for which it gets rewarded, then the probability of making that same response on the next trial increases. The models specify the manner of these changes.

Let p_n be the probability of going to the right-hand side (probability of an "error") on trial n; let $q_n = 1 - p_n$; let $\alpha_1, \alpha_2, \beta_1$ and β_2 be nonnegative parameters such that α_1 and β_1 are associated with reward and α_2 and β_2 are associated with nonreward. The models can then be defined in the following way:

[1] Based on the author's PhD dissertation supervised by R. R. Bush, and read by R. D. Luce and J. Beck. The data analysis was performed at the Computer Center of the University of Pennsylvania with the assistance of S. Gorn and P. Z. Ingerman.

[2] Now at General Dynamics/Electronics, Rochester, New York.

This article appeared in *J. exp. Psychol.*, 1961, **61**, 455–461. Reprinted with permission.

Alpha Model	*Response*	*Outcome*	*Beta Model*
$p_{n+1} = \alpha_1 p_n$	left turn	reward	$p_{n+1} = \dfrac{p_n}{p_n + \beta_1(1 - p_n)}$
$p_{n+1} = \alpha_2 p_n$	right turn	nonreward	$p_{n+1} = \dfrac{p_n}{p_n + \beta_2(1 - p_n)}$
$q_{n+1} = \alpha_1 q_n$	right turn	reward	$p_{n+1} = \dfrac{\beta_1 p_n}{\beta_1 p_n + 1 - p_n}$
$q_{n+1} = \alpha_2 q_n$	left turn	nonreward	$p_{n+1} = \dfrac{\beta_2 p_n}{\beta_2 p_n + 1 - p_n}$

Mathematical properties of the alpha model were listed by Galanter and Bush (1959, pp. 272–273) for the special condition that a left response is always rewarded and a right-hand response is never rewarded, (100:0). For the beta model the mathematical properties have been determined by Kanal (1960, 1961), Bush, Galanter, and Luce (1959, p. 387), and Bush (1960).

METHOD[3]

Subjects.—The Ss were male hooded rats of the Long-Evans strain, from Rockland Farms, New York City, New York. They weighed about 75 gm. on arrival. Eight rats were used for the preliminary experiment. In the main experiment 63 rats were used, but the final $N = 50$, because 13 died during the experiment.

[3] For details see Fey, 1960.

TABLE 1

PERIOD 2, 100:0 GROUP

COMPARISON OF STATISTICS FROM THE FIRST 35 TRIALS OF EXPERIMENTAL GROUP WITH CORRESPONDING MODEL VALUES CALCULATED WITH $p_1 = 1$, $\alpha_1 = .858$, AND $\alpha_2 = .955$ FOR ALPHA MODEL AND $p_1 = .97$, $\beta_1 = .952$, AND $\beta_2 = .642$, FOR BETA MODEL

Statistic	Means			Standard Errors		
	Exp.	α Model	β Model	Exp.	α Model	β Model
Number of Ss	25	100	500			
Number of trials	35	35	35			
Total number of errors	12.28	12.28	12.39	.76	.00	.012
Trial of last error	23.16	22.10	26.45	1.00	.25	.028
Trial of first success	6.88	6.87	6.49	.48	.00	.024
Number of RR sequences	7.48	7.32	7.01	.56	.00	.014
RL	4.76	4.85	5.32	.28	.09	.016
LR	3.80	3.85	4.41	.28	.10	.014
LL	17.96	17.98	17.26	.80	.22	.024
Number of L runs of:						
Length 1	2.00	1.81	1.86	.20	.10	.012
2	.56	.81	.87	.08	.03	.014
3	.44	.51	.57	.08	.03	.006
4	.32	.37	.38	.04	.04	.006
5	.08	.28	.30	.04	.02	.004
Number of R runs of:						
Length 1	2.60	2.70	3.12	.24	.00	.014
2	.80	.81	.83	.16	.00	.008
3	.40	.40	.36	.08	.00	.006
4	.24	.27	.28	.04	.00	.008
5	.20	.20	.20	.04	.00	.004
Total number of R runs	4.80	4.96	5.38	.28	.00	.018

Note.—Standard error of the mean was computed from range approximation.

TABLE 2

PERIOD 2, 75:25 GROUP

COMPARISON OF STATISTICS OF 75:25 EXPERIMENTAL GROUP WITH CORRESPONDING
MODEL VALUES CALCULATED WITH $p_1 = 1$, $\alpha_1 = .858$, AND $\alpha_2 = .955$ FOR
ALPHA MODEL AND $p_1 = .97$, $\beta_1 = .952$, AND $\beta_2 = .642$
FOR BETA MODEL

Statistic	Means			Standard Errors		
	Exp.	α Model	β Model	Exp.	α Model	β Model
Number of animals	25	100	200			
Total number of errors	15.92	19.21	19.43	1.04	.22	.03
Trial of last error	27.32	32.71	33.59	1.04	.21	.045
Trial of first success	7.52	7.19	7.56	.64	.16	.07
Number of RR sequences	10.24	11.85	11.81	.88	.25	.045
RL	5.44	7.09	7.33	.28	.10	.035
LR	4.68	6.37	6.75	.32	.09	.035
LL	13.64	8.69	8.11	1.12	.24	.08
Number of L runs of:						
Length 1	2.48	3.63	3.55	.20	.10	.045
2	1.16	1.62	1.68	.20	.05	.03
3	.40	.77	1.09	.08	.03	.02
4	.24	.41	.52	.04	.02	.015
5	.16	.23	.21	.04	.02	.01
Number of R runs of:						
Length 1	2.88	3.52	3.70	.20	.10	.035
2	1.16	1.50	1.63	.12	.05	.03
3	.48	.66	.79	.12	.04	.015
4	.36	.54	.47	.08	.03	.02
5	.20	.38	.29	.08	.02	.01
Total number of R runs	5.68	7.36	7.62	.32	.09	.035

Note.—The model parameters were estimated from the 100.0 group. Standard error was computed from range approximation.

Apparatus.—The T maze was a replica of that used by Galanter and Bush (1959). It consisted of a straight alley runway for pretraining and a T maze for the main experiment. The T maze was built in such a way that the crossbar and the start arm of the T could be separated and a goalbox could be hooked to the stem of the T, thereby changing the maze into a straight runway. The maze was built of plywood with a removable wire mesh top and pressed wood doors. The inside of the stem and the attachable goalbox were painted medium gray, the right arm was painted light gray, and the left, dark gray. The length of the cross arm was 60 in., the length of the stem was 26 in., and the attachable goalbox was 10 in. The alleys were 4 in. wide and the walls were 8 in. high. The starting compartment was 10 in. long with a guillotine door on the maze side and a hinged door on the outside. Another guillotine door was at the choice point. The goal cups were placed at the end of each arm. The metal goal cups had double floors, the bottom part contained inaccessible wet food mash to balance olfactory cues, and the top contained the reward pellet.

Procedure.—This experiment consisted of three parts: (a) preliminary handling; (b) straight alley pretraining; and (c) T-maze learning.

The Ss were kept in the laboratory for 23 days at ad lib. food and water and were handled daily. Then Ss were deprived of food for 18, 21, 21½, 21¾, and 22 hr. on Days 24, 25, 26, 27, and 28, respectively.

The pretraining started on Day 29. For the remainder of the experiment Ss were under 18 hr. food deprivation at the beginning of each daily run. They were fed 4 hr. later for a 2-hr. period. Water was always available in the cages.

The Ss were given one trial per day of pretraining on the straight alley runway. Pretraining lasted for three days.

During the 30 days of Period 1 of the T-maze learning, the following procedure was adhered to: .038-gm. pellet was deposited in the right goal cup; nothing was placed in the left goal cup. The S was placed in the startbox and the startbox door was raised. As S passed the choice point, its door was lowered. The S was left in the maze until it ate the pellet, until it investigated the goal cup (on the nonrewarded side), or until 3 min. were up, whichever occurred first.

At the end of Period 1 Ss were divided at random into two groups. One group was always rewarded on the left side during Period 2, and the other was rewarded according to the following schedule obtained from a random number table with $P(L) = 0.75$: L L L R L L R L L R L L L L L R L R L L L L L R L L R R R R L L L L L L. Period 2 lasted for 35 days.

Estimation of parameters.—The parameters of the alpha model were estimated in the following way: The initial probability p_1 was taken to be 1.00. The other two parameters were estimated from the Period 2 data of the 100:0 group by equating the observed mean number of trials before the first success and the observed mean total number of errors to their respective expected values.

Initial estimates of the beta model parameters were determined by methods similar to those used for finding the alpha model parameters. These estimates were modified by exploration of the parameter space until the response probabilities (Monte Carlo computations) were similar to the experimental data of the 100:0 group. The following criteria were used: the total number of errors generated by the model had to match the data, and a plot of trial-by-trial mean response probabilities produced by the model had to appear similar to the corresponding plot of the data.

RESULTS

The results of the experiment are summarized in Fig. 1 and 2 and Tables 1 and 2. Figure 1 presents the proportions of R response of the 100:0 group during Period 2 and the corresponding curves generated by the models. Figure 2 depicts the same data for the 75:25 group during Period 2. Tables 2 and 1 give

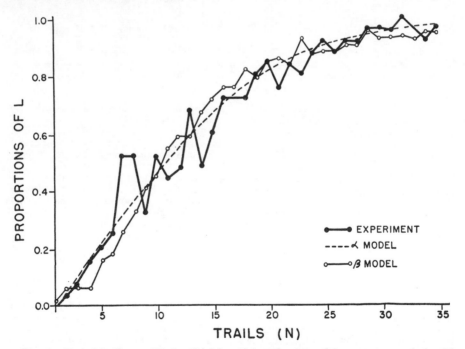

FIG. 1. Period 2, Group 100:0. Trial by trial proportions of L responses made by 25 experimental Ss (filled circles); generated by alpha model (smooth line) computed with $p_1 = 1.00$, $\alpha_1 = 0.858$, and $\alpha_2 = 0.955$; and generated by 500 beta model Monte Carlo analogs (open circles) computed with $p_1 = 0.97$, $\beta_1 = 0.952$, and $\beta_2 = 0.647$.

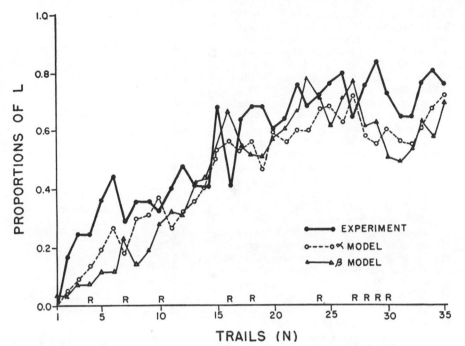

FIG. 2. Period 2, Group 75:75. Trial by trial proportions of L responses made by 25 experimental Ss (filled circles); by 100 alpha model Monte Carlo analogs (open circles) computed with $p_1 = 1.00$, $\alpha_1 = 0.858$, and $\alpha_2 = 0.955$; and by 200 beta model Monte Carlo analogs (triangles) computed with $p_1 = 0.97$, $\beta_1 = 0.952$, and $\beta_2 = 0.647$. (R = food reward is in right maze arm, otherwise the left arm is baited.)

comparative results of this experiment and corresponding model values. A more detailed analysis of results is presented by Fey (1960).

DISCUSSION

The merit of a mathematical model of learning lies not so much in describing the data of any one experiment with the aid of parameters estimated from that particular experiment as in its ability to represent accurately the learning process of a variety of different experimental situations using the *same* set of parameters. In other words once the parameters are estimated for one experimental situation the model should be able to predict the course of learning in other experiments. Models which will handle a variety of experimental situations with the same set of parameters are called *parameter invariant*.

This experiment indicates that the models under consideration fit the Period 2, 100:0 group data, from which their parameters were estimated, quite well, but the fit to the Period 2, 75:25 group data (using parameters estimated from the Period 2, 100:0 group) is less successful. Both models show an apparent lack of parameter invariance of approximately equal magnitude.

Tables 1 and 2 might give the impression that the alpha model fits the data slightly better than the beta model. This conclusion is hardly warranted if the magnitudes of the differences and the methods of estimating the parameters are considered. The alpha model parameters were determined analytically; those of the beta model were estimated by Monte Carlo procedures. Thus the alpha model parameters were determined more exactly than those of the beta model.

The lack of long runs seems to be a basic difficulty of the models. This is of little consequence in 100:0 animal learning, but it does seem to be important in partial reinforcement schedules for animals as well as in human choice behavior (Derks, 1960). This lack of long runs is not generally manifested in mean learning curves, but only in a sequential analysis of the data.

The fact that the 75:25 "stat rats" learn more slowly than the experimental Ss is not as serious as the lack of long runs. A change in the size of the model parameters will correct the former deficiency. The data indicate that by reducing the beta model parameters by about 25%, the total number of errors made by the model analogs will match those of the experimental Ss for the 75:25 group. These reduced parameters decrease the fit to the 100:0 group.

The slow learning of the 75:25 model analogs could be handled by specifying the manner in which the parameters are modified when the schedule changes from 100:0 to 75:25. With respect to the lack of perseverance, no small change in parameter values would increase the fit of model to data.

Galanter and Bush (1959) noted in three of their experiments that the probability of turning to the more frequently rewarded side tended to decrease slightly during the first few acquisition trials before it began to rise. This phenomenon occurs also in other experi-

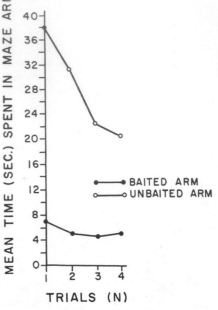

FIG. 4. Trial by trial distribution of time spent in baited, left (filled circles) and unbaited, right (open circles) maze arm by 50 Ss of Period 1.

mental situations (Gibson & Walk, 1956; Jensen, 1960; Kendler & Lachman, 1958). In the present experiment, the initial dip is hardly noticeable.

A look at the time the rats spent in the baited and in the unbaited arms of the maze (Fig. 3 and 4) indicates that initially our Ss and those of the Galanter and Bush (1959) Exp. III[4] were removed more quickly from the unbaited than from the baited side of the maze; later in the experiment, removal occurred after approximately the same time interval in either arm of the maze. The reason for this is found in the criteria for removing S from the maze: S is left in the maze until it investigates the food cup on the unbaited side, until it eats the pellet on the baited side, or until 3 min. are up, whichever occurs first. The Ss investigate the food cup on the

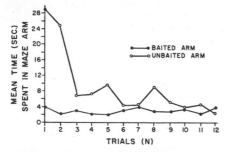

FIG. 3. Trial by trial distribution of time spent in baited, left (filled circles) and unbaited, right (open circles) maze arm by 20 Ss of Galanter and Bush (1959) Exp. III.

[4] The data plotted in Fig. 3 were obtained from the original protocols of the experiment reported by Galanter and Bush (1959).

baited side before they start eating the pellet. In fact, S may take a pellet in its mouth, drop it, and not eat it; thus investigation of the food cup occurs before the eating (Fig. 3 and 4).

Should S initially prefer removal from the maze to eating the pellet, the non-rewarded side may actually be more attractive to S than the rewarded side, since S has to stay in the nonrewarded side for a shorter period of time. The Ss behave initially as if they were much more interested in escaping from the maze than in eating. As S becomes accustomed to the experimental situation, interest in escaping decreases and the food pellet gradually becomes more attractive.

This explanation can handle the dip in our experiment, but it fails in the case of other experiments such as a Skinner-box situation.

SUMMARY

This paper investigated two models for learning: a linear model proposed by Bush and Mosteller and a nonlinear model developed by Luce. Specifically, an attempt was made to determine whether data obtained from two different experimental situations could be described by the models without changing the parameters.

Two groups of rats were trained in a T maze. One group was always rewarded with food on one side; the other group received a food reward with probability .75 on one side and .25 on the other side. Model statistics were computed for both groups, using parameters estimated from the group that was always rewarded on the same side, and compared with the experimental data.

It was found that there is good agreement between the models and the data of the continuously reinforced group, from which the model parameters were estimated. The fit to the data of the partially reinforced group, however, leaves something to be desired.

Both models fit the data about equally well.

REFERENCES

BUSH, R. R. Some properties of Luce's beta model for learning. In K. J. Arrow, S. Karlin, & P. Suppes (Eds.), *Proceedings of the first Stanford symposium on mathematical methods in the social sciences.* Stanford, Calif.: Stanford Univer. Press, 1960.

BUSH, R. R., GALANTER, E., & LUCE, R. D. Tests of the "beta model." In R. R. Bush & W. K. Estes (Eds.), *Studies in mathematical learning theory.* Stanford, Calif.: Stanford Univer. Press, 1959.

BUSH, R. R., & MOSTELLER, R. *Stochastic models for learning.* New York: Wiley, 1955.

DERKS, P. Human binary prediction and the "conditioning axiom" under temporal, incentive, contingency, and experimental variations. Unpublished doctoral dissertation, University of Pennsylvania, 1960.

FEY, C. F. Parameter invariance in models for learning. Unpublished doctoral dissertation, University of Pennsylvania, 1960.

GALANTER, E., & BUSH, R. R. Some T-maze experiments. In R. R. Bush & W. K. Estes (Eds.), *Studies in mathematical learning theory.* Stanford, Calif.: Stanford Univer. Press, 1959.

GIBSON, E. J., & WALK, R. D. The effect of prolonged exposure to visually presented patterns on learning to discriminate them. *J. comp. physiol. Psychol.*, 1956, **49**, 239–242.

JENSEN, G. D. Learning and performance as functions of ration size, hours of privation, and effort requirement. *J. exp. Psychol.*, 1960, **59**, 261–268.

KANAL, L. Analysis of some stochastic processes arising from a learning model. Unpublished docotral dissertation, University of Pennsylvania, 1960.

KANAL, L. On a random walk related to a nonlinear learning model. *IRE Nat. convention Rec.*, 1961, in press.

KENDLER, H. H., & LACHMAN, R. Habit reversal as a function of schedule of reinforcement and drive strength. *J. exp. Psychol.*, 1958, **55**, 584–591.

LUCE, R. D. *Individual choice behavior: A theoretical analysis.* New York: Wiley, 1959.

(Early publication received December 6, 1960)

A FUNCTIONAL EQUATION ANALYSIS OF TWO LEARNING MODELS*

Laveen Kanal†

GENERAL DYNAMICS/ELECTRONICS

ROCHESTER, NEW YORK

One-absorbing barrier random walks arising from Luce's nonlinear beta model for learning and a linear commuting-operator model (called the alpha model) are considered. Functional equations for various statistics are derived from the branching processes defined by the two models. Solutions to general functional equations, satisfied by statistics of the alpha and beta models, are obtained. The methods presented have application to other learning models.

The two-response, two-event, path-independent, contingent version of a number of stochastic models for learning is given by the equations

$$(1) \qquad p_{n+1} = \begin{cases} Q_1 p_n & \text{with probability } p_n \\ Q_2 p_n & \text{with probability } (1 - p_n), \end{cases}$$

where Q_1 and Q_2 represent transition operators, and p_n and $(1 - p_n)$ are, respectively, the probabilities of responses A_1 and A_2 on trial n. A linear model discussed by Bush and Mosteller [8] is obtained when the operators in (1) are defined by the equations

$$(2) \qquad \begin{aligned} Q_1 p_n &= \alpha_1 p_n & (0 \leq \alpha_1 \leq 1), \\ Q_2 p_n &= \alpha_2 p_n & (0 \leq \alpha_2 \leq 1). \end{aligned}$$

In this paper, this linear model is called the "alpha" model. A specialization of the nonlinear "beta" model proposed by Luce [13] is obtained when the operators are defined by the equations:

$$(3) \qquad Q_i p_n = \frac{\beta_i p_n}{1 + (\beta_i - 1)p_n}, \qquad i = 1, 2; \qquad \beta_i > 0; \qquad 0 \neq p_1 \neq 1.$$

In terms of the variable $v_n = p_n/(1 - p_n)$ the transition equations for this

*Abstracted from portions of the author's doctoral dissertation, University of Pennsylvania, June 1960. The author is indebted to Robert R. Bush, his dissertation supervisor for the valuable help and encouragement received from him and to R. Duncan Luce for many helpful discussions and for partial support from an NSF grant.

†Formerly at the Moore School of Electrical Engineering, University of Pennsylvania, Philadelphia, Pa. The author is grateful to J. G. Brainerd, S. Gorn, and C. N. Weygandt of the Moore School, and N. F. Finkelstein, D. Parkhill and A. A. Wolf of General Dynamics for their encouragement.

This article appeared in *Psychometrika*, 1962, **27**, 89–104. Reprinted with permission.

version of the beta model are

$$
(4) \qquad v_{n+1} = \begin{cases} \beta_1 v_n & \text{with probability } p_n \\ \beta_2 v_n & \text{with probability } (1 - p_n), \end{cases}
$$

where

$$
0 < v < \infty; \qquad \beta_i > 0; \qquad i = 1, 2.
$$

In the beta model response probabilities undergo nonlinear rather than linear transformations from trial to trial. Since the probabilities of choice inevitably enter into the derivation of stochastic properties of the model, the methods generally used to derive properties of linear learning models do not apply to the beta model.

Analytical methods applicable to both the alpha and beta models are presented in this paper. The approach used is to consider the branching process defined by the decision rules of the two models, and from it to formulate functional equations for various statistics of interest. Tatsuoka and Mosteller [15] used a functional equation approach to obtain some statistics for the alpha model. Their techniques differ somewhat from those presented here; the approach developed here leads to a unified method of attack for the alpha and beta models and can be extended to others.

Some Random Walks Arising from the Beta Model

In (4), $\beta_i > 1$ and $\beta_i < 1$ may be identified, respectively, with reward and nonreward of the response. If response A_1 is never rewarded and response A_2 is always rewarded $\beta_1 < 1, \beta_2 < 1$. If both responses are always rewarded $\beta_1 > 1, \beta_2 < 1$. If neither response is ever rewarded $\beta_1 < 1, \beta_2 > 1$. It is shown in [11] that these three cases lead to one-absorbing-barrier (OAB), two-absorbing-barrier (TAB), and two-reflecting-barrier (TRB) walks. Rigorous proof of the nature of the barriers for these and other random walks resulting from the two-alternative, two-outcome beta model is given by Lamperti and Suppes [12]. Only the OAB beta model ($\beta_1 \leq 1, \beta_2 \leq 1$) is considered in this paper. Except for the case when $\alpha_i = 1$, in the alpha model either response diminishes the probability of response A_1; the alpha model is a one-absorbing-barrier model.

Functional Equations for Statistics of the One-Absorbing Barrier Models

The OAB alpha and beta models lead to an asymptotic distribution of p_n which has all its density at $p = 0$. (Considering response A_1 as an error on the part of organisms which are learning, this means that all organisms eventually learn not to make errors). Additional information about the processes is obtained from various statistics. Following the work of Bush and Sternberg [9] on a simple single-operator model, the statistics considered are those which describe the rate of approach to the asymptote, such as the mean, weighted mean, and variance of the rate of approach; sequential statistics concerning runs of responses; other statistics, such as those describing the first occurrence of an A_2 response (success) and the last occurrence of an A_1 response (failure). Functional equations satisfied by these statistics are derived by considering the branching processes shown in Fig. 1.

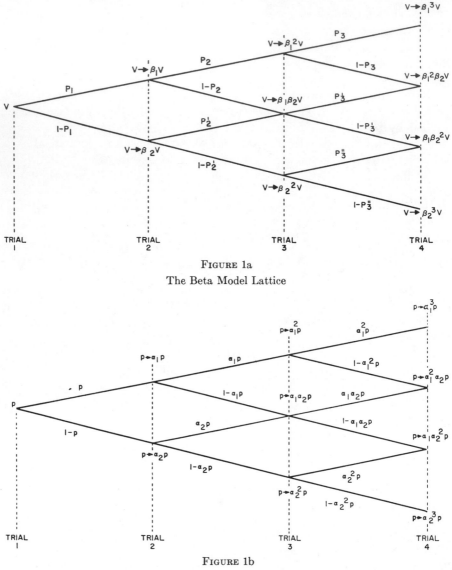

FIGURE 1a

The Beta Model Lattice

FIGURE 1b

The Alpha Model Lattice

For the analysis which follows, a sequence x_1, x_2, $\cdots$, x_n of random variables is defined such that

$$x_n = \begin{cases} 1 \text{ if response } A_1 \text{ occurs on trial } n \\ 0 \text{ if response } A_2 \text{ occurs on trial } n. \end{cases}$$

The random variables have expectations p_n.

The mean number of A_1 responses

In terms of the random variables x_n, the total number of A_1 responses in N trials is given by the random variable $X_N = \sum_{n=1}^{N} x_n$ with expectation $E(X_N) = \sum_{n=1}^{N} p_n$. In the one-absorbing barrier models, both responses decrease the probability of response A_1 and

$$E(X) = \lim_{N \to \infty} E(X_N)$$

is of interest. In fact, by replacing the parameters of the models by $\beta = \max (\beta_1, \beta_2)$ and $\alpha = \max (\alpha_1, \alpha_2)$ finite upper bounds for $E(X)$ in the two models are obtained. Now the number X_N of A_1 responses in N trials starting from trial 1 will be equal to the number, X_{N-1}, of A_1 responses in $(N - 1)$ trials starting from trial 2 if the result of trial 1 is an A_2 response and be equal to $1 + X_{N-1}$ if the result of trial 1 is an A_1 response. Letting ϕ denote the expected number of A_1 responses, the functional equations for ϕ are obtained from Fig. 1 to be

$$\phi_\beta(v, N) = p_1[1 + \phi_\beta(\beta_1 v, N - 1)] + (1 - p_1)\phi_\beta(\beta_2 v, N - 1)$$

$$= \frac{v}{1 + v} [\phi_\beta(\beta_1 v, N - 1) + 1] + \frac{1}{1 + v} \phi_\beta(\beta_2 v, N - 1),$$

and

$$\phi_\alpha(p, N) = p[\phi_\alpha(\alpha_1 p, N - 1) + 1] + (1 - p)\phi_\alpha(\alpha_2 p, N - 1).$$

When $N \to \infty$ these equations become

$$(5) \qquad \phi_\beta(v) = \frac{v}{1 + v} \phi_\beta(\beta_1 v) + \frac{1}{1 + v} \phi_\beta(\beta_2 v) + \frac{v}{1 + v},$$

$$(6) \qquad \phi_\alpha(p) = p\phi_\alpha(\alpha_1 p) + (1 - p)\phi_\alpha(\alpha_2 p) + p.$$

Both the above functions must, of course, satisfy the boundary condition $\phi(0) = 0$.

The second moment of the number of A_1 responses

Letting θ denote $E(X_N^2)$ the functional equations for the second moment are then, as $N \to \infty$,

$$(7) \qquad \theta_\beta(v) = \frac{v}{1 + v} \theta_\beta(\beta_1 v) + \frac{1}{1 + v} \theta_\beta(\beta_2 v) + \frac{v}{1 + v} [1 + 2\phi_\beta(\beta_1 v)],$$

(8) $\theta_\alpha(p) = p\theta_\alpha(\alpha_1 p) + (1 - p)\theta_\alpha(\alpha_2 p) + p[1 + 2\phi_\alpha(\alpha_1 p)].$

$\theta(0) = 0$ is a boundary condition. Finite upper bounds exist for $\theta_\beta(v)$ and $\theta_\alpha(p)$; replacing the parameters by $\beta = \max (\beta_1 , \beta_2)$ and $\alpha = \max (\alpha_1 , \alpha_2)$ the variance of X_N is $\sum_{n=1}^{N} p_n(1 - p_n)$ which remains finite as $N \to \infty$ if $\sum_1^N p_n$ does. Functional equations for higher moments are easily obtained in this manner.

The functional equations for the mean and second moment of the number of A_1 responses have been previously obtained by Tatsuoka [14] and Tatsuoka and Mosteller [15]. Their method of derivation is somewhat different from that presented here.

The weighted number of A_1 responses

Define the random variable

$$Y_{\omega,N} = \sum_{n=1}^{N} (n + \omega)x_n .$$

Then $Y_{0,N}$ represents the weighted number of A_1 responses in N trials with the weighting function being the trial number n. From trial 2 on, the weighted number of A_1 responses is $\sum_{n=2}^{N} nx_n$, which by relabeling the random variables $x_2 , x_3 , \cdots$ as $x_1 , x_2 , \cdots$ can be represented by the random variable

$$Y_{1,(N-1)} = \sum_{n=1}^{N-1} (n + 1)x_n = Y_{0,N-1} + X_{N-1} .$$

If ψ stands for the expectation of the weighted number of A_1 responses, the functional equations are obtained by noting that $Y_{0,N}$ is equal to $Y_{1,N-1}$ if the result of the first trial is an A_2 response and is equal to $(1 + Y_{1,(N-1)})$ if the result of the first trial is an A_1 response. For an infinite number of trials,

(9) $\psi_\beta(v) = \dfrac{v}{1 + v} \psi_\beta(\beta_1 v) + \dfrac{1}{1 + v} \psi_\beta(\beta_2 v) + \phi_\beta(v),$

(10) $\psi_\alpha(p) = p\psi_\alpha(\alpha_1 p) + (1 - p)\psi(\alpha_2 p) + \phi_\alpha(p).$

A boundary condition is $\psi(0) = 0$.

Number of trials before the first A_2 response (success) occurs

Let $F_1 + 1$ denote the trial number on which response A_2 occurs for the first time so that F_1 is the number of trials before the first A_2 . F_1 is equal to zero if A_2 occurs on the first trial and is equal to $(1 + F_2)$, where F_2 denotes the number of trials, before the first A_2 response occurs, starting at trial 2, if trial 1 results in an A_1 response. Letting ν denote the expectation of the random variables F, the functional equations for ν are

(11) $\nu_\beta(v) = p_1[\nu_\beta(\beta_1 v) + 1] + [(1 - p_1)0] = \dfrac{v}{1 + v} \nu_\beta(\beta_1 v) + \dfrac{v}{1 + v} ;$

(12) $$\nu_\alpha(p) = p\nu_\alpha(\alpha_1 p) + p.$$

If ρ denotes the second moment of the random variables F, the functional equations for ρ are

(13) $$\rho_\beta(v) = \frac{v}{1+v}[1 + 2\nu_\beta(\beta_1 v) + \rho_\beta(\beta_1 v)]$$

$$= \frac{v}{1+v}\rho_\beta(\beta_1 v) + \frac{v}{1+v}[1 + 2\nu_\beta(\beta_1 v)];$$

(14) $$\rho_\alpha(p) = p\rho_\alpha(\alpha_1, p) + p[1 + 2\nu(\alpha_1 p)].$$

Trial number at which last A_1 response occurs

Let

$$L_n = \begin{cases} 0 \text{ if no } A_1 \text{ response occurs on, or after trial } n \\ 1 \text{ if the last } A_1 \text{ response occurs on trial } n \\ (N+1) - n \text{ if the last } A_1 \text{ response occurs on trial } N > n. \end{cases}$$

Then the random variable L_1 represents the trial number at which the last A_1 response occurs, and by definition L_1 is zero if no A_1 response occurs on any trial. In the following development, the sequence of responses $A_2 A_2 A_1$ denotes the occurrence of A_2 on the first trial followed by A_2 on the second trial and by A_1 on the third trial. It is evident that

$$L_1 = \begin{cases} L_2 + 1 & \text{if } A_1 \text{ occurs} \\ L_3 + 2 & \text{if } A_2 A_1 \text{ occurs} \\ L_4 + 3 & \text{if } A_2 A_2 A_1 \text{ occurs} \\ L_5 + 4 & \text{if } A_2 A_2 A_2 A_1 \text{ occurs} \\ \text{and so on.} \end{cases}$$

Letting μ denote the expectation of the random variables L, the functional equation for μ_α is developed from Fig. 1. For an infinite number of trials

$$\mu_\alpha(p) = p[\mu_\alpha(\alpha_{1v}) + 1] + (1 - p)\alpha_2 p[\mu_\alpha(\alpha_1\alpha_2 p) + 2]$$
$$+ (1 - p)(1 - \alpha_2 p)\alpha_2^2 p[\mu_\alpha(\alpha_1\alpha_2^2 p) + 3] + \cdots$$
$$= p\mu_\alpha(\alpha_1 p) + p + (1 - p)\alpha_2 p + (1 - p)(1 - \alpha_2 p)\alpha_2^2 p + \cdots$$
$$+ [(1 - p)\alpha_2 p + 2(1 - p)(1 - \alpha_2 p)\alpha_2^2 p$$
$$+ 3(1 - p)(1 - \alpha_2 p)(1 - \alpha_2^2 p)\alpha_2^3 p + \cdots + (1 - p)\alpha_2 p\mu_\alpha(\alpha_1\alpha_2 p)$$
$$+ (1 - p)(1 - \alpha_2 p)\alpha_2^2 p\mu_\alpha(\alpha_1\alpha_2^2 p) + \cdots].$$

But the term in brackets in the last expression is just $(1 - p)\mu_\alpha(\alpha_2 p)$ as may be deduced from the expression for $\mu_\alpha(p)$. Also

$$p + (1 - p)\alpha_2 p + (1 - p)(1 - \alpha_2 p)\alpha_2^2 p + \cdots = 1 - \prod_{i=0}^{\infty}(1 - \alpha_2^i p).$$

A similar development for $\mu_\beta(v)$ results in the functional equations

$$(15) \qquad \mu_\beta(v) = \frac{v}{1+v} \mu_\beta(\beta_1 v) + \frac{1}{1+v} \mu_\beta(\beta_2 v) + 1 - \prod_{i=0}^{\infty} \frac{1}{(1 + \beta_2^i v)} \,,$$

$$(16) \qquad \mu_\alpha(p) = p\mu_\alpha(\alpha_1 p) + (1 - p)\mu_\alpha(\alpha_2 p) + 1 - \prod_{i=0}^{\infty} (1 - \alpha_2^i p),$$

with $\mu(0) = 0$, since for $p = 0$ no A_1 response ever occurs. A different derivation for the mean of the trial number at which the last A_1 response occurs in
the alpha model will be found in Tatsuoka and Mosteller [15].

For the expectation of L_1^2 it is necessary to consider the expectations of
$(L_2 + 1)^2$, etc. Denoting the second moment of the random variables L
by γ the functional equations for γ are

$$(17) \quad \gamma_\beta(v) = \frac{v}{1+v} \gamma_\beta(\beta_1 v) + \frac{1}{1+v} \gamma_\beta(\beta_2 v) + \left[2\mu_\beta(v) + \prod_{i=0}^{\infty} \frac{1}{1 + \beta_2^i v} - 1 \right],$$

and

$$(18) \quad \gamma_\alpha(p) = p\gamma_\alpha(\alpha_1 p) + (1 - p)\gamma_\alpha(\alpha_2 p) + \left[2\mu_\alpha(p) + \prod_{i=0}^{\infty} (1 - \alpha_2^i p) - 1 \right],$$

with $\gamma(0) = 0$. Functional equations for higher moments of L_1 can easily
be generated in the above manner.

Number of runs, of length j, of A_1 responses

The sequence of responses

$$\underbrace{A_1 A_1 A_1 \cdots A_1 A_2}_{j \text{ trials}}$$

is termed a run, of A_1 responses, of length j. Statistics concerning the number
of runs of A_1 responses of length exactly equal to j, and of length greater
than or equal to j $(j = 1, 2 \cdots)$, are of interest. Let $R_{n,j}$ denote the number
of runs of length j, which occur between trial n and the termination of the
process. The total number of runs of length j is then $R_{1,j}$. From the branching
process of Fig. 1 it is seen that $R_{1,j} = R_{n,j} + \delta_{n,j+2}$, where $\delta_{n,j+2}$ is the
Kronecker delta function. Letting σ_j denote the expectation of the number
of runs of length j, the functional equation for $\sigma_{j\beta}$ is developed from the beta
model lattice of Fig. 1(a). For an infinite number of trials

$$\sigma_{j\beta}(v) = \sum_{k=0}^{\infty} \left(\prod_{i=1}^{k} p_i \right)(1 - p_{k+1})[\sigma_{j\beta}(\beta_1^k \beta_2 v) + \delta_{k,j}],$$

where $\delta_{k,j}$ is the Kronecker delta function. Substituting $\sigma_{j\beta}(\beta_1 v)$ for part of
the expression gives,

$$\sigma_{j\beta}(v) = p_1\sigma_{j\beta}(\beta_1 v) + (1 - p_1)\sigma_{j\beta}(\beta_2 v) + \prod_{i=1}^{j} p_i[(1 - p_{i+1}) - p_{i+1}(1 - p_{i+2})].$$

A similar development gives the functional equation for $\sigma_{i\alpha}(p)$. The functional equations are

$$(19) \quad \sigma_{i\beta}(v) = \frac{v}{1+v} \sigma_{i\beta}(\beta_1 v) + \frac{1}{1+v} \sigma_{i\beta}(\beta_2 v)$$

$$+ \prod_{i=1}^{j+1} \left(\frac{\beta_1^{i-1} v}{1 + \beta_1^{i-1} v} \right) \left(\frac{1}{\beta_1^i v} - \frac{1}{1 + \beta_1^{i+1} v} \right);$$

$$(20) \quad \sigma_{i\alpha}(p) = p\sigma_{i\alpha}(\alpha_1 p) + (1-p)\sigma_{i\alpha}(\alpha_2 p)$$

$$+ \alpha_1 \frac{j(j-1)}{2} p^i (1 - 2\alpha_1^i p + \alpha_1^{2i+1} p^2),$$

with $\sigma_i(0) = 0$.

Number of runs of length greater than or equal to j

Let $T_{n,j}$ stand for the number of runs of length greater than or equal to j of A_1 responses, which occur from trial n to the termination of the process. Then $T_{1,j}$ denotes the total number of such runs. Now, for an infinite number of trials

$$T_{1,j} = T_{n,j} + \delta_{n,j+i} \qquad (i = 2, 3, \cdots).$$

Letting λ_j be the expectation of the number of runs of length $\geq j$, a development similar to that previously outlined gives

$$(21) \quad \lambda_{j\beta}(v) = p_1\lambda_{j\beta}(\beta_1 v) + (1 - p_1)\lambda_{j\beta}(\beta_2 v) + (1 - p_{i+1}) \prod_{i=1}^{j+1} p_i$$

$$= \frac{v}{1+v} \lambda_{j\beta}(\beta_1 v) + \frac{1}{1+v} \lambda_{j\beta}(\beta_2 v) + \frac{1}{\beta_1^i v} \prod_{i=1}^{j+1} \frac{\beta_1^{i-1} v}{1 + \beta_1^{i-1} v},$$

$$(22) \quad \lambda_{j\alpha}(p) = p\lambda_{j\alpha}(\alpha_1 p) + (1-p)\lambda_{j\alpha}(\alpha_2 p) + (1 - \alpha_1^i p)\alpha_1 \frac{j(j-1)}{2} p^i.$$

The expectation of the total number of runs of A_1 responses in an infinite number of trials is obtained when $j = 1$. Denoting this statistic by λ,

$$(23) \quad \lambda_\beta(v) = \frac{v}{1+v} \lambda_\beta(\beta_1 v) + \frac{1}{1+v} \lambda_\beta(\beta_2 v) + \frac{v}{1+v} \cdot \frac{1}{(1 + \beta_1 v)},$$

$$(24) \quad \lambda_\alpha(p) = p\lambda_\alpha(\alpha_1 p) + (1-p)\lambda_\alpha(\alpha_2 p) + p(1 - \alpha_1 p),$$

with $\lambda(0) = 0$. Additional functional equations for other random variables of interest, such as runs of A_2 responses, have been derived in [11].

General Functional Equations for the One-Absorbing-Barrier Models

The functional equations presented for statistics of the beta model have the general form

(25) $\quad f(v, \beta_1, \beta_2) = \dfrac{v}{1+v} f(\beta_1 v, \beta_1, \beta_2) + \dfrac{1}{1+v} f(\beta_2 v, \beta_1, \beta_2) + g(v, \beta_1, \beta_2)$

where

$$0 \leq v < \infty, \qquad 0 \leq \beta_1 \leq 1, \qquad 0 \leq \beta_2 \leq 1.$$

The term $g(v, \beta_1, \beta_2)$ is, in general, different for each statistic considered. For all except the run statistics

$$g(v, \beta_1, \beta_2) \geq 0,$$

(26) $\qquad\qquad\qquad g(0, \beta_1, \beta_2) = 0,$

$$\lim_{v \to \infty} g(v, \beta_1, \beta_2) \geq 1.$$

For these statistics

(27) $\qquad\qquad\qquad f(0, \beta_1, \beta_2) = 0,$

$$\lim_{v \to \infty} f(v, \beta_1, \beta_2) = \infty.$$

Equation (26) does not hold for the run statistics and the boundary conditions for the run statistics have to be defined separately.

The functional equations for statistics of the alpha model are seen to have the general form

(28) $\quad y(p, \alpha_1, \alpha_2) = py(\alpha_1 p, \alpha_1, \alpha_2) + (1 - p)y(\alpha_2 p, \alpha_1, \alpha_2) + z(p, \alpha_1, \alpha_2)$

where

$$0 \leq p \leq 1, \qquad 0 \leq \alpha_1 \leq 1, \qquad 0 \leq \alpha_2 \leq 1.$$

For the statistics of the alpha model

$$z(0, \alpha_1, \alpha_2) = 0,$$

(29) $\qquad\qquad\qquad z(1, \alpha_1, \alpha_2) \geq 0,$

and the boundary conditions for all the statistics considered are

(30) $\qquad\qquad\qquad y(0, \alpha_1, \alpha_2) = 0$

and

$$\lim_{p \to 1} y(p, \alpha_1, \alpha_2) \quad \text{is finite.}$$

The functional equations for the run statistics of the beta model differ in nature from the functional equations for the other statistics considered. A discussion of the functional equations for the run statistics is presented in [11].

The sections which follow present formal solutions to (25) and (28) under the boundary conditions (27) and (30) respectively. Theorems concerning existence, uniqueness and other properties of the solutions have been proved in [11] by methods similar to those of Bellman [3]. Some of these theorems are stated here without proof.

On the functional equation for the OAB beta model

Writing $f(v, \beta_1, \beta_2)$ simply as $f(v)$, (25) takes the form

$$(31) \qquad f(v) = \frac{v}{1+v} f(\beta_1 v) + \frac{1}{1+v} f(\beta_2 v) + g(v),$$

where

$$g(v) \geq 0, \qquad g(0) = 0, \qquad \lim_{v \to \infty} g(v) \geq 1,$$

and

$$f(0) = 0; \qquad \lim_{v \to \infty} f(v) = \infty.$$

Further, let $0 \leq \beta_1 < 1; 0 \leq \beta_2 < 1$. The cases $(\beta_1 = 1, \beta_2 < 1)$ and $(\beta_1 < 1, \beta_2 = 1)$ can be considered separately.

Existence of solution. For any function $r(v)$ define the operator T by

$$(32) \qquad T \cdot r(v) = \frac{v}{1+v} r(\beta_1 v) + \frac{1}{1+v} r(\beta_2 v) + g(v).$$

THEOREM 1.

$$f(v) = \lim_{n \to \infty} T^{(n)} g(v)$$

when the limit exists.

THEOREM 2. *If $g(v)$ is a monotone increasing function of v, then a solution $f(v)$ exists if*

$$\sum_{i=0}^{\infty} g(\beta^i v)$$

is finite for $0 \leq v < \infty$, where $0 \leq \beta = \max(\beta_1, \beta_2) < 1$.

As almost all the $g(v)$ occurring in the beta model first-moment equations are monotone increasing functions of v which satisfy the conditions of Theorem 2, the existence of the mean of most of the random variables introduced for the OAB beta model is assured.

From a proof similar to that for Theorem 2 it follows that when $g(v)$ is a monotone increasing function of v,

$$(33) \qquad \sum_{i=0}^{\infty} g(\beta_n^i v) \leq f(v) \leq \sum_{i=0}^{\infty} g(\beta_m^i v),$$

where

$$\beta_m = \max(\beta_1, \beta_2) \quad \text{and} \quad \beta_n = \min(\beta_1, \beta_2).$$

Continuity. If $|g(v)|$ is bounded in $0 \leq v < \infty$, the solution $f(v)$ is continuous.

Monotonicity. If $g(v)$ is a monotone increasing function of v, and if $\beta_1 \geq \beta_2$, then $f(v)$ is a monotone increasing function of v.

Uniqueness. The solution $f(v)$ is unique in $0 \leq v < \infty$.

On the functional equation for the OAB alpha models

For the functional equation

$$(34) \qquad y(p) = \acute{p} \cdot y(\alpha_1 p) + (1 - p)y(\alpha_2 p) + z(p)$$

the development of existence, uniqueness and other properties of the solution is similar to that for (31). Some properties of $y(p)$ are stated without proof.

Existence. For any function $Q(p)$, define the operator

$$(35) \qquad \Lambda Q(p) = pQ(\alpha_1 p) + (1 - p)Q(\alpha_2 p) + z(p)$$

and let

$$\lim_{n \to \infty} \Lambda^{(n)} \cdot z(p) \big|_{p \to 1} = c(\alpha_1, \alpha_2).$$

THEOREM 3.

$$y(p) = \lim_{n \to \infty} \Lambda^{(n)} \cdot z(p).$$

THEOREM 4.   *If $z(p)$ is monotone increasing in p, then*

$$\sum_{i=0}^{\infty} z(\alpha_n^i p) \leq y(p) \leq \sum_{i=0}^{\infty} z(\alpha_m^i p)$$

where

$$\alpha_m = \max (\alpha_1, \alpha_2), \qquad \alpha_n = \min (\alpha_1, \alpha_2).$$

Monotonicity. If $z(p)$ is monotone increasing in p, and $\alpha_1 \geq \alpha_2$, then $y(p)$ is monotone increasing in p.

Convexity. If $z(p)$ is convex and $\alpha_1 \geq \alpha_2$, then $y(p)$ is convex.

Solution of the Functional Equation for the OAB Beta Model

The solution to (31) is obtained by generalizing from solutions of the equation for special parameter values. The parameter space of the OAB beta model is shown in Fig. 2. One solution for special parameter values is derived here. A detailed presentation will be found in [11].

THEOREM 5.   *Along sides (1) and (2) of Fig. 2,*

$$(36) \qquad f(v) = \sum_{n=0}^{\infty} \sum_{m=0}^{\infty} g(\beta_1^m \beta_2^n v) \prod_{j=0}^{m-1} \frac{\beta_2^n \beta_1^j v}{(1 + \beta_2^n \beta_1^j v)}.$$

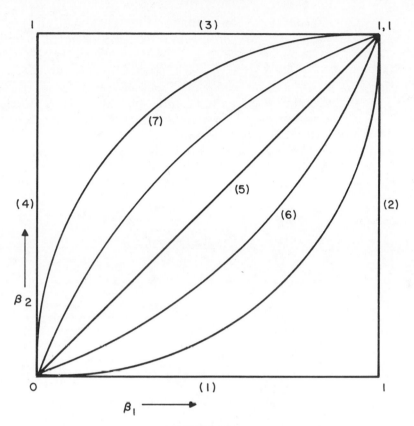

FIGURE 2

Parameter Space of OAB Beta Model

PROOF. Along side (1), $\beta_2 = 0$, $\beta_1 \leq 1$, and only the $n = 0$ term of the summation over n, is nonzero. The resulting expression is the one obtained from the functional equation, for in this case

$$f(v) = \frac{v}{1+v} f(\beta_1 v) + g(v),$$

giving

$$f(\beta_1^m v) = \frac{\beta_1^m v}{(1 + \beta_1^m v)} f(\beta_1^{m+1} v) + g(\beta_1^m v),$$

for $m = 0, 1, \cdots$, from which the desired result is obtained by successive substitution. Along side (2), $\beta_1 = 1$, $\beta_2 \leq 1$, and (36) becomes

$$\sum_{n=0}^{\infty} g(\beta_2^n v) \sum_{m=0}^{\infty} \prod_{j=0}^{m-1} \frac{\beta_2^n v}{(1 + \beta_2^n v)} = \sum_{n=0}^{\infty} (1 + \beta_2^n v) g(\beta_2^n v),$$

the last expression being also the one obtained from the functional equation for the case $\beta_1 = 1$, $\beta_2 < 1$, for which case the functional equation reduces to $f(v) - f(\beta_2 v) = (1 + v)g(v)$. Q.E.D.

Note that at the point $(1, 1)$ of the parameter space the solutions diverge. By letting $\beta_1 = \beta_2^k$, $\beta_2 = \beta_1^k$ $(k = 1, 2, \cdots)$, solutions along arcs of the form (6) and (7) of the parameter space can be obtained. The resulting functional equations may be written in the form of q-difference equations for which there exists an extensive body of literature [1, 2].

Examination of the solutions for various special parameter values suggests the form of the general solution. The general solution to (31) is given by the following theorem.

THEOREM 6.

$$f(v) = \sum_{m=0}^{\infty} \sum_{n=0}^{\infty} A_{m,n}(v) \cdot g(\beta_1^m \beta_2^n v).$$

where

$$A_{0,0}(v) = 1,$$

$$A_{m,0}(v) = \prod_{i=1}^{m} \frac{\beta_1^{i-1} v}{1 + \beta_1^{i-1} v} \qquad (m = 1, 2, \cdots),$$

$$A_{0,n}(v) = \prod_{j=1}^{n} \frac{1}{1 + \beta_2^{j-1} v} \qquad (n = 1, 2, \cdots),$$

$$A_{m,n}(v) = \sum_{k=0}^{n} A_{0,k}(v) A_{1,0}(\beta_2^k v) A_{m-1,n-k}(\beta_1 \beta_2^k v) \qquad (m, n = 1, 2, \cdots).$$

PROOF. Substitution in (31) gives

$$\sum_{m=0}^{\infty} \sum_{n=0}^{\infty} A_{m,n}(v) g(\beta_1^m \beta_2^n v) = \frac{v}{1 + v} \sum_{m=0}^{\infty} \sum_{n=0}^{\infty} A_{m,n}(\beta_1 v) g(\beta_1^{m+1} \beta_2^n v)$$

$$+ \frac{1}{1 + v} \sum_{m=0}^{\infty} \sum_{n=0}^{\infty} A_{m,n}(\beta_2 v) g(\beta_1^m \beta_2^{n+1} v) + g(v)$$

so that

(37) $$\sum_{m=0}^{\infty} A_{m,0}(v) g(\beta_1^m v) = g(v) + \frac{v}{1 + v} \sum_{m=1}^{\infty} A_{m-1,0}(\beta_1 v) g(\beta_1^m v),$$

which gives

$$A_{0,0}(v) = 1; \qquad A_{m,0}(v) = \frac{v}{1 + v} A_{m-1,0}(\beta_1 v) = \prod_{i=1}^{m} \frac{\beta_1^{i-1} v}{1 + \beta_1^{i-1} v}.$$

(38) $$\sum_{n=1}^{\infty} A_{0,n}(v) g(\beta_2^n v) = \frac{1}{1 + v} \sum_{n=1}^{\infty} A_{0,n-1}(\beta_2 v) g(\beta_2^n v),$$

which gives,

$$A_{0,1}(v) = \frac{1}{1+v} A_{0,0}(\beta_2 v) = \frac{1}{1+v},$$

$$A_{0,n}(v) = \frac{1}{1+v} A_{0,n-1}(\beta_2 v) = \prod_{i=1}^{n} \frac{1}{(1 + \beta_2^{i-1} v)},$$

and

(39) $$\sum_{m=1}^{\infty} \sum_{n=1}^{\infty} A_{m,n}(v) g(\beta_2^m \beta_2^n v) = \frac{v}{1+v} \sum_{m=1}^{\infty} \sum_{n=1}^{\infty} A_{m-1,n}(\beta_1 v) g(\beta_1^m \beta_2^n v)$$

$$+ \frac{1}{1+v} \sum_{m=1}^{\infty} \sum_{n=1}^{\infty} A_{m,n-1}(\beta_2 v) g(\beta_1^m \beta_2^n v).$$

The coefficients in this last expression satisfy the difference equation

$$A_{m,n}(v) = \frac{v}{1+v} A_{m-1,n}(\beta_1 v) + \frac{1}{1+v} A_{m,n-1}(\beta_2 v),$$

from which follows [11]

$$A_{1,n}(v) = \sum_{k=0}^{n} A_{0,k}(v) A_{1,0}(\beta_2^k v) A_{0,n-k}(\beta_1 \beta_2^k v)$$

$$= \sum_{k=0}^{n} \frac{\beta_2^k v}{1 + \beta_2^k v} \prod_{i=1}^{k} \frac{1}{(1 + \beta_2^{i-1} v)} \prod_{i=1}^{n-k} \frac{1}{(1 + \beta_1 \beta_2^{i+k-1} v)},$$

$$A_{m,n}(v) = \sum_{k=0}^{n} A_{0,k}(v) A_{1,0}(\beta_2^k v) A_{m-1,n-k}(\beta_1 \beta_2^k v). \qquad \text{Q.E.D.}$$

General Solution to the OAB Alpha Model Functional Equation

Replacing β_2 and β_1 by α_2 and α_1 in Fig. 2 gives the parameter space of the OAB alpha model. The general solution for (34) can be derived [11] in a manner similar to that used for the beta model functional equation. The solution is given by

THEOREM 7.

$$y(p) = \sum_{m=0}^{\infty} \sum_{n=0}^{\infty} b_{m,n}(p) \cdot z(\alpha_1^m \alpha_2^n p),$$

where

$$b_{0,0}(p) = 1,$$

$$b_{m,0}(p) = p^m \alpha_1 \frac{m(m-1)}{2} \qquad (m = 1, 2, \cdots),$$

$$b_{0,n}(p) = \prod_{j=1}^{n} (1 - \alpha_2^{j-1} p) \qquad (n = 1, 2, \cdots),$$

$$b_{m,n}(p) = \sum_{k=0}^{n} b_{1,0}(\alpha_2^k p) b_{0,k}(p) b_{m-1,n-k}(\alpha_1 \alpha_2^k p) \qquad (m, n = 1, 2, \cdots).$$

PROOF.   The proof is similar to that used for the beta model equation. Details are given in [11].

Discussion

Analytical techniques applicable to a class of learning models have been presented. Functional equations for various statistics of two learning models, viz., Luce's nonlinear beta model and a linear commuting-operator model called the alpha model, have been derived from the branching processes defined by the models.

The results on stochastic properties of Luce's beta model are new. For the alpha model, power series solutions to the functional equations for the first and second moments of the total number of A_1 responses and the trial number at which the last A_1 occurs had been obtained by Tatsuoka and Mosteller [15]. However, the techniques of expanding the functions in a power series in the variable often fails, as is illustrated by the fact that the power series solutions (obtained by Tatsuoka [14]) to the functional equations for the first and second moments of the total number of A_1 responses for the one-absorbing-barrier (OAB) beta model are not valid for $v \geq 1$.

By investigating two general equations, the problem of solving the individual functional equations for the OAB models was simplified. The functional equations for the sequential statistics of the OAB beta model do not have the same boundary conditions as the general equation presented in this paper, and their solutions require additional investigation.

Because of the complexity of the expressions obtained for the statistics of the OAB models, an attempt was made to find some close bounds which could be easily computed. Some upper and lower bounds for statistics of the OAB alpha model have been presented in ([11], ch. 5). An upper bound for one statistic of the OAB beta model has also been derived in [11], mainly to illustrate the methods used to obtain upper bounds for a few statistics of the OAB beta model. These methods failed for a number of the statistics. Furthermore, a method for the derivation of close lower bounds for the OAB beta model remains to be found.

Empirical tests and comparisons of the beta model with other models have been presented by Bush, Galanter, and Luce [6] and Fey [10]. The use of statistics such as those derived in this paper for the estimation of parameters and for measuring the goodness of fit has been discussed by Bush and Mosteller [8], Bush, Galanter, and Luce [6] and by others (see [5]).

REFERENCES

[1] Adams, C. R. On the linear ordinary q-difference equation. *Ann. Math.*, 2nd ser., **30**, 1929, 195–205.
[2] Adams, C. R. Linear q-difference equations. *Bull. Amer. math. Soc.*, 2nd ser., **37**, 1931, 361–400.

[3] Bellman, R. On a certain class of functional equations. In T. E. Harris, R. Bellman, and H. N. Shapiro (Eds.), *Functional equations occurring in decision processes*. Research memo. RM-898, Rand Corp., Santa Monica, Calif., 1952.

[4] Bush, R. R. Some properties of Luce's beta model for learning. In K. J. Arrow, S. Karlin, and P. Suppes (Eds.), *Proceedings of the First Stanford Symposium on mathematical methods in the social sciences*. Stanford, Calif.: Stanford Univ. Press, 1960.

[5] Bush, R. R. and Estes, W. K. (Eds.) *Studies in mathematical learning theory*. Stanford, Calif.: Stanford Univ. Press, 1959.

[6] Bush, R. R., Galanter, E., and Luce, R. D. Tests of the beta model. In R. R. Bush and W. K. Estes (Eds.), *Studies in mathematical learning theory*. Stanford, Calif.: Stanford Univ. Press, 1959. Ch. 18.

[7] Bush, R. R. and Mosteller, F. A comparison of eight models. In R. R. Bush and W. K. Estes (Eds.), *Studies in mathematical learning theory*. Stanford, Calif.: Stanford Univ. Press, 1959. Ch. 15.

[8] Bush, R. R. and Mosteller, F. *Stochastic models for learning*. New York: Wiley, 1955.

[9] Bush, R. R. and Sternberg, S. A single-operator model. In R. R. Bush and W. K. Estes (Eds.), *Studies in mathematical learning theory*. Stanford, Calif.: Stanford Univ. Press, 1959. Ch. 10.

[10] Fey, C. Investigation of some mathematical models for learning. *J. exp. Psychol.*, **61**, 1961, 455–461.

[11] Kanal, L. Analysis of some stochastic process arising from a learning model. Unpublished doctoral thesis, Univ. Penn., 1960.

[12] Lamperti, J. and Suppes, P. Some asymptotic properties of Luce's beta learning model. *Psychometrika*, **25**, 1960, 233–241.

[13] Luce, R. D. *Individual choice behavior*. New York: Wiley, 1959.

[14] Tatsuoka, M. Asymptotic mean and variance of number of errors for the beta model. Unpublished memo. PC-11, 1958.

[15] Tatsuoka, M. and Mosteller, F. A commuting-operator model. In R. R. Bush and W. K. Estes (Eds.), *Studies in mathematical learning theories*. Stanford, Calif.: Stanford Univ. Press, 1959. Ch. 12.

Manuscript received 12/3/60

Revised manuscript received 7/23/61

THE ASYMPTOTIC DISTRIBUTION FOR THE TWO-ABSORBING-BARRIER BETA MODEL*

LAVEEN KANAL†

GENERAL DYNAMICS/ELECTRONICS

ROCHESTER, NEW YORK

For the two-absorbing-barrier specialization of Luce's beta learning model, the asymptotic distribution of the response probability has all its density at $p = 0$ and $p = 1$. The functional equation for the amount of the density at $p = 1$ is investigated in this paper.

Luce's beta learning model [5] for the two-response, two-event, contingent case is given by the transition equations

$$(1) \qquad v_{n+1} = \begin{cases} \beta_1 v_n & \text{with probability } p_n \\ \beta_2 v_n & \text{with probability } 1 - p_n \end{cases} \qquad 0 < v < \infty, \quad \beta_i > 0, \quad i = 1, 2.$$

where p_n and $1 - p_n$ are respectively the probabilities of response A_1 and response A_2, and where $v_n = p_n/(1 - p_n)$. In a companion paper [3] statistics for the one-absorbing-barrier (OAB) beta model obtained when $\beta_1 \leq 1$, $\beta_2 \leq 1$, are derived. In this paper a statistic for the two-absorbing-barrier (TAB) beta model arising when $\beta_1 > 1$, $\beta_2 < 1$ is presented. Some statistics for the two-reflecting-barrier beta model are considered in [4].

For the two-absorbing-barrier beta model the asymptotic distribution of p_n has all its density at $p = 0$ and $p = 1$. The amount of the density at $p = 1$ is a useful statistic for these models. If $f(v)$ is the probability that a "particle" starting at v is eventually absorbed at $+\infty$, i.e., at $p = 1$, the functional equation for $f(v)$ is

$$(2) \qquad f(v) = \frac{v}{1 + v} f(\beta_1 v) + \frac{1}{1 + v} f(\beta_2 v),$$

where

$$0 \leq v < \infty, \quad \beta_1 > 1, \quad \beta_2 < 1, \quad f(0) = 0, \quad \lim_{v \to \infty} f(v) = 1.$$

*Abstracted from a portion of the author's doctoral dissertation, University of Pennsylvania, June 1960. The author is indebted to Prof. B. Epstein and to Prof. Robert R. Bush, his dissertation supervisor, for the valuable help and encouragement received from them.

†Formerly at the Moore School of Electrical Engineering, University of Pennsylvania, Philadelphia, Pa. The author is grateful to the Moore School for the support extended to him during his doctoral studies. He also wishes to thank D. Parkhill and N. Finkelstein of General Dynamics for their encouragement of his work.

This article appeared in *Psychometrika*, 1962, **27**, 105–109. Reprinted with permission.

The solution of (2) is the subject of this paper. Existence, uniqueness, and monotonicity of the solution are shown in [4] by methods similar to those of Bellman [1].

Solution for the symmetric model

For the two-absorbing-barrier symmetric beta model

$$\beta_2 = \frac{1}{\beta_1} < 1.$$

Let $x = \log_e v$ and $b = \log_e \beta_1$. Then (2) becomes

(3) $$\tilde{f}(x) = \frac{e^x}{1 + e^x} \tilde{f}(x + b) + \frac{1}{1 + e^x} \tilde{f}(x - b).$$

The solution of (3) is given by Theorem 1.

THEOREM 1*.

$$\tilde{f}(x) = \frac{\sum\limits_{k=0}^{\infty} \exp \left\{ -\frac{1}{2b} [x - (k + \tfrac{1}{2})b]^2 \right\}}{\sum\limits_{k=-\infty}^{\infty} \exp \left\{ -\frac{1}{2b} [x - (k + \tfrac{1}{2})b]^2 \right\}}.$$

PROOF. From (3), letting $\tilde{g}(x) = \tilde{f}(x) - \tilde{f}(x - b)$, $h(x) = \log_e \tilde{g}(x)$, one gets $h(x) - h(x + b) = x$. Assuming $h(x) = c_0 + c_1 x + c_2 x^2$, and substituting gives

$$\tilde{g}(x) - p(x) \exp \left[-\frac{1}{2b} (x - b/2)^2 \right],$$

where $p(x)$ is a periodic function of period b. As

$$\tilde{f}(x + b) - \tilde{f}(x) = \tilde{g}(x + b), \qquad \tilde{f}(x) = \tilde{f}(x + nb) - \sum_{k=1}^{n} \tilde{g}(x + kb).$$

Then as $n \to \infty$, $\tilde{f}(x + nb) \to 1$ and

$$\tilde{f}(x) = 1 - p(x) \sum_{k=1}^{\infty} \exp \left\{ -\frac{1}{2b} [x + (k - \tfrac{1}{2})b]^2 \right\}.$$

Furthermore

$$\tilde{f}(x + nb) = 1 - p(x) \sum_{k=n+1}^{\infty} \exp \left\{ -\frac{1}{2b} [x + (k - \tfrac{1}{2})b]^2 \right\},$$

and letting $n \to -\infty$ gives

$$p(x) = \frac{1}{\sum\limits_{k=-\infty}^{\infty} \exp \left\{ -\frac{1}{2b} [x + (k - \tfrac{1}{2})b]^2 \right\}}.$$

*Prof. B. Epstein pointed out the error in taking limits in an earlier version of Theorem 1 presented by Bush [2].

so that

$$\tilde{f}(x) = 1 - \frac{\sum_{k=1}^{\infty} \exp\left\{-\frac{1}{2b}\left[x + (k - \frac{1}{2})b\right]^2\right\}}{\sum_{k=-\infty}^{\infty} \exp\left\{-\frac{1}{2b}\left[x + (k - \frac{1}{2})b\right]^2\right\}},$$

from which Theorem 1 follows. Note that $\tilde{f}(0) = \frac{1}{2}$ as the symmetry of the problem indicates. Q.E.D.

COROLLARY 1.   When $x \to -\infty$, i.e., for large negative values of x,

$$\tilde{f}(x) = p(x) \exp\left[-\frac{1}{2b}(x - b/2)^2\right],$$

as $p(x)$ is of period b and the term corresponding to $k = 0$ dominates in the numerator.

COROLLARY 2.   For large positive x,

$$\tilde{f}(x) = 1 - p(x) \exp\left[-\frac{1}{2b}(x + b/2)^2\right].$$

COROLLARY 3.   When $b \leq 4$ the denominator of Theorem 1 is given by

$$\frac{1}{p(x)} \approx \sqrt{\frac{2\pi}{b}},$$

obtained by performing a fourier series analysis.

COROLLARY 4.   When $b \leq 4$,

$$\tilde{f}(x) = \frac{1}{\sqrt{2\pi}} \int_{-\infty}^{x/\sqrt{b}} e^{-\nu^2/2} \, dy,$$

for then by Corollary 3, the denominator of Theorem 1 is closely approximated by a constant and the numerator may be approximated by replacing the sum from zero to infinity by an integral from $-1/2$ to infinity. Using the transformation

$$y = \sqrt{b}\left[\frac{x}{b} - k - \frac{1}{2}\right],$$

gives the corollary.

Solution for the general TAB beta model

For the general case $\beta_1 > 1$, $\beta_2 < 1$, it is convenient to obtain the solution in terms of the solution for the symmetric model. Let the solution for the symmetric model given in Theorem 1 be denoted by $R(v)$. Then the solution for the general model is given by Theorem 2.

THEOREM 2. *For $\beta_1 > 1$, $\beta_2 < 1$*

$$f(v) = \frac{1}{C(\beta_1)} \sum_{n=0}^{\infty} \sum_{m=0}^{\infty} \sum_{k=0}^{\infty} B_n(\beta_1^{-1}) B_m(\beta_2) \beta_1^{-(n+1)k} R(\beta_1^{-k} \beta_2^m v),$$

where

$$C(\beta_1) = \prod_{i=1}^{\infty} (1 - \beta_1^{-i}),$$

$$B_m(\beta_2) = \frac{(-1)^m \beta_2^{m(m+1)/2}}{\prod_{i=1}^{m} (1 - \beta_2^i)},$$

$$B_n(\beta_1^{-1}) = \frac{(-1)^n \beta_1^{-n(n+1)/2}}{\prod_{i=1}^{n} (1 - \beta_1^{-i})}.$$

PROOF. Define the transform

$$F(s) = \int_0^{\infty} f(v) v^{-s-1} \, dv.$$

Writing (2) in the form

$$\left(1 + \frac{1}{v}\right) f(v) = f(\beta_1 v) + \frac{1}{v} f(\beta_2 v),$$

and applying the transform gives

$$F(s) + F(s+1) = \beta_1^s F(s) + \beta_2^{(s+1)} F(s+1).$$

If $R(s)$ is the transform of $R(v)$, it is shown in [4] that

$$F(s) = R(s) \prod_{i=1}^{\infty} \frac{[1 - \beta_2^{(s+i)}]}{[1 - \beta_1^{-(s+i)}]},$$

from which, by expanding the numerator and denominator terms in the product, one gets

$$F(s) = \frac{1}{C(\beta_1)} \sum_{n=0}^{\infty} B_n(\beta_1^{-1}) \sum_{k=0}^{\infty} \beta_1^{-(n+1)k} \sum_{m=0}^{\infty} B_m(\beta_2) \beta_1^{-sk} \beta_2^{sm} R(s).$$

The inverse transform of $\beta_1^{-sk} \beta_2^{sm} R(s)$ being $R(\beta_1^{-k} \beta_2^m v)$, taking the inverse transform of $F(s)$ gives Theorem 2. Q.E.D.

It is noted that the coefficients in the series of Theorem 2 tend to zero rather rapidly.

REFERENCES

[1] Bellman, R. On a certain class of functional equations. In T. E. Harris, R. Bellman, and H. Shapiro (Eds.), *Functional equations occurring in decision processes*. Research memo. RM-878, Rand Corp., Santa Monica, Calif., 1952.

[2] Bush, R. R. Some properties of Luce's beta model for learning. In K. J. Arrow, S. Karlin, and P. Suppes (Eds.), *Proceedings of the First Stanford Symposium on mathematical methods in the social sciences*. Stanford, Calif.: Stanford Univ. Press, 1960.
[3] Kanal, L. A functional equation analysis for two learning models. *Psychometrika*, **27**, 1962, 89–104.
[4] Kanal, L. Analysis of some stochastic processes arising from a learning model. Unpublished doctoral thesis, Univ. Pennsylvania, 1960.
[5] Luce, R. D. *Individual choice behavior*. New York: Wiley, 1959.

Manuscript received 12/3/60

Revised manuscript received 7/23/61

SOME RANDOM WALKS ARISING IN
LEARNING MODELS I

Samuel Karlin

Introduction

The present paper presents an analysis of certain transition operators arising in some learning models introduced by Bush and Mosteller [2]. They suppose that the organism makes a sequence of responses among a fixed finite set of alternatives and there is a probability p_s^n at moment n that response s will occur. They suppose further that the probabilities $p_s^{(n+1)}$ are determined by the p_s^n, the response s_n made after moment n, and the outcome or event r_n that follows response s_n. We shall examine in detail the one-dimensional models which occur in their theory. These models can be described in simplest form as follows: There exist two alternatives A_1 and A_2, and two possible outcomes r_1 and r_2, for each experiment. There exists a set of Markoff matrices F_{ij} which will apply where choice i was made and outcome r_j occurs. Let p represent the initial probability of choosing alternative A_2, and $1 - p$ the probability of choosing A_1. Depending on the choice and outcome, the vector $(p, 1 - p)$ is transformed by the appropriate F_{ij} into a new probability vector which represents the new probabilities of preference of A_2 and A_1, respectively, by the organism. The psychologist is interested in knowing the limiting form of the probability choice vector $(p, 1 - p)$.

The mathematical description of the simplest process of this type can be formulated as follows: A particle on the unit interval executes a random walk subject to two impulses. If it is located at the point x, then $x \to F_1 x = \sigma x$ with probability $1 - \phi(x)$, and $x \to F_2 x = 1 - \alpha + \alpha x$ with probability $\phi(x)$. The actual limiting behavior of x depends on the nature of $\phi(x)$. The transition operator representing the change of the distribution describing the position of the particle is given by

$$(TF)(x) = \int_0^{x/\sigma} [1 - \phi(t)] \, dF + \int_0^{(x-1+\alpha)/\alpha} \phi(t) \, dF.$$

We introduce an additional operator, acting on continuous functions, and given by

$$U\pi(t) = [1 - \phi(t)]\pi(\sigma t) + \phi(t)\pi(1 - \alpha + \alpha t).$$

It turns out that T is conjugate to U; hence knowing the behavior of U one obtains much information about T. This interplay shall be exploited considerably. The operator T is not weakly completely continuous nor does it possess any kind of compactness property; thus none of the classical ergodic theorems apply to this type [3]. The limiting behavior of $T^n F$ depends very sensitively on the assumptions made about the operators F_i and the probabilities $\phi(x)$.

This article is from *Pacific J. Math.*, 1953, 3, 725–756. Reprinted with permission.

Section 1 treats the case where $\phi(x) = x$. This causes the boundaries 0 and 1 to be absorbing states, and thus the limiting distribution concentrates only at these points. However, the concentration depends on the initial distribution. By examining the corresponding U in detail, we have been able to obtain much additional knowledge. For example, we have shown that if π is m times continuously differentiable then $(U^n\pi)^{(r)}$ converges uniformly for each $0 \leq r \leq m - 1$. It is worth emphasizing that the knowledge of the convergence of the distributions does not imply the uniform convergence of $U^n\pi$ for any continuous function π. Additional arguments are needed for this conclusion. In this connection, we finally remark that R. Bellman, T. Harris, and H. N. Shapiro [1] have analyzed only this case independently. They did not point out the connection between the operators T and U. The methods they used to establish the convergence of T^nF are probabilistic. Our paper in § 1 overlaps with theirs in some of the theorems, notably 6, 8, 9, 12, and 15; our results subsume theirs, and their proofs are entirely different from ours. Section 2 considers the case where $\phi(x)$ is monotone increasing and

$$|\phi(x) - \phi(y)| \leq u < 1.$$

This leads to the ergodic phenomonon, or steady-state situation, where the limiting distributions are independent of the starting distributions.

In § 3, we examine the situation $\phi(x) = 1 - x$. This corresponds to completely reflecting boundaries, and of course the ergodic phenomenon holds. Other interesting properties of the operators are also developed. We consider in § 4 the case where $\phi(x)$ is linear and monotonic decreasing. Section 5 introduces a further possibility where we allow the particle to stand still with certain probability. This type has been statistically examined by M. M. Flood [5]. In § 6 we investigate the general ergodic type where $\phi(x)$ is not necessarily linear. The arguments here combine both abstract analysis and probabilistic reasoning involving recurrent event theory. Furthermore, it is worth emphasizing, the proofs given in § 6 apply without any modifications to the case where we allow any finite number of impulses acting on the particle. In a future paper we shall present the extension of this model to the circumstance where changes in time occur continuously and the possible motion of the particle has a continuous or infinite discrete range of values.

The last section studies some of the properties of the limiting distribution in the ergodic types. It is shown in all circumstances that the limiting distribution is either singular or absolutely continuous, and the actual form depends on the value of $\alpha + \sigma$.

Most of the analysis carries over to higher dimensional models where more alternatives are allowed. In a subsequent paper we shall present this theory with other generalizations. We finally note that this paper represents a combination of abstract analysis and probability; it is hoped that the methods used will be useful for future investigations of this type.

It has been brought to my attention by the referee that the material of [6], [7], [8], and [9] relate closely to the content of this paper. Their techniques seem to be different.

1. *A particle undergoes a random walk* on the unit interval subject to the following law: If the particle is at x, then after unit time $x \rightarrow \alpha + (1 - \alpha)x$ with probability x, and $x \rightarrow \sigma x$ with probability $1 - x$, where $0 < \alpha, \sigma < 1$. If $F(x)$ represents the cumulative distribution describing the location of x at the beginning of the time interval

with the understanding that $F(x) \equiv 1$ for $x \geq 1$ and $F(x) = 0$ for $x < 0$, then the new distribution locating the position of the particle at the end of the time interval is given by

$$G(x) = TF = \int_0^{x/\sigma} (1 - t) \, dF(t) + \int_0^{(x-\alpha)/(1-\alpha)} t \, dF(t). \tag{1}$$

Indeed, the probability $dG(x)$ that after unit time the particle is located at x can materialize in two ways; namely, the particle was at x/σ and moved with probability $1 - x/\sigma$ to x, or it jumped with probability $(x - \alpha)/(1 - \alpha)$ from $(x - \alpha)/(1 - \alpha)$ to x during the unit time interval. This yields

$$dG(x) = \left(1 - \frac{x}{\sigma}\right) dF\left(\frac{x}{\sigma}\right) + \frac{x - \alpha}{1 - \alpha} dF\left(\frac{x - \alpha}{1 - \alpha}\right),$$

which easily implies the conclusion of equation (1).

Equation (1) represents the transition law for the particular Markoff process on hand.

The transformation T is easily seen to furnish a linear bounded mapping of the space of functions of bounded variation (V) on the unit interval into itself. Furthermore, T takes distributions into distributions and is of norm 1. This section investigates the behavior of T^n for large n with the aim of determining limiting properties of T^n.

We consider the following additional mapping U applied to the space of continuous functions defined on the unit interval $C(0, 1)$:

$$(U\pi)(t) = (1 - t)\pi(\sigma t) + t\pi[\alpha + (1 - \alpha)t]. \tag{2}$$

The operator U has a probabilistic interpretation which we shall speak about later; but its direct relevance to T is given in Theorem 1. The inner-product notation

$$(\pi, F) = \int_0^1 \pi(t) \, dF(t)$$

will be extensively used.

THEOREM 1. *The conjugate map U^* to U is T.*

PROOF. It is necessary to verify that $(U\pi, F) = (\pi, TF)$ for any continuous function $\pi(t)$ and any distribution $F(t)$ with $F(t) \equiv 1$ for $t \geq 1$ and $F(t) = 0$ for $t < 0$. Indeed,

$$(U\pi, F) = \int (1 - t)\pi(\sigma t) \, dF(t) + \int t\pi[\alpha + (1 - \alpha)t] \, dF(t).$$

By a change of variable, we get

$$(U\pi, F) = \int \left(1 - \frac{t}{\sigma}\right) \pi(t) \, dF\left(\frac{t}{\sigma}\right) + \int \pi(t) \frac{t - \alpha}{1 - \alpha} \, dF\left(\frac{t - \alpha}{1 - \alpha}\right)$$

$$= \int \pi(t) \, dG(t) \quad \text{where} \quad G = TF.$$

The value of Theorem 1 is that, by studying the iterates of U^n, we deduce corresponding results about the conjugate operators T^n. We proceed now to study this operator U. To be complete, we should denote the operator by $U_{\sigma,\alpha}$, but where no ambiguity arises we shall drop the subscripts. Let W denote the isometry

$$W\pi(t) = \pi(1 - t).$$

Clearly $W^{-1} = W$. We now observe the identity

$$U_{1-\alpha,1-\sigma} = WU_{\sigma,\alpha}W. \qquad (3)$$

The mapping $(\sigma, \alpha) \to (1 - \alpha, 1 - \sigma)$ of the parameter space into itself has the effect of mapping the triangle of the unit square bounded above by $1 - \alpha - \sigma = 0$ into the other triangle located in the unit square. This isomorphism property enables us to restrict our attention to the case where $1 - \alpha - \sigma \geq 0$. Corresponding theorems valid for the other circumstances, where $1 - \alpha - \sigma < 0$, are deduced easily by virtue of (3) and will be summarized at the end of this section. From now on in § 2, unless explicitly stated otherwise, we shall assume that $1 - \alpha - \sigma \geq 0$.

The next two theorems, which we state for completeness, are immediate from (2).

THEOREM 2. *The operator U preserves the values at 0 and 1.*

THEOREM 3. *The operator U is positive; that is, it transforms positive continuous functions into positive continuous functions.*

In particular, if $\pi_1(t) \geq \pi_2(t)$, for all t, then $U\pi_1 \geq U\pi_2$.

THEOREM 4. *If $\pi, \pi', \ldots, \pi^{(n)} \geq 0$, then $U\pi, (U\pi)', \ldots, (U\pi)^{(n)} \geq 0$.*

PROOF. A simple calculation yields

$$(U\pi)^{(n)} = (1 - t)\sigma^n\pi^{(n)}(\sigma t) + t(1 - \alpha)^n\pi^{(n)}(\alpha + (1 - \alpha)t)$$
$$+ n(1 - \alpha)^{n-1}\pi^{(n-1)}(\alpha + (1 - \alpha)t) - n\sigma^{n-1}\pi^{(n-1)}(\sigma t). \qquad (4)$$

Since

$$\sigma t < t < \alpha + (1 - \alpha)t,$$

we conclude since $\pi^{(n-1)}(t)$ is monotonic increasing that

$$\pi^{(n-1)}(\alpha + (1 - \alpha)t) \geq \pi^{(n-1)}(\sigma t) \geq 0.$$

The assumption that $1 - \alpha \geq \sigma$ implies that $(1 - \alpha)^{n-1} \geq \sigma^{n-1}$. As $\pi^{(n)}(t) \geq 0$, it follows that $(U\pi)^{(n)} \geq 0$. The same conclusion and argument apply to $(U\pi)^{(i)}$ for $0 \leq i \leq n - 1$.

In particular, U transforms positive monotonic convex functions into functions of the same kind. Although in the proof of Theorem 4 we assumed the existence of derivatives, the argument can be carried through routinely at the expense of elegance, by use of the general definitions of convexity and monotonicity.

THEOREM 5. *If $c \geq \pi^{(i)}(t) \geq 0$ for $0 \leq i \leq n$, then $(U^r\pi)^{(i)}(1) \leq K_i$ for $0 \leq i \leq n$ and hence $(U^r\pi)^{(i)}(t) \leq K_i$.*

PROOF. The proof is by induction. By Theorem 2, the theorem is trivially true for $i = 0$. Suppose we have established the result for the ith derivative with $0 \leq i \leq n - 1$. Equation (4) yields

$$(U\pi)^{(n)}(1) - \pi^{(n)}(1) = c_1(\alpha)\pi^{(n-1)}(1) - c_2(\sigma)\pi^{(n-1)}(\sigma) + [(1 - \alpha)^n - 1]\pi^{(n)}(1), \qquad (5)$$

where $c_1(\alpha)$ and $c_2(\sigma)$ are constants depending only on α and σ respectively, and on n. If

$$\pi^{(n)}(1) > M(\alpha, \sigma, c),$$

where M is a constant sufficiently large, then (5) yields

$$(U\pi)^{(n)}(1) < \pi^{(n)}(1).$$

Since $c_1(\alpha)$ and $c_2(\sigma)$ do not depend on k, and by the induction hypotheses

$$|(U^k\pi)^{n-1}(x)| \leq M$$

uniformly in k and x, we find in general that when $(U^k\pi)^{(n)}(1)$ becomes larger than $M(\alpha, \sigma, c)$, then

$$(U^{k+1}\pi)^{(n)}(1) < (U^k\pi)^{(n)}(1).$$

Consequently, the iterates $(U^k\pi)^{(n)}(1)$ for $k \geq k_0$ are bounded by

$$M(\alpha, \sigma, c) + c_1(\alpha)M + c_2(\sigma)M.$$

This trivially implies the conclusion of Theorem 5.

The proof of the next theorem is due originally to R. Bellman. We present it for completeness.

THEOREM 6. *There exists at most one continuous solution of $U\pi = \pi$ for which $\pi(0) = 0$ and $\pi(1) = 1$.*

PROOF. (By contradiction.) Let π_1 and π_2 denote two solutions with the prescribed boundary conditions. Put $\pi_0 = \pi_1 - \pi_2$; then $\pi_0(0) = \pi_0(1) = 0$. Let t_0 be a point where π_0 achieves its maximum. Since

$$\pi(t_0) = (1 - t_0)\pi(\sigma t_0) + t_0\pi(\alpha + (1 - \alpha)t_0),$$

we deduce that σt_0 is also a maximum point. Iterating, we find by continuity that $\pi(0) \equiv 0$ is the maximum value of $\pi(t)$. A similar argument shows that $0 = \min \pi(t)$, which implies that $\pi_1 = \pi_2$.

THEOREM 7. *For any function $\pi(t) = t^r$ with $\infty > r \geq 1$, $U^n(t^r)$ converges uniformly as $n \to \infty$.*

PROOF. Clearly $t \geq t^r > p(t)$, where

$$p(t) = \begin{cases} 0, & \text{for } 0 \leq t \leq t_0; \\ \dfrac{t - t_0}{1 - t_0}, & \text{for } t_0 \leq t \leq 1; \end{cases}$$

and t_0 is close to 1 with r fixed. Since Ut is convex by Theorem 4, and the values at 0 and 1 are fixed, we find that $t \geq Ut$. Hence

$$U^n t \geq U^{n+1} t \geq 0,$$

and $\lim U^n t = \theta(t)$ for every t. Since $\theta(t)$ is convex, and by Theorem 5 the derivatives of $U^n t$ at 1 are uniformly bounded, we conclude that $\theta(t)$ is continuous. By Dini's theorem the convergence of $U^n t$ to $\theta(t)$ is uniform. Obviously, $U\theta = \theta$. On the other hand, if t_0 is close to 1 then $(Up)'(1) < p'(1)$ (see the proof of Theorem 5). Since

Theorem 4 guarantees the convexity of Up, and the slope at 0 is 0, it follows that $Up \leq p$, and hence $U^n p \leq U^{n+1} p$; therefore $\lim U^n p = \phi(t)$. Again, $\phi(t)$ is a continuous fixed point, and therefore by Theorem 6 we infer that $\phi(t) = \theta(t)$. On account of $U^n t \geq U^n t^r \geq U^n p$, we deduce that $\lim U^n t = \phi(t)$ with the convergence being uniform.

We denote this unique fixed point of U by $\phi_{\sigma,\alpha}(t)$, or by $\phi(t)$ whenever no ambiguity arises.

THEOREM 8. *The iterates U^n converge strongly (that is, $U^n \pi$ converges uniformly for any continuous function π).*

PROOF. The constant functions are fixed points of U^n. Consequently by Theorem 7, $U^n q$ converges uniformly for any function $q(t)$ in the linear space L spanned by the functions $(1, t^r)$. The set L is dense in the space of continuous functions. Moreover, as $\|U^n\| = 1$, by a well-known theorem of Banach, $U^n q$ converges strongly when applied to any continuous function $q(t)$.

The actual limit is easily seen to be given by

$$\lim_{n \to \infty} U^n q(t) = q(1)\phi_{\sigma,\alpha}(t) + q(0) [1 - \phi_{\sigma,\alpha}(t)]. \tag{6}$$

This is an immediate consequence of the fact that the fixed points of U consist of the two dimensional space spanned by the function 1 and $\phi_{\sigma,\alpha}$. Equation (6) shows that two functions q_1 and q_2 which agree at 0 and 1 have the same limit. This enables us to show:

THEOREM 9. *If $q(t)$ is any bounded function continuous at 0 and 1, then $U^n q$ converges strongly.*

PROOF. Let $q(t)$, in addition to being continuous at 0 and 1, possess finite derivatives at 0 and 1. Then clearly there exist two continuous functions $h_1(t)$ and $h_2(t)$ with

$$h_1(t) \geq q(t) \geq h_2(t),$$

where $h_1(0) = h_2(0)$ and $h_1(1) = h_2(1)$. We conclude the result from this using the argument of Theorem 7 and equation (6). If now $q(t)$ is only continuous at 0 and 1, then we can find for any ϵ a $q_\epsilon(t)$ satisfying the properties assumed about $q(t)$ in the first part of the proof with $|q(t) - q_\epsilon(t)| \leq \epsilon$. As $\|U^n\| = 1$, the conclusion of the theorem now follows by a standard argument.

THEOREM 10. *If $|\pi^{(i)}(t)| \leq c_i$ for $0 \leq i \leq m$, then $|U^n \pi^{(i)}(t)| \leq c_i$ for $0 \leq i \leq m$.*

PROOF. The proof is by induction. For $r = 0$, the result is trivial since U preserves positivity, and the constant functions are fixed points of U. Suppose we have established the result for $r = m - 1$. We note that

$$U\pi^{(m)} = (1 - t)\sigma^m \pi^{(m)}(\sigma t) + t(1 - \alpha)^{(m)} \pi^{(m)}[\alpha + (1 - \alpha)t]$$
$$+ m(1 - \alpha)^{m-1} \pi^{(m-1)}[\alpha + (1 - \alpha)t] - m\sigma^{m-1}\pi^{(m-1)}(\sigma t).$$

This easily yields that

$$\max_t |U\pi^{(m)}(t)| \leq \lambda \max_t |\pi^{(m)}(t)| + C \max_t |\pi^{(m-1)}(t)| ,$$

where

$$\lambda = \max_{t} [(1 - t)\sigma^m + t(1 - \alpha)^m] < 1.$$

Therefore,

$$\max_{t} |(U^k \pi)^{(m)}(t)| \leq \lambda \max_{t} |(U^{k-1} \pi)^{(m)}(t)| + C \max_{t} |(U^{k-1} \pi)^{m-1}(t)|$$

$$\leq \lambda \max_{t} |(U^{(k-1)} \pi)^{(m)}(t)| + K$$

by our induction hypothesis. Iterating this last inequality yields

$$\max_{t} |(U^k \pi)^{(m)}(t)| \leq \sum_{i=0}^{k-1} \lambda^i K + \lambda^k \max_{t} |\pi^{(m)}(t)| \leq M.$$

This establishes the theorem.

THEOREM 11. *If $q(t)$ belongs to C^n (n continuous derivatives), then*

$$\lim_{m \to \infty} [U^m q(t)]^{(r)}$$

converges uniformly for $0 \leq r \leq n - 1$.

PROOF. We prove the theorem only for $r = 1$, for the other cases are similar. On account of Theorem 10, the uniform boundedness of $(U^m q)^{(2)}$ implies the equicontinuity of $U^m q^{(1)}$. Thus we can select a subsequence converging uniformly since $U^m q^{(1)}$ are also uniformly bounded. Let

$$\Psi(t) = \lim_{i \to \infty} U^{m_i} q^{(1)}.$$

Since $\lim U^{m_i} q$ converges uniformly to a unique limit $\theta(t)$, we obtain $\theta'(t) = \Psi(t)$. As $\theta'(t)$ is independent of the subsequence chosen, the conclusion of the theorem easily follows.

THEOREM 12. *The fixed point $\phi_{\sigma,\alpha}$ is analytic for $0 \leq t \leq 1$ with $\phi_{\sigma,\alpha}^{(r)} \geq 0$.*

PROOF. Let $p(t)$ denote a function infinitely differentiable with $p^{(r)}(t) \geq 0$ and $p(0) = 0$, $p(1) = 1$. By virtue of Theorem 11 and Theorem 4 we deduce that

$$\lim_{n \to \infty} (U^n p)^{(r)} = \phi_{\sigma,\alpha}^{(r)} \geq 0.$$

Therefore $\phi_{\sigma,\alpha}$ is absolutely monotonic and hence, by a well-known theorem, is analytic.

At this point it seems desirable to summarize the analogous results of Theorems 2 through Theorem 12 for the case where $\alpha + \sigma \leq 1$. We enumerate the corresponding theorems.

THEOREM 4'. *If $(-1)^{i-1} \pi^{(i)}(t) \geq 0$ for $i = 0, 1, 2, \ldots, n$, and $\pi(t) \geq 0$, then $(-1)^{i-1}(U\pi)^{(i)}(t) \geq 0$.*

In particular, positive increasing concave functions are transformed into functions of the same kind.

THEOREM 5'. *If $C \geq \pi(t) \geq 0$ and $C \geq (-1)^{i-1}\pi^{(i)}(t) \geq 0$ for $1 \leq i \leq n$, then $0 \leq (-1)^{i-1}(U^r \pi)^{(i)}(0) \leq K_i$, and hence $|U^r \pi^{(i)}(t)| \leq K_i$ for $1 \leq i \leq n$.*

Theorem 6 remains unchanged and is valid independent of the conditions on α and σ, provided only they lie in the open unit interval.

Theorem 7 holds with a modification of the proof where $p(t)$ is replaced by the concave function

$$p(t) = \left\{ \begin{array}{ll} 1, & \text{for } 1 \geq t \geq t_0 \\ \dfrac{1}{t_0} t, & \text{for } 0 \leq t \leq t_0 \end{array} \right\},$$

and the functions t^r are replaced by $1 - (1 - t)^r$. These also constitute, with the constant function, a family of functions whose linear span is dense in $C[0, 1]$. This enables us to infer the validity of Theorem 8. Theorems 9, 10, and 11, with suitable changes in their statements which we leave for the reader, are established by simple appropriate modifications similar to that indicated above for Theorem 7. The unique solution $\phi_{\sigma,\alpha}$ for this situation, where $\alpha + \sigma \leq 1$, is completely monotonic and hence analytic. In the remainder of this section the theorems are established without any specification as to the value of $\alpha + \sigma$.

THEOREM 13. *The functions*

$$\phi_m(t) = \sum_{n=m}^{\infty} U^n[t(1 - t)]$$

converge geometrically to 0.

PROOF. It is immediate from (6) that

$$U^n[t(1 - t)] = \Psi'_n(t)$$

tends uniformly to zero. Since the derivative at 0 and 1 of $t(1 - t)$ is 1 and -1, we conclude by Theorem 11 that for n sufficiently large there exists an $n_0(\lambda)$ such that

$$U^{n_0}[t(1 - t)] \leq \lambda t(1 - t)$$

with $\lambda < 1$. Let kn_0 denote the last integer k for which $kn_0 \leq m$. We obtain

$$0 \leq \phi_m(t) \leq \phi_{kn_0}(t) \leq \frac{\lambda^k}{1 - \lambda} \sum_{i=0}^{n_0-1} U^i[t(1 - t)] \leq C\lambda^k \leq C\rho^{(n_0+1)k} < C\rho^m,$$

where

$$\rho = \lambda^{1/(n_0+1)} < 1.$$

THEOREM 14. *If $q(t)$ is continuous, $|q'(1)| < \infty$ and $|q'(0)| < \infty$, then $\lim U^n[q(t)]$ converges geometrically.*

PROOF. We first establish the result for special functions t^r with $1 \leq r \leq \infty$. A simple calculation shows that

$$-Ct(1 - t) \leq U(t^r) - t^r \leq Ct(1 - t).$$

For $n < m$, we obtain upon continued application of U and summation that

$$-C \sum_{i=m}^{n} U^i[t(1 - t)] \leq U^n(t^r) - U^m(t^r) \leq C \sum_{i=m}^{n} U^i(t(1 - t)).$$

The conclusion now follows from Theorem 13. The general function $q(t)$, satisfying the hypothesis of Theorem 14, can be bounded from above and below by two poly-nomials $P_1(t)$ and $P_2(t)$ which agree at 0 and 1. The result now follows directly from this fact and the first part of this proof.

We observe easily the identity

$$Ut - t = (\alpha + \sigma - 1)t(1 - t).$$

Applying successively U and adding, we obtain

$$\phi_{\sigma,\alpha} = \lim_{n \to \infty} U^m t = t + (\alpha + \sigma - 1) \sum_{n=1}^{\infty} U_{\sigma,\alpha}^n t(1 - t). \tag{7}$$

This is useful for purposes of calculation.

Some remarks describing the dependence of $\phi_{\sigma,\alpha}$ on σ and α are in order. We consider the following identity:

$$U_{\sigma,\alpha}^n - U_{\sigma',\alpha'}^n = \sum_{i=0}^{n-1} U_{\sigma,\alpha}^i (U_{\sigma,\alpha} - U_{\sigma',\alpha'}) U_{\sigma',\alpha'}^{n-i-1}. \tag{8}$$

If $f(t)$ is any function with bounded derivatives, then we obtain by the mean-value theorem that

$$|(U_{\sigma,\alpha} - U_{\sigma',\alpha'})f| \leq |(1 - t)\,[f(\sigma t) - f(\sigma' t)] + t[f(\alpha + (1 - \alpha)t)$$
$$- f(\alpha' + (1 - \alpha')t)]|$$
$$\leq C(|\sigma - \sigma'| + |\alpha - \alpha'|)\, t(1 - t).$$

Applying equation 8 to $f(t) = \phi_{\sigma',\alpha'}$, and remembering that inequalities are preserved by Theorem 2, we obtain

$$|U_{\sigma,\alpha}^n \phi_{\sigma',\alpha'} - \phi_{\sigma',\alpha'}| \leq C(|\sigma - \sigma'| + |\alpha - \alpha'|) \sum_{i=0}^{n-1} U^i(t(1 - t)).$$

Allowing n to go to ∞, we have easily that

$$|\phi_{\sigma,\alpha} - \phi_{\sigma',\alpha'}| \leq K(|\sigma - \sigma'| + |\alpha - \alpha'|),$$

where $K(\eta)$ is finite, provided that $0 < \eta < \alpha,\ \alpha'\sigma,\ \sigma' < 1 - \eta < 1$.

It is worthwhile to discuss the nature of $\phi_{\sigma,\alpha}$ for (σ, α) lying on the boundary of the unit square. First, we observe by direct verification that when $\alpha + \sigma = 1$, then $\phi_{\sigma,\alpha}(x) = x$. Next let $\alpha = 0$ and $\sigma < 1$; then

$$U\phi = (1 - x)\phi(\sigma x) + x\phi(x).$$

Therefore, if ϕ is a fixed point with $\phi(0) = 0$ and $\phi(1) = 1$, then for $x \neq 1$ we have that $\phi(x) = \phi(\sigma x)$, and hence $\phi(x) \equiv \phi(0) = 0$ $(0 \leq x < 1)$ provided that ϕ is continuous at 0. Similarly, when $\sigma = 1$ and $\alpha < 1$ then the only fixed point ϕ continuous at 1 and satisfying $\phi(0) = 0$, $\phi(1) = 1$, is $\phi(x) \equiv 1$ for $0 < x \leq 1$. On the other two boundaries of the unit square the solutions are easily calculated and turn out as follows: If $0 < \sigma < 1$ is arbitrary and $\alpha = 1$, then

$$\phi_{\sigma,1} = 1 - \prod_{r=0}^{\infty} (1 - \sigma^r x),$$

while when $\sigma = 0$, $0 < \alpha < 1$, then

$$\phi_{\sigma,\alpha} = \prod_{r=0}^{\infty} L^r x,$$

where $L^0 = I$ and the operation L applied to x gives $\alpha + (1 - \alpha)x$. Finally for $\alpha = 0$, $\sigma = 1$ the operator U reduces to the identity mapping. We now investigate the dependence of $\phi_{\sigma,\alpha}$ on σ and α as we allow σ and α to tend to the boundary. We limit our attention for definiteness to studying the case where $(\sigma, \alpha) \to (\sigma_0, 0)$ with $\sigma_0 < 1$, and we show that $\phi_{\sigma,\alpha}$ converges pointwise to 0 for $0 \le x < 1$, and $\phi_{\sigma,\alpha}(1) \equiv 1$ otherwise. Moreover, the convergence is uniform in any interval $0 \le x \le 1 - \delta < 1$. Let $(\sigma_n, \alpha_n) \to (\sigma_0, 0)$; then without loss of generality we may assume that $1 - \sigma_n - \alpha_n > 0$. Therefore the ϕ_{σ_n,α_n} are convex, monotonic increasing and positive, with $\phi_{\sigma_n,\alpha_n}(0) = 0$. Also, for any interior interval $0 \le x \le 1 - \sigma < 1$, the first derivatives $\phi'_{\sigma_n,\alpha_n}$ are uniformly bounded. Since this implies the ϕ_{σ_n,α_n} are equi-continuous over the subinterval, and as $0 \le \phi_{\sigma_n,\alpha_n} \le 1$, we can select a subsequence which may be denoted as ϕ_{σ_r,α_r} converging to $\Psi(t)$ uniformly, for any interval of the form $0 \le x \le 1 - \delta < 1$. As

$$\phi_{\sigma_r,\alpha_r}(1) = 1,$$

we get $\Psi(1) = 1$ and similarly $\Psi(0) = 0$. The uniform convergence of ϕ_{σ_r,α_r} guarantees the continuity of Ψ at zero.

Put

$$U_r = U_{\sigma_r,\alpha_r}, \quad U_0 = U_{\sigma_0,0}, \quad \text{and } \phi_r = \phi_{\sigma_r,\alpha_r}.$$

We consider the following identity:

$$\Psi - U_0\Psi = (\Psi - \phi_r) + (\phi_r - U_r\Psi) + (U_r\Psi - U_0\Psi) = I_1 + I_2 + I_3.$$

We take a fixed $x < 1$; then trivially $|I_1| = |\Psi - \phi_r| \le \epsilon$ when r is sufficiently large. Also

$$|I_2| = |\phi_r - U_r\Psi| = |U_r\phi_r - U_r\Psi| = |(1 - x)[\phi_r(\sigma_r x) - \Psi(\sigma_r x)]$$
$$+ x[\phi_r(\alpha_r + (1 - \alpha_r)x) - \Psi(\alpha_r + (1 - \alpha_r)x)]|.$$

But for $x = x_0 < 1$ fixed, we observe that $\alpha_r + (1 - \alpha_r)x_0$ varies in an interval $\le 1 - \delta$ as $\alpha_r \to 0$, and the same applies to $\sigma_r x$. The uniform convergence of $\phi_r \to \Psi$ inside $0 \le x \le 1 - \delta$ yields $|I_2| \le \epsilon$. By construction, $|I_3| \le \epsilon$ for r large. Thus we infer the equality $\Psi = U_0\Psi$ for $0 \le x < 1$, and by direct verification for $x = 1$. However, the fixed point to the equation $U_0\Psi = \Psi$ with $\Psi(0) = 0$, $\Psi(1) = 1$ and Ψ continuous at 0 is $\Psi(x) = 1$ for $0 \le x < 1$ and $\Psi(1) = 1$. Thus the limit function Ψ is the same for every subsequence of $\alpha_{\sigma_n,\alpha_n}$, and hence we deduce that ϕ_{σ_n,α_n} converges pointwise. We furthermore note that Ψ is independent of $\sigma_0 < 1$. A similar analysis applies to the case where $(\sigma, \alpha) \to (1, \alpha)$ $(\alpha > 0)$. The continuity properties of the solution for the other two boundaries yield to simpler analysis. Summarizing, we have established the following theorem:

THEOREM 15. *The fixed points $\phi_{\sigma,\alpha}$ satisfy the following continuity properties: If $0 < \eta < \alpha$, $\alpha' \le 1$ and $0 \le \sigma$, $\sigma' \le 1 - \eta$, then*

$$|\phi_{\sigma,\alpha} - \phi_{\sigma',\alpha'}| \le K(\eta)[|\sigma - \sigma'| + |\alpha - \alpha'|].$$

If $(\sigma, \alpha) \to (\sigma_0, 0)$ with $\sigma_0 < 1$, then $\phi_{\sigma,\alpha}(x) \to 0$ pointwise for $0 \le x < 1$ and $\phi_{\sigma,\alpha}(1) \equiv 1$. If $(\sigma, \alpha) \to (1, \alpha_0)$ with $\alpha_0 > 0$, then $\phi_{\sigma,\alpha}(x) \to 1$ pointwise for $0 < x \le 1$.

Finally, a word concerning convergence of $U^n\pi$ for π continuous when the parameter values lie on the boundary. When $\alpha = 0$, $\sigma < 1$, then $U^n\pi$ converges pointwise. The same conclusion holds when $\alpha > 0$ and $\sigma = 1$. On the other two boundaries the convergence is uniform for $U^n \pi$. We omit the proofs.

We now return to the study of the operator T.

THEOREM 16. *For any distribution the iterates $T^n F$ converge in the sense of distributions to the distribution*

$$G(x) = I_1(x) \int \phi_{\sigma,\alpha} \, dF + I_0(x) \int (1 - \phi_{\sigma,\alpha}) \, dF,$$

where $I_0(x)$ and $I_1(x)$ are the distributions concentrating fully at 0 and 1 respectively.

PROOF. From the convergence of $U^n \pi$ for any continuous function π and Theorem 1 follows the weak*convergence of $T^n F$. This is equivalent to the convergence of $T^n F$ in the sense of distributions. The actual form of

$$\lim_{n \to \infty} T^n F = G$$

as given in the theorem follows directly from (6).

By choosing the distribution $F = I_{x_0}$, we obtain from Theorem 6 that $\phi_{\sigma,\alpha}(x_0)$ represents the probability with which the limiting distribution concentrates at 1, or in other words—as can be easily shown—the probability with which the particle beginning at x_0 will converge to 1. This furnishes a probability interpretation to the fixed point of the operator U which is different from a constant.

In connection with Theorem 8, we remark that $U^n \pi$ cannot converge for an arbitrary Lebesgue measurable bounded function. In fact, if we assume that $U^n \pi$ converges for every bounded measurable function $\pi(t)$, then $T^n F$ would converge weakly if F were absolutely continuous. Since the space of all integrable functions $L[0, 1]$ is weakly complete, and T maps distributions into distributions, we could find a fixed point $TF = F$ with F absolutely continuous and total variation 1. However, in view of (16) the only fixed distributions which exist concentrate only at 0 and 1, and hence cannot be absolutely continuous.

Finally, we present a slight application of Theorem 14. We show that the expected position of the particle converges geometrically for any starting distribution, although the iterated distributions converge slowly to the limiting distribution. The expected position of the particle is given by

$$\int_0^1 x \, dF(x) = (x, F),$$

where F is the cumulative distribution describing the position. The expected position at the nth step is given by

$$(x, T^n F) = (U^n x, F).$$

On account of Theorem 14, $U^n x$ converges geometrically, which establishes the assertion. The same conclusion applies to all the moments. This observation is very useful for computational and estimation purposes.

Finally, we note that the spectrum of the operator T cannot consist of the isolated point 1. Otherwise, by standard techniques one can show that $U^n \pi$ converges for any measurable bounded function π.

2. *In this second model the random walk* is described as follows: If the particle is at x, then $x \rightarrow \alpha + (1 - \alpha)x$ with probability $\phi(x)$ and $x \rightarrow \sigma x$ with probability $1 - \phi(x)$, where

$$|\phi(x) - \phi(y)| \leq \mu < 1.$$

The analogous transition operator to (1) becomes

$$G(x) = TF = \int_0^{x/\sigma} (1 - \phi(t)) \, (dF(t)) + \int_0^{(x-\alpha)/(1-\alpha)} \phi(t) \, dF(t), \tag{9}$$

with the same understanding concerning F applying as before. Let

$$U\pi = [1 - \phi(t)]\pi(\sigma t) + \phi(t)\pi[\alpha + (1 - \alpha)t]. \tag{10}$$

In this section, we take $0 < \alpha, \sigma < 1$; the case where boundary values for α and σ are considered is easy to handle but not of great interest. The spaces on which they operate are the same as in § 1. Again, in a similar manner to Theorem 1, we obtain:

THEOREM 17.   *The operator T is conjugate to the operator U.*

We now further assume that $\phi(t)$ is monotonic increasing. This model includes the important case where $\phi(t) = \lambda + \mu t$, where $\lambda + \mu \leq 1$; and whenever $\lambda + \mu = 1$ then $\lambda > 0$.

THEOREM 18.   *The operator U preserves positivity and positive monotonic increasing functions.*

PROOF.   Direct verification.

Since the hypothesis on $\phi(t)$ implies either $\phi(1) < 1$ or $\phi(0) > 0$, we analyze the case where $\phi(1) < 1$. The other circumstance can be treated in an analogous manner. Furthermore, we now assume that if $\phi(0) = 0$, then $\phi'(0)$ exists and is finite.

THEOREM 19.   *If $\pi(t)$ is monotonic increasing bounded and positive, then $U^n\pi$ converges uniformly to a constant.*

The proof can be carried out easily using the techniques employed above. The hypothesis on $\phi(t)$ easily yields the fact that the only continuous fixed points of $U\pi = \pi$ are constant functions. The proof is similar to the proof used in Theorem 6. This fact directly connects with the result of Theorem 21 below. First, we complete the proof of convergence of $U^n\pi$ for any continuous function $\pi(t)$.

THEOREM 20.   *The operators $U^n\pi$ converge uniformly for any continuous function.*

PROOF.   Since $\|U^n\| = 1$, and the space of all monotonic positive continuous functions spans a dense subset of the set of all continuous functions, the theorem follows by a well-known theorem of Banach.

THEOREM 21.   *For any distribution F, the distributions T^nF converge as distributions to a unique distribution G for which $TG = G$ which is independent of F.*

PROOF.   The weak*convergence of T^nF follows directly from Theorem 20 and Theorem 16. To complete the proof we must establish that if $\lim T^nF = G$ and

$\lim T^n H = K$, then $G = K$. Indeed, let Ψ denote any continuous function. We have that

$$(\Psi, G - K) = \lim_{n \to \infty} (\Psi, T^n(F - H)) = \lim_{n \to \infty} (U^n \Psi, F - H) = a\left(\int dF - \int dH\right) \equiv 0 \tag{11}$$

as F and H are distributions. Hence

$$\int \Psi(t)\, dF(t) = \int \Psi(t)\, dK(t)$$

for any continuous function Ψ, and therefore $G = K$.

It seems extremely difficult to determine the complete nature of this unique fixed distribution. We shall say more about it in a later section. We denote it by $F_{\sigma,\alpha}$.

THEOREM 22. *The distribution $F_{\sigma,\alpha}$ is a continuous function of σ, α; that is, if $(\sigma_n, \alpha_n) \to (\sigma, \alpha)$ with $0 < \sigma, \alpha < 1$, then $F_{\sigma_n,\alpha_n} \to F_{\sigma,\alpha}$ at every point of continuity of $F_{\sigma,\alpha}$.*

PROOF. Let $(\sigma_n, \alpha_n) \to (\sigma, \alpha)$; by Helly's theorem we can choose a subsequence $F_r = F_{\sigma_{n_r}, \alpha_{n_r}}$ converging to the distribution F at every continuity point. Write T_r for $T_{\sigma_{n_r}, \alpha_{n_r}}$ and T for $T_{\sigma,\alpha}$. Let $\pi(t)$ denote any fixed continuous function. We consider the quantity

$$(\pi, F - TF) = (\pi, F - F_r) + (\pi, F_r) - (\pi, TF_r) + (\pi, TF_r - TF).$$

Since $F_r \to F$ as distributions, we find for r sufficiently large that $|(\pi, F - F_r)| < \epsilon$. Now we note that

$$|(\pi, F_r) - (\pi, TF_r)| = |(\pi, T_r F_r) - (\pi, TF_r)| = |(U_r \pi - U\pi, F_r)|.$$

Since $U = U_{\sigma_{n_r}, \alpha_{n_r}}$ converges strongly to $U = U_{\sigma,\alpha}$, as is trivial to verify, it follows that $U_r \pi$ converges uniformly to $U\pi$. Whence, as F_r are distributions, we infer that

$$|(U_r \pi - U\pi, F_r)| \leq \max_t |U_r \pi - U\pi| < \epsilon$$

when r is chosen large enough. Evidently, with r large we get as before that

$$|(\pi, T(F_r - F))| = |(U\pi, F_r - F)| \leq \epsilon.$$

Therefore we obtain for r large that $|(\pi, F - TF)| \leq 3\epsilon$, and hence $(\pi, F) = (\pi, TF)$. Since π is any continuous function, we infer $F = TF$ and therefore $F = F_{\sigma,\alpha}$ by Theorem 21. Consequently, as any limit distribution of F_{σ_n,α_n} must be $F_{\sigma,\alpha}$ the conclusion of Theorem 22 is now immediate.

3. *The model considered in this section* is with $\phi(x) = 1 - x$. In this case ϕ is monotonic decreasing. The operator U becomes

$$U\pi(t) = t\pi(\sigma t) + (1 - t)\pi(1 - \alpha + \alpha t). \tag{12}$$

Note that we have replaced α by $1 - \alpha$. This is only for convenience in Theorem 28, and does not restrict any generality. In this model the closer the particle moves to the ends 0 and 1 the greater probability there is of moving back into the interior. The situation described here is of completely reflecting boundaries. Again it is easy to show that the only continuous fixed points $U\pi = \pi$ are the constant function. Therefore, we shall find as in § 2 that the distributions describing the position of the particle converge to a limit distribution independent of the initial distribution. We first proceed to analyze convergence properties of $U^n\pi$. In this case it is no longer true that U preserves the class of positive monotonic functions. Only positivity is conserved by the mapping U. However, a new quality as described in Theorem 23 serves here well.

Throughout this section in order to avoid trivial changes of proof and different results at times, we suppose that $0 < \alpha,\ \sigma < 1$.

THEOREM 23. *If $\pi(t)$ has a continuous derivative, then*

$$\max_t |(U\pi)'(t)| \le \max_t |\pi'(t)|,$$

with equality holding if and only if $\pi(t)$ is linear.

PROOF. By direct computation, we obtain

$$U\pi'(t) = t\sigma\pi'(\sigma t) + (1 - t)\alpha\pi'(1 - \alpha + \alpha t) + \pi(\sigma t) - \pi(1 - \alpha + \alpha t).$$

Hence, with the aid of the mean-value theorem we get

$$\max_t |U\pi'(t)| \le \max_t |t\sigma\pi'(\sigma t) + (1 - t)\alpha\pi'(1 - \alpha + \alpha t)| \tag{13}$$

$$+ (\sigma t - (1 - \alpha) - \alpha t)\left|\frac{\pi(\sigma t) - \pi(1 - \alpha + \alpha t)}{\sigma t - (1 - \alpha) - \alpha t}\right|$$

$$\le \max_t [t\sigma + (1 - t)\alpha + 1 - \alpha - (\sigma - \alpha)t] \max_t |\pi'(t)| = \max_t |\pi'(t)|.$$

If equality holds, then let t_0 denote a point where

$$\max_t |\pi'(t)| = |\pi'(t_0)|.$$

It follows easily from (13) that

$$\max_t |\pi'(t)| = |\pi'(\sigma t_0)| = |\pi'(1 - \alpha + \alpha t_0)| = \left|\frac{\pi(\sigma t_0) - \pi(1 - \alpha + \alpha t_0)}{\sigma t_0 - (1 - \alpha) - \alpha t_0}\right|. \tag{14}$$

This yields that $\pi(t)$ is linear for $\sigma t_0 \le t \le 1 - \alpha + \alpha t_0$, or otherwise somewhere between σt_0 and $1 - \alpha + \alpha t_0$ the slope has greater magnitude than the slope of the chord subtended by $\pi(t)$ at these points. Equation (14) shows also that σt_0 and $(1 - \alpha + \alpha t_0)$ are maximum points of $\pi'(t)$. Repeating this argument successively then implies that equality in (13) requires $\pi(t)$ to be linear.

THEOREM 24. *If $\pi(t)$ belongs to C^m [$\pi(t)$ possesses m continuous derivatives], then $\max_t |(U^n\pi)^{(r)}(t)|$ is uniformly bounded in n for each r $(0 \le r \le m)$.*

PROOF. The proof is similar to that of Theorem 10.

THEOREM 25. *If $\pi(t)$ possesses two continuous derivatives, and $\sigma \ne \alpha$, then $U^n\pi$ converges uniformly to a constant.*

Remark. The reason why the two cases $\sigma = \alpha$ and $\sigma \ne \alpha$ are distinguished, and necessarily so, will be explained later.

PROOF. In view of Theorem 23 and Theorem 24, the first and second derivatives of $U^n\pi$ are uniformly bounded. Thus $U^n\pi$ and $(U^n\pi)'$ constitute equicontinuous families of functions. We can thus select a subsequence n_i such that $U^{n_i}\pi$ converges uniformly to $\phi(t)$, and $(U^{n_i}\pi)'$ converges uniformly to $\phi'(t)$. It follows trivially that $U^{n_i+1}\pi$ tends uniformly to $U\phi$ and

$$U^{n_i+2}\pi \to U^2\phi.$$

Moreover, by virtue of Theorem 23,

$$\max_t |(U^{n_i}\pi)'| \geq \max_t |(U^{n_i+1}\pi)'| \geq \max_t |(U^{n_i+1}\pi)'|. \tag{15}$$

Hence

$$\lim_{i\to\infty} \max_t |(U^{n_i}\pi)'| = \lim_{i\to\infty} \max_t |(U^{n_i+1}\pi)'| = \lim_{i\to\infty} \max_t |(U^{n_i+2}\pi)'|.$$

Therefore, by the uniform convergence of the derivatives, we secure

$$\max_t |\phi'(t)| = \max_t |(U\phi)'(t)| = \max_t |(U^2\phi)'(t)|.$$

Invoking Theorem 23 yields that $\phi(t)$ and $U\phi(t)$ are linear. However, if $\alpha \neq \sigma$ and $\phi(t)$ contains a term with t, then $U\phi$ is quadratic. This impossibility forces $\phi(t)$ to be identically a constant. Let i be chosen sufficiently large so that

$$|U^{n_i}\pi - c| \leq \epsilon.$$

Then

$$|U^{n_i+1}\pi - c| \leq t|U^{n_i}\pi(\sigma t) - c| + (1-t)|U^{n_i}\pi(1 - \alpha + \alpha t) - c| < \epsilon.$$

Repeating this argument shows that

$$|U^{n_i+p}\pi - c| \leq \epsilon$$

for any p. This establishes that $U^n\pi$ converges uniformly to c.

THEOREM 26. *If $\pi(t)$ is continuous and $\sigma \neq \alpha$, then $U^n\pi$ converges uniformly.*

PROOF. The space of all functions with two continuous derivatives spans linearly a dense subset of the space of all continuous functions. Since $\|U^n\| = 1$, we obtain the result using Theorem 25 and a well-known theorem of Banach.

In the next two theorems we establish the uniform convergence of $U^n\pi$ for the case where $1 > \sigma = \alpha > 0$. We note in this case the interesting fact that U applied to a polynomial does not increase its degree. Particularly,

$$Ux^n = [\alpha^n - n\alpha^{n-1}(1-\alpha)]x^n + P_{n-1}(x),$$

where $P_{n-1}(x)$ denotes a polynomial of degree $n-1$.

THEOREM 27. *If $P(t)$ is any polynomial, then U^kP converges uniformly to a constant and the convergence is geometric.*

PROOF. The proof is by induction on the degree of the polynomial. Clearly if P is a constant $= c$ then $U^kP \equiv c$. Suppose we have shown for any polynomial P_{n-1} of degree $\leq n-1$ that the iterates U^kP_{n-1} converge uniformly. To complete the proof, it is enough to verify that U^kx^n converges uniformly. Let

$$\lambda = \alpha^n - n\alpha^{n-1}(1-\alpha);$$

then $|\lambda| < 1$ since $1 > \alpha > 0$. We obtain

$$Ux^n = \lambda x^n + P_{n-1}(x).$$

Repeating, we get, for $k \geq 1$,

$$U^k x^n = \lambda^k x^n + \sum_{r=0}^{k-1} \lambda^r U^{k-r-1} P_{n-1}.$$

This last sum is of the form

$$c_k = \sum_{r=0}^{k} a_r b_{k-r},$$

with $\Sigma \, |a_r| < \infty$, and $\lim_{k=\infty} b_k(x)$ exists. It is a well-known theorem that $\lim c_k(x)$ exists uniformly whenever

$$b_k(x) = U^{k-1} P_{n-1}$$

converges uniformly. Thus, $U^k x^n$ converges uniformly to a fixed point which must be a constant function. Finally we note that in the case where $\sigma = \alpha$ (the rate of learning, so to speak, is the same regardless of the outcome of the experiment), then $U^n P$ for any polynomial converges geometrically. The proof can be carried through by using induction.

This yields the fact that the expected position converges geometrically to a limiting expected position with similar results valid for higher moments.

THEOREM 28.   *If $\pi(t)$ is continuous and $\sigma = \alpha > 0$, then $U^n \pi$ converges uniformly.*

PROOF.   Similar to Theorem 26, since the set of all polynomials is dense.

We now note the important example that when $\alpha = \sigma = 0$ it is no longer true that $U^n \pi$ converges. It is easily verified that in this case $U^{2n} \pi$ and $U^{2n+1} \pi$ converge separately but that a periodic phenomenon occurs otherwise. The argument of Theorem 27 breaks down in this case as the quantity λ is -1. We only mention that other difficult convergence behavior occurs when α, σ traverse the boundary of the unit square for this model. In particular, when $\alpha = 1$ and $\sigma < 1$ it is not hard to show that $U^n_{\sigma,\alpha} \pi$ does not necessarily converge for every continuous function π, and even for the circumstance where π is a polynomial. The case where $\sigma = \alpha = 1$ produces for U the identity operator for which the convergence of U^n is trivial. For $\alpha < 1$ and $\sigma = 1$ we can conclude again a lack of convergence. However, when $\alpha = 0$ and $1 > \sigma > 0$, or $\sigma = 0$ and $1 > \alpha > 0$, then $U^n_{\sigma,\alpha} \pi$ converges for every continuous function π.

We return now to the hypothesis $0 < \alpha, \sigma < 1$.

THEOREM 29.   *If $\pi(t)$ belongs to C^m, then $(U^k \pi)^{(r)}(t)$ converges uniformly for $0 \leq r \leq m$.*

PROOF.   This follows easily from Theorems 24, 26, and 28. Let

$$TF = \int_0^{x/\sigma} t \, dF(t) + \int_0^{(x+\alpha-1)/\alpha} (1-t) \, dF(t).$$

This represents the transition law for the distribution describing the position of the particle for this model. By arguments analogous to those employed in the preceding sections, we can establish the following theorems, using the conjugate relationship between T and U.

THEOREM 30. *For any distribution F the distributions $T^n F$ converge as distributions to a unique distribution $F_{\sigma,\alpha}$ for which $TF_{\sigma,\alpha} = F_{\sigma,\alpha}$, which is independent of F.*

THEOREM 31. *The distributions $F_{\sigma,\alpha}$ constitute a continuous family of distributions in the sense of Theorem 22.*

Again it seems very difficult to determine any more explicit information about $F_{\sigma,\alpha}$.

4. *The model examined here* is such that $1 - \phi(x) = \lambda x + \mu$, with $\lambda + \mu \leq 1$ and at least $1 > \lambda$ or $0 < \mu$. The operator U has the form

$$U\pi = (\lambda x + \mu)\pi(\sigma x) + (1 - \lambda x - \mu)\pi(1 - \alpha + \alpha x). \tag{16}$$

Of course, as before, $0 < \alpha, \sigma < 1$. Convergence questions for $U^n \pi$ turn out to be very elementary in this case in view of the following theorem which is easily proven.

THEOREM 32. *If $\pi(x)$ has a bounded derivative, then*

$$\max_x |(U\pi)'(x)| \leq a \max_x |\pi'(x)|$$

with $a < 1$.

An immediate consequence of Theorem 32 is that $(U^k \pi)'$ converges geometrically to 0. Let T denote the transition operator of distributions for this model. In the standard way, we obtain:

THEOREM 33. *For any distribution F the distributions $T^n F$ converge to the distribution $F_{\sigma,\alpha}$ which is a continuous function of (σ, α), and $TF_{\sigma,\alpha} = F_{\sigma,\alpha}$. Moreover, $F_{\sigma,\alpha}$ is independent of F.*

5. *This section is devoted to some variations* of the preceding models. A new feature added first is that we allow in addition to the two impulses of motions towards the two fixed points 0 and 1 by the transformations

$$F_1 x = \sigma x \quad \text{and} \quad F_2 x = 1 - \alpha + \alpha x$$

the possibility of a third motion where the particle stands still with certain probability. These models are particularly important in learning problems, and much statistical investigation on this type has been done by M. M. Flood [5]. They are referred to as the pure models. The mathematical description of the first model of this type is as follows: A particle x on the unit interval is subject to three random impulses: (1) $x \to \sigma x$ with probability $\pi_1(1 - x)$; (2) $x \to 1 - \alpha + \alpha x$ with probability $\pi_2 x$; and (3) $x \to x$ with probability $(1 - \pi_1)(1 - x) + (1 - \pi_2)x$, where $0 \leq \pi_1, \pi_2 \leq 1$. This is similar to model I where absorption takes place at the boundaries 0 and 1. The operator analogous to (2) becomes

$$U\pi = \pi_1(1 - x)\pi(\sigma x) + [(1 - \pi_1)(1 - x) + (1 - \pi_2)x]\pi(x)$$

$$+ \pi_2 x \pi(1 - \alpha + \alpha x). \tag{17}$$

Again, let T denote the transition operator which maps the distribution locating the particle into the corresponding distribution at the end of the experiment. Theorem 1 is valid for this setup, and T is consequently conjugate to U. It is easy to verify that U fulfills the conditions of Theorems 2 and 3 and also preserves the property of monotone increasing functions. Furthermore, we obtain:

THEOREM 34. *If π, π' and $\pi'' \geq 0$, then $(U\pi)'' \geq 0$ if and only if*

$$(1 - \sigma)\pi_1 + \pi_2(\alpha - 1) \geq 0,$$

and otherwise $U\pi$ preserves with π and $\pi' \geq 0$ the property of concavity.

PROOF. The proof can be carried through by direct computation.

We remark that the remainder of the analogue to Theorem 4 does not carry over under the condition stated in Theorem 34. Moreover, noting that we have here changed α into $1 - \alpha$ as compared to § 2, we obtain for $\pi_1 = \pi_2 = 1$ the condition of § 1 for preservation of convexity, and so on.

The analogues of Theorems 5, 6, 7, and 8 easily extend to this model by the same methods, and we obtain that $U^n \pi$ converges uniformly to a limit given by

$$[1 - \phi_{\sigma,\alpha,\pi_1,\pi_2}(x)]\pi(0) + \phi_{\sigma,\alpha,\pi_1,\pi_2}(x)\pi(1), \tag{18}$$

where $\phi_{\sigma,\alpha,\pi_1,\pi_2}$ is the unique continuous fixed point of $U\phi = \phi$ with $\phi(0) = 0$ and $\phi(1) = 1$. The entire theory of geometric convergence, continuity of ϕ as a function of σ, α, π_1, and π_2, and the form of the limiting distribution of the particle established for the model of § 1 remains valid with slight changes in the proofs. The general conclusion is that introducing a probability of standing still has no effect on the convergence of the distributions or its limiting form provided only the essential feature of absorbing boundaries still prevails. Finally, in this connection we remark that for special boundary values of the parameters π_1 and π_2 the motion may become a drift to one or other of the end points; for example, $\pi_1 = 0$, $\pi_2 > 0$.

6. *We treat in this section,* the following general nonlinear one-dimensional learning model. The particle moves with probability $\phi(x)$ from x to $1 - \alpha + \alpha x$ and with probability $1 - \phi(x)$ from x to σx. The function is only continuous with the additional important requirement for this case that $\phi(x) \geq \delta > 0$ and $1 - \phi(x) > \delta > 0$ for all x in the unit interval. This excludes the types of models discussed in §§ 1 and 3, but includes some subcases of the examples investigated in §§ 2 and 4. However, in those cases we obtained much stronger results about the rate of convergence of derivatives, and so on. The transition operators become

$$TF = \int_0^{x/\sigma} [1 - \phi(t)] \, dF(t) + \int_0^{(x-1+\alpha)/\alpha} \phi(t) \, dF(t), \tag{20}$$

and T is adjoint to

$$(U\pi)(t) = (1 - \phi(t))\pi(\sigma t) + \phi(t)\pi(1 - \alpha + \alpha t). \tag{21}$$

We shall show that $U^n \pi$ converges uniformly for any continuous function $\pi(t)$. The proof of this fact shall be based on the following highly intuitive proposition. Let an experiment be repeated with only two possible outcomes, success or failure at each trial. Suppose further that the probability of success p_n at the nth trial depends on the outcome of the previous trial, but that these conditional probabilities satisfy $p_n \geq \eta > 0$; that is, regardless of the previous number of failures the conditional probability of success is always at least $\eta > 0$. Then the recurrent event of a success run of length r with r fixed is a certain event; that is, with probability 1 it will occur in finite time. This result can be deduced in a standard way using the theory of recurrent events [4].

We turn back now to the examination of $U^n \pi$. Let

$$F_1 x = \sigma x \quad \text{and} \quad F_2 x = 1 - \alpha + \alpha x$$

and by Fx denote the operation that either F_1 or F_2 is applied. We note the important obvious fact that

$$|F^r x - F^r y| \leq \lambda^r |x - y|, \tag{22}$$

with $0 < \lambda < 1$, where F^r denotes r applications of F_1 and F_2 in some order acting on x and y in the same way.

Next, we need the important lemma:

LEMMA. *If* $|\phi^{(m)}(t)| \leq K$ *for* $m = 0, 1, \ldots,$ *and* $|\pi^{(m)}(t)| \leq K_1,$ *then* $|U^n \pi^{(m)}(t)| \leq K_2$ *uniformly in n and t.*

PROOF. The proof is similar to that of Theorem 24.

Now let $\pi(t)$ denote a continuously differentiable function. Consider the following identity:

$$
\begin{aligned}
U^n \pi(x) - U^n \pi(y) = {} & (1 - \phi(x))(1 - \phi(y))[U^{n-1}\pi(F_1 x) - U^{n-1}\pi(F_1 y)] \\
& + \phi(x)\phi(y)[U^{n-1}\pi(F_2 x) - U^{n-2}\pi(F_2 y)] \\
& + (1 - \phi(y))\phi(x)[U^{n-1}\pi(F_2 x) - U^{n-1}\pi(F_1 y)] \\
& + \phi(y)(1 - \phi(x))[U^{n-1}\pi(F_1 x) - U^{n-1}\pi(F_2 y)].
\end{aligned}
\tag{23}
$$

We continue to apply this identity to the factors $U^{n-1}\pi(\cdot) - U^{n-1}\pi(\cdot)$; and when any term of the form $U^m \pi(F^r w) - U^n \pi(F^r z)$ is achieved, then that factor is allowed to stand without any further reduction. All other terms are reduced to expressions involving as factors $\pi(\cdot) - \pi(\cdot)$. Thus we obtain

$$U^n \pi(x) - U^n \pi(y) = I_1^n + I_2^n,$$

when I_1 consists of terms of the form

$$\sum p_k [U^{m_k} \pi(F^r w_k) - U^{m_k} \pi(F^r z_k)],$$

and $\sum p_k \leq 1$ while I_2 consists of the remaining terms. We now conceive of the following probability model. Let two particles undergo the random walk described by this model starting from x and y, respectively. We say a success occurs if the same impulse activates both particles, and otherwise failure occurs. The probability of success is given initially by

$$\phi(x)\phi(y) + [1 - \phi(x)][1 - \phi(y)] \geq 2\delta^2 > 0,$$

and it is easily seen that each p_k, where p_k is the conditional probability of success occurring on the kth trial, satisfies

$$p_k \geq 2\delta^2 > 0.$$

Consequently, a success run of length r is certain to happen in finite time. In particular as $n \to \infty$, $I_2^n \to 0$, since I_2^n is bounded by twice the probability of no success run in n trials times K. On the other hand, in view of the lemma and equation (22) we secure that $I_1^n \leq C\lambda^r$. Therefore,

$$\overline{\lim_{n \to \infty}} |U^n \pi(x) - U^n \pi(y)| \leq C\lambda^r,$$

which can be made arbitrarily small as $r \to \infty$. Hence, if

$$\lim U^n \pi(y) = a$$

exists for a single y, then

$$\lim_{n \to \infty} U^n \pi(x) = a$$

for every x. Since a subsequence can be found so that

$$\lim_{i \to \infty} U^{n_i} \pi(x) = a$$

for one x and hence for all x, an argument used in the close of the proof of Theorem 25 shows that

$$\lim_{n \to \infty} U^n \pi(x) = a.$$

The lemma easily implies that the convergence is uniform. Using the fact that $\|U^n\| = 1$, we can sum up the conclusions for this nonlinear model as follows:

THEOREM 35.   *If $\pi(t)$ is continuous, then $\lim\limits_{n \to \infty} U^n \pi$ exists uniformly converging to a constant limit.*

THEOREM 36.   *If $\phi(t)$ belongs to C^m, and $\pi(t)$ is in C^m, then*

$$\lim_{n \to \infty} (U^n \pi)^{(m)}(t) = 0$$

with convergence uniform in t.

THEOREM 37.   *For any distributions F, $T^n F$ converges to a distribution $F_{\sigma, \alpha}$ independent of F with $TF_{\sigma, \alpha} = F_{\sigma, \alpha}$ and $F_{\sigma, \alpha}$ continuous with respect to σ, α.*

This last theorem follows on account of the conjugate relationship of T and U.

Finally, we note that the method used in this section can be employed to analyze the random walks with any number of impulses.

$$F_i x = (1 - \alpha_i) m_i + \alpha_i x.$$

7. *In the present section we investigate* the nature of the limiting distribution obtained in the various models. In the case where the boundaries were absorbing states as in §§ 1 and 5, we find that the limiting distribution is discrete and concentrates at the two ends 0 and 1. The weight at 1 depends on the starting distribution F and is given by

$$\int_0^1 \phi_{\sigma, \alpha}(x) \, dF(x),$$

where $\phi_{\sigma, \alpha}$ is the unique continuous fixed point of $U\phi = \phi$ with $\phi(0) = 0$ and $\phi(1) = 1$. Many properties of $\phi_{\sigma, \alpha}$ are developed in those sections. In all the other types the ergodic property was seen to hold and the limiting distribution was independent of the initial distribution. Let us deal with the following general type. The random walk is given by $x \to F_1 x = \sigma x$ with probability $1 - \phi(x)$, and $x \to F_2 x = 1 - \alpha + \alpha x$ with probability $\phi(x)$, where $1 - \delta \geq \phi(x) \geq \delta > 0$. The relevant operators are given by equations (20) and (21). Let the limiting distribution be denoted by $F_{\sigma, \alpha}$.

We now distinguish two cases: (a) $\sigma \geq 1 - \alpha$ and (b) $\sigma < 1 - \alpha$. Let us examine case (b) first. We note that the union of the image sets $F_1[0, 1] + F_2[0, 1]$ of F_1 and F_2 applied to the unit interval does not overlap with the open subinterval $(\sigma, 1 - \alpha)$. Any two applications of F_1 and F_2 leave empty the two additional open intervals $(\sigma^2, (1 - \alpha)\sigma)$ and $(\sigma(1 - \alpha), (1 - \alpha)^2)$. Proceeding in this way, we find that the limit of the total set covered by n applications of F_i ($i = 1, 2$) in any arrangement is a Cantor set C. It is easily seen that $F_{\sigma, \alpha}$ must concentrate its full probability on this set C.

Now let

$$\pi_{t_0}(x) = \begin{cases} 1, & \text{if } x = t_0 \\ 0, & \text{if } x \neq t_0 \end{cases}.$$

We show that $U^n \pi_{t_0}(x)$ converges uniformly to zero. Note that $U\pi_{t_0}(t)$ is zero for every t except at most one value of t; namely, $F_1^{-1} t_0$ or $F_2^{-1} t_0$. Of course, if $\sigma < t_0 < 1 - \alpha$, then neither inverse exists for that t_0; and otherwise only one exists and

$$|U\pi_{t_0}| \leq \max_x [\phi(x), 1 - \phi(x)] \leq 1 - \delta.$$

Similarly, $U^n \pi_{t_0} \leq (1 - \delta)^n$, from which the assertion follows. We now observe that

$$(\pi_{t_0}, F_{\sigma, \alpha}) = (\pi_{t_0}, T^n F_{\sigma, \alpha}) = (U^n \pi_{t_0}, F_{\sigma, \alpha}) \to 0.$$

Consequently, the probability of $F_{\sigma, \alpha}$ at t_0 is zero for any t_0 with $0 \leq t_0 \leq 1$. Summing up, we have established:

THEOREM 38. *If $\sigma < 1 - \alpha$, then the limiting distribution $F_{\sigma, \alpha}$ is a singular distribution (probability zero at every point) spread on a Cantor-like set.*

We now turn to examine case (a) where $\sigma \geq 1 - \alpha$. We note first that at least one of the two mappings F_1^{-1} or F_2^{-1} is defined for every x in the unit interval. Let $\pi(t)$ denote any continuous positive function defined on the unit interval so that $\pi(t) \geq \eta > 0$ for some subinterval $t_0 - h \leq t \leq t_0 + h$ ($h > 0$). Since at least F_1^{-1} or F_2^{-1} exists at t_0 (say F_1^{-1}), we obtain $F_1^{-1} t_0 = t_1$. We construct t_2 from t_1 in the same way and continue this for n steps, obtaining $t_n = F^{-n} t_0$, where F^{-n} denotes a specific order of application of F_1^{-1} or F_2^{-1} a total of n times. Let F^n denote the reverse order of the operators obtained by passing from t_0 to t_n. We note that

$$|F^n x - F^n y| \leq \lambda^n |x - y| \leq \lambda^n,$$

where $\lambda < 1$. Choose n so large that $\lambda^n < h$; then for every x we get that

$$|F^n x - F^n t_n| = |F^n x - t_0| < h.$$

Consequently, as

$$1 > 1 - \delta \geq \phi(x) \geq \delta > 0,$$

$U^n \pi$ is positive for all x since $F^{-n}[t_0 - h, t_0 + h]$ covers the entire unit interval and $\pi(t) \geq \eta > 0$ on this initial interval which is spread out by the term in U^n involving F^n. We have thus shown:

THEOREM 39.   *If $\sigma > 1 - \alpha$, the operator U is strictly positive; that is, for each positive continuous function $\pi(t)$ there exists an n depending upon π so that $U^n \pi$ is strictly positive.*

Now let $\pi_{t_0}(t)$ be defined as before. Again we establish that $U^n \pi_{t_0}$ converges uniformly to zero. To this end we observe that $U\pi_{t_0}$ has at most two possible values at $F_1^{-1} t_0$ and $F_2^{-1} t_0$ given by $1 - \phi(F_1^{-1} t_0)$ and $\phi(F_2^{-1} t_0)$, respectively, while $U\pi_{t_0} \equiv 0$ elsewhere. Also, $U^2 \pi_{t_0}$ has at most four possible values and the maximum value that could be achieved for $U^2 \pi_{t_0}$ is

$$\max \{[1 - \phi(F_1^{-1} t_0)][1 - \phi(F_1^{-2} t_0)], \ \phi(F_2^{-1} t_0)\phi(F_2^{-2} t_0),$$
$$[1 - \phi(F_1^{-1} t_0)]\phi(F_2^{-1} F_1^{-1} t_0) + \phi(F_2^{-1} t_0)[1 - \phi(F_1^{-1} F_2^{-1} t_0)]\}$$

To secure a bound for the maximum of $U^n \pi_{t_0}$, let us consider the same repeated-experiment model set up in the previous section. The conditional probabilities of success p_n at the nth trial satisfy the uniform inequalities $1 > 1 - \eta \geq p_n \geq \eta > 0$, where success in this case is taken to be an application of the impulse F_1 to the particle. It is readily seen by standard inequalities that the probability of securing k ($k \leq n$) successes converges uniformly to zero as $n \to \infty$. Moreover, it follows directly that $\max_k(\text{probability of } k \text{ successes})$ is a bound for $U^n \pi_{t_0}$, and hence $U^n \pi_{t_0} \to 0$. We deduce as before that $F_{\sigma,\alpha}$ has probability zero for every t. Thus the cumulative distribution of F is continuous. Let $F = F_1 + F_2$, where F_1 is absolutely continuous and F_2 is singular. Observing that the transition operator transforms absolutely continuous measures into absolutely continuous measures and singular measures into singular measures, we find that $TF_1 = F_1$ and $TF_2 = F_2$. However, as the fixed distribution is unique, we deduce that either F_1 or F_2 vanishes.

THEOREM 40.   *If $\sigma \geq 1 - \alpha$, then the unique distribution $F_{\sigma,\alpha}$ is either absolutely continuous or singular. Furthermore, $F_{\sigma,\alpha}$ has positive measure in every open interval.*

PROOF.   We have demonstrated all the conclusions of the theorem but the last. Let $\pi(t)$ denote a continuous function bounded by 1, and zero outside an open interval I, and 1 on a closed subinterval I' of I. By virtue of Theorem 39 there exists an n such that $U^n \pi \geq \delta > 0$ for all t. We note that

$$(\pi, F_{\sigma,\alpha}) = (\pi, T^n F_{\sigma,\alpha}) = (U^n \pi, F_{\sigma,\alpha}) \geq \delta > 0.$$

But

$$\int_I dF_{\sigma,\alpha} \geq (\pi, F_{\sigma,\alpha}) \geq \delta > 0,$$

and the proof of the theorem is complete.

We close with the conjecture that when $\sigma \geq 1 - \alpha$, then $F_{\sigma,\alpha}$ is always absolutely continuous. An example where this is the case is furnished by $\phi(x) \equiv 1/2$, $\sigma = 1/2 = 1 - \alpha$, where $F_{\sigma,\alpha}(x) = x$.

REFERENCES

[1] R. Bellman, T. Harris, and H. N. Shapiro. *Studies on functional equations occurring in decision processes.* RM 878, RAND Corporation, July, 1952.

[2] R. R. Bush and C. F. Mosteller. A mathematical model for simple learning. *Psych. Rev.*, 1951, **58**, 313–323.

[3] J. L. Doob. Asymptotic properties of Markoff transition probabilities, *Trans. Amer. Math. Soc.*, 1948, **63**, 393–421.

[4] W. Feller. *An introduction to probability theory and its applications.* New York: Wiley, 1950.

[5] M. M. Flood. *On game learning theory.* RM 853, RAND Corporation, May 30, 1952.

[6] O. Onicescu and G. Mihoc. Sur les chaînes de variables statistiques. *Bull. Sci. Math.*, 1935, 2, **59**, 174–192.

[7] W. Doeblin and R. Fortet. Sur les chaînes à liaisons complètes. *Bull. Soc. Math. France*, 1937, **65**, 132–148.

[8] R. Fortet. (Thèse) Sur l'iteration des substitutions algébrique linéaires à une infinité de variables. *Revista*, No. 424, Año **40**, Lima, 1938.

[9] Ionescu Tulcea and G. Marinescu. Sur certaines chaînes à liaisons complètes. *C.R. Acad. Sci. Paris*, 1948, **227**, 667–669.

Received December 19, 1952.

SOME ASYMPTOTIC PROPERTIES OF LUCE'S BETA LEARNING MODEL*

JOHN LAMPERTI AND PATRICK SUPPES

APPLIED MATHEMATICS AND STATISTICS LABORATORIES

STANFORD UNIVERSITY

This paper studies asymptotic properties of Luce's beta model. Asymptotic results are given for the two-operator and four-operator cases of contingent and noncontingent reinforcement.

For application to various simple learning situations, Luce and his collaborators, Bush and Galanter, [1, 7] have considered a learning model in which the changes in probability of response from trial to trial are not linear functions of the probability of response on the preceding trial. Both theoretical and empirical considerations have motivated the development of the beta model. Some learning theorists like Hull and Spence believe that overt response behavior may best be explained in terms of a construct like that of response strength. From this viewpoint stochastic learning models which postulate a linear transformation of the probability of response from one trial to the next, with the transformation depending on the reinforcing event, are unsatisfactory in so far as they offer no more general psychological justification of their postulates. From an empirical standpoint there is evidence in some experiments, particularly certain T-maze experiments with rats, that the linear stochastic models do not yield good predictions of actual behavior [1, 7].

On the basis of some very simple postulates [7] on choice behavior, Luce has shown that there exists a ratio scale v over the set of responses with the property that

$$p_{i,n} = \frac{v_n(i)}{\sum_i v_n(i)} ,$$

where $p_{i,n}$ is the probability of response A_i on trial n, and $v_n(i)$ is the strength of this response on trial n. Additional simple postulates lead to the result that the $v_n(i)$ are transformed linearly from trial to trial, and this unobservable stochastic process on response strengths then determines a stochastic process

*This research was supported in part by the Group Psychology Branch of the Office of Naval Research and in part by the Rockefeller Foundation.

This article appeared in *Psychometrika*, 1960, **25**, 233–241. Reprinted with permission.

in the response probabilities. Superficially, it would seem that the simplest way to study the asymptotic behavior of the response probabilities—a subject of interest in connection with nearly any learning data—would be to determine the asymptotic behavior of the response strengths $v_n(i)$ and then infer by means of the equation given above the behavior of the response probabilities. This course is pursued rather far by Luce [7] and encounters numerous mathematical difficulties. We have taken the alternative path of studying directly the properties of the nonlinear transformations on the response probabilities to obtain results on their asymptotic behavior.

We restrict ourselves to situations in which one of two responses, A_1 and A_2, is made. Let p_n be the probability of response A_1 on trial n, and let E_1 be the event of reinforcing response A_1, and E_2 the event of reinforcing response A_2.

Luce's beta model is then characterized by the following transformations: if A_j and E_k occurred on trial n, then for $j = 1, 2$ and $k = 1, 2$,

$$(1) \qquad p_{n+1} = \frac{p_n}{p_n + \beta_{jk}(1 - p_n)},$$

where $\beta_{jk} > 0$. Luce [7] gives a more general formulation. (Generally, we want $\beta_{j1} < 1$ and $\beta_{j2} > 1$, to reflect the primary effects of reinforcement; moreover, it is ordinarily assumed that $\beta_{11} < \beta_{21} < \beta_{12} < \beta_{22}$.) Throughout this paper it is assumed that $0 \neq p_1 \neq 1$.

The most important fact about (1) is that the operators commute. For example, suppose in the first n trials there are b_1 occurrences of A_1E_1, b_2 occurrences of A_2E_1, b_3 occurrences of A_1E_2, b_4 occurrences of A_2E_2; then it is easily shown that

$$(2) \qquad p_{n+1} = \frac{p_1}{p_1 + \beta_{11}^{b_1}\beta_{21}^{b_2}\beta_{12}^{b_3}\beta_{22}^{b_4}(1 - p_1)}.$$

The aim of the present paper is to study asymptotic properties of the beta model for certain standard probabilistic schedules of reinforcement. The methods of attack used by Karlin [4] and by Lamperti and Suppes [6] for linear learning models do not directly apply to the nonlinear beta model.

The basis of our approach is to change the state space (the probability p_n is the state) from the unit interval to the whole real line in such a way that the transformations (1) become simply translations. The noncontingent case (the next section) then reduces to sums of independent random variables; the contingent cases can also be studied by "comparing" the resulting random walks with the case of sums of random variables. The probabilistic tool for this is developed and applied in later sections. The general conclusion to be drawn from our results is that for all but one case of noncontingent reinforcement individual response probabilities are ultimately either zero or one, which is in marked contrast to corresponding results for linear learning models. Absorption at zero or one also occurs for many, but not all, cases of contingent reinforcement.

Noncontingent Reinforcement with Two Operators

If the probability of a reinforcement is independent of response and trial number, we have what is called simple noncontingent reinforcement. Let π be the probability of an E_1 reinforcement, and for simplicity let

$$(3) \qquad \begin{cases} \beta_{11} = \beta_{21} = \beta, \\ \beta_{12} = \beta_{22} = \gamma, \\ 0 < \beta < 1, \\ \gamma > 1. \end{cases}$$

We seek an expression for the asymptotic probability distribution of response probabilities in terms of the numbers π, β, and γ.

The random variable η_n is defined recursively as follows:

$$\eta_1 = \begin{cases} \beta & \text{with prob } \pi, \\ \gamma & \text{with prob } (1 - \pi); \end{cases}$$

$$\eta_{n+1} = \begin{cases} \eta_n \beta & \text{with prob } \pi, \\ \eta_n \gamma & \text{with prob } (1 - \pi). \end{cases}$$

The random variable X_n is defined as follows:

$$X_n = \log \eta_n .$$

Then

$$(4) \qquad X_{n+1} = \begin{cases} X_n + \log \beta & \text{with prob } \pi, \\ X_n + \log \gamma & \text{with prob } (1 - \pi). \end{cases}$$

It is clear from (4) and what has preceded that X_n is the sum of n independent identically distributed random variables Y_i defined by

$$Y_i = \begin{cases} \log \beta & \text{with prob } \pi, \\ \log \gamma & \text{with prob } (1 - \pi). \end{cases}$$

By the strong law of large numbers, with probability one as $n \to \infty$

$$(5) \qquad \begin{aligned} X_n &\to \infty \quad \text{if} \quad \pi \log \beta + (1 - \pi) \log \gamma > 0, \\ X_n &\to -\infty \quad \text{if} \quad \pi \log \beta + (1 - \pi) \log \gamma < 0. \end{aligned}$$

Define now for any real number x

$$(6) \qquad F_x(p_1) = \frac{p_1}{p_1 + e^x(1 - p_1)}.$$

Then $p_{n+1} = F_{X_n}(p_1)$ for the sequence of reinforcements η_n, where $X_n = \log \eta_n$. These results are utilized to prove the following theorem.

THEOREM 1. *Let $c = \pi \log \beta + (1 - \pi) \log \gamma$. Then with probability one*

$$p_\infty = \begin{cases} 0 & if \quad c > 0, \\ 1 & if \quad c < 0. \end{cases}$$

If $c = 0$, then p_n oscillates between 0 and 1, so that with probability one

$$\limsup p_n = 1$$

$$\liminf p_n = 0.$$

Despite this oscillation, there is a limiting distribution for p_n ; it is concentrated at 0 and 1 with equal probabilities $\frac{1}{2}$.

PROOF. The results for $c > 0$ and $c < 0$ follow immediately from (5), (6), and the remark following. In case $c = 0$, note that $E(Y_i) = 0$. It is known [2] that the sums X_n are then recurrent; that is, they repeatedly take on values arbitrarily close to any possible value. In particular, X_n takes on repeatedly arbitrarily large and arbitrarily small values (with probability one), which upon recalling (6) proves the second statement. The third statement is a consequence of the central limit theorem, which implies that for any A, $\Pr(X_n > A)$ and $\Pr(X_n < -A)$ both converge to one-half as n increases. Again the assertion of the theorem follows from this fact and (6).

Two Theorems on Random Walks

The results of this section are special cases of those in [5]. However, the present approach has the advantages of simplicity and directness.

We have seen that the two-operator, noncontingent beta model gives rise to a Markov process on the real line such that from x the "moving particle" goes to $x + a$ or $x - b$ with (constant) probabilities φ and $1 - \varphi$. The contingent case leads to a similar process, except that the transition probabilities become functions of x. The four-operator model gives rise to a process with four possible transitions, from x to $x + a_i$, say, $i = 1, 2, 3, 4$. In this section some simple results on processes of these sorts will be obtained, in preparation for the study of the more general cases of the beta model. In the interest of clarity, only the two-operator case will be treated in full; the more general case can be handled in a similar way, but the details are cumbersome. Our approach was suggested by the work of Hodges and Rosenblatt [3].

Let $\{X_n\}$ be a real Markov process such that if $X_n = x$,

$$(9) \qquad X_{n+1} = \begin{cases} x + a & \text{with prob } \varphi(x), \\ x - b & \text{with prob } [1 - \varphi(x)], \end{cases}$$

where $0 < a, b, \varphi(x), 1 - \varphi(x)$. Let $\{Y_n\}$ be another process of the same type (and with the same a and b) but with constants θ and $1 - \theta$ as the transition probabilities in place of $\varphi(x)$ and $1 - \varphi(x)$.

LEMMA. *If for all $x \geq M$, one has $\varphi(x) \geq \theta$, and if $\Pr(Y_n \to + \infty) > 0$, then $\Pr(X_n \to + \infty) > 0$. If, on the other hand, for $x \geq M$, $\varphi(x) \leq \theta$ and if $\Pr(Y_n \to + \infty) = 0$, then $\Pr(X_n \to + \infty) = 0$.*

PROOF. Let $\{\xi_n\}$ be a sequence of independent random variables, each uniformly distributed on $[0, 1]$. The $\{X_n\}$ process will be referred to $\{\xi_n\}$ by letting

(10)
$$X_{n+1} = \begin{cases} X_n + a & \text{if } \xi_{n+1} \leq \varphi(X_n), \\ X_n - b & \text{otherwise.} \end{cases}$$

This does lead to the transition law (9) as may easily be seen. The $\{Y_n\}$ process can be linked to $\{X_n\}$ by referring it after the manner of (10) to the *same* sequence $\{\xi_n\}$, so that $Y_{n+1} = Y_n + a$ if and only if $\xi_{n+1} \leq \theta$.

Choose $Y_0 > M$. Whatever the value of X_0, since $\varphi(x) > 0$ there is positive probability that $X_m \geq Y_0$ for some m; therefore assume $X_0 \geq Y_0$. We now assert that for those sequences $\{Y_n\}$ with the property that $Y_n \geq M$ for all n, the inequality $X_n \geq Y_n$ is also valid for all n. This follows from our construction "linking" the processes, and the assumption that $\varphi(x) \geq \theta$ for $x \geq M$; the transition $X_{n+1} = X_n - b$ and $Y_{n+1} = Y_n + a$ is impossible, so $X_n - Y_n$ can only increase.

To complete the proof, note that since $\Pr(Y_n \to + \infty)$ is positive, so is $\Pr(Y_n \to + \infty, Y_n \geq M \text{ for all } n)$. But the event $Y_n \to + \infty, Y_n \geq M$ for all n may be considered as a set S in the sample space of the sequence $\{\xi_n\}$; S is a set of positive probability, and is contained in the set $X_n \to \infty$ since on S, $X_n \geq Y_n$ and $Y_n \to \infty$. Hence $\Pr(X_n \to + \infty) > 0$. The second part of the lemma is proved in a similar way, using the same construction linking $\{X_n\}$ and $\{Y_n\}$.

THEOREM 2. *Let $b/(a + b) = c$, and suppose that*

(11)
$$\lim_{x \to + \infty} \varphi(x) = \alpha \quad \text{and} \quad \lim_{x \to - \infty} \varphi(x) = \beta$$

exist. Then if $\alpha < c$ and $\beta > c$,

(12) $\Pr(\limsup X_n = + \infty, \liminf X_n = - \infty) = 1$ ($\{X_n\}$ *is recurrent*),

while if $\alpha < (>) c$ and $\beta < (>)c$, then

(13)
$$\Pr(X_n \to - \infty (+\infty)) = 1.$$

Finally, if $\alpha > c$ and $\beta < c$,

(14) $\Pr(X_n \to +\infty) = \delta, \qquad \Pr(X_n \to -\infty) = 1 - \delta$

for some $0 < \delta < 1$.

PROOF. Suppose, for instance, that $\alpha < c$. Let $\{Y_n\}$ (as in the lemma) be a process with constant transition probabilities θ and $1 - \theta$ where $\alpha < \theta < c$. The $\{Y_n\}$ process may be regarded as sums of random variables

(15)
$$Y_n = Y_0 + \sum_{i=1}^{n} Z_i , \quad \text{where} \quad \Pr (Z_i = a) = \theta \quad \text{and}$$
$$\Pr (Z_i = -b) = 1 - \theta.$$

But $E(Z_i) = a\theta - b(1 - \theta) < 0$, since $\theta < c$; this implies that $\Pr(Y_n \to - \infty) = 1$ by the law of large numbers. From the lemma, $\Pr(X_n \to + \infty) = 0$.

Similarly, if $\alpha > c$ it follows that $\Pr(X_n \to + \infty) > 0$. Since the lemma also holds for convergence to $- \infty$ (with φ and θ replaced by $1 - \varphi$ and $1 - \theta$), we obtain in the same way that $\beta < c$ makes $\Pr(X_n \to - \infty) > 0$, while if $\beta > c$ this probability is zero.

Consider the case when $\alpha < c$ and $\beta < c$; there is then positive probability of absorption at $- \infty$, but not at $+ \infty$. It is not hard to see that $X_n \to - \infty$ with probability one; the idea is roughly as follows. Since $X_n \not\to + \infty$, we have $X_n \leq N$ infinitely often with probability arbitrarily close to 1 for some N. Now the probability that from or to the left of N the random walk goes and remains to the left of $N - M$ must be positive since $\Pr(X_n \to - \infty) > 0$. But in an infinite sequence of not necessarily independent trials, an event whose probability on each trial is bounded away from zero is certain to occur. Hence for any M, the random walk will eventually become and remain to the left of $N - M$, and therefore $X_n \to - \infty$ with probability arbitrarily close to 1 (and so equal to one). The other cases are similar; one can think of $\alpha > c$ or $\alpha < c$ as the conditions under which $+ \infty$ is an absorbing or reflecting barrier, etc., and the process behaves accordingly.

The generalization to the four-operator case will now be described. Let $\{X_n\}$ be a real Markov process such that if $X_n = x$, then

(17)
$$X_{n+1} = x + a_i \quad \text{with prob } \varphi_i(x),$$

where $a_1 , a_2 > 0 > a_3, a_4$ and $\varphi_i(x) > 0$. Suppose

(18)
$$\lim_{x \to + \infty} \varphi_i(x) = \alpha_i \quad \text{and} \quad \lim_{x \to - \infty} \varphi_i(x) = \beta_i$$

exist, and let

$$\mu_+ = \sum_{i=1}^{4} a_i\alpha_i \quad \text{and} \quad \mu_- = \sum_{i=1}^{4} a_i\beta_i .$$

By methods entirely similar to those used above, but rather more involved, it is possible to prove the following.

THEOREM 3. *For the process $\{X_n\}$ described above, if $\mu_+ < 0$ and $\mu_- > 0$ then (12) holds; if $\mu_+ < (>)0$ and $\mu_- < (>)0$ then (13) applies; while if $\mu_+ > 0$ and $\mu_- < 0$, (14) is valid.*

Contingent Reinforcement with Two Operators

If the probability of reinforcement depends only on the immediately preceding response (on the same trial), one has (*simple*) *contingent reinforcement*. Let $\Pr(E_1 \mid A_1) = \pi_1$ and $\Pr(E_1 \mid A_2) = \pi_2$, and let the two operators β and γ be specified as in (3). Using (6), define the random variable X_n recursively. (Note that $\log \gamma$ appears first, since $\log \gamma > 0$ and $\log \beta < 0$, in order most directly to apply Theorem 2.)

$$(19) \qquad X_{n+1} = \begin{cases} X_n + \log \gamma & \text{with prob } F_{X_n}(p_1)(1 - \pi_1) \\ \qquad\qquad\qquad + (1 - F_{X_n}(p_1))(1 - \pi_2) = \varphi(X_n), \\ X_n + \log \beta & \text{with prob } [1 - \varphi(X_n)]. \end{cases}$$

Observe that

$$(20) \qquad \lim_{x \to +\infty} \varphi(x) = 1 - \pi_2 \quad \text{and} \quad \lim_{x \to -\infty} \varphi(x) = 1 - \pi_1.$$

Combining (20) and Theorem 2, one then has immediately Theorem 4.

THEOREM 4. *For the contingent case of the two-operator model, let* $c = -\log \beta/\log(\gamma/\beta)$. *Then with probability one*

(i) *if* $1 - \pi_2 < c$ *and* $1 - \pi_1 > c$ *then*

$$\limsup_n p_n = 1 \quad and \quad \liminf_n p_n = 0,$$

(ii) *if* $1 - \pi_2 < c$ *and* $1 - \pi_1 < c$ *then* $p_\infty = 1,$

(iii) *if* $1 - \pi_2 > c$ *and* $1 - \pi_1 > c$ *then* $p_\infty = 0.$

Moreover,

(iv) *if* $1 - \pi_2 > c$ *and* $1 - \pi_1 < c$ *then for some* δ *with* $0 < \delta < 1$

$$\Pr(p_n \to 1) = \delta, \qquad \Pr(p_n \to 0) = 1 - \delta.$$

The intuitive character of the distinction between the results expressed in (i) and (iv) of this theorem should be clear. If $1 - \pi_2 < c$ and $1 - \pi_1 > c$, then probability zero of an A_1 response and probability one of an A_1 response are both reflecting barriers, whereas if $1 - \pi_2 > c$ and $1 - \pi_1 < c$, they are both absorbing barriers.

It is also to be noticed that except when $1 - \pi_1 = c$ or $1 - \pi_2 = c$, Theorem 4 covers all values of β, γ, π_1, and π_2 for the contingent case. It can be shown [5] by deeper methods that if $1 - \pi_1 = c$ (or $1 - \pi_2 = c$) then probability one (respectively zero) of an A_1 response is again a reflecting barrier. These results agree with those given by Luce ([7], p. 124) and in addition settle most of the open questions in his Table 6. Detailed comparison is tedious because his classification of cases differs considerably from ours as given in the above theorem.

Contingent Reinforcement with Four Operators

We want finally to apply Theorem 3 to the contingent case of the general four-operator model formulated in (1). Analogous to (19),

$$
(21) \quad X_{n+1} = \begin{cases} X_n + \log \beta_{22} & \text{with prob } (1 - \pi_2)(1 - F_{X_n}(p_1)) = \varphi_{22}(X_n), \\ X_n + \log \beta_{12} & \text{with prob } (1 - \pi_1)F_{X_n}(p_1) = \varphi_{12}(X_n), \\ X_n + \log \beta_{21} & \text{with prob } \pi_2(1 - F_{X_n}(p_1)) = \varphi_{21}(X_n), \\ X_n + \log \beta_{11} & \text{with prob } \pi_1 F_{X_n}(p_1) = \varphi_{11}(X_n). \end{cases}
$$

Also,

$$
(22) \quad \begin{cases} \lim_{x \to +\infty} \varphi_{22}(x) = 1 - \pi_2 , & \lim_{x \to -\infty} \varphi_{22} = 0, \\[1mm] \lim_{x \to +\infty} \varphi_{12}(x) = 0, & \lim_{x \to -\infty} \varphi_{12}(x) = 1 - \pi_1 , \\[1mm] \lim_{x \to +\infty} \varphi_{21}(x) = \pi_2 , & \lim_{x \to -\infty} \varphi_{21}(x) = 0, \\[1mm] \lim_{x \to +\infty} \varphi_{11}(x) = 0, & \lim_{x \to -\infty} \varphi_{11}(x) = \pi_1 . \end{cases}
$$

Then

$$
(23) \quad \mu_+ = \sum_{j,k} \log \beta_{jk} \lim_{x \to +\infty} \varphi_{jk}(x) = \pi_2 \log \beta_{21} + (1 - \pi_2) \log \beta_{22} ,
$$

and

$$
(24) \quad \mu_- = \sum_{j,k} \log \beta_{jk} \lim_{x \to -\infty} \varphi_{jk}(x) = \pi_1 \log \beta_{11} + (1 - \pi_1) \log \beta_{12} .
$$

To apply Theorem 3 one also assumes that $\beta_{22}, \beta_{12} > 1 > \beta_{21}, \beta_{11} > 0$. On this assumption, and utilizing (23) and (24), we infer Theorem 5.

·THEOREM 5. *For the contingent case of the four-operator model, with probability one*

(i) *if $\mu_+ < 0$ and $\mu_- > 0$ then* $\limsup_n p_n = 1$ *and* $\liminf_n p_n = 0$,

(ii) *if $\mu_+ < 0$ and $\mu_- < 0$ then* $p_\infty = 1$,

(iii) *if $\mu_+ > 0$ and $\mu_- > 0$ then* $p_\infty = 0$;

and if $\mu_+ > 0$ and $\mu_- < 0$, then for some δ with $0 < \delta < 1$

(iv) $\Pr(p_n \to 1) = \delta, \Pr(p_n \to 0) = 1 - \delta$.

Specialization of this theorem to cover the noncontingent case is immediate.

REFERENCES

[1] Bush, R. R., Galanter, E., and Luce, R. D. Tests of the "beta model." In R. R. Bush and W. K. Estes (Eds.), *Studies in mathematical learning theory.* Stanford: Stanford Univ. Press, 1959. Ch. 18.

[2] Chung, K. L. and Fuchs, W. H. J. On the distribution of values of sums of random variables. *Mem. Amer. Math. Soc.,* 1951, **6**, 1–12.

[3] Hodges, J. L. and Rosenblatt, M. Recurrence time moments in random walks. *Pac. J. Math.,* 1953, **3**, 127–136.

[4] Karlin, S. Some random walks arising in learning models I. *Pac. J. Math.,* 1953, **3**, 725–756.

[5] Lamperti, J. Criteria for the recurrence or transience of stochastic processes I. *J. math. Anal. Applications,* (in press).

[6] Lamperti, J. and Suppes, P. Chains of infinite order and their application to learning theory. *Pac. J. Math.,* 1959, **9**, 739–754.

[7] Luce, R. D. *Individual choice behavior.* New York: Wiley, 1959.

Manuscript received 4/27/59

Revised manuscript received 11/10/59

CHAINS OF INFINITE ORDER AND THEIR
APPLICATION TO LEARNING THEORY

JOHN LAMPERTI AND PATRICK SUPPES

1. Introduction. The purpose of this paper is to study the asymptotic behavior of a large class of stochastic processes which have been used as models of learning experiments. We will do this by applying a theory of so-called "chains of infinite order" or "chaînes à liaisons complètes." Namely, we shall employ certain limit theorems for stochastic processes whose transition probabilities depend on the entire past history of the process, but only slightly on the remote past. Such theorems were given by Doeblin and Fortet [3] in a form close to that we employ; however, in order to accomodate certain cases of learning models we found it necessary to relax somewhat their hypotheses. A self-contained discussion of these and some additional results is the content of §2.

We should emphasize that this section is included to serve as preparation for the theorems of §4, and it is original with us only in some details and extensions. In addition to [3], papers by Harris [7] and Karlin [8] contain very closely related results and arguments, but not quite in the form we require.

The processes which we shall study with these tools are called "linear earning models." From a psychological standpoint these models are very simple. A subject is presented a series of *trials*, and on each trial he makes a *response*, which consists of a choice from a finite set of possible actions. This response is followed by a *reinforcement* (again one of a finite number). The assumption of the model is that the subject's response probabilities on the next trial are linear functions of the probabilities on the present trial, where the form of the functions depends upon which reinforcement has occurred. Many results about such models may be found in Bush and Mosteller [2], Estes [4], and Estes and Suppes [6]. We will also study here models constructed along similar lines for experiments involving two or more subjects and a type of interaction between them [6, Section 9] and Atkinson and Suppes [1]. Precise definitions of these processes are given below in §3.

The references mentioned above do not, except in very special cases, give a thorough treatment of asymptotic properties. We shall prove that under general conditions linear learning models exhibit "ergodic" behavior; that is, that after much time has passed these processes become approximately stationary and the influence of the initial distributions

Received November 20, 1958. This research was supported by the Group Psychology and Statistics Branches of the Office of Naval Research under contracts with Stanford University.

This article appeared in the *Pacific J. Math.*, 1959, **9**, 739–754. Reprinted with permission.

goes to zero. This is not the case for all models which have been used in experimental work, but it seems as if ergodic behavior can be proved by our method in almost all the cases in which one might expect it. Our theorems to this effect, their proofs and some corollaries are given in §4.

The major work so far on limiting behavior of learning models is Karlin [8], who obtains detailed limit theorems for certain classes of models. However, the results and even the techniques of Karlin's paper do not apply to many cases of interest. His starting point is a representation of the linear model as a Markov process whose states are the response probabilities. Two typical situations when such a representation is impractical arise (i) when the probabilities with which the reinforcement is selected depend on two or more previous responses, and (ii) in the many-person situations mentioned above. Both these situations can (and will) be studied using infinite order chains, and ergodic behavior established under mild restrictions. On the other hand, Karlin's work treats interesting non-ergodic cases outside the scope of our approach. For example, consider a *T*-maze experiment in which the subject (a rat, say) is reinforced (rewarded) on each trial regardless of whether he goes left or right. In the appropriate linear model, the probability of a left turn eventually is either nearly 0 or nearly 1, and which it is depends upon the rat's initial response probabilities. The model of this experiment has been thoroughly studied in [8, Section 2], and these results have been generalized by Kennedy [9].

In conclusion we comment that both more detailed results and other applications seem possible using the ideas of "infinite order chains." We hope to contribute further to this development in the future.

2. Chains of infinite order. In this section we present a theory of non-Markov stochastic processes where the transition probabilities are influenced only slightly by the remote past. The original convergence theorems for this type of process are due to Doeblin and Fortet [3]; they are given here in a generalized form (Theorems 2.1 and 2.2). The weaker hypotheses make the proof of Lemma 2.1 more complicated than it is in [3], but the other proofs are not much affected. T. E. Harris has also studied these chains; we shall not use his results but remark that his paper [7] gives additional references and background on the subject. Finally we point out that the restriction to a finite number of states is not essential, and the theorems can be extended to the denumerable case without much change of methods.

Let *I* consist of the integers from 1 to *N* (to represent the states of the chain); we shall use the notation x for a finite sequence $i_0, i_1, \cdots$ of integers from *I*. The subscript "m" on x_m merely adds the specification that the sequence has m terms; the "sum" $x_m + x'$ will be the combined sequence $i_0, \cdots, i_{m-1}, i_0', i_1' \cdots$. The starting point for the theory will be a set of functions $p_i(x)$ defined for all $i \in I$ and all sequences x (including the sequence φ of length zero) and having the properties

$$(2.1) \qquad p_i(x) \geqq 0, \; \sum_i p_i(x) = 1 \; .$$

The function $p_i(x)$ will be interpreted as the conditional probability that a path function of the random process will go next to state i, having just occupied state i_0, previously i_1, etc. With this interpretation in mind we define inductively the "higher transition probabilities":

$$(2.2) \qquad p_i^{(n)}(x) = \sum_{j \in I} p_j(x) p_i^{(n-1)}(j + x) \; ,$$

where of course $p_i^{(1)}(x) = p_i(x)$, the given function. It is easy to see that these higher probabilities also satisfy condition (2.1). The functions $p_i^{(n)}(x)$ are the analogues of the terms of the matrix P^n for a Markov chain with transition matrix P; the theorems we shall give generalize the convergence properties of the matrices P^n.

We shall first impose a positivity condition on the transition probabilities; specifically we assume that for some state j_0, some positive integer n_0, and some $\delta > 0$,

$$(2.3) \qquad p_{j_0}^{(n_0)}(x) > \delta \text{ for every } x \; .$$

We also need to make precise the "slight" dependence of these probabilities on the remote past; indeed, this is the crux of the whole theory. Define

$$(2.4) \qquad \varepsilon_m = \sup |p_i(x + x') - p_i(x + x'')|$$

where the sup is taken over all states i, all sequences x' and x'', and all sequences x which contain the state j_0 at least m times. We shall use the postulate

$$(2.5) \qquad \sum_{m=0}^{\infty} \varepsilon_m < \infty \; .$$

(In [3], ε_m is defined in the same way except that the sup is taken over all x of length at least m. Since this results in larger $\varepsilon_m's$, and since it is also assumed there that $\sum \varepsilon_m < \infty$, our hypotheses are strictly weaker.) Throughout this section, (2.3) and (2.5) will be assumed.

LEMMA 2.1.

$$(2.6) \qquad \lim_{m \to \infty} [\sup |p_i^{(n)}(x + x') - p_i^{(n)}(x + x'')|] = 0 \; ,$$

where the sup is the same as in (2.4) (i.e., x contains j_0 at least m times); the convergence is uniform in n.

Proof. We define quantites $\varepsilon_m^{(k)}$ by using $p_i^{(k)}$ instead of p_i in (2.4); then of course $\varepsilon_m^{(1)} = \varepsilon_m$, and the conclusion of the lemma is equivalent to $\varepsilon_m^{(k)} \to 0$ uniformly in k as $m \to \infty$. Now

$$| p_i^{(k)}(x + x') - p_i^{(k)}(x + x'') |$$
$$= | \sum_j \{p_i^{(k-1)}(j + x + x')p_j(x + x') - p_i^{(k-1)}(j + x + x'')p_j(x + x'')\} |$$
$$\leq \sum_j p_j(x + x')| p_i^{(k-1)}(j + x + x') - p_i^{(k-1)}(j + x + x'')|$$
$$+ \sum_j | p_j(x + x') - p_j(x + x'')| p_i^{(k-1)}(j + x + x'') .$$

Suppose that x contains j_0 m times. Then the second term of the above estimate is less than $N\varepsilon_m$. The absolute value in the first term is less than $\varepsilon_m^{(k-1)}$, but if $j = j_0$ this can be improved to $\varepsilon_{m+1}^{(k-1)}$. Taking account of (2.3) and assuming that $n_0 = 1$, we obtain the estimate

$$(2.7) \qquad \varepsilon_m^{(k)} \leq N\varepsilon_m + \delta\varepsilon_{m+1}^{(k-1)} + (1 - \delta)\varepsilon_m^{(k-1)} .$$

(In case $n_0 > 1$, the same idea can be carried out; the details are more cumbersome and will not be given.)

Now (2.7) can be iterated to obtain an estimate of $\varepsilon_m^{(k)}$ in terms of ε_m. After some computation the result is

$$\varepsilon_m^{(k)} \leq N\varepsilon_m \sum_{i=0}^{k-1}(1 - \delta)^i + N\varepsilon_{m+1}\delta\sum_{i=0}^{k-2}(i + 1)(1 - \delta)^i$$
$$+ \cdots + N\varepsilon_{m+l}\delta^l \sum_{i=0}^{k-l-1}\binom{i + l}{i}(1 - \delta)^i + \cdots + N\delta^{k-1}\varepsilon_{m+k-1} .$$

If the series are extended to infinity, the inequality remains true; calling these (infinite) series $A_0, A_1, \cdots, A_{k-1}$ we have

$$\varepsilon_m^{(k)} \leq N\sum_{i=0}^{k-1}\varepsilon_{m+i}\delta^i A_i .$$

But it can be shown without much difficulty that

$$A_{l+1} - A_l = (1 - \delta)A_{l+1} ,$$

or $A_{l+1} = A_l/\delta$. Since $A_0 = \delta^{-1}$ we obtain $A_l = \delta^{-(l+1)}$, and hence

$$(2.8) \qquad \varepsilon_m^{(k)} \leq \delta^{-1}\sum_{i=0}^{k-1}\varepsilon_{m+i} .$$

Recalling hypothesis (2.5), the uniform convergence of $\varepsilon_m^{(k)}$ follows from (2.8).

LEMMA 2.2.

$$(2.9) \qquad \lim_{n\to\infty} | p_i^{(n)}(x') - p_i^{(n)}(x'')| = 0$$

and the convergence is uniform in x' and x''.

Proof. For clarity we shall use probabilistic arguments, although a purely analytic rephrasing is not hard. Consider two stochastic processes operating independently with transition probabilities $p_i(x)$, one with the sequence x' for its past history up to time 0 and the other with x''. In view of Lemma 2.1, for any $\varepsilon > 0$ there is an m such that if the two processes have occupied the same states for a period which includes j_0 at least m times and ends sometime before time n, then their probabilities of being in state i at time n differ by at most $\varepsilon/2$. But it follows from condition (2.3) that with probability one, there will sometime be a period of length m during which both processes remain in state j_0. We can take n large enough so that this simultaneous "run" of state j_0 will occur before time n with probability not less than $1 - \varepsilon/2$. For this and all greater values of n, therefore, the two processes have probabilities of occupying state i at time n which differ by at most ε, and this proves (2.9). It is also easy to see from (2.3) and Lemma 2.1 that n can be chosen uniformly in x' and x''.

With this much preparation we shall now prove the first theorem:

THEOREM 2.1. *The quantities*

$$(2.10) \qquad \lim_{n \to \infty} p_i^{(n)}(x) = \pi_i$$

exist, are independent of x, and satisfy $\sum_i \pi_i = 1$; the convergence is uniform in x.

Proof. Applying (2.2) repeatedly, we have

$$p_i^{(n+m)}(x)$$
$$= \sum_{x_m} p_{i_{m-1}}(x) p_{i_{m-2}}(i_{m-1} + x) \cdots p_{i_0}(i_1 + \cdots + i_{m-1} + x) p_i^{(n)}(x_m + x)$$

where $x_m = i_0, i_1, \cdots, i_{m-1}$. Therefore

$$|p_i^{(n+m)}(x) - p_i^{(n)}(x)|$$
$$\leq \sum_{x_m} p_{i_{m-1}}(x) \cdots p_{i_0}(i_1 + \cdots + i_{m-1} + x) | p_i^{(n)}(x_m + x) - p_i^{(n)}(x)|$$

and by Lemma 2.2, for any ε there is an n such that each term within absolute value signs on the right is less than ε. Since the weights $p_{i_{m-1}}(x) \cdots p_{i_0}(i_1 + \cdots + i_{m-1} + x)$ sum to one, we have

$$|p_i^{(n+m)}(x) - p_i^{(n)}(x)| < \varepsilon ,$$

and so $p_i^{(n)}(x)$ has a (uniform in x) limit π_i. Since there are a finite number of states,

$$\sum_i \pi_i = \sum_i \lim_{n \to \infty} p_i^{(n)}(x) = \lim_{n \to \infty} \sum_i p_i^{(n)}(x) = 1 ,$$

and this completes the proof.

Next we shall define joint probabilities. If x_m is $i_0, i_1, \cdots, i_{m-1}$, let

$$(2.11) \qquad p_{x_m}(x') = p_{x_m}^{(1)}(x')$$
$$= p_{i_{m-1}}(x')p_{i_{m-2}}(i_{m-1} + x') \cdots p_{i_0}(i_1 + \cdots + i_{m-1} + x') .$$

This is, of course, the probabilility of executing the sequence of states x_m starting with past history x'. We can define also the higher joint probabilities:

$$(2.12) \qquad p_{x_m}^{(n)}(x') = \sum_{j \in I} p_j(x')p_{x_m}^{(n-1)}(j + x') .$$

Analogues of Lemmas 2.1 and 2.2 can be proved for these quantities by the same arguments used already; in this way it is not difficult to prove

THEOREM 2.2. *The quantities*

$$(2.13) \qquad \lim_{n \to \infty} p_{x_m}^{(n)}(x') = \pi_{x_m}$$

exist, are independent of x', and satisfy $\sum\limits_{i_0 \cdots i_{m-1}} \pi_{x_m} = 1$; *the convergence is uniform in x'.*

REMARK. These two theorems imply the existence of a stationary stochastic process with the $p_i(x)$ for transition probabilities. The idea is that the quantities π_{x_m} can be used to define a probability measure on the "cylinder sets" in the space of infinite sequences of members of I, and this measure can then be extended. This stationary process need not concern us further here.

Finally we will prove convergence theorems for certain "moments" which are useful in studying experimental data. The idea is that if we have a stochastic process with the functions $p_i(x)$ for transition probabilities, the probability $p_i(x_m)$ that the state at time m is i given the past history x_m is itself a random variable, and so it makes sense to study $E(p_i^\nu(x_m))$. More formally, define

$$(2.14) \qquad \alpha_i^\nu(m, x) = \sum_{i_0, \cdots, i_{m-1}} p_i^\nu(x_m + x)p_{x_m}(x)$$

where $p_{x_m}(x)$ is defined by (2.11). Thus $\alpha_i^1(m, x)$ is the same as $p_i^{(m)}(x)$. Theorem 2.1 states that $\lim\limits_{m \to \infty} \alpha_i^1(m, x) = \pi_i$ exists. We shall now prove

THEOREM 2.3. *The quantities*

$$(2.15) \qquad \lim_{m \to \infty} \alpha_i^\nu(m, x) = \alpha_i^\nu$$

exist for every positive integer ν; convergence is uniform in x and the limit is independent of x.

Proof. We use a simple estimate to show that $\alpha_i^\gamma(m, x)$ is a Cauchy sequence:

$$|\alpha_i^\gamma(m + k + h, x) - \alpha_i^\gamma(m + k, x)|$$

$$= |\sum_{x_{m+k+h}} p_i^\gamma(x_{m+k+h} + x)p_{x_{m+k+h}}(x) - \sum_{x_{m+k}} p_i^\gamma(x_{m+k} + x)p_{x_{m+k}}(x)|$$

$$\leq \sum_{x_{m+k+h}} |p_i^\gamma(x_{m+k+h} + x) - p_i^\gamma(x_m + x)|p_{x_{m+k+h}}(x)$$

$$+ \sum_{x_{m+k}} |p_i^\gamma(x_{m+k} + x) - p_i^\gamma(x_m + x)|p_{x_{m+k}}(x)$$

$$+ |\sum_{x_{m+k+h}} p_i^\gamma(x_m + x)p_{x_{m+k+h}}(x) - \sum_{x_{m+k}} p_i^\gamma(x_m + x)p_{x_{m+k}}(x)| .$$

If m is chosen large enough, the first two terms will be arbitrarily small; this involves nothing more than the conditions (resulting from (2.3) and (2.5)) that $\varepsilon_m \to 0$, and that a long sequence x contains j_0 many times with high probability. The last term may be rewritten by carrying out the summation over all the indices except those in x_m; this yields

$$|\sum_{x_m} p_i^\gamma(x_m + x)(p_{x_m}^{(k+h)}(x) - p_{x_m}^{(k)}(x))| \leq \sum_{x_m} |p_{x_m}^{(k+h)}(x) - p_{x_m}^{(k)}(x)|$$

which is small for all h (and for all x) if k is large enough, by Theorem 2.2. Thus if $n = m + k$, $|\alpha_i^\gamma(n + h, x) - \alpha_i^\gamma(n, x)|$ is small for all h, and this proves that the limit (2.15) must exist; the limit is uniform in x since $\alpha_i^\gamma(m, x)$ is uniformly Cauchy. Another estimate along much the same line can be made to show that for any $\varepsilon > 0$,

$$|\alpha_i^\gamma(m + k, x) - \alpha_i^\gamma(m + k, x')| \leq \varepsilon$$

provided m and k are large. Since the limit of $\alpha_i^\gamma(m + k, x)$ exists as $m + k \to \infty$, we can conclude that the limit is the same for all x.

It is also desirable to consider some additional "cross" moments involving $p_i(x_m)$ for several states at once; accordingly we define

$$(2.16) \qquad \alpha_{j_1 j_2 \cdots j_k}^{\nu_1 \nu_2 \cdots \nu_k}(m, x) = \sum_{x_m} p_{j_1}^{\nu_1}(x_m + x)p_{j_2}^{\nu_2}(x_m + x) \cdots p_{j_k}^{\nu_k}(x_m + x)p_{x_m}(x) .$$

The following theorem is then a generalization of Theorem 2.3, which treats the case $k = 1$:

THEOREM 2.4. *The quantities*

$$(2.17) \qquad \lim_{m \to \infty} \alpha_{j_1 \cdots j_k}^{\nu_1 \cdots \nu_k}(m, x) = \alpha_{j_1 \cdots j_k}^{\nu_1 \cdots \nu_k}$$

exist uniformly in x for all non-negative integers $\nu_1 \cdots \nu_k$ and all $j_1 \cdots j_k \in I$, and the limits are independent of x.

The argument used in proving Theorem 2.3 works in this case also with only trivial changes, and need not be repeated. Finally we remark that moments involving several values of n can be considered, and it

can be shown that their limits exist also. This provides a generalization of Theorem 2.2.

3. **Definition of linear learning models.** The models we consider
apply to an experimental situation which consists of a sequence of trials.
On each trial the subject of the experiment makes a response, which is
followed by a reinforcing event. Thus an experiment may be represented
by a sequence $(A_1, E_1, A_2, E_2, \cdots A_n, E_n, \cdots)$ of random variables, where
the choice of letters follows conventions established in the literature:
the value of the random variable A_n is a number j representing the
actual response on trial n, and the value of E_n is a number k representing the reinforcing event on trial n. The relevant data on each trial
may then be represented by an ordered pair (j, k) of integers with
$1 \leq j \leq r$, and $0 \leq k \leq t$, that is, we envisage in general r responses
and $t + 1$ reinforcing events. Any sequence of these pairs of integers
is a sequence of values of the random variables and thus represents a
possible experimental outcome. The general aim of the theory is to
predict the probability distribution of the response random variable when
a particular distribution, or class of distributions, is imposed on the reinforcement random variable.

In dealing with the general linear model with r responses and
$t + 1$ reinforcing events we are following the formulation in Chapter 1
of Bush and Mosteller [2], although our notation is somewhat different,
being closer to Estes [4] and Estes and Suppes [6].

The theory is formulated for the probability of a response on trial
$n + 1$ *given* the entire preceding sequence of responses and reinforcements. For this preceding sequence we use the notation x_n. Thus

$$x_n = (k_n, j_n, k_{n-1}, j_{n-1}, \cdots, k_1, j_1) .$$

(It is convenient to write these sequences in this order, but note that
the numbering here is from past to present, not the reverse as in §2.)
Our single axiom is the following linearity assumption:

Axiom L.   *If $E_n = k$ and $P(x_n) > 0$ then*

$$(3.1) \qquad P(A_{n+1} = j | x_n) = (1 - \theta_k) P(A_n = j | x_{n-1}) + \theta_k \lambda_{jk} ,$$

where $0 \leq \theta_k, \lambda_{jk} \leq 1$ and $\sum_j \lambda_{jk} = 1$.

We obtain the linear model studied intensitively in [6] by setting:

$$(3.2) \qquad \begin{cases} \theta_k = \theta & \text{for } k \neq 0 \\ \theta_k = 0 & \text{for } k = 0 \\ \lambda_{jj} = 1 \\ \lambda_{jk} = 0 & \text{for } j \neq k \\ \quad t = r . \end{cases}$$

A linear model satisfying (3.2) we shall term an *Estes Model*, and for such models (3.1) may be replaced by the simpler condition:

$$(3.3) \quad P(A_{n+1} = j \,|\, x_n) = \begin{cases} (1 - \theta)P(A_n = j \,|\, x_{n-1}) + \theta & \text{if } E_n = j \\ (1 - \theta)P(A_n = j \,|\, x_{n-1}) & \text{if } E_n = k,\ k \neq 0,\ k \neq j \\ P(A_n = j \,|\, x_{n-1}) & \text{if } E_n = 0 \,. \end{cases}$$

Axiom L satisfies the combining classes condition of Bush and Mosteller. Upon replacing θ by $1 - \alpha$ in (3.1) essentially their general formulation of the linear model is obtained, although they do not explicitly indicate dependence on the sequence x_n.

We also define here certain moments which are of experimental interest and whose asymptotic properties we investigate subsequently. The *moments* $\alpha^\nu_{j,n}$ of the response probabilities at trial n are:

$$(3.4) \qquad \alpha^\nu_{j,n} = \sum_{x_{n-1}} P^\nu(A_n = j \,|\, x_{n-1})P(x_{n-1}) \,.$$

And if the appropriate limits exist, we define

$$(3.5) \qquad \alpha^\nu_j = \lim_{n \to \infty} \alpha^\nu_{j,n} \,.$$

The moments (3.4) are formed in an unsymmetrical way; however, they enter in a natural way in the expression of quantities which are easily observed experimentally—for instance, the joint probability $P(A_{n+1} = j, A_n = j)$. (For other examples, see [6].)

We are also interested in studying extensions of the linear model to multiperson situations. We may suppose that we have s subjects in a situation such that the probability of a particular reinforcing event for any one subject will depend in general on preceding responses and reinforcements of the other $s - 1$ subjects as well as on his own prior responses and reinforcements. The data on each trial may then be represented by an ordered $2s$-tuple $(j_1, k_1, \cdots, j_s, k_s)$ of integers with $1 \leq j_i \leq r_i$, $0 \leq k_i \leq t_i$, for $i = 1, \cdots, s$, and any sequence of such tuples represents a possible experimental outcome. Let $A^{(i)}_n$ and $E^{(i)}_n$ be the response and reinforcement random variables for the ith subject on trial n. We may then generalize Axiom L to:

Axiom M. For $1 \leq i \leq s$, if $E^{(i)}_n = k$ and $P(x_n) > 0$ then

$$(3.6) \qquad P(A^{(i)}_{n+1} = j \,|\, x_n) = (1 - \theta^{(i)}_\nu)P(A^{(i)}_n = j \,|\, x_{n-1}) + \theta^{(i)}_k \lambda^{(i)}_{jk} \,,$$

where $0 \leq \theta^{(i)}_k$, $\lambda^{(i)}_{jk} \leq 1$ *and* $\sum_j \lambda^{(i)}_{jk} = 1$.

Experimental tests of Axiom M for two-person situations are reported in Estes [5] and in Atkinson and Suppes [1]. Let $x^{(i)}_{n-1}$ be just the sequence of first $n - 1$ responses and reinforcements of subject i. It is a consequence[1] of Axiom M that

$$P(A_n^{(i)} = j \mid x_{n-1}^{(i)}) = P(A_n^{(i)} = j \mid x_{n-1}) \,,$$

and it is in terms of $x_{n-1}^{(i)}$ that we define moments $\alpha_{\nu,j,n}^{(i)}$ exactly analogous to (3.4). We shall also be interested in the joint moments

$$(3.7) \qquad \gamma_{j_1,\dots,j_s,n}^{\nu} = \sum_{x_{n-1}} P^{\nu}(A_n^{(1)} = j_1, \cdots, A_n^{(s)} = j_s \mid x_{n-1}) P(x_{n-1}) \,,$$

and their asymptotes $\gamma_{j_1,\dots,j_s}^{\nu}$ if they exist. To work with these latter moments in terms of Axiom M we need the additional reasonable assumption that when all the $n - 1$ preceding responses and reinforcements are given, the s responses on trial n are statistically independent:

AXIOM I.   If $P(x_{n-1}) > 0$ then

$$P(A_n^{(1)} = j_1, \cdots, A_n^{(s)} = j_s \mid x_{n-1}) = \prod_{i=1}^{s} P(A_n^{(i)} = j_i \mid x_{n-1}) \,.$$

The experimental restriction implied by Axiom I has been satisfied in the multiperson studies employing the linear model.

4. Asymptotic theorems for learning models.   After dealing with some matters of notation, we state general theorems on the existence of asymptotic moments. The hypotheses of the theorems give some broad conditions which guarantee ergodic behavior. We begin with the one-person models satisfying Axiom L.

In this section it will be convenient to use some of the notation of §2. Thus we may write $P(A_n = j \mid x_m + x')$ in place of $P(A_n = j \mid x_{n-1})$ to indicate we are interested in the last m terms of x_{n-1}. The "sum" $x_m + x'$ is just the combined sequence x_{n-1}. We reserve the subscript m for counting back m trials from a given trial n.

To clarify the general theorem it is desirable to define in an exact way the notion of the conditional probability of a reinforcing event depending on only a finite number m of past trial outcomes and independent of the trial number.

DEFINITION.   A linear model has a *reinforcement schedule with past dependence of length* m if, and only if, for all k, n and n' with n, $n' > m$ and all x_m, x' and x''

$$(4.1) \qquad P(E_n = k \mid x_m + x') = P(E_{n'} = k \mid x_m + x'') \,.$$

(It is understood that x_m includes the response $A_{j,n}$ which precedes $E_{k,n}$ on trial n.) It is to be noticed that the use of n on one side and n' on the other side of (4.1) yields independence of trial number. The term

---

[1] Proof of this fact is analogous to that of Theorem 4.8 of [6].

reinforcement schedule has been used because of its frequent occurrence with approximately this meaning in the experimental literature. For the conditional probabilities of (4.1) we shall use the notation

(4.2) $$\pi_{k, x_m} = P(E_n = k \mid x_m + x) .$$

We may now state the first general theorem.

THEOREM 4.1.   *Let $\mathscr{L}$ be a linear model such that*

(i)   *$\mathscr{L}$ has a reinforcement schedule with past dependence of length m^*,*

(ii)   *there is an integer k^* such that*

(a)   *$\theta_{k^*} \neq 0$*

(b)   *there is a δ^* and an m_0 such that for all sequences x and all integers n*

$$P(E_{n+m_0} = k^* \mid x_n) \geqq \delta^* > 0 .$$

Then the asymptotic moments $\alpha_j^{\prime}$ of $\mathscr{L}$ all exist and are independent of the initial distribution of responses.

Proof.   The central task is to characterize $\mathscr{L}$ as a chain of infinite order and show that satisfaction of the hypotheses of the theorem implies satisfaction of conditions (2.3) and (2.5). With this accomplished the asymptotic theorems of §2 may be applied to $\mathscr{L}$. It is most convenient to take as states of the chain the ordered pairs (j, k), where j is the response on trial n, say, and k is the reinforcement on the *preceding* trial. Consider now the reinforcement k^* of the hypothesis of the theorem. Let j^* be a response such that $\lambda_{j^* k^*} \neq 0$. (There is at least one such j^* since $\sum_j \lambda_{jk} = 1$; in the Estes model $j^* = k^*$.) With the pair (j^*, k^*) as the state j_0 of the infinite order chain, we shall establish (2.3) and (2.5).

To verify (2.3), we use (ii)b of the hypothesis and the following equalities and inequalities, which hold for all x and n:

$$P(A_{n+m_0+1} = j^*, E_{n+m_0} = k^* \mid x_n)$$
$$= \sum_{x_{m_0-1}} P(A_{n+m_0+1} = j^* \mid E_{n+m_0} = k^*, x_{m_0-1} + x_n)$$
$$\cdot P(E_{n+m_0} \mid x_{m_0-1} + x_n) P(x_{m_0-1} \mid x_n) .$$

Applying Axiom, L, the right-hand side becomes:

$$= \sum_{x_{m_0-1}} [(1 - \theta_{k^*}) P(A_{n+m_0} = j^* \mid x_{m_0-1} + x_n) + \theta_{k^*} \lambda_{j^* k^*}]$$
$$\cdot P(E_{n+m_0} = k^* \mid x_{m_0-1} + x_n) \cdot P(x_{m_0-1} \mid x_n)$$
$$\geqq \theta_{k^*} \lambda_{j^* k^*} \sum_{x_{m_0-1}} P(E_{n+m_0} = k^* \mid x_{m_0-1} + x_n) P(x_{m_0-1} \mid x_n)$$
$$\geqq \theta_{k^*} \lambda_{j^* k^*} P(E_{n+m_0} = k^* \mid x_n)$$
$$\geqq \theta_{k^*} \lambda_{j^* k^*} \delta^* \qquad\qquad\qquad\qquad\qquad \text{by (ii)b .}$$

To establish (2.5), consider the following equalities and inequalities:

(4.3) $|P(A_{n'+1} = j, E_{n'} = k \,|\, x + x') - P(A_{n''+1} = j, E_{n''} = k \,|\, x + x'')|$

$= \pi_{k, x_{m*}} |P(A_{n'+1} = j \,|\, E_{n'} = k, x + x') - P(A_{n''+1} = j \,|\, E_{n''} = k, x + x'')|\,,$

where x_{m*} means the last m^* terms of x, and where the sequence x contains at least m occurrences of k^*, with $m > m^*$. The equality follows from (i) of the hypothesis, for by virtue of (i)

$$\pi_{k, x_{m*}} = P(E_{n'} = k \,|\, x + x') = P(E_{n''} = k \,|\, x + x'') \,.$$

Applying Axiom L once to the right-hand side of (4.3) we get, ignoring $\pi_{k, x_{m*}}$:

$$|P(A_{n'+1} = j \,|\, E_{n'} = k, x + x') - P(A_{n''+1} = j \,|\, E_{n''} = k, x + x'')|$$
$$= (1 - \theta_k) |P(A_{n'} = j \,|\, x + x') - P(A_{n''} = j \,|\, x + x'')| \,.$$

We do not know that $\theta_k \neq 0$, but as we apply Axiom L repeatedly, we obtain the factor $(1 - \theta_{k*})$ at least m times, so that

(4.4) $|P(A_{n'+1} = j, E_{n'} = k \,|\, x + x') - P(A_{n''+1} = j, E_{n''} = k \,|\, x + x'')|$

$\leq (1 - \theta_{k*})^m |P(A_{n'-h} = j \,|\, x') - P(A_{n''-h} \,|\, x'')| \,,$

where h is the length of x^2. The difference term on the right of this inequality is not more than 1, so that from (4.4) we obtain the estimate for $m > m^*$

$$\varepsilon_m \leq (1 - \theta_{k*})^m \,,$$

whence

$$\sum_{m=0}^{\infty} \varepsilon_m < \infty \,,$$

which is (2.5).

On the basis of (2.3) and (2.5) we know from Theorem 2.4 that the asymptotic cross-moments of $\mathcal{L}$ exist and are independent of the initial distribution of responses. But

$$P(A_n = j \,|\, x_{n-1}) = \sum_k P(A_n = j, E_{n-1} = k \,|\, x_{n-1}) \,,$$

and so the moments $\alpha_{j,n}^{\nu}$ can be expressed as sums of the cross-moments for the infinite order chain $\mathcal{L}$, which insures the existence of the limiting moments (3.5) and that they do not depend upon initial conditions.

There are several remarks to be made about the theorem just

---

[2] If all $\theta_k \neq 0$, the original condition given in [3] would be satisfied; our weaker condition (2.5) allows inclusion of cases where some of the θ_k are 0 (i.e. where there can be trials without a reinforcement).

proved. First, we observe that a simple sufficient (but not necessary) condition for (ii)b is

$$(4.5) \qquad\qquad \min_{x_{m*}} \pi_{k^*, x_{m*}} \neq 0 .$$

The interpretation of (4.5) is that the reinforcing event k^* has positive probability on every trial no matter what sequence x_{m*} of responses and reinforcements preceded. A number of interesting experimental cases of the linear model can be described in terms of (4.5), (i) and (ii)a of Theorem 4.1.

I. *Contingent case with lag v.* In the Estes model let $P(E_n = k \,|\, A_{n-v} = j, x) = \pi_{kj}(v)$, for all x such that $P(A_{n-v} = j, x) > 0$. To satisfy (4.5), we need only that for some k, $\pi_{jk}(v) \neq 0$ for all j. Experimental data for $v = 0, 1, 2$ are given in Estes [5].

II. *Double contingent case.* Let

$$P(E_n = k \,|\, A_n = j, A_{n-1} = j', x) = \pi_{k, jj'} ,$$

for all x such that $P(A_n = j, A_{n-1} = j', x) > 0$.

Then (i) of Theorem (4.1) is immediately satisfied, and for (ii)a and (4.5) we need a k such that $\theta_k \neq 0$ and for all j and j', $\pi_{k,jj'} \neq 0$.

An interesting fact about (I) and (II) is that although they are simple to test experimentally and their asymptotic response moments exist on the basis of Theorem 4.1, there is no known constructive method for computing the actual asymptotes. (The Estes [5] test of (I) excludes non-reinforced trials which cause the computational difficulties.) It may also be noted that the convergence theorems in Karlin [8] do not in general apply to (II), and apply to (I) only if $v = 0$.

On the basis of the proof of Theorem 4.1 we may, by virtue of Theorem 2.2, conclude that the asymptotic joint probabilities of successive responses also exist:

COROLLARY 1. *If the hypothesis of Theorem 4.1 is satisfied, then for every m the limit as $n \to \infty$ of*

$$P(A_{n+m} = j_m, A_{n+m-1} = j_{m-1}, \cdots, A_n = j_0)$$

exists.

We may regard the quantities $P(A_n = j \,|\, x_{n-1})$, for $1 \leq j \leq r$ as a random probability vector with an arbitrary joint distribution F_1 on trial 1, and distribution F_n on trial n. The following corollary is a consequence of the existence of the moments α_j^γ independent of the initial response probabilities.

COROLLARY 2. *If the hypothesis of Theorem 4.1 is satisfied, then there is a unique asymptotic distribution F_∞, independent of F_1 to which the distributions F_n converge.*

For the multiperson situation characterized by Axioms I and M, we have a theorem analogous to Theorem 4.1. For use in the hypothesis of this theorem we define the notion of *reinforcement schedule with past dependence of length m*, exactly as we did in (4.1), namely, we have such a schedule if for all k, $1 \leq i \leq s$, all n and n' with $n, n' > m$ and all x_m, x' and x''

$$\pi_{k^{(1)}, \cdots, k^{(s)}, x_m} = P(\underline{E}_n^{(1)} = k^{(1)}, \cdots, \underline{E}_n^{(s)} = k^{(s)} | x_m + x')$$
$$= P(E_n^{(1)} = k^{(1)}, \cdots, E_n^{(s)} = k^{(s)} | x_m + x'') .$$

THEOREM 4.2. *Let $\mathscr{M}$ be an s-person linear model such that*

(i) *$\mathscr{M}$ has a reinforcement schedule with past dependence of length m^*,*

(ii) *there are integers $k^{(i)*}$, for $1 \leq i \leq s$, such that*

(a) *$\theta_{k^{(i)*}}^{(i)} \neq 0$,*

(b) *there is a δ^* and an m_0 such that for all sequences x and all integers n*

$$P(E_{n+m_0}^{(1)} = k^{(1)*}, \cdots, E_{n+m_0}^{(s)} = k^{(s)*} | x_n) \geq \delta^* > 0 .$$

Then the asymptotic moments $\gamma_{j^{(1)}, j^{(2)}, \cdots, j^{(s)}}^\nu$ of $\mathscr{M}$ all exist and are independent of the initial distribution of responses.

Proof. The states of the chain are now defined as $2s$-tuples $(i^{(1)}, \cdots, j^{(s)}, k^{(1)}, \cdots, k^{(s)})$, where $j^{(i)}$ is the response made by the ith subject and $k^{(i)}$ is the reinforcement for that subject on the preceding trial. Using the reinforcements $k^{(i)*}$ of the hypothesis, let $j^{(i)*}$ be such that $\lambda_{j^{(i)*}k^{(i)*}}^{(i)} \neq 0$. We take $(j^{(1)*}, \cdots, j^{(s)*}, k^{(1)*}, \cdots, k^{(s)*})$ as the state j_0 for which we establish (2.3) and (2.5). To simplify notation, it is convenient to define:

$$P_{n+1}(j, k | x) = P(A_{n+1}^{(1)} = j^{(1)}, \cdots, A_{n+1}^{(s)} = j^{(s)}, E_n^{(1)} = k^{(1)}, \cdots, E_n^{(s)} = k^{(s)} | x),$$
$$p_{n+1}(j^{(i)} | k, x) = P(A_{n+1}^{(i)} = j^{(i)} | E_n^{(1)} = k^{(1)}, \cdots, E_n^{(s)} = k^{(s)}, x) ,$$
$$\pi_{k, m^*} = \pi_{k^{(1)}, \cdots, k^{(s)*}, x_{m^*}} .$$

Moreover, we omit the superscript notation from θ and λ.

To verify (2.3) we proceed exactly as in the proof of Theorem 4.1, applying now Axioms I and M instead of L, and we obtain that

$$p_{n+m_0+1}(j, k | x_n) \geq \prod_{i=1}^{s} \theta_{k^{(i)*}} \lambda_{j^{(i)*} k^{(i)*}} \delta^* .$$

For (2.5), we first observe that by virtue of (i) of the hypothesis and Axiom I

$$|p_{n'+1}(j, k | x + x') - p_{n''+1}(j, k | x + x'')|$$
$$= \pi_{k,m*}|\prod_{i=1}^{s} p_{n'+1}(j^{(i)}|k, x + x') - \prod_{i=1}^{s} p_{n''+1}(j^{(i)}|k, x + x'')| .$$

We notice next that the right-hand side is

$$\leq \pi_{k,m*}\Big\{ p_{n'+1}(j^{(1)}|k, x + x')|\prod_{i=2}^{s} p_{n'+1}(j^{(i)}|k, x + x')$$
$$- \prod_{i=2}^{s} p_{n''+1}(j^{(i)}|k, x + x'')|$$
$$+ \prod_{i=2}^{s} p_{n''+1}(j^{(i)}|k, x+x'')|p_{n'+1}(j^{(1)}|k, x + x')-p_{n''+1}(j^{(1)}|k, x + x'')| .$$

Continuing this same development, we obtain:

$$\leq \sum_{i=1}^{s} |p_{n'+1}(j^{(i)}|k, x + x') - p_{n''+1}(j^{(i)}|k, x + x'')| .$$

And by the line of reasoning used in the proof of Theorem 4.1, if the sequence x contains state $(j^{(1)*}, \cdots, k^{(s)*})$ at least m times the last quantity is

$$\leq \sum_{i=1}^{s} (1 - \theta_{k^{(i)*}})^{m} .$$

Provided $m > m^*$ this inequality yields an estimate of ε_m from which we conclude that (2.5) holds. The existence of the asymptotic moments then follows from the theory of §2 as in the case of Theorem 4.1. Q.E.D.

A pair of corollaries follow from the theorem just proved which are exactly like the two given after Theorem 4.1.

Finally, we want to remark that Axiom L involves linear functions which are distance diminishing, i.e., have slope less than one. The asymptotic results of this section apply to many learning models in which these linear functions are replaced by non-linear functions having this property.

REFERENCES

1. Richard C. Atkinson, and Patrick Suppes, *An analysis of two-person game situations in terms of statistical learning theory*, J. of Experimental Psychology, **55** (1958), 369–378.
2. Robert R. Bush, and Frederick Mosteller, *Stochastic Models for Learning*, New York, 1955.
3. W. Doeblin, and R. Fortet, *Sur des chaines à liaisons complètes*, Bull. Soc. Math. France, **65** (1937), 132–148.
4. W. K. Estes, *Theory of learning with constant, variable, or contingent probabilities of reinforcement*, Psychometrika, **22** (1957), 113–132.
5. ———, *Of models and men*, Amer. Psychologist, **12** (1957), 609–617.

6. W. K. Estes, and Patrick Suppes, *Foundations of Statistical Learning Theory*, I. *The Linear Model for Simple Learning*, Technical Report No. 16, Contract Nonr 225(17), Applied Mathematics and Statistics Laboratory, Stanford University, 1957. An abridged version appears as Chapter 8 of *Studies in Mathematical Learning Theory*, edited by R. R. Bush and W. K. Estes, Stanford University Press, 1959.

7. T. E., Harris, *On chains of of infinite order*, Pacific J. Math., **5** (1955), 707–724.

8. Samuel Karlin, *Some random walks arising in learning models* I, Pacific J. Math., **3** (1953), 725–756.

9. Maurice Kennedy, *A convergence theorem for a certain class of Markoff processes*, Pacific J. Math., **7** (1957), 1107–1124.

STANFORD UNIVERSITY

FINITE MARKOV PROCESSES IN PSYCHOLOGY*

GEORGE A. MILLER

MASSACHUSETTS INSTITUTE OF TECHNOLOGY

Finite Markov processes are reviewed and considered for their usefulness in the description of behavioral data. The various alternative responses in an experimental situation define a vector space, and changes in the probabilities of these alternatives are represented by movements in this space. Methods of fitting the theory to experimental data are considered.

The simplest process, with a constant matrix of transitional probabilities that is applied repeatedly to represent the effect of successive trials, seems inadequate for most learning data. A matrix function that may be useful for learning theory is presented.

In the two general areas where psychology has been relatively successful as a quantitative science, i.e., sensory psychology and test construction, probabilistic considerations long ago proved their worth. It is characteristic of these two areas, however, that the observations are relatively invariant in time. The basic parameters can be explored at length because sequential effects of measurement are secondary and can be ignored or randomized. This fortunate situation makes it possible to use familiar probability models based upon independent random variables.

With the more dynamic problems of psychology, however, this familiar model has not often led to profitable results. For example, it is intrinsic in the very notion of learning that successive measurements are not independent; attempts to use a theory of independent variables must either fail or misrepresent the basic process. Such failures may lead to a rejection of statistical concepts as inadequate; a more proper attitude is to abandon the assumption of independence and ask what help can be had from dependent probabilities. The simplest mathematical models incorporating dependent probabilities are the finite Markov processes. In this paper such processes are examined for their usefulness and their limitations for describing psychological data.

1. *Simple Markov Chains with Two Alternatives.* The data from psychological experiments usually come in the form of sequences of choices embedded in the time continuum. Often it is possible to ignore the temporal order in which alternative choices occur. The purpose of this discussion,

*This article was written at the Institute for Advanced Study in Princeton, New Jersey, while the author was on sabbatical leave from Harvard University.

This article appeared in *Psychometrika,* 1952, **17**, 149–167. Reprinted with permission.

however, is to examine situations in which the temporal sequence should not be ignored. We shall adopt the Markovian model of dependent probabilities to discuss such sequences. We begin, therefore, with the simplest possible example of a Markov chain.

Consider an experiment in which only two alternative responses are possible. A trial consists of a choice of one of these two alternatives. If the letters A and B designate these choices, then a sequence of trials might produce the sequence of responses $ABBAAABA \ldots$, where the durations and latencies are ignored. We shall assume that this sequence is produced by a Markov process; i.e., that the distribution of probabilities at trial $n + 1$ depends upon the outcome of trial n. However, the knowledge of outcomes prior to n does not change our description of the system if we know the outcome of trial n. In other words, the present state of the system governs its future development.

We adopt the following notation:

n	number of the trial: 0, 1, 2, $\ldots$.
A and B	the two alternative responses.
$p^{(n)}(A)$	probability of alternative A at trial n.
$p(A)$	asymptotic value of $p^{(n)}(A)$ as $n \to \infty$.
d_n	the set of absolute probabilities at trial n, considered as a vector; $[p^{(n)}(A), p^{(n)}(B)]$.
$p_A(B)$	given A at n, the conditional probability of B at $n + 1$.
$p_A^{(m)}(B)$	given A at n, the conditional probability of B at $n + m$, $m = 2, 3, \ldots$.
T	matrix of transitional probabilities.
λ_i	characteristic roots of the matrix T.

Alternative A can occur at trial $n + 1$ in either of two ways. Either it follows an A on trial n, or it follows a B on trial n. Similarly, B can occur at $n + 1$ in either of two ways. This obvious fact leads to the following equations:

$$p^{(n)}(A)p_A(A) + p^{(n)}(B)p_B(A) = p^{(n+1)}(A)$$
$$p^{(n)}(A)p_A(B) + p^{(n)}(B)p_B(B) = p^{(n+1)}(B). \tag{1}$$

In matrix notation these equations can be written

$$\begin{Bmatrix} p_A(A) & p_B(A) \\ p_A(B) & p_B(B) \end{Bmatrix} \begin{Bmatrix} p^{(n)}(A) \\ p^{(n)}(B) \end{Bmatrix} = \begin{Bmatrix} p^{(n+1)}(A) \\ p^{(n+1)}(B) \end{Bmatrix}. \tag{2}$$

The reader is assumed to be familiar with the elements of matrix theory. If the distribution of probabilities on trials n and $n + 1$ is regarded as the vectors d_n and d_{n+1} in a two-dimensional space, then the square matrix of transitional probabilities is a linear transformation or operator mapping d_n into d_{n+1}. Thus we can write Eq. (2) as

$$Td_n = d_{n+1} . \tag{3}$$

Any sequence of distributions can be produced by operating upon the successive d_i by appropriate transformations. For the moment, however, we shall consider a special case. We shall assume that repeated trials can be represented as repeated transformations by the same operator. Thus we can write for the initial trial:

$$Td_0 = d_1 .$$

A second trial carries d_1 into d_2 :

$$Td_1 = d_2 .$$

In terms of d_0 , therefore, we can write:

$$Td_1 = T(Td_0) = T^2 d_0 = d_2 .$$

Or more generally,

$$T^n d_0 = d_n . \tag{4}$$

Since the probabilities of A and B on successive trials are given by $T^n d_0$, we proceed to examine the powers of T. The elements of T^n are $p_i^{(n)}(j)$, where $i = A,B$; $j = A,B$. We wish to find a general expression for T^n in terms of $p_i(j)$ and n. From matrix theory we know that every square matrix with distinct roots is similar* to a diagonal matrix whose diagonal elements are the characteristic roots λ_i of T. We designate this similar diagonal matrix by Λ, and write

$$\Lambda = S^{-1}TS,$$

where S is a matrix whose columns are the characteristic vectors of T. From this we obtain

$$T = S\Lambda S^{-1}.$$

To obtain the powers of T we note that

$$T^2 = S\Lambda S^{-1}S\Lambda S^{-1} = S\Lambda^2 S^{-1},$$

or more generally,

$$T^n = S\Lambda^n S^{-1}. \tag{5}$$

Powers of Λ are simply calculated, for since Λ is a diagonal matrix, its powers are given by the powers of the diagonal elements λ_i .

To find Λ for the matrix of Eq. (2) we first write the characteristic equation for the matrix T. If we use the fact that $p_A(A) + p_A(B) = 1$ (and

---

*Two matrices are said to be similar when they have the same characteristic roots.

similarly for B subscripts), the determinantal equation can be written in the convenient form

$$\det (T - \lambda I) = \lambda^2 - [p_A(A) + p_B(B)]\lambda + [p_A(A) - p_B(A)] = 0.$$

The roots of this equation are the characteristic roots of the matrix:

$$\lambda_1 = 1 \quad \text{and} \quad \lambda_2 = p_A(A) - p_B(A).$$

Since the sums of all the columns of T are unity, we note that unity is always a root of these matrices. Substituting these roots into $Tv_i = \lambda_i v_i$ and solving for the characteristic vectors, v_i , we obtain the vectors $[1, p_A(B)/p_B(A)]$ and $(1, -1)$. These vectors comprise the columns of S, and so from Eq. (5) we obtain, after inverting S,

$$T^n = \begin{Bmatrix} 1 & 1 \\ \dfrac{p_A(B)}{p_B(A)} & -1 \end{Bmatrix} \begin{Bmatrix} 1^n & 0 \\ 0 & [p_A(A) - p_B(A)]^n \end{Bmatrix} \dfrac{1}{p_A(B) + p_B(A)}$$

$$\cdot \begin{Bmatrix} p_B(A) & p_B(A) \\ p_A(B) & -p_B(A) \end{Bmatrix}. \quad (6)$$

Eq. (6) can be written more conveniently

$$T^n = \dfrac{1}{p_A(B) + p_B(A)} \begin{Bmatrix} p_B(A) & p_B(A) \\ p_A(B) & p_A(B) \end{Bmatrix}$$

$$+ \dfrac{[p_A(A) - p_B(A)]^n}{p_A(B) + p_B(A)} \begin{Bmatrix} p_A(B) & -p_B(A) \\ -p_A(B) & p_B(A) \end{Bmatrix}. \quad (7)$$

Since $| p_A(A) - p_B(A) | < 1$, the second term on the right of Eq. (7) goes to zero as $n \to \infty$, so the first term represents the asymptotic form of T^n.

With Eq. (7) we can calculate $T^n d_0$, and so obtain the probability of A on successive trials:

$$p^{(n)}(A) = \dfrac{p_B(A)}{p_A(B) + p_B(A)}$$

$$+ [p(A) - p(A)]^n \dfrac{p^{(0)}(A)p_A(B) - p^{(0)}(B)p_B(A)}{p_A(B) + p_B(A)}. \quad (8)$$

The value of

$$p^{(n)}(A) \to \dfrac{p_B(A)}{p_A(B) + p_B(A)} \text{ as } n \to \infty.$$

It is apparent that Eq. (8) can be written

$$p^{(n)}(A) = a(1 - be^{-cn}), \quad (9)$$

where

$$a = \frac{p_B(A)}{p_A(B) + p_B(A)},$$

$$b = -p^{(0)}(A) \frac{p_A(B)}{p_B(A)} + p^{(0)}(B),$$

$$c = -\ln [p_A(A) - p_B(A)].$$

Eq. (9) is an exponential growth function—a form frequently used to describe data from learning experiments. It should be noted, however, that while the average subject may follow such a learning function, the individual subjects are generating stationary time series that do not represent learning. The term "learning" probably should be reserved for those cases in which the matrix operator changes on successive trials.

We shall illustrate the use of the Markov chain with a numerical example. Suppose that two alternative responses are called right (R) and wrong (W), that $p^{(n)}(R)$ and $p^{(n)}(W)$ are measured by the percentage of subjects in a large sample that choose R and W on trial n, and that the transitional probabilities observed on successive pairs of trials are constant. Assume the following numerical values for $T\, d_0 = d_1$:

$$\begin{Bmatrix} .97 & .27 \\ .03 & .73 \end{Bmatrix} \begin{Bmatrix} 0 \\ 1 \end{Bmatrix} = \begin{Bmatrix} .27 \\ .73 \end{Bmatrix}.$$

A right response is followed by another right response 97 per cent of the time; wrong follows wrong 73 per cent of the time. From Eq. (8) we calculate that the successive values of $p^{(n)}(R)$ are 0, .27, .46, .59, .68, etc., approaching the asymptote of .90. The equation is

$$p^{(n)}(R) = .9(1 - .7^n) \qquad (n = 0, 1, 2, \ldots)$$

If we know that on a particular trial a W occurred, this equation gives the probability of R on the nth succeeding trial.

2. *Autocorrelation Function.* A simple parameter of such Markov chains is the autocorrelation function. We will mention it now because for the more complex cases we wish to consider next the autocorrelation function is either not defined or is most tedious to compute from the matrix of transitional probabilities.

The autocorrelation function is the correlation of a time series with itself displaced 0, 1, 2, $\ldots$ steps. With zero displacement the correlation of the series with itself is, of course, +1. With a displacement of one step, the responses on trials 1, 2, 3, $\ldots$ are correlated with the responses on trials

2, 3, 4, ... If the series of binary choices is fairly long, the autocorrelation after a displacement of one step is given by

$$r_1 = p_A(A) - p_B(A). \tag{10}$$

We note that r_1 is a characteristic root of the matrix of transitional probabilities. More generally,

$$r_m = p_A^{(m)}(A) - p_B^{(m)}(A), \tag{11}$$

where $p_A^{(m)}(A)$ and $p_B^{(m)}(A)$ are elements of T^m. From Eq. (7) we observe that these elements of T^m are

$$p_A^{(m)}(A) = \frac{p_B(A) + p_A(B)[p_A(A) - p_B(A)]^m}{p_A(B) + p_B(A)}$$

and

$$p_B^{(m)}(A) = \frac{p_B(A) - p_B(A)[p_A(A) - p_B(A)]^m}{p_A(B) + p_B(A)}.$$

When these values are substituted in Eq. (11), we obtain

$$r_m = [p_A(A) - p_B(A)]^m = r_1^m. \tag{12}$$

In short, for a simple Markov chain, the autocorrelation between positions n and $n + m$ is the mth power of the autocorrelation between n and $n + 1$. If $|r_1| < 1$, then $|r_m|$ declines monotonically toward zero.

A simple example is provided by the Samoan language. E. B. Newman has noted that the sequence of consonants (C) and vowels (V) in Samoan writing is adequately described as a Markov chain with the following matrix of transitional probabilities:

$$\begin{Bmatrix} p_C(C) & p_V(C) \\ p_C(V) & p_V(V) \end{Bmatrix} = \begin{Bmatrix} 0 & .49 \\ 1 & .51 \end{Bmatrix}.$$

Consonants never follow consonants in written Samoan. The autocorrelation function is easily computed from this matrix. For successive displacements of one letter the value of the correlation coefficient is 1, $-.49$, $.24$, $-.12$, $.06$, $-.03$, etc.

The autocorrelation function for this simple process can also be described as the determinant of T^n. Thus r_0 is the determinant of $T^0 = I$, r_1 is the determinant of T, r_2 is the determinant of T^2, etc.

When the distribution of probabilities at $n + 1$ depends upon events prior to n as well as upon n itself, Eq. (10) still holds as a definition of the autocorrelation function, but Eq. (11) does not hold. When more than two unscaled alternatives are used, the autocorrelation function is not defined.

3. *Extension to More than Two Alternatives.* The extension of the matrix equations to experiments involving more than two alternative responses is straightforward. Designate the alternatives $A, B, C, \ldots, N$. Then we have

$$
\left\{
\begin{matrix}
p_A(A) & p_B(A) & \cdots & p_N(A) \\
p_A(B) & p_B(B) & \cdots & p_N(B) \\
 & & & \\
 \cdot & \cdot & \cdot & \cdot \\
 \cdot & \cdot & \cdot & \cdot \\
 \cdot & \cdot & \cdot & \cdot \\
p_A(N) & p_B(N) & \cdots & p_N(N)
\end{matrix}
\right\}
\left\{
\begin{matrix}
p^{(n)}(A) \\
p^{(n)}(B) \\
\cdot \\
\cdot \\
\cdot \\
p^{(n)}(N)
\end{matrix}
\right\}
=
\left\{
\begin{matrix}
p^{(n+1)}(A) \\
p^{(n+1)}(B) \\
\cdot \\
\cdot \\
\cdot \\
p^{(n+1)}(N)
\end{matrix}
\right\}.
\quad (13)
$$

General solutions are known for certain types of operators. These are of considerable interest in physics and genetics, where the elements of T are given by theory. The present use of such operators is almost purely descriptive, however, for we do not know what special types of matrices will be of the greatest psychological interest.

It is not always necessary to find a general solution. A qualitative understanding of an experimental situation is often provided by simply transforming the initial distribution five or ten steps by direct matrix multiplication. For example, a learning situation might be analyzed into three kinds of responses: correct (C), slightly wrong (S), and grossly wrong (G). During the course of learning a subject begins by making gross mistakes, then slight mistakes, and finally manages to make correct responses. Such a situation could produce a matrix equation like the following:

$$
Td_0 =
\left\{
\begin{matrix}
p_C(C) & p_S(C) & p_G(C) \\
p_C(S) & p_S(S) & p_G(S) \\
p_C(G) & p_S(G) & p_G(G)
\end{matrix}
\right\}
\left\{
\begin{matrix}
p^{(0)}(C) \\
p^{(0)}(S) \\
p^{(0)}(G)
\end{matrix}
\right\}
=
\left\{
\begin{matrix}
.9 & .3 & 0 \\
.1 & .6 & .3 \\
0 & .1 & .7
\end{matrix}
\right\}
\left\{
\begin{matrix}
0 \\
0 \\
1
\end{matrix}
\right\}.
$$

It is tedious to find the general solution of T^n, and it is easy to see by direct multiplication what happens. The proportion of grossly wrong responses declines steadily: 1, .7, .52, .40, .32, .26, $\cdots$, .08. The proportion of small errors on successive trials at first increases, then decreases: 0, .3, .39, .40, .38, .35, $\cdots$, .23. The proportion of correct responses gives a roughly S-shaped function: 0, 0, .09, .20, .30, .38, .45, $\cdots$, .69. This situation is analogous to pouring water from one vessel into a second, which in turn pours the water into a third. The asymptotic distribution can always be found by solving the equation $Td_n = d_n$.

The form of a general solution can be indicated, for finite matrices with distinct roots, as follows. Let λ_i represent the N characteristic roots of the polynomial det $(T - \lambda I)$. We define a set of matrices $f_i(T)$ by

$$
f_i(T)
$$

$$
= \frac{(T - \lambda_1 I)(T - \lambda_2 I) \cdots (T - \lambda_{i-1} I)(T - \lambda_{i+1} I) \cdots (T - \lambda_N I)}{(\lambda_i - \lambda_1)(\lambda_i - \lambda_2) \cdots (\lambda_i - \lambda_{i-1})(\lambda_i - \lambda_{i+1}) \cdots (\lambda_i - \lambda_N)}. \quad (14)
$$

In terms of these matrices, T can be expressed

$$T = \lambda_1 f_1(T) + \lambda_2 f_2(T) + \cdots + \lambda_N f_N(T). \tag{15}$$

If $g(\lambda)$ is a rational scalar polynomial, then

$$g(T) = g(\lambda_1)f_1(T) + g(\lambda_2)f_2(T) + \cdots + g(\lambda_N)f_N(T). \tag{16}$$

In particular, if $g(\lambda) = \lambda^n$, we have

$$T^n = \lambda_1^n f_1(T) + \lambda_2^n f_2(T) + \cdots + \lambda_N^n f_N(T). \tag{17}$$

The 2×2 transformation is expressed in this form in Eq. (7). Concerning the roots λ_i , we know that λ_1 can be assigned the value 1, and that all the other roots fall between -1 and $+1$. Thus the asymptotic value of T^n is given by $f_1(T)$.

The solution for a particular matrix can always be obtained by (a) finding the roots of the characteristic polynomial, $\det(T - \lambda I)$; (b) determining the $f_i(T)$ according to Eq. (14); (c) substituting into Eq. (17); and (d) solving $T^n d_0$ for the given boundary conditions of d_0 . This procedure has the advantage of avoiding the problem of inverting a large matrix, but if two or more roots are nearly the same, the computations may be quite difficult.

The autocorrelation function is not defined for more than two unordered alternatives, because the value of the correlation coefficient varies according to the various possible assignments of numerical values to the different alternatives. However, the determinant of the matrix of transitional probabilities has many of the characteristics of a correlation coefficient, and in the 2×2 case the determinant and the autocorrelation coefficient are identical. The determinant of T^n, as a function of n, lies between $+1$ and -1, declines toward 0 for the Markov processes, and can reveal periodicities in much the same way as an autocorrelation function. The possible usefulness of this extension to $N \times N$ transformations needs to be explored.

4. *Extension to Compound Responses.*   For psychological purposes it is an inconvenience that Markov processes have no memory. We must now remove the restriction that, if the outcome of the trial n is known, events prior to n are irrelevant for predicting the outcome at $n + 1$. We must consider the non-Markovian case. What we must do is to expand the definition of a state of the system in order to make such systems Markovian in a larger space.

If the probabilities at trial $n + 1$ depend upon the outcomes of trials n and $n - 1$, but knowledge of events prior to $n - 1$ does not change our prediction for $n + 1$, we have a non-Markovian system. This system is made to be Markovian by changing the definition of an event. Instead of characterizing the state of the system by the occurrence of a single response, we characterize it by pairs of responses. If there are two atomic alternatives,

A and B, in the original system, then there are four compound alternatives, AA, AB, BA, and BB, in the new system. Thus we must define a distribution d_n over four alternatives, and T is a square matrix of fourth order:

$$Td_n = \begin{Bmatrix} p_{AA}(AA) & 0 & p_{BA}(AA) & 0 \\ p_{AA}(AB) & 0 & p_{BA}(AB) & 0 \\ 0 & p_{AB}(BA) & 0 & p_{BB}(BA) \\ 0 & p_{AB}(BB) & 0 & p_{BB}(BB) \end{Bmatrix} \begin{Bmatrix} p^{(n)}(AA) \\ p^{(n)}(AB) \\ p^{(n)}(BA) \\ p^{(n)}(BB) \end{Bmatrix}$$

$$= \begin{Bmatrix} p^{(n+1)}(AA) \\ p^{(n+1)}(AB) \\ p^{(n+1)}(BA) \\ p^{(n+1)}(BB) \end{Bmatrix} = d_{n+1} \; . \quad (18)$$

Note that many of the transitional probabilities are zero; it is not possible for the system to move from some state to others in a single step. For example, the system cannot move from AA to BB in less than two steps: $AA \rightarrow AB \rightarrow BB$ as in the sequence $AABB$.

Tabulations of sequences of vowels and consonants in written Hebrew have been made by E. B. Newman. The sequence of consonants (A) and vowels (B) can be adequately represented by a matrix of the form of Eq. (18):

$$\begin{Bmatrix} 0 & 0 & .23 & 0 \\ 1 & 0 & .77 & 0 \\ 0 & .81 & 0 & .90 \\ 0 & .19 & 0 & .10 \end{Bmatrix} \begin{Bmatrix} .095 \\ .410 \\ .410 \\ .085 \end{Bmatrix}$$

As before, the transformation T can be applied iteratively to carry any initial distribution into a final, unique, stable distribution.

This extension of the Markov process can be carried as far as the data seem to merit. For example, fixed-ratio reinforcement in operant conditioning requires an animal to respond m times in one way, then approach the food tray. In order to keep track of the sequential aspects of this behavior we could define a state of the system to include all the possible sequences of responses and approaches of length $m + 1$. Thus there would be 2^{m+1} alternative states, and the transformation would be of order 2^{m+1}. More complex sequential dependencies arise in human verbal behavior and can be treated in a similar manner. The verbal case is so complex, however, that it cannot be adequately discussed in this paper.

In principle it is possible to extend the Markov definition indefinitely to take into account as much of the past history of the system as one desires.

Cases are known, however, in which the extension would need to be carried infinitely far into the past in order for the Markov model to summarize all the information. Such cases are better handled in other ways. At present, it seems likely that most learning situations will need to be described by these other methods, and that Markov processes using a single matrix of transitional probabilities are most valuable when the behavior has settled into a relatively stable pattern.

5. *Least-Squares Fit to Data.*   Under the assumption that a single transformation describes the behavior, every trial can be considered a measurement of the single transformation T. We wish to find a least-squares solution that will give the best estimate for T from the available data. The following procedures may not be the most efficient for Markov processes, but they represent one fairly natural extension of the procedures used with more familiar statistical problems.

We introduce a matrix M to represent the observed data. This matrix is formed by placing in successive columns the distributions observed on successive trials, from trial 1 through trial $n - 1$. If each distribution contains a alternative quantities, and n such distributions are known for successive trials, then M is an $a \times (n - 1)$ matrix. A matrix N is formed analogously by placing in successive columns the distributions observed on the successive trials from 2 through n. Thus N is also an $a \times (n - 1)$ matrix. The matrix $\overline{N}$ represents the best estimate of the successive distributions:

$$\overline{N} = N + C, \tag{19}$$

where the elements of the matrix C are the corrections that must be added to the observed values in N to give the best estimate $\overline{N}$.

We wish to determine $\overline{T}$, the best estimate of the transformation. From the definition of M and $\overline{N}$ and the assumption of a single operator throughout learning, we have the equation:

$$\overline{T}M = \overline{N} = N + C. \tag{20}$$

From Eq. (20) we obtain an expression for C:

$$C = -N + \overline{T}M. \tag{21}$$

For a least-squares solution, CC' must be a minimum. This is obtained by putting the partial derivative with respect to $\overline{T}$ to zero:

$$\frac{\partial}{\partial \overline{T}} CC' = MC' = 0. \tag{22}$$

We now substitute for C' from Eq. (21) into Eq. (22) and obtain

$$M(-N + \overline{T}M)' = -MN' + MM'\overline{T}' = 0.$$

Rearranging terms gives

$$\overline{T}' = (MM')^{-1}MN',$$

or

$$\overline{T} = NM'(MM')^{-1}. \tag{23}$$

Eq. 23 provides a best estimate of T on the basis of the data matrices M and N.

As an example, consider an experiment in a T-maze. We decide from an examination of the data that the learning process can be described by a Markov process with a single transformation. Suppose that 10 rats were run for 20 trials, and that on successive trials the following numbers of rats made the correct choice: 5, 7, 6, 6, 8, 8, 8, 7, 8, 9, 8, 7, 8, 9, 10, 10, 8, 8, 9, 9. From these data we construct the matrices:

$$M = \begin{cases} .5 & .7 & .6 & .6 & .8 & .8 & .8 & .7 & .8 & .9 & .8 & .7 & .8 & .9 \\ .5 & .3 & .4 & .4 & .2 & .2 & .2 & .3 & .2 & .1 & .2 & .3 & .2 & .1 \end{cases}$$
$$\begin{aligned} 1.0 & \quad 1.0 & \quad .8 & \quad .8 & \quad .9 \\ 0 & \quad .0 & \quad .2 & \quad .2 & \quad .1 \end{aligned} \Big\}$$

$$N = \begin{cases} .7 & .6 & .6 & .8 & .8 & .8 & .7 & .8 & .9 & .8 & .7 & .8 & .9 & 1.0 \\ .3 & .4 & .4 & .2 & .2 & .2 & .3 & .2 & .1 & .2 & .3 & .2 & .1 & 0 \end{cases}$$
$$\begin{aligned} 1.0 & \quad .8 & \quad .8 & \quad .9 & \quad .9 \\ 0 & \quad .2 & \quad .2 & \quad .1 & \quad .1 \end{aligned} \Big\}.$$

Next we multiply these matrices to obtain

$$NM' = \begin{cases} 12.16 & 3.14 \\ 2.74 & .96 \end{cases}, \qquad MM' = \begin{cases} 11.99 & 2.91 \\ 2.91 & 1.19 \end{cases}.$$

The matrix MM' is easily inverted, and we have

$$\overline{T} = NM'(MM')^{-1} = \begin{cases} 12.16 & 3.14 \\ 2.74 & .96 \end{cases} \begin{cases} 1.19 & -2.91 \\ -2.91 & 11.99 \end{cases} \frac{1}{5.8},$$

$$\overline{T} = \begin{cases} .92 & .39 \\ .08 & .61 \end{cases}.$$

The initial distribution d_0 is $(.5, .5)$, and from Eq. (8) we obtain

$$p^{(n)}(R) = .83 - .33(.63)^n.$$

The values calculated from this equation are .500, .665, .738, .785, .804, ..., approaching .83 as the asymptote. Note that we do not have a least-squares fit of this function, $p^{(n)}(R)$, to the observed data; we have a least-squares fit for the transformation T.

From Eq. (21) we can calculate the corrections that are added to N:

$$\overline{TM} = \begin{cases} .655 & .761 & .708 & .708 & .814 & .814 & .814 & .761 & .814 & .867 \\ .345 & .239 & .292 & .292 & .186 & .186 & .186 & .239 & .186 & .133 \end{cases}$$

$$\begin{matrix} .814 & .761 & .814 & .867 & .920 & .920 & .814 & .814 & .867 \\ .186 & .239 & .186 & .133 & .080 & .080 & .186 & .186 & .133 \end{matrix} \Big\},$$

$$C = \begin{cases} -.045 & .161 & .108 & -.092 & .014 & .014 & .114 & -.039 \\ .045 & -.161 & -.108 & .092 & -.014 & -.014 & -.114 & .039 \end{cases}$$

$$\begin{matrix} -.086 & .067 & .114 & -.039 & -.086 & -.133 & -.080 \\ .086 & -.067 & -.114 & .039 & .086 & .133 & .080 \end{matrix}$$

$$\begin{matrix} .120 & .014 & -.086 & -.033 \\ -.120 & -.014 & .086 & .033 \end{matrix} \Big\}.$$

The squared deviations are given by

$$CC' = \begin{cases} .144 & -.144 \\ -.144 & .144 \end{cases}.$$

The best estimate of the dispersion of the calculated from the observed values is

$$\sigma = \sqrt{\frac{cc'}{n - a - 1}} = \sqrt{\frac{.144}{17}} = .092. \tag{24}$$

The variance-covariance matrix V is given by

$$V = \sigma^2 (MM')^{-1} = \frac{.00847}{5.8} \begin{cases} 1.19 & -2.91 \\ -2.91 & 11.99 \end{cases}. \tag{25}$$

From Eq. (25) we compute the standard deviations of the estimates of $p_A(A)$ and $p_B(B)$:

$$\sigma[p_A(A)] = .092 \sqrt{\frac{1.19}{5.8}} = .04 ,$$

$$\sigma[p_B(B)] = .092 \sqrt{\frac{11.99}{5.8}} = .132.$$

The same procedure can be applied to the data from a single animal. The data matrices M and N then have either 0 or 1 on successive trials; e.g.,

$$M = \begin{Bmatrix} 1 & 0 & 1 & 1 & 1 & 0 & 0 & 1 & 0 & 1 & 1 & \cdots & 0 & 1 & 1 \\ 0 & 1 & 0 & 0 & 0 & 1 & 1 & 0 & 1 & 0 & 0 & \cdots & 1 & 0 & 0 \end{Bmatrix}$$

$$N = \begin{Bmatrix} 0 & 1 & 1 & 1 & 0 & 0 & 1 & 0 & 1 & 1 & 0 & \cdots & 1 & 1 & 1 \\ 1 & 0 & 0 & 0 & 1 & 1 & 0 & 1 & 0 & 0 & 1 & \cdots & 0 & 0 & 0 \end{Bmatrix}.$$

In order to solve for $\overline{T}$ we determine

$$NM' = \begin{Bmatrix} m(1,1) & m(0,1) \\ m(1,0) & m(0,0) \end{Bmatrix}, \qquad MM' = \begin{Bmatrix} m(1) & 0 \\ 0 & m(0) \end{Bmatrix}.$$

The symbol $m(i,j)$ represents the number of occurrences of the ordered pair i,j; $m(i)$ represents the number of occurrences of i; and $m(0) + m(1) = n - 1$, where n is the number of trials. Next we invert MM' and solve for $\overline{T}$:

$$\overline{T} = NM'(MM')^{-1} = \begin{Bmatrix} m(1,1) & m(0,1) \\ m(1,0) & m(0,0) \end{Bmatrix} \begin{Bmatrix} \dfrac{1}{m(1)} & 0 \\ 0 & \dfrac{1}{m(0)} \end{Bmatrix}$$

(26)

$$\overline{T} = \begin{Bmatrix} \dfrac{m(1,1)}{m(1)} & \dfrac{m(0,1)}{m(0)} \\ \dfrac{m(1,0)}{m(1)} & \dfrac{m(0,0)}{m(0)} \end{Bmatrix}.$$

Eq. (26) is the result that would be expected from the definition of the transitional probabilities.

In order to estimate the dispersion we calculate

$$\overline{T}M = \begin{Bmatrix} \dfrac{m(1,1)}{m(1)} & \dfrac{m(0,1)}{m(0)} & \dfrac{m(1,1)}{m(1)} & \cdots & \dfrac{m(1,1)}{m(1)} \\ \dfrac{m(1,0)}{m(1)} & \dfrac{m(0,0)}{m(0)} & \dfrac{m(1,0)}{m(1)} & \cdots & \dfrac{m(1,0)}{m(1)} \end{Bmatrix}.$$

Then from Eq. (21) we find

$$C = \overline{T}M - N = \begin{Bmatrix} \dfrac{m(1,1)}{m(1)} & \dfrac{-m(0,0)}{m(0)} & \dfrac{-m(1,0)}{m(1)} & \cdots & \dfrac{-m(1,0)}{m(1)} \\ \dfrac{-m(1,1)}{m(1)} & \dfrac{m(0,0)}{m(0)} & \dfrac{m(1,0)}{m(1)} & \cdots & \dfrac{m(1,0)}{m(1)} \end{Bmatrix}$$

The squared deviations are given by

$$CC' = \begin{Bmatrix} c & -c \\ -c & c \end{Bmatrix}$$

where

$$c = m(1,1)\left[\frac{m(1,0)}{m(1)}\right]^2 + m(1,0)\left[\frac{m(1,1)}{m(1)}\right]^2 + m(0,1)\left[\frac{m(0,0)}{m(0)}\right]^2$$

$$+ m(0,0)\left[\frac{m(0,1)}{m(0)}\right]^2$$

$$= [m(1,0) + m(1,1)]\left[\frac{m(1,1)}{m(1)}\frac{m(1,0)}{m(1)}\right] + [m(0,0) + m(0,1)]\left[\frac{m(0,1)}{m(0)}\frac{m(0,0)}{m(0)}\right]$$

$$= m(1)\left[\frac{m(1,1)}{m(1)} \cdot \frac{m(1,0)}{m(1)}\right] + m(0)\left[\frac{m(0,1)}{m(0)} \cdot \frac{m(0,0)}{m(0)}\right].$$

The dispersion is, therefore,

$$\sigma = \sqrt{\frac{c}{n - 1 - a}} = \left\{\left[\frac{m(1)}{n - 3} \cdot \frac{m(1,1)}{m(1)} \cdot \frac{m(1,0)}{m(1)}\right]\right.$$

$$\left. + \left[\frac{m(0)}{n - 3} \cdot \frac{m(0,1)}{m(0)} \cdot \frac{m(0,0)}{m(0)}\right]\right\}^{1/2}. \quad (27)$$

The variance-covariance matrix is

$$V = \sigma^2(MM')^{-1} = \frac{c}{n - 3}\left\{\begin{matrix} \frac{1}{m(1)} & 0 \\ 0 & \frac{1}{m(0)} \end{matrix}\right\}$$

and from this matrix we compute

$$\sigma[p_A(A)] = \sigma\sqrt{\frac{1}{m(1)}} \quad \text{and} \quad \sigma[p_B(B)] = \sigma\sqrt{\frac{1}{m(0)}}. \quad (28)$$

Although these examples are worked out for the Markov case with two alternatives, the same procedures can be used with more than two alternatives or with Markov processes defined for compound responses. It should be stressed, however, that the statistical properties of Markov chains are neither simple nor well understood. Better techniques will undoubtedly develop as the Markov process becomes more widely applied.

6. *Variable Transformations.* Up to this point we have made the explicit assumption that a single transformation could describe the successive changes in the probabilities of the alternative responses or alternative sequences of responses. This assumption greatly simplifies the theoretical landscape and should be made whenever the data hint that it might be true. Simplicity is not, however, an intrinsic property of the behavior of living organisms, and so we must be prepared to deal with situations that obviously violate the assumption.

The assumption that a single transformation is adequate means that the transitional probabilities are fixed from the first through the last trial. Since the transitional probabilities determine the sequences of responses that are probable or improbable, we are assuming that the animal's course of action or strategy is fixed throughout the experiment. In a certain sense, therefore, such an assumption means that there is no learning at all; as soon as the experimental situation is encountered for the first time, the subject adopts the set of transitional probabilities that will later describe the statistical properties of his behavior after he has had long experience in the situation.

The assumption of a single transformation would be justified, for example, after a long series of alternate conditioning and extinction. In this experiment the subject is able to evolve a single transformation for the reinforcement conditions and another for the extinction conditions. Or if an animal has adopted a stable mode of behavior in a situation and then is temporarily distracted in some way, his return to normal when the impediment is removed might be expected to follow a single transformation. But in most of the situations that are studied experimentally there is no *a priori* reason to expect that a single transformation will be adequate, and there are several reasons to expect that it will not be.

In order to illustrate what is involved in the assumption of a single transformation, Table I has been prepared to show one case where the assumption is correct and another where the assumption is wrong. Once more we consider the data from 10 rats on 20 consecutive choices in a T-maze. The symbol 1 represents a correct choice, and 0 represents an incorrect choice. In Tables IA and IB the numbers of rats making the correct choice are the same, and both are the same as the example fitted in the preceding section.

TABLE 1

Hypothetical Data for Ten Rats on Twenty Trials in a T-Maze

IA.   Constant Transformation
Trial

Rat	1	2	3	4	5		6	7	8	9	10		11	12	13	14	15		16	17	18	19	20
1	1	1	0	0	0		0	0	0	1	1		1	1	1	1	1		1	1	1	1	1
2	0	0	0	0	0		1	1	1	1	1		1	1	1	1	1		1	0	1	1	1
3	1	1	1	1	1		1	1	1	1	1		1	1	1	1	1		1	1	0	0	0
4	0	1	1	1	1		1	1	1	1	1		0	0	0	0	1		1	1	1	1	1
5	1	1	1	1	1		1	1	1	1	1		1	1	1	1	1		1	0	0	1	1
6	0	1	1	1	1		1	1	1	1	1		1	1	1	1	1		1	1	1	1	1
7	0	0	0	0	1		1	1	1	1	1		1	1	1	1	1		1	1	1	1	1
8	1	1	1	1	1		0	0	0	0	0		0	0	1	1	1		1	1	1	1	1
9	0	0	0	0	1		1	1	1	1	1		1	0	0	1	1		1	1	1	1	1
10	1	1	1	1	1		1	1	0	0	1		1	1	1	1	1		1	1	1	1	1
Σ	5	7	6	6	8		8	8	7	8	9		8	7	8	9	10		10	8	8	9	9

TABLE 1 (*Continued*)

IB. Variable Transformation

Rat	1	2	3	4	5		6	7	8	9	10		11	12	13	14	15		16	17	18	19	20
11	1	0	1	1	1		1	1	1	0	1		1	1	1	1	1		1	1	1	1	1
12	0	0	0	0	1		1	1	1	1	1		0	1	1	1	1		1	0	1	1	1
13	1	1	1	1	1		0	0	1	1	1		1	1	0	0	1		1	1	0	0	0
14	1	1	0	1	1		1	1	1	1	1		1	0	0	1	1		1	1	1	1	1
15	1	1	1	0	1		1	0	0	1	1		1	1	1	1	1		1	0	0	1	1
16	0	1	0	1	1		1	1	1	0	0		1	1	1	1	1		1	1	1	1	1
17	0	1	1	1	0		1	1	1	1	1		1	0	1	1	1		1	1	1	1	1
18	0	1	1	0	0		1	1	0	1	1		1	1	1	1	1		1	1	1	1	1
19	1	0	0	0	1		0	1	0	1	1		1	1	1	1	1		1	1	1	1	1
20	0	1	1	1	1		1	1	1	1	1		0	0	1	1	1		1	1	1	1	1
Σ	5	7	6	6	8		8	8	7	8	9		8	7	8	9	10		10	8	8	9	9

From the data in Table I we can estimate the values of $p_1(1)$ and $p_0(0)$ on successive pairs of trials by $[m(i,j)]/m(i)$:

IA Trial	$p_1(1)$	$p_0(0)$	IB Trial	$p_1(1)$	$p_0(0)$
1–2	1.00	0.60	1–2	0.60	0.20
2–3	0.86	1.00	2–3	0.72	0.67
3–4	1.00	1.00	3–4	0.60	0.50
4–5	1.00	0.25	4–5	0.83	0.25
5–6	0.88	0.50	5–6	0.75	0.00
6–7	1.00	1.00	6–7	0.88	0.50
7–8	0.88	1.00	7–8	0.75	0.50
8–9	1.00	0.67	8–9	0.72	0.00
9–10	1.00	0.50	9–10	0.88	0.50
10–11	0.89	1.00	10–11	0.78	0.00
11–12	0.88	1.00	11–12	0.75	0.50
12–13	1.00	0.67	12–13	0.86	0.33
13–14	1.00	0.50	13–14	1.00	0.50
14–15	1.00	0.00	14–15	1.00	0.00
15–16	1.00	....	15–16	1.00	....
16–17	0.80	....	16–17	0.80	....
17–18	0.88	0.50	17–18	0.88	0.50
18–19	1.00	0.50	18–19	1.00	0.50
19–20	1.00	1.00	19–20	1.00	1.00

There seems to be a clear trend in IB for $p_1(1)$ to increase on successive trials, whereas no trend for $p_1(1)$ is observable in IA. If we group the trials by fives to secure more reliable estimates, we get

IA Trials	$p_1(1)$	$p_0(0)$	IB Trials	$p_1(1)$	$p_0(0)$
1–6	0.94	0.67	1–6	0.72	0.33
6–11	0.95	0.89	6–11	0.85	0.30
11–16	0.98	0.63	11–16	0.93	0.38
16–20	0.92	0.60	16–20	0.92	0.60

Comparisons such as these show that the assumption of a constant transformation cannot be checked by the successive distributions alone, for IA and IB are identical in this respect. The assumption is justified if the analysis of short sequences of trials shows relatively constant transitional frequencies, as in IA. If the transitional frequencies show a definite trend, as in IB, the assumption is not justified.

The question is what to do when we face variable transformations. Whatever we do, the situation will not be simple. If $\ldots PQRST \, d_0$ cannot be translated into $\ldots TTTTT \, d_0$, the matrix products may get quite complex. If we could choose P, Q, R, S, T as commutative matrices, it would be possible to find a simultaneous solution for all of them; all matrices would have the same characteristic vectors but different characteristic roots. Unfortunately, however, it does not seem possible in general to choose commutative matrices with the properties demanded by the data.

If the complexity of the problem is admitted as inevitable, we can still look for a matrix function of n, $T(n)$, that changes in some reasonable way on successive trials. The following argument illustrates one possible approach. We assume that at the beginning of the experiment the subjects are equipped with transitional preferences given by the matrix U. After long experience in the situation the subjects develop transitional preferences given by the matrix V. As the experiment progresses the tendencies represented by U are slowly extinguished and those represented by V are slowly strengthened. Consider the following sequence of equations:

$$T(0) = U$$
$$T(1) = wT(0) + (1 - w)V$$
$$T(2) = wT(1) + (1 - w)V \qquad (29)$$
$$\ldots\ldots\ldots\ldots\ldots\ldots\ldots$$
$$T(n) = wT(n - 1) + (1 - w)V,$$

where $0 \leq w < 1$. The rationale for this set of equations is that w represents the perseveration of the tendencies on the preceding trial, and $(1 - w)$ represents the ability to adopt the new mode of response symbolized by V. If the extinction of the old pattern of responses is slow, w is near unity; if the old pattern extinguishes rapidly, w is near zero.

Eq. (29) can be written in terms of U and V:

$$T(0) = U \qquad\qquad\qquad = w^0(U - V) + V$$
$$T(1) = wU + (1 - w)V \quad = w^1(U - V) + V.$$
$$T(2) = w^2U + (1 - w^2)V = w^2(U - V) + V. \qquad (30)$$
$$\ldots\ldots\ldots\ldots\ldots\ldots\ldots\ldots\ldots\ldots\ldots\ldots$$
$$T(n) = w^nU + (1 - w^n)V = w^n(U - V) + V.$$

In this form it is clear that, since $0 \leq w < 1$, $T(n)$ approaches V as n increases. The importance of U becomes progressively smaller as the subject has more and more experience in the experimental situation. This formulation has the advantage that it is relatively easy to compute the successive values of $T(n)$, given U and V. The initial and final matrices, U and V, can be given theoretically or can be determined from data obtained prior to the first trial and after the learned behavior has stabilized again in the new course of action.

For illustrative purposes, assume that U and V are known to be

$$U = \begin{Bmatrix} .5 & .5 \\ .5 & .5 \end{Bmatrix} \quad \text{and} \quad V = \begin{Bmatrix} .9 & .4 \\ .1 & .6 \end{Bmatrix},$$

and that the weight w is calculated to be 0.8. Then Eq. (30) gives

$$T(n) = .8^n \begin{Bmatrix} -.4 & .1 \\ .4 & -.1 \end{Bmatrix} + \begin{Bmatrix} .9 & .4 \\ .1 & .6 \end{Bmatrix}.$$

Then on successive learning trials we have:

n:	0	1	2	3	4	5	6	7	8	9	10	$\cdots$
$p_A(A)$:	.5	.58	.644	.695	.736	.768	.796	.816	.832	.846	.857	$\cdots$
$p_B(B)$:	.5	.52	.536	.549	.559	.567	.574	.579	.583	.587	.589	$\cdots$

Next we calculate the proportions of right and wrong responses on successive trials. This is given by the equation:

$$T(0)d_0 = d_1$$
$$T(1)d_1 = d_2 \quad = T(1)T(0)d_0$$
$$T(2)d_2 = d_3 \quad = T(2)T(1)T(0)d_0 \qquad\qquad (31)$$
$$\cdots\cdots\cdots\cdots\cdots\cdots\cdots\cdots$$
$$T(n)d_n = d_{n+1} = \prod_{n}^{0} T(i)d_0.$$

It is assumed that $T(0) = U$ and d_0 are known from preliminary experimentation. Assume the boundary condition $d_0' = (.5, .5)$. Then direct computation gives the values:

n:	1	2	3	4	5	6	7	8	9	10	$\cdots$	∞
$p(R)$:	.5	.53	.559	.587	.614	.639	.662	.683	.700	.716	$\cdots$	.800

Considerable care must be taken with such iterated computation, for the errors are cumulative.

It should be noted that if $w = 0$, the variable case reduces to the constant case, for then $T(n) = V$ and $\Pi T(i) = T^n$. Similarly, if $w = 1$, then $T(n) = U$ and we again have a single transformation.

A special case arises if U and V commute, $UV = VU$, for then $T(n)$ and $T(n + k)$ also commute. If two matrices with distinct roots commute, then one can be written as a polynomial in terms of the other, with scalar coefficients. Thus if the matrices A and B commute, we can write, according to Eq. (15) and (16),

$$B = \lambda_1 f_1(B) + \lambda_2 f_2(B) + \cdots + \lambda_N f_N(B)$$

$$A = g(B) = g(\lambda_1)f_1(B) + g(\lambda_2)f_2(B) + \cdots + g(\lambda_N)f_N(B),$$

(32)

where λ_1 is the characteristic root of B; $g(\lambda_1)$ is the characteristic root of A; and for matrices of transitional probabilities $\lambda_1 = g(\lambda_1) = 1$. Thus A and B have different roots, but $f_i(A) = f_i(B)$. Another way of saying the same thing is to note that commutative matrices are transformed into their diagonal form by the same operator. Thus if S transforms A into the diagonal form Λ_A, S also transforms B into its diagonal form Λ_B. The product of A and B is (since the diagonal matrices Λ_A and Λ_B obviously commute)

$$AB = (S\Lambda_A S^{-1})(S\Lambda_B S^{-1}) = S\Lambda_A\Lambda_B S^{-1} = S\Lambda_B\Lambda_A S^{-1}$$

$$= (S\Lambda_B S^{-1})(S\Lambda_A S^{-1}) = BA.$$

If the matrices $T(i)$ commute, then

$$\prod_n^0 T(i) = S\left[\prod_n^0 \Lambda(i) \right]S^{-1},$$

(33)

where the $\Lambda(i)$ are the diagonal matrices similar to $T(i)$. The product of the $T(i)$ reduces to the product of diagonal matrices. If all of the $\Lambda(i)$'s are equal, then Eq. (33) reduces to the constant case given by Eq. (5).

Commutative matrices occur when the distribution over the several alternative responses does not change, although the transitional probabilities do change. If U has been applied repeatedly, U^n approaches $f_1(U)$ as a limit; after V has been applied repeatedly, V^n approaches $f_1(V)$. When U and V commute, $f_1(U) = f_1(V)$, and so both transformations lead to the same stable distribution. Such a situation might arise in learning a simple alternation between left and right. The learning might leave $p(L) = p(R) = .5$, although the transitional probabilities were altered.

This discussion of learning should suggest some of the descriptive possibilities of systems of dependent probabilities. By this general development we arrived at a mathematical description of complex behavioral changes— a description that enables us to talk about the gradual replacement of one pattern of responses by another.

Manuscript received 2/8/51

Revised manuscript received 9/17/51

ON THE MAXIMUM LIKELIHOOD ESTIMATE OF THE SHANNON-WIENER MEASURE OF INFORMATION

GEORGE A. MILLER

AND

WILLIAM G. MADOW

The limiting form and the first two asymptotic moments of the sampling distribution of the maximum likelihood estimate of the Shannon-Wiener measure of amount of information per observation drawn from a multinomial distribution are determined. Also, approximations to the bias and the mean square error of the estimate are given.

Preface

The statistic defined by Shannon (3) and by Wiener (4) to measure the amount of information in an event drawn from a multinomial distribution has been adopted by some psychologists to measure certain aspects of stimulus and response events in psychological experiments (2). In these applications, however, the psychologist is usually forced to work with relatively small samples and the sampling distribution of the measure becomes of real interest. In the present paper the first two moments of the asymptotic distribution are derived and the bias of the statistic for small samples is explored.

1. The Limiting Distribution of the Maximum Likelihood Estimate of Amount of Information

If an experiment or operation has k possible results, the ith of which has probability $p_i > 0$, $i = 1, \ldots, k$, the Shannon-Wiener measure of the amount of information per performance of this operation or event is

$$H = -\sum_{i=1}^{k} p_i \log_2 p_i.$$

We propose to consider the properties of the maximum likelihood estimate H' of H obtained from n independent performances of the operation. Since H is a continuous and differentiable function of $p_i, \ldots, p_k$ for all positive values of the probabilities, it follows that the maximum likelihood estimate, H', is

$$H' = -\sum_{i=1}^{k} \frac{n_i}{n} \log_2 \frac{n_i}{n},$$

where n_i is the frequency with which the ith of the k possible outcomes occurs in the n

This article is from the Operational Applications Laboratory, Air Force Cambridge Research Center, Air Research and Development Command, Bolling Air Force Base, 1954, AFCRC-TR-54-75, contract AF 18(600)-322. Reprinted with permission.

448

performances, and where, if $n_i = 0$ for one or more values of i, we define the corresponding terms $(n_i/n) \log_2 n_i/n$ of H' to be 0.

We will now show: (a) If the p_i are not all equal, then H' has a normal limiting distribution; and (b) if $p_i = 1/k$, $i = 1, \ldots, k$, then H' has a chi-square limiting distribution with $k - 1$ degrees of freedom.

As a preliminary, we obtain $H - H'$ in a form that simplifies the further calculations.

LEMMA.   *The difference $H - H'$ is given by the following equations:*
Let

$$U_n = \sum_{i=1}^{k} \frac{n_i}{n} \log_2 \frac{n_i}{np_i}$$

and

$$V_n = \sum_{i=1}^{k} \left(\frac{n_i}{n} - p_i \right) \log_2 p_i. \tag{1}$$

Then

$$H - H' = U_n + V_n$$

where $p_i > 0$, $i = 1, \ldots, k$. Terms in U_n that have $n_i = 0$ are themselves defined to vanish, but terms in V_n that have $n_i = 0$ still yield $-p_i \log_2 p_i$.

PROOF.   By simple substitutions we can expand H' as follows:

$$H' = -\sum_{i=1}^{k} \frac{n_i}{n} \log_2 \frac{n_i}{np_i} - \sum_{i=1}^{k} \frac{n_i}{n} \log_2 p_i$$

$$= -\sum_{i=1}^{k} \frac{n_i}{n} \log_2 \frac{n_i}{np_i} - \sum_{i=1}^{k} \left(\frac{n_i}{n} - p_i \right) \log_2 p_i - \sum_{i=1}^{k} p_i \log_2 p_i$$

$$= -U_n - V_n + H.$$

All we need to do is verify that the effects of $n_i = 0$ are as stated. Suppose, for example, that $n_1 = 0$ but $n_i > 0$ otherwise. Then from the definitions of H and H' we have

$$H - H' = -\sum_{i=1}^{k} p_i \log_2 p_i + \sum_{i=2}^{k} \frac{n_i}{n} \log_2 \frac{n_i}{n}$$

and

$$U_n = \sum_{i=2}^{k} \frac{n_i}{n} \log_2 \frac{n_i}{np_i} = \sum_{i=2}^{k} \frac{n_i}{n} \log_2 \frac{n_i}{n} - \sum_{i=2}^{k} \frac{n_i}{n} \log_2 p_i$$

$$V_n = \sum_{i=1}^{k} \frac{n_i}{n} \log_2 p_i + H,$$

so that if we combine the values of U_n and V_n, we verify that $H - H' = U_n + V_n$.

THEOREM 1.

a. *If the p_i are not all equal, then $\sqrt{n}(H - H')$ has a normal limiting distribution with mean 0 and variance*

$$\sigma^2 = \sum_{i=1}^{k} p_i (\log_2 p_i + H)^2.$$

b. If $p_i = 1/k$, $i = 1, \ldots, k$ then $(2n/\log_2 e)\,(H - H')$ has a chi-square limiting distribution with $k - 1$ degrees of freedom.

The first part of Theorem 1 holds for maximum likelihood estimates almost without exception (e.g. [1], p. 500). Also, maximum likelihood estimates are asymptotically efficient. We will prove both parts of the theorem since most of the calculations made would be needed in any case for the asymptotic moments. Because of the preceding lemma, the problem of evaluating $\sqrt{n}(H - H')$ can be replaced by the equivalent problem of evaluating $\sqrt{n}U_n + \sqrt{n}V_n$.

PROOF. We first note that if the p_i are not all equal then $\sqrt{n}V_n$ has a normal limiting distribution with mean 0 and variance σ^2. We sketch the proof: The random variables $\sqrt{n}(n_i/n - p_i)$, $i = 1, \ldots, k - 1$, have a $(k - 1)$-variate limiting normal distribution with mean values 0, variances $p_i q_i$, $(q_i = 1 - p_i)$, and covariances $-p_i p_j$, $i, j = 1, \ldots, k - 1$, $(i \neq j)$. Since the log p_i are constant weights applied to these random variables, it is clear that $\sqrt{n}V_n$ is a linear combination of the random variables. Therefore, $\sqrt{n}V_n$ has a limiting normal distribution with mean value

$$\sqrt{n}EV_n = \sqrt{n}E \sum_{i=1}^{k} \left(\frac{n_i}{n} - p_i \right) \log_2 p_i$$

$$= \sqrt{n} \sum_{i=1}^{k} \log_2 p_i E \left(\frac{n_i}{n} - p_i \right) = 0,$$

and a variance

$$\sigma^2 = \operatorname{Var} \left[\sum_{i=1}^{k} \sqrt{n} \left(\frac{n_i}{n} - p_i \right) \log_2 p_i \right]$$

$$= \sum_{i=1}^{k} (\log_2 p_i)^2 \operatorname{Var} \left[\sqrt{n} \left(\frac{n_i}{n} - p_i \right) \right] + \sum_{i \neq j} (\log_2 p_i)\,(\log_2 p_j) \operatorname{Cov} \left[\sqrt{n} \left(\frac{n_i}{n} - p_i \right) \right]$$

$$= \sum_{i=1}^{k} (\log_2 p_i)^2 p_i q_i - \sum_{i \neq j} (\log_2 p_i)\,(\log_2 p_j)\, p_i p_j$$

$$= \sum_{i=1}^{k} p_i (\log_2 p_i)^2 - \sum_{\substack{i=1 \\ j=1}}^{k} (p_i \log_2 p_i)\,(p_j \log_2 p_j)$$

$$= \sum_{i=1}^{k} p_i (\log_2 p_i)^2 - H^2$$

$$= \sum_{i=1}^{k} p_i (\log_2 p_i + H)^2.$$

We next show that $\sqrt{n}U_n$ converges in probability to zero as n increases, and that $2nU_n/\log_2 e$ has a chi-square limiting distribution with $k - 1$ degrees of freedom.

Let us define

$$x_i = \frac{n_i - np_i}{np_i}, \quad i = 1, \ldots, k.$$

Then

$$U_n = \sum_{i=1}^{k} \frac{n_i}{n} \log_2 \frac{n_i}{np_i}$$

$$= \sum_{i=1}^{k} p_i(1 + x_i) \log_2 (1 + x_i), \tag{2}$$

and since $n_i \geq 1$, it follows that $x_i \geq x_{i0} = -1 + 1/np_i > -1$. Hence we can apply Lemma A.2* and we obtain

$$\frac{1}{\log_2 e} U_n = \sum_{i=1}^{k} p_i \left[\frac{n_i - np_i}{np_i} + \sum_{v=2}^{j} \frac{(-1)^v}{v(v-1)} \left(\frac{n_i - np_i}{np_i} \right)^v \right] + R'_{j+1}, \tag{3}$$

where

$$R'_{j+1} \leq \sum_{i=1}^{k} \frac{np_i^2}{j(j+1)} \left| \frac{n_i - np_i}{np_i} \right|^{j+1} = \sum_{i=1}^{k} \frac{p_i}{j(j+1)} \frac{|n_i - np_i|^{j+1}}{(np_i)^j}.$$

Furthermore, since

$$\sum_{i=1}^{k} (n_i - np_i) = 0,$$

we have

$$\frac{n}{\log_2 e} U_n = \sum_{v=2}^{j} \frac{(-1)^v}{v(v-1)} \sum_{i=1}^{k} \frac{(n_i - np_i)^v}{(np_i)^{v-1}} + R''_{j+1}, \tag{4}$$

where

$$R''_{j+1} \leq \frac{1}{j(j+1)} \sum_{i=1}^{k} \frac{|n_i - np_i|^{j+1}}{(np_i)^{j-1}}.$$

It follows from (2) that we do not need any special treatment of terms with $n_i = 0$ in the approximations to U_n yielded by (3), since the appearance of n_i as a multiplier will automatically cause the corresponding term of (2) to vanish when $n_i = 0$. The elimination of terms involving $n_i = 0$ has made it possible for the remainder terms to be bounded, for if we did not require $n_i \log_2 n_i$ to vanish when $n_i = 0$, it would follow that there would be positive probability that H' would be indeterminate.

Furthermore, from Lemma B.1 and Lemma C.2 it can be seen that

$$Pr(R''_{j+1} > \epsilon) = O\left(\frac{1}{n^{2j-2-j-1}} \right) = O\left(\frac{1}{n^{j-3}} \right)$$

and

$$ER''_{j+1} = O\left(\frac{1}{n^{j-1-\eta}} \right), \text{ where } \eta = \frac{j+1}{2} \quad \text{if } j \text{ is odd}$$

$$= \frac{j}{2} \quad \text{if } j \text{ is even.}$$

Actually, it is easy to see from (4) that we have

$$R''_{j+1} = \frac{(-1)^{j+1}}{(j+1)j} \sum_{i=1}^{k} \frac{(n_i - np_i)^{j+1}}{(np_i)^j} + \frac{(-1)^{j+2}}{(j+2)(j+1)} \sum_{i=1}^{k} \frac{(n_i - np_i)^{j+2}}{(np_i)^{j+1}} + R''_{j+3},$$

* The letter "A" in "Lemma A.2" indicates that this lemma will be found in Appendix A.

and hence, symbolically,

$$R''_{j+1} = O\left(\frac{1}{n^{j-1}}\right) + O\left(\frac{1}{n^j}\right) + O\left(\frac{1}{n^{j-1}}\right) = O\left(\frac{1}{n^{j-1}}\right). \tag{5}$$

Thus Eq. (5) shows that the upper bound of $O(1/n^{j-3})$ that we have found for R''_{j+1} is unnecessarily large, but the above device is sufficient to prove that R''_{j+1} and ER''_{j+1} converge to 0 as fast as

$$\sum_{i=1}^{k} \frac{(n_i - np_i)^{j+1}}{(np_i)^j}$$

and

$$E \sum_{i=1}^{k} \frac{(n_i - np_i)^{j+1}}{(np_i)^j}.$$

Now the first term of $\dfrac{2n\,U_n}{\log_2 e}$ is

$$\sum_{i=1}^{k} \frac{(n_i - np_i)^2}{np_i},$$

which is well known to have a chi-square limiting distribution with $k - 1$ degrees of freedom, whereas all other terms of $2n\,U_n/\log_2 e$ converge in probability to zero by Lemma C.2. Hence $2n\,U_n/\log_2 e$ has a limiting chi-square distribution. On the other hand, since

$$\sqrt{n}\,U_n = \left(\frac{2n\,U_n}{\log_2 e}\right)\left(\frac{\log_2 e}{2\sqrt{n}}\right)$$

is the product of a random variable that has a limiting distribution by a variable that converges to 0, it follows that $\sqrt{n}\,U_n$ converges in probability to 0.

Thus, if the p_i are not all equal, $\sqrt{n}(H - H') = \sqrt{n}V_n + \sqrt{n}U_n$ is the sum of two random variables, one of which has a normal limiting distribution, whereas the other converges in probability to zero. Hence $\sqrt{n}(H - H')$ has the same limiting distribution as $\sqrt{n}V_n$.

On the other hand, if the p_i are all equal, then $V_n = 0$ and $[2n/(\log_2 e)]\,(H - H')$ has the same limiting distribution as $[2n/(\log_2 e)]\,U_n$, namely, chi-square with $k - 1$ degrees of freedom.

2. The Limiting First Moment of $H - H'$

By (1)

$$EH' = H - EU_n - EV_n.$$

Since $EV_n = 0$, it follows that $-EU_n$ is the bias of H'. In order to evaluate this bias we now approximate EU_n.

From (4) we have

$$\frac{U_n}{\log_2 e} = \frac{1}{2n}\sum_{i=1}^{k} \frac{(n_i - np_i)^2}{np_i} - \frac{1}{6n}\sum_{i=1}^{k} \frac{(n_i - np_i)^3}{(np_i)^2}$$

$$+ \frac{1}{12n}\sum_{i=1}^{k} \frac{(n_i - np_i)^4}{(np_i)^3} - \frac{1}{20n}\sum_{i=1}^{k} \frac{(n_i - np_i)^5}{(np_i)^4} + \frac{1}{n}R''_6.$$

From Lemma B.1 we see that

$$\frac{EU_n}{\log_2 e} = \frac{1}{2n}\sum_{i=1}^{k}\frac{np_iq_i}{np_i} - \frac{1}{6n}\sum_{i=1}^{k}\frac{np_iq_i(q_i - p_i)}{(np_i)^2} + \frac{1}{12n}\sum_{i=1}^{k}\frac{3n^2p_i^2q_i^2 + np_iq_i(1 - 6p_iq_i)}{(np_i)^3}$$

$$- \frac{1}{20n}\sum_{i=1}^{k}\frac{10n^2p_i^2q_i^2(q_i - p_i) + np_iq_i(q_i - p_i)(1 - 12p_iq_i)}{(np_i)^4} + \frac{ER_6''}{n}$$

$$= \frac{k - 1}{2n} - \frac{1}{6n^2}\sum_{i=1}^{k}\frac{q_i(q_i - p_i)}{p_i} + \frac{1}{12n^2}\sum_{i=1}^{k}\frac{3q_i^2}{p_i} + O\left(\frac{1}{n^3}\right),$$

or, combining terms, we have

$$\frac{EU_n}{\log_2 e} = \frac{k - 1}{2n} + \frac{1}{12n^2}\sum_{i=1}^{k}\frac{1 - p_i^2}{p_i} + O\left(\frac{1}{n^3}\right)$$

$$= \frac{k - 1}{2n} - \frac{1}{12n^2} + \frac{1}{12n^2}\sum_{i=1}^{k}\frac{1}{p_i} + O\left(\frac{1}{n^3}\right).$$

Hence, an estimate of H that is unbiased to terms of order $1/n$ is $H' + (\log_2 e)(k - 1)/2n$, and an estimate of H that is unbiased to terms of order $1/n^2$ is

$$H' + (\log_2 e)\frac{k - 1}{2n} - \frac{\log_2 e}{12n^2} + \frac{\log_2 e}{12n^2}\sum_{i=1}^{k}\frac{1}{p_i}.$$

Thus, we have proved the following theorem:

THEOREM 2. *Under the stated conditions*

$$H - EH' = \log_2 e\left(\frac{k - 1}{2n} - \frac{1}{12n^2} + \frac{1}{12n^2}\sum_{i=1}^{k}\frac{1}{p_i}\right) + O\left(\frac{1}{n^3}\right).$$

Furthermore, if we let

$$H'' = H' + (\log_2 e)\frac{k - 1}{2n}$$

and let

$$H''' = H'' - \frac{\log_2 e}{12n^2} + \frac{\log_2 e}{12n^2}\sum_{i=1}^{k}\frac{1}{p_i},$$

then

$$H = EH' + O(1/n),$$

$$H = EH'' + O(1/n^2),$$

and

$$H = EH''' + O(1/n^3).$$

Theorem 2 enables us to make several observations about the bias: (1) the term of order n^{-1}, namely, $(k - 1)/2n$, does not depend on the probabilities p_i and hence H'' has a bias of lower order than H' for all values of the p_i. (2) Since $(k - 1)/2n$ and $[(\sum 1/p_i) - 1]/12n^2$ are both positive quantities, H' is biased downward even to terms of order n^{-2} for all possible values of the p_i. (Terms of higher order may be negative, of course, so that EH'' or EH''' may be greater than H for small values of n.) (3) An

TABLE I

Expected Values of the Estimators H', H'', and H''' for the Binomial Case when $p_i = 0.50$ and when $p_i = 0.05$ for Sample Sizes up to 20

Sample size	When $p_i = 0.5$			When $p_i = 0.05$		
N	EH'	EH''	EH'''	EH'	EH''	EH'''
1	0	.721	1.082	0	.721	3.132
2	.500	.861	.951	.095	.456	1.058
3	.689	.929	.969	.131	.371	.640
4	.781	.961	.983	.153	.333	.484
5	.832	.977	.990	.169	.313	.410
6	.865	.985	.995	.181	.301	.368
7	.887	.990	.997	.191	.294	.343
8	.903	.993	.998	.199	.289	.327
9	.914	.994	.999	.206	.286	.316
10	.924	.996	.999	.212	.284	.308
11	.931	.997	1.000	.217	.283	.302
12	.937	.997	1.000	.222	.282	.298
13	.942	.998	1.000	.226	.281	.296
14	.947	.998	1.000	.229	.281	.293
15	.951	.999	1.000	.232	.280	.291
16	.954	.999	1.000	.235	.280	.289
17	.957	.999	1.000	.238	.280	.288
18	.959	.999	1.000	.240	.280	.287
19	.961	.999	1.000	.242	.280	.287
20	.963	.999	1.000	.244	.280	.286
∞	1.000	1.000	1.000	.286	.286	.286

increase in bias results if one uses $[(k - 1)/2n] - 1/12n^2$ as an overall correction and omits $(\Sigma 1/p_i)/12n^2$. (4) When all the p_i are equal, H''' becomes

$$H' + \log_2 e \left(\frac{k - 1}{2n} + \frac{k^2 - 1}{12n^2} \right),$$

which is a lower bound for H''' (that is to say, if the p_i are unequal, $\Sigma 1/p_i \geq k^2$).

In order to illustrate the use of the bias corrections of Theorem 2 for a simple case, we state the following:

COROLLARY. *For the binomial case, $k = 2$, we obtain the following estimates of H to terms of order n^{-2}:*
If $k = 2$ and $p_i = 0.5$, then

$$H''' = H' + (\log_2 e) \left(\frac{1}{2n} + \frac{1}{4n^2} \right).$$

If $k = 2$ and $p_i = 0.05$, then

$$H''' = H' + (\log_2 e)\left(\frac{1}{2n} + \frac{381}{228n^2}\right).$$

In Table 1 the expected values of the estimates, EH', EH'', and EH''', are compared with H for the binomial case for sizes of sample up to $n = 20$. When $p_i = 0.5$, samples as small as 5 give satisfactory estimates of H, but when $p_i = 0.05$, the size of sample needed becomes larger.

3. *The Limiting Second Moment of $H - H'$*

Since $E(H - H')^2 = EV_n^2 + 2EU_nV_n + EU_n^2$, we will now consider each of these three terms in order.

a. *Evaluation of EV_n^2*

We have already seen that

$$EV_n^2 = \frac{1}{n} \sum_{i=1}^{k} p_i (\log_2 p_i + H)^2, \tag{6}$$

b. *Evaluation of EU_nV_n*

By (4), we have

$$U_nV_n = \left[\frac{1}{n}\sum_{i=1}^{k}(n_i - np_i)\log_2 p_i\right]\left[\frac{\log_2 e}{n}\sum_{\nu=2}^{j}\frac{(-1)^\nu}{\nu(\nu-1)}\sum_{i=1}^{k}\frac{(n_i - np_i)^\nu}{(np_i)^{\nu-1}}\right] + R'''_{j+1},$$

where

$$R'''_{j+1} = \left[\frac{1}{n}\sum_{i=1}^{k}(n - np_i)\log_2 p_i\right]\left[\frac{\log_2 e}{n} R''_{j+1}\right].$$

By an analysis such as that summarized in (5) we can ignore ER'''_{j+1} as involving terms that approach 0 more rapidly than the terms we shall retain. Hence

$$\frac{n^2}{\log_2 e} EU_nV_n$$
$$\cong \sum_{\nu=2}^{j}\frac{(-1)^\nu}{\nu(\nu-1)}\left[\sum_{i=1}^{k} E\frac{(n_i - np_i)^{\nu+1}}{(np_i)^{\nu-1}}\log_2 p_i + \sum_{i\neq h} E\frac{(n_i - np_i)^\nu(n_h - np_h)}{(np_i)^{\nu-1}}\log_2 p_h\right].$$

By Lemma B.3

$$E[(n_h - np_h) \mid n_i] = -\frac{p_h}{q_i}(n_i - np_i)$$

so that

$$D = \sum_{i\neq h}\frac{E(n_i - np_i)^\nu(n_h - np_h)}{(np_i)^{\nu-1}}\log_2 p_h = -\sum_{i\neq h}\frac{E(n_i - np_i)^{\nu+1}}{(np_i)^{\nu-1}}\frac{p_h}{q_i}\log_2 p_h.$$

Now

$$-\sum_{\substack{h\\h\neq 1}} p_h \log_2 p_h = H + p_i \log_2 p_i$$

so that

$$D = H\sum_{i=1}^{k}\frac{E(n_i - np_i)^{\nu+1}}{(np_i)^{\nu-1}q_i} + \sum_{i=1}^{k}\frac{(p_i \log_2 p_i)E(n_i - np_i)^{\nu+1}}{(np_i)^{\nu-1}q_i}.$$

Hence

$$
\begin{aligned}
\frac{n^2 E U_n V_n}{\log_2 e} &\simeq \sum_{\nu=2}^{j} \frac{(-1)^\nu}{\nu(\nu-1)} \sum_{i=1}^{k} \frac{E(n_i - np_i)^{\nu+1}}{(np_i)^{\nu-1}} \left[\log_2 p_i + \frac{p_i \log p_i}{q_i} + \frac{H}{q_i} \right] \\
&= \sum_{\nu=2}^{j} \frac{(-1)^\nu}{\nu(\nu-1)} \sum_{i=1}^{k} \frac{E(n_i - np_i)^{\nu+1}}{(np_i)^{\nu-1}} \left[\frac{\log_2 p_i + H}{q_i} \right] \\
&= \sum_{i=1}^{k} \frac{\log_2 p_i + H}{q_i} \left[\sum_{\nu=2}^{k} \frac{(-1)^\nu}{\nu(\nu-1)} \frac{E(n_i - np_i)^{\nu+1}}{(np_i)^{\nu-1}} \right]. \quad (7)
\end{aligned}
$$

We shall want to retain all terms of (7) in order $(1/n)$ or lower. From Lemma B.1 it is clear that we need consider only terms to $j = 4$. Hence, we begin by evaluating

$$
F_i = \frac{1}{2} \frac{np_i q_i (q_i - p_i)}{np_i} - \frac{1}{6} \frac{3n^2 p_i^2 q_i^2 + np_i q_i (1 - 6p_i q_i)}{n^2 p_i^2} + \frac{1}{12} \frac{10n^2 p_i^2 q_i^2 (q_i - p_i)}{n^3 p_i^3}
$$

where we omit the second term of the fifth moment of n_i since it will yield a term of order $1/n^2$. Then

$$
\begin{aligned}
F_i &= \frac{1}{2} q_i (q_i - p_i) - \frac{1}{2} q_i^2 - \frac{q_i(1 - 6p_i q_i)}{6np_i} + \frac{5q_i^2(q_i - p_i)}{6np_i} \\
&= -\frac{p_i q_i}{2} + \frac{q_i}{6np_i} (4p^2 - pq_i + 4).
\end{aligned}
$$

By substituting in (7) we obtain

$$
\begin{aligned}
\frac{n^2 E U_n V_n}{\log_2 e} &\simeq -\frac{1}{2} \sum_{i=1}^{k} p_i (\log_2 p_i + H) + \frac{1}{6n} \sum_{i=1}^{k} \frac{(4p_i^2 - qp_i + 4)(\log_2 p_i + H)}{p_i} \\
&\simeq -\frac{3}{2n} \sum_{i=1}^{k} (\log_2 p_i + H) + \frac{2}{3n} \sum_{i=1}^{k} \frac{\log_2 p_i + H}{p_i}, \quad (8)
\end{aligned}
$$

since

$$
\sum_{i=1}^{k} p_i (\log_2 p_i + H) = 0.
$$

c. *Evaluation of* EU_n^2

The first three terms of the approximation to U_n given by (4) will be used, namely,

$$
\frac{nU_n}{\log_2 e} \simeq \frac{1}{2} \sum_{i=1}^{k} \frac{(n_i - np_i)^2}{np_i} - \frac{1}{6} \sum_{i=1}^{k} \frac{(n_i - np_i)^3}{(np_i)^2} + \frac{1}{12} \sum_{i=1}^{k} \frac{(n_i - np_i)^4}{(np_i)^3}.
$$

Since the details are very tedious, they have been put in Appendix D. Here we state the result.

THEOREM 3. *Including terms of order* $1/n$ *we have*

$$
E\left(\frac{nU_n}{\log_2 e} \right)^2 = \frac{k^2 - 1}{4} + \frac{7k - 11}{12n} \sum_{i=1}^{k} \frac{1}{p_i} - \frac{9k^2 - 20k + 7}{12n}
$$

and if $k = 2$, $p_i = \frac{1}{2}$ *we have*

$$
E\left(\frac{nU_n}{\log_2 e} \right)^2 = \frac{3}{4} + \frac{3}{4n}.
$$

Finally, from (6), (8), and Theorem 3, we obtain

THEOREM 4. *In general*

$$E(H - H')^2 = \frac{1}{n} \sum_{i=1}^{k} p_i (\log_2 p_i + H)^2 - \frac{3 \log_2 e}{2n^2} \sum_{i=1}^{k} (\log_2 p_i + H)$$

$$+ \frac{2 \log_2 e}{3n^2} \sum_{i=1}^{k} \frac{\log_2 p_i + H}{p_i} + \frac{(\log_2 e)^2 (k^2 - 1)}{4n^2}$$

$$+ \frac{(\log_2 e)^2 7k - 11}{12n^3} \sum_{i=1}^{k} \frac{1}{p_i} - \frac{(\log_2 e)^2}{12n^3} (9k^2 - 20k + 7) + O\left(\frac{1}{n^4}\right),$$

but if all the p_i are equal, then

$$E(H - H')^2 = \frac{(\log_2 e)^2 (k^2 - 1)}{4n^2} + \frac{(\log_2 e)^2}{12n^3} (7k - 11)k^2$$

$$- \frac{(\log_2 e)^2}{12n^3} (9k^2 - 20k + 7) + O\left(\frac{1}{n^4}\right).$$

Furthermore, if $k = 2$ and $p_i = \frac{1}{2}$, then

$$E(H - H')^2 = \frac{3 (\log_2 e)^2}{4n^2} \left(\frac{n + 1}{n}\right) + O\left(\frac{1}{n^4}\right).$$

In Theorem 4 we have approximated the mean square error of H' about H. For any random variable H' we have

$$E(H - H')^2 = \sigma_{H'}^2 + (EH' - H)^2$$

where $\sigma_{H'}^2$ is the variance of H', i.e.

$$\sigma_{H'}^2 = E(H' - EH')^2.$$

Since $(EH' - H)$ is given by Theorem 2, we can approximate $\sigma_{H'}^2$ by using

$$\sigma_{H'}^2 = E(H - H')^2 - (\log_2 e)^2 \left[\frac{(k - 1)^2}{4n^2} + \frac{k - 1}{12n^3} \left(-1 + \sum_{i=1}^{k} \frac{1}{p_i} \right) \right] + O\left(\frac{1}{n^4}\right)$$

where the mean square error $E(H - H')^2$ will be obtained from Theorem 4. For estimating H, the mean square error is the more fundamental quantity.

By way of illustration, consider the binomial case where $k = 2$ and $p_i = 0.5$. Then we have the approximation

$$\sigma_{H'}^2 = \frac{3 (\log_2 e)^2}{4n^2} \left(\frac{n + 1}{n}\right) - \frac{(\log_2 e)^2}{4n^2} \left(\frac{n + 1}{n}\right) = \frac{(\log_2 e)^2}{2n^2} \left(\frac{n + 1}{n}\right).$$

Appendix A. An Expansion for $(1 + x) \log (1 + x)$

We begin with an expansion of $\log (1 + x)$ and then derive the expansion of $(1 + x) \log (1 + x)$.

LEMMA A.1. *Let $-1 < x_0 \le x$. Then*

$$\log (1 + x) = x - \frac{x^2}{2} + \cdots + (-1)^{j-1} \frac{x^j}{j} + R_{j+1}, \qquad \text{(A.1)}$$

where

$$R_{j+1} = (-1)^j \int_0^x \frac{t^j}{1 + t} \cdot dt, \tag{A.2}$$

and hence, if $x_0 < 0$,

$$|R_{j+1}| \le \frac{|x|^{j+1}}{(j + 1)(1 + x_0)}, \tag{A.3}$$

while, if $x_0 > 0$

$$|R_{j+1}| \le \frac{|x|^{j+1}}{(j + 1)}. \tag{A.4}$$

PROOF. If $-1 < x$, then

$$\log(1 + x) = \int_0^x \frac{1}{1 + t} \cdot dt$$

and, if we expand $1/(1 + t)$, we obtain

$$\log(1 + x) = \sum_{i=1}^{j} (-1)^{i-1} \frac{x^i}{i} + (-1)^j \int_0^x \frac{t^j}{1 + t} dt.$$

Thus (A.1) and (A.2) hold. Then (A.3) follows from the fact that $1/(1 + t) \le 1/(1 + x_0)$ if $x_0 < 0$ and (A.4) follows from the fact that $1/(1 + t) \le 0$ if $x_0 \ge 0$.

LEMMA A.2. *Let $-1 < x_0 \le x$. Then*

$$(1 + x) \log(1 + x) = x + \sum_{i=2}^{j} \frac{(-1)^i x^i}{(i - 1)i} + R'_{j+1}, \tag{A.5}$$

where

$$R'_{j+1} = (-1)^j \int_0^x \int_0^t \frac{u^{i-1}}{1 + u} \, du \, dt, \tag{A.6}$$

and hence, if $x_0 < 0$, then

$$|R'_{j+1}| \le \frac{|x|^{j+1}}{(1 + x_0)j(j + 1)}, \tag{A.7}$$

while, if $x_0 \ge 0$, then

$$|R'_{j+1}| \le \frac{|x|^{j+1}}{j(j + 1)}. \tag{A.8}$$

PROOF. If $-1 < x$, then

$$\int_0^x \frac{1 + t}{1 + t} \, dt = x$$

and also, integrating by parts,

$$\int_0^x \frac{1 + t}{1 + t} \, dt = [(1 + t) \log(1 + t)]_0^x - \int_0^x \log(1 + t) \, dt,$$

so that

$$(1 + x) \log(1 + x) = x + \int_0^x \log(1 + t) \, dt.$$

From Lemma A.1, it follows that if $x > -1$, then

$$\int_0^x \log(1 + t) \, dt = \sum_{i=2}^{j} \frac{(-1)^i x^i}{(i - 1)i} + \int_0^x (-1)^j \int_0^t \frac{u^{j-1}}{1 + u} \, du \, dt,$$

and hence (A.5) and (A.6) hold. If $x_0 < 0$ then, from (A.3) it follows that

$$|R'_{j+1}| \le \int_0^{|x|} \frac{t^j}{(1 + x_0)j} \, dt = \frac{|x|^{j+1}}{(1 + x_0)j(j + 1)}$$

so that (A.7) is proved. Then (A.8) follows in a similar fashion from (A.4).

Appendix B. Multinomial Moments

Let an operation having k possible outcomes be independently performed n times and let n_i be the number of occurrences of the ith of the possible outcomes in the n performances. Then,

$$\frac{n!}{n_1! \, n_2! \cdots n_k!} \, p_1^{n_1} p_2^{n_2} \cdots p_k^{n_k}$$

is the probability of obtaining any specified values of $n_1, \cdots, n_k$ where $n_1 + \cdots + n_k = n$, $p_i \ge 0$, $p_1 + \cdots + p_k = 1$, and p_i is the probability of the occurrence of the ith of the possible outcomes in each operation, $i = 1, \cdots, k$.

Then, it is possible, by easy but tedious calculations to prove the following lemma.

LEMMA B.1. *The first six moments of n_i are given by the following equations.*

$$En_i = np_i$$
$$E(n_i - np_i)^2 = np_i q_i \quad (\text{where } q_i = 1 - p_i)$$
$$E(n_i - np_i)^3 = np_i q_i (q_i - p_i)$$
$$E(n_i - np_i)^4 = 3n^2 p_i^2 q_i^2 + np_i q_i (1 - 6p_i q_i)$$
$$E(n_i - np_i)^5 = 10n^2 p_i^2 q_i^2 (q_i - p_i) + np_i q_i (q_i p_i)(1 - 12p_i q_i)$$
$$E(n_i - np_i)^6 = 15n^3 p_i^3 q_i^3 + 5n^2 p_i^2 q_i^2[5 - 26p_i q_i] + np_i q_i[1 - 30p_i q_i + 120p_i^2 q_i^2].$$

In general, if m is an integer, then

$$E(n_i - np_i)^{2m} = 0(n^m)$$

and

$$E(n_i - np_i)^{2m+1} = 0(n^m).$$

The proof of Lemma B.1 is omitted.

We shall need not only the moments of n_i about its mean but also certain of the product moments

$$E(n_i - np_i)^a (n_j - np_j)^b.$$

The following lemma will be helpful in deriving these moments. Its usefulness results from the fact that the needed conditional moments will be obtainable easily from Lemma B.1.

LEMMA B.2. *Let x' be a random variable and let A' be a random event. Then*

$$E(x' - Ex')^\nu = \sum_{\alpha=0}^{\nu} \frac{\nu!}{\alpha! \, (\nu - \alpha)!} \, E\{[E(x' \mid A') - Ex']^{\nu-\alpha} E([x' - E(x' \mid A')]^\alpha \mid A')\}. \quad \text{(B.1)}$$

PROOF. In general, if u is any random variable, then

$$Eu = E\{E(u \mid A')\} \quad \text{(B.2)}$$

where A' is a random event and the "$|$" denotes conditional expectation. To apply to general formula we put $u = (x' - Ex')^v$ and note that

$$(x' - Ex')^v = \sum_{\alpha=0}^{v} \frac{v!}{\alpha! \, (v - \alpha)!} \, [E(x' \mid A') - Ex']^{v-\alpha}[x' - E(x' \mid A')]^\alpha.$$

Then, since

$$E\{[E(x' \mid A') - Ex']^{v-\alpha} \mid A'\} = [E(x' \mid A') - Ex']^{v-\alpha},$$

the Lemma follows by substituting for $x' - Ex'$ in (B.1).

Since we will apply (B.1) for $v = 1, 2, 3$ in the following Lemma, we now write out $E[(x' - Ex')^v \mid A']$ for $v = 1, 2, 3$.

$$E[(x' - Ex') \mid A'] = E(x' \mid A') - Ex' \tag{B.3}$$

$$E[(x' - Ex')^2 \mid A'] = [E(x' \mid A') - Ex']^2 + E\{[x' - E(x' \mid A')]^2 \mid A'\} \tag{B.4}$$

$$E[(x' - Ex')^3 \mid A'] = [E(x' \mid A') - Ex']^3 + 3[E(x' \mid A') - Ex']E\{[x' - E(x' \mid A')]^3 \mid A'\}$$
$$+ E\{[x' - E(x' \mid A')]^3 \mid A'\}. \tag{B.5}$$

Let us now evaluate some joint moments for a multinomial distribution. In all cases, the random event A will be "n_i has a specified value."

LEMMA B.3. *We assume a multinomial population and suppose $i \neq j$. Then*

$$E(n_j \mid n_i) = np_j - \frac{p_j}{q_i}(n_i - np_i)$$

$$E[(n_j - np_j) \mid n_i] = -\frac{p_j}{q_i}(n_i - np_i)$$

$$E[(n_j - np_j)^2 \mid n_i] = \frac{p_j^2}{q_i^2}(n_i - np_i)^2 - \frac{p_j(q_i - p_j)}{q_i^2}(n_i - np_i) + \frac{np_j(q_i - p_j)}{q_i}$$

$$E[(n_j - np_j)^3 \mid n_i] = -\frac{p_j^3}{p_i^3}(n_i - np_i)^3$$

$$+ 3\frac{p_j^2(q_i - p_j)}{q_i^3}(n_i - np_i)^2 - 3n\frac{p_j^2(q_i - p_j)}{q_i^2}(n_i - np_i)$$

$$- \frac{p_j(q_i - p_j)(q_i - 2p_j)}{q_i^3}(n_i - np_i) + \frac{np_j(q_i - p_j)(q_i - 2p_j)}{q_i^2}.$$

PROOF. If n_i is fixed the conditional size of sample is $n - n_i$ and the conditional probability of the jth possible outcome is p_j/q_i. Hence

$$E(n_j \mid n_i) = (n - n_i)\frac{p_j}{q_i} = np_j - \frac{p_j}{q_i}(n_i - np_i),$$

$$E[(n_j - np_j) \mid n_i] = (n - n_i)\frac{p_j}{q_i} - np_j$$

$$= -\frac{p_j}{q_i}(n_i - np_i).$$

Also

$$E(n_j \mid n_i) - E n_j = -\frac{p_j}{q_i}(n_i - n p_i).$$

Hence

$$E[(n_j - n p_j)^2 \mid n_i] = \frac{p_j^2}{q_i^2}(n_i - n p_i)^2 + (n - n_i)\frac{p_j(q_i - p_j)}{q_i^2}$$

$$= \frac{p_j^2}{q_i^2}(n_i - n p_i)^2 - \frac{p_j(q_i - p_j)}{q_i^2}(n_i - n p_i) + \frac{n p_j(q_i - p_j)}{q_i},$$

since $n - n_i = n q_i - (n_i - n p_i)$. Finally,

$$E[(n_j - n p_j)^3 \mid n_i] = -\frac{p_j^3}{q_i^3}(n_i - n p_i)^2 - 3\frac{p_j}{q_i}(n_i - n p_i)(n - n_i)\frac{p_j(q_i - p_j)}{q_i^2}$$

$$+ (n - n_i)\frac{p_j}{q_i}\left(\frac{q_i - p_j}{q_i}\right)\left(\frac{q_i - 2p_j}{q_i}\right)$$

$$= -\frac{p_j^3}{q_i^3}(n_i - n p_i)^3 + 3\frac{p_j^2(q_i - p_j)}{q_i^3}(n_i - n p_i)^2$$

$$- 3n\frac{p_j^2(q_i - p_j)}{q_i^2}(n_i - n p_i)$$

$$- \frac{p_j(q_i - p_j)(q_i - 2p_j)}{q_i^3}(n_i - n p_i)$$

$$+ \frac{n p_j(q_i - p_j)(q_i - 2p_j)}{q_i^2}.$$

Hence

$$E(n_i - n p_i)(n_j - n p_j) = E(n_i - n p_i)\left[-\frac{p_j}{q_i}(n_i - n p_i)\right]$$

$$= -\frac{p_j}{q_i} n p_i q_i = -n p_i q_i,$$

$$E(n_i - n p_i)^2(n_j - n p_j)^2$$

$$= E(n_i - n p_i)^2\left[\frac{p_j^2}{q_i^2}(n_i - n p_i)^2 - \frac{p_j(q_i - p_j)}{q_i^2}(n_i - n p_i) + \frac{n p_j(q_i - p_i)}{q_i}\right]$$

$$= \frac{p_j^2}{q_i^2}[3n^2 p_i^2 q_i^2 + n p_i q_i(1 - 6 p_i q_i)]$$

$$- \frac{p_j(q_i - p_j)}{q_i^2} n p_i q_i(q_i - p_i) + \frac{n p_j(q_i - p_j)}{q_i} n p_i q_i$$

$$= 3n^2 p_i^2 q_i^2 + \frac{n p_i p_j^2(1 - 6 p_i q_i)}{q_i} - \frac{n p_i p_j}{q_i}(q_i - p_i)(q_i - p_j)$$

$$+ n^2 p_i p_j(q_i - p_j),$$

$$\sum_{i \neq j} E\frac{(n_i - n p_i)^2(n_j - n p_j)^2}{n^2 p_i p_j} = \sum_{i \neq j}[3 p_i p_j + (q_i - p_j)]$$

$$+ \sum_{i \neq j}\left[\frac{p_j(1 - 6 p_i q_i)}{n q_i} - \frac{(q_i - p_i)(q_i - p_j)}{n q_i}\right].$$

Now

$$\sum_{\substack{j \\ j \neq i}} p_j = 1 - p_i = q_i, \quad \sum_{\substack{j \\ j \neq i}} (q_i - p_j) = (k - 1)q_i - q_i = (k - 2)q_i.$$

Hence

$$\sum_{i \neq j} E \frac{(n_i - np_i)^2 (n_j - np_j)^2}{n^2 p_i p_j} = \sum_i \left[3p_i q_i + (k - 2)q_i + \frac{1 - 6p_i q_i}{n} - \frac{(k - 2)(q_i - p_i)}{n} \right]$$

$$= 3 \sum_i p_i q_i + (k - 1)(k - 2) + \frac{1}{n} \left[k - 6 \sum_i p_i q_i - (k - 2)^2 \right].$$

Appendix C. Order of Convergence and Convergence in Probability

If

$$\lim_{n \to \infty} n^\alpha f(n)$$

is bounded, we say that $f(n)$ is at most of order $1/n^\alpha$ and write

$$f(n) = O\left(\frac{1}{n^\alpha}\right).$$

If

$$\lim_{n \to \infty} n^\alpha f(n) = 0,$$

we say that $f(n)$ is of lower order than $1/n^\alpha$ and write

$$f(n) = o\left(\frac{1}{n^\alpha}\right).$$

A sequence of random variables $u_1, u_2 \cdots$ converges in probability to 0 if, for every $\epsilon > 0$, we have

$$\lim_{n \to \infty} Pr(|u_n| > \epsilon) = 0.$$

LEMMA C.1. *If $2\alpha > \beta$, then* $\dfrac{(n_i - np_i)^\beta}{n^\alpha}$ *converges in probability to 0 as n becomes infinite.*

PROOF. Using some simple manipulations and the Tchebycheff inequality, we have

$$Pr\left(\frac{|n_i - np_i|^\beta}{n^\alpha} > \epsilon\right) = Pr\left(\left|\frac{n_i}{n} - p_i\right| > \epsilon^{1/\beta} n^{(\alpha/\beta)-1}\right) \le \frac{p_i q_i}{n \epsilon^{2/\beta} n^{(2\alpha/\beta)-1}}$$

so that convergence in probability occurs if

$$\frac{2\alpha}{\beta} - 1 > 0,$$

i.e., if $2\alpha > \beta$.

LEMMA C.2. *If $2\alpha > \beta$, then*

$$\sum_{i=1}^k \frac{|n_i - np_i|^\beta}{(np_i)^\alpha}$$

converges in probability to 0 as n becomes infinite.

PROOF. Since

$$Pr\left(\sum_{i=1}^{k} \frac{|n_i - np_i|^\beta}{(np_i)^\alpha} > \epsilon\right) \leq Pr\left(\text{at least one of } \frac{|n_i - np_i|^\beta}{(np_i)^\alpha} > \frac{\epsilon}{k}\right)$$

$$\leq \sum_{i=1}^{k} Pr\left(\frac{|n_i - np_i|^\beta}{n^\alpha} > \frac{\epsilon}{k} p_i^\alpha\right)$$

$$\leq \frac{k^{2/\beta}}{n^{2\alpha-\beta}\epsilon^{2/\beta}} \sum_{i=1}^{k} \frac{p_i q_i}{p_i^{2\alpha/\beta}},$$

the result follows if $2\alpha > \beta$.

Appendix D. Evaluation of EU_n^2

The first three terms of the approximation to U_n given by (4) will be the basis for the approximation we use, i.e.,

$$\frac{nU_n}{\log_2 e} \cong \frac{1}{2}\sum_{i=1}^{k} \frac{(n_i - np_i)^2}{np_i} - \frac{1}{6}\sum_{i=1}^{k} \frac{(n_i - np_i)^3}{(np_i)^2} + \frac{1}{12}\sum_{i=1}^{k} \frac{(n_i - np_i)^4}{(np_i)^3}.$$

Let us define

$$w_{ij} = \frac{(n_i - np_i)^j}{(np_i)^{j-1}}.$$

Then, excluding terms that will yield moments $E(n_i - np_i)^j$ where $j \geq 7$, we have

$$\left(\frac{nU_n}{\log_2 e}\right)^2 \cong \frac{1}{4}\left(\sum_{i=1}^{k} w_{i2}^2 + \sum_{i \neq h} w_{h2}w_{i2}\right)$$

$$- \frac{1}{6}\left(\sum_{i=1}^{k} w_{i2}w_{i3} + \sum_{i \neq h} w_{h2}w_{i3}\right)$$

$$+ \frac{1}{36}\left(\sum_{i=1}^{k} w_{i3}^2 + \sum_{i \neq h} w_{h3}w_{i3}\right)$$

$$+ \frac{1}{12}\left(\sum_{i=1}^{k} w_{i2}w_{i4} + \sum_{i \neq h} w_{h2}w_{i4}\right).$$

We now evaluate the necessary expected values. Inasmuch as we wish to retain only terms of $O(1/n)$ or lower we shall drop the terms of higher order as they appear indicating their omission by " $\cdots$ ".

$$Ew_{i2}^2 = E\frac{(n_i - np_i)^4}{(np_i)^3} = \frac{3n^2p_i^2q_i^2 + np_iq_i(1 - 6p_iq_i)}{n^2p_i^2} = 3q_i^2 + \frac{q_i(1 - 6p_iq_i)}{np_i},$$

$$Ew_{i2}w_{i3} = E\frac{(n_i - np_i)^5}{(np_i)^3} = \frac{10n^2p_i^2q_i^2(q_i - p_i) + np_iq_i(q_i - p_i)(1 - 12p_iq_i)}{n^3p_i^3}$$

$$= \frac{10q_i^2(q_i - p_i)}{np_i} + \frac{q_i(q_i - p_i)(1 - 12p_iq_i)}{n^2p_i^2},$$

$$Ew_{i3}^2 = Ew_{i2}w_{i4} = E\frac{(n_i - np_i)^6}{(np_i)^4}$$

$$= \frac{15n^3p_i^3q_i^3 + 5n^2p_i^2q_i^2[5 - 26p_iq_i] + np_iq_i[1 - 30p_iq_i + 120p_i^2q_i^2]}{n^4p_i^4}$$

$$= \frac{15q_i^3}{np_i} + \frac{5q_i^2(5 - 26p_iq_i)}{n^2p_i^2} + \frac{q_i(1 - 30p_iq_i + 120p_i^2q_i^2)}{n^3p_i^3}.$$

Now since the first term of, say,

$$Ew_{i3}w_{i4} = \frac{n^3k}{n^5p_i^5} = O\left(\frac{1}{n^2}\right),$$

it follows that in obtaining the expected values of the terms of (6) we can ignore all terms that are $O(1/n^2)$ where $d \geq 2$. We shall do this in the following evaluations. From Lemma B.3 we have

$$E[(n_h - np_h)^2 \mid n_i] = \frac{p_h^2}{q_h^2}(n_i - np_i)^2 - \frac{p_h(q_i - p_h)}{q_i^2}(n_i - np_i) + \frac{np_h(q_i - p_h)}{q_i},$$

so that

$$Ew_{h2}w_{i2} = \frac{p_h^2}{n^2p_ip_hq_i^2}E(n_i - np_i)^4 - \frac{p_h(q_i - p_h)}{n^2p_ip_hq_i^2}E(n_i - np_i)^3$$

$$+ \frac{np_h(q_i - p_h)}{n^2p_ip_hq_i^2}E(n_i - np_i)^2$$

$$= \frac{p_h}{n^2p_iq_i^2}[3n^2p_i^2q_i^2 + np_iq_i(1 - 6p_iq_i)]$$

$$- \frac{(q_i - p_h)}{n^2p_iq_i^2}[np_iq_i(q_i - p_i)] + \frac{(q_i - p_h)}{np_iq_i}np_iq_i,$$

and hence,

$$E\sum_{\substack{h \\ h \neq i}} w_{h2}w_{i2} = 3p_iq_i + \frac{1 - 6p_iq_i}{n} - \frac{(k-2)(q_i - p_i)}{n} + (k-2)q_i.$$

Also,

$$Ew_{h2}w_{i3} = \frac{p_h^2}{n^3p_i^2p_hq_i^2}E(n_i - np_i)^5 - \frac{p_h(q_i - p_h)}{n^3p_i^2p_hq_i^2}E(n_i - np_i)^4$$

$$+ \frac{np_h(q_i - p_h)}{n^3q_ip_i^2p_h}E(n_i - np_i)^3$$

$$= \frac{p_h}{n^3p_i^2q_i^2}[10n^2p_i^2q_i^2(q_i - p_i) + \cdots]$$

$$- \frac{(q_i - p_h)}{n^3p_i^2q_i^2}[3n^2p_i^2q_i^2 + \cdots]$$

$$+ \frac{(q_i - p_h)}{n^2p_i^2q_i}np_iq_i(q_i - p_i),$$

where "$\cdots$" stands for quantities that will yield terms $O(1/n^2)$ or higher. Hence,

$$Ew_{h2}w_{i3} \cong \frac{10p_h(q_i - p_i)}{n} - \frac{3(q_i - p_h)}{n} + \frac{(q_i - p_h)(q_i - p_i)}{np_i},$$

and

$$E \sum_{\substack{h \\ h \neq i}} w_{h2} w_{i3} \cong \frac{10 q_i (q_i - p_i)}{n} - \frac{3(k-2)q_i}{n} + \frac{(k-2)q_i(q_i - p_i)}{np_i}.$$

Also,

$$Ew_{h2}w_{i4} = \frac{p_h^2}{n^4 p_i^3 p_h q_i^2} E(n_i - np_i)^6 - \frac{p_h(q_i - p_h)}{n^4 p_i^3 p_h q_i^2} E(n_i - np_i)^5$$

$$+ \frac{np_h(q_i - p_h)}{n^4 p_i^3 p_h q_i} E(n_i - np_i)^4$$

$$= \frac{p_h}{n^4 p_i^3 q_i^2} [15 n^3 p_i^3 q_i^3 + \cdots] - \frac{(q_i - p_h)}{n^4 p_i^3 q_i^2} [\cdots] + \frac{(q_i - p_h)}{n^3 p_i^3 q_i} [3 n^2 p_i^2 q_i^2 + \cdots]$$

$$= \frac{15 p_h q_i}{n} + \frac{3(q_i - p_h)q_i}{np_i}.$$

Hence,

$$E \sum_{\substack{h \\ h \neq i}} w_{h2} w_{i4} = \frac{15 q_i^2}{n} + \frac{3(k-2)q_i^2}{np_i}.$$

Finally,

$$Ew_{h3}w_{i3} = E \frac{(n_h - np_h)^3 (n_i - np_i)^3}{n^4 p_h^2 p_i^2}$$

$$= E \frac{(n_i - np_i)^3}{n^4 p_h^2 p_i^2} \left[-\frac{p_h^3}{q_i^3} (n_i - np_i)^3 + \cdots \right]$$

$$\cong - \frac{p_h^3}{n^4 p_h^2 p_i^2 q_i^3} E(n_i - np_i)^6$$

$$= - \frac{p_h}{n^4 p_i^2 q_i^3} [15 n^3 p_i^3 q_i^3 + \cdots]$$

$$= - \frac{15 p_h p_i}{n},$$

and

$$E \sum_{\substack{h \\ h \neq i}} w_{h3} w_{i3} = - \sum_{\substack{h \\ h \neq i}} \frac{15 p_h p_i}{n} = - \frac{15 p_i q_i}{n}.$$

First, we note that

$$Ew_{i2}^2 = 3q_i^2 + \frac{q_i(1 - 6p_i q_i)}{np_i}$$

and that

$$E \sum_{\substack{h \\ h \neq i}} w_{h2} w_{i2} = 3p_i q_i + (k-2)q_i + \frac{1 - 6p_i q_i - (k-2)(q_i - p_i)}{n},$$

so that

$$E\left[\sum_{i=1}^{k} w_{i2}^2 + \sum_{i \neq 1} w_{h2}w_{i2}\right]$$

$$= 3\sum_{i=1}^{k} q_i^2 + 3(k-1) - 3\sum_{i=1}^{k} q_i^2 + (k-2)(k-1)$$

$$+ \frac{1}{n}\left[\sum_{i=1}^{k} \frac{p_i}{q_i} - 6\sum_{i=1}^{k} q_i^2 + k - 6(k-1) + 6\sum_{i=1}^{k} q_i^2 - (k-2)^2\right]$$

$$= (k-1)(k+1) + \frac{1}{n}\left[\sum_{i=1}^{k} \frac{1}{p_i} - k + k - 6(k-1) - (k-2)^2\right]$$

$$= k^2 - 1 + \frac{1}{n}\left[\sum_{i=1}^{k} \frac{1}{p_i} - k^2 - 2k + 2\right].$$

Similarly, for the second term,

$$E\left[\sum_{i=1}^{k} w_{i2}w_{i3} + \sum_{i \neq h} w_{h2}w_{i3}\right]$$

$$= \sum_{i=1}^{k}\left[\frac{10q_i(q_i - p_i)}{np_i} + \frac{10q_i(q_i - p_i)}{n} - \frac{3(k-2)q_i}{n} + \frac{(k-2)q_i(q_i - p_i)}{np_i}\right]$$

$$= \sum_{i=1}^{k} \frac{10q_i(q_i - p_i) - (k-2)q_i(4p_i - q_i)}{np_i}$$

$$= \sum_{i=1}^{k} \frac{(k+8)q_i^2 - (4k+2)p_iq_i}{np_i} = \sum_{i=1}^{k} \frac{q_i}{np_i}[(k+8) - 5p_i(k+2)].$$

For the third term,

$$E\left[\sum_{i=1}^{k} w_{i3}^2 + \sum w_{h3}w_{i3}\right] = \sum_{i=1}^{k}\left(\frac{15q_i}{np_i} - \frac{15p_iq_i}{n}\right)$$

$$= \sum_{i=1}^{k} \frac{15q_i}{np_i}(q_i^2 - p_i^2) = \sum_{i=1}^{k} \frac{15q_i}{np_i}(q_i - p_i).$$

For the final term,

$$E\left[\sum_{i=1}^{k} w_{i2} \cdot w_{i4} + \sum_{i \neq h} w_{h2} \cdot w_{i4}\right] = \sum_{i=1}^{k}\left[\frac{15q_i^3}{np_i} + \frac{15q_i^2}{n} + \frac{3(k-2)q_i^2}{np_i}\right]$$

$$= \sum_{i=1}^{k} \frac{3q_i^2}{np_i}[5q_i + 5p_i + 3(k-2)] = \sum_{i=1}^{k} \frac{3q_i^2}{np_i}(3k-1).$$

Hence,

$$E\left(\frac{nU_n}{\log_2 e}\right)^2 \cong \frac{k^2-1}{4} + \frac{1}{4n}\left[\sum_{i=1}^{k}\frac{1}{p_i} - k^2 - 2k + 2\right] - \frac{(k+8)}{6n}\sum_{i=1}^{k}\frac{q_i}{p_i}$$

$$+ 5\frac{k+2}{6n}(k-1) + \frac{15}{36n}\sum_{i=1}^{k}\frac{q_i^2}{p_i} - \frac{15}{36n}(k-1) + \frac{3(3k-1)}{12n}\sum_{i=1}^{k}\frac{q_i^2}{p_i}$$

$$= \frac{k^2-1}{4} + \frac{1}{4n}\sum_{i=1}^{k}\frac{1}{p_i} + \frac{2-2k-k^2}{4n} - \frac{k+8}{6n}\sum_{i=1}^{k}\frac{1}{p_i}$$

$$+ \frac{k+8}{6n}k + \frac{5(k+2)(k-1)}{6n} - \frac{5}{12n}(k-1)$$

$$+ \frac{5}{12n}\sum_{i=1}^{k}\frac{q_i^2}{p_i} + \frac{3(3k-1)}{12n}\sum\frac{q_i^2}{p_i}.$$

Finally,

$$E\left(\frac{nU_n}{\log_2 e}\right)^2 = \frac{k^2-1}{4} + \frac{1}{12n}\left(\sum_{i=1}^{k}\frac{1}{p_i}\right)(3 - 2k - 16 + 9k + 2)$$

$$+ \frac{1}{12n}[6 - 6k - 3k^2 + 2k^2 + 16k + 10k^2$$

$$+ 10k - 20 - 5k + 5 + 2 + 5k - 18k]$$

$$= \frac{k^2-1}{4} + \frac{7k-11}{12n}\sum_{i=1}^{k}\frac{1}{p_i} - \frac{9k^2-20k+7}{12n}.$$

As a check, $E\left(\frac{nU_n}{\log_2 e}\right)^2$ was computed for a special case. Let $k = 2$ so that

$$n_1 + n_2 = n, \qquad n_2 = n - n_1,$$

$$n_2 - np_2 = n - n_1 - np_2 = -(n_1 - np_1).$$

Hence,

$$\frac{nU_n}{\log_2 e} \cong \frac{1}{2}\frac{(n_1-np_1)^2}{n}\left(\frac{1}{p_1} + \frac{1}{q_1}\right) - \frac{1}{6}\frac{(n_1-np_1)^3}{n^2}\left(\frac{1}{p_1^2} - \frac{1}{q_1^2}\right)$$

$$+ \frac{1}{12}\frac{(n_1-np_1)^4}{n^3}\left(\frac{1}{p_1^3} - \frac{1}{q_1^3}\right),$$

and

$$\left(\frac{nU_n}{\log_2 e}\right)^2 \cong \frac{1}{4}\frac{(n_1 - np_1)^4}{n^2 p_1^2 q_1^2} + \frac{1}{36}\frac{(n_1 - np_1)^6}{n^4 p_1^4 q_1^4}(q_1 - p_1)^2 - \frac{1}{6}\frac{(n_1 - np_1)^5}{n^3 p_1^3 q_1^3}(q_1 - p_1)$$

$$+ \frac{1}{12}\frac{(n_1 - np_1)^6}{n^4 p_1^4 q_1^4}(q_1^3 + p_1^3).$$

$$E\left(\frac{nU_n}{\log_2 e}\right)^2 \cong \frac{1}{4n^2 p_1^2 q_1^2}(3n^2 p_1^2 q_1^2 + np_1 q_1[1 - 6p_1 q_1])$$

$$+ \frac{15n^3 p_1^3 q_1^3(q_1 - p_1)^2}{36n^4 p_1^4 q_1^4} - \frac{10n^2 p_1^2 q_1^2(q_1 - p_1)^2}{6n^3 p_1^3 q_1^3}$$

$$+ \frac{15n^3 p_1^3 q_1^3(q_1^3 + p_1^3)}{12n^4 p_1^4 q_1^4}$$

$$= \frac{3}{4} + \frac{1 - 6p_1 q_1}{4np_1 q_1} + \frac{5(q_1 - p_1)^2}{12np_1 q_1} - \frac{5(q_1 - p_1)^2}{3np_1 q_1} + \frac{5(q_1^3 + p_1^3)}{4np_1 q_1}$$

$$= \frac{3}{4} + \frac{1}{12np_1 q_1}[3 - 18p_1 q_1 + 5(q_1 - p_1)^2 - 20(q_1 - p_1)^2 + 15(q_1^3 + p_1^3)].$$

Let $p_1 = q_1 = 1/2$, so that

$$E\left(\frac{nU_n}{\log_2 e}\right)^2 \cong \frac{3}{4} + \frac{1}{3n}\left(3 - \frac{9}{2} + \frac{15}{4}\right)$$

$$= \frac{3}{4} + \frac{1}{3n}\left(\frac{12 - 18 + 15}{4}\right) = \frac{3}{4} + \frac{3}{4n}.$$

If $k = 2$ and $p_1 = q_1 = 1/2$,

$$E\left(\frac{nU_n}{\log_2 e}\right)^2 \cong \frac{3}{4} + \frac{1}{n}\left(1 - \frac{6}{4}\right) \qquad \text{(from square of 1st term)}$$

$$+ 0 \qquad \text{(from square of 2nd term)}$$

$$+ 0 \qquad \text{(from product of 1st by 2nd)}$$

$$+ \frac{5}{4n} \qquad \text{(from product of 1st by 3rd).}$$

From general formula

1st term squared $\dfrac{3}{4} + \dfrac{1}{4n}[4 - 4 - 4 + 2] = \dfrac{3}{4} - \dfrac{1}{2n}$

2nd term squared $\dfrac{1}{36}\cdot\dfrac{15}{n}\left(2\dfrac{1/4}{1/2}\right) - \dfrac{15}{36n} = \dfrac{15}{36n} - \dfrac{15}{36n} = 0$.

product of 1st by 2nd $-\dfrac{10}{6n}2 + \dfrac{5 \times 4}{6n} = 0$

product of 1st by 3rd term $\dfrac{3 \times 5}{12n}\left(\dfrac{1}{2} + \dfrac{1}{2}\right) = \dfrac{15}{12n} = \dfrac{5}{4n}.$

Hence each part checks.

REFERENCES

[1] Cramer, H. *Mathematical methods of statistics*. Princeton: Princeton University Press, 1946.
[2] Miller, G. A. What is information measurement? *Amer. Psychologist*, 1953, **8**, 3–11.
[3] Shannon, C. E. A mathematical theory of communication. *Bell System Tech. J.*, 1948, **27**, 379–423.
[4] Wiener, N. *Cybernetics*. New York: Wiley, 1948.

A STATISTICAL DESCRIPTION OF VERBAL LEARNING*

GEORGE A. MILLER AND WILLIAM J. McGILL

MASSACHUSETTS INSTITUTE OF TECHNOLOGY

Free-recall verbal learning is analyzed in terms of a probability model. The general theory assumes that the probability of recalling a word on any trial is completely determined by the number of times the word has been recalled on previous trials. Three particular cases of this general theory are examined. In these three cases, specific restrictions are placed upon the relation between probability of recall and number of previous recalls. The application of these special cases to typical experimental data is illustrated. An interpretation of the model in terms of set theory is suggested but is not essential to the argument.

The verbal learning considered in this paper is the kind observed in the following experiment: A list of words is presented to the learner. At the end of the presentation he writes down all the words he can remember. This procedure is repeated through a series of n trials. At the present time we are not prepared to extend the statistical theory to a wider range of experimental procedures.

The General Model

We shall assume that the degree to which any word in the test material has been learned is completely specified by the number of times the word has been recalled on preceding trials. In other words, the probability that a word will be recalled on trial $n + 1$ is a function of k, the number of times it has been recalled previously. (Symbols and their meanings are listed in Appendix C at the end of the paper.)

Let the probability of recall after k previous recalls be symbolized by τ_k. Then the corresponding probability of failing to recall the word is $1 - \tau_k$. When a word has been recalled exactly k times on the preceding trials, we shall say that the word is in state A_k. Thus before the first trial all the words are in state A_0; that is to say, they have been recalled zero times on previous trials. Ideally, on the first trial a proportion τ_0 of these words is recalled and so passes from state A_0 to state A_1. The proportion $1 - \tau_0$ is not recalled and so remains in state A_0. On the second trial the

*This research was facilitated by the authors' membership in the Inter-University Summer seminar of the Social Science Research Council, entitled Mathematical Models for Behavior Theory, held at Tufts College, June 28–August 24, 1951. The authors are especially grateful to Dr. F. Mosteller for advice and criticism that proved helpful on many different occasions.

This article appeared in *Psychometrika*, 1952, **17**, 369–396. Reprinted with permission.

words that remained in A_0 undergo the same transformation as before. Of those in A_1, however, the proportion $1 - \tau_1$ is not recalled and so remains in A_1.

One general problem is to determine the proportion of words expected in state A_k on trial n. Let $p(A_k,n)$ represent the probability that a word is in state A_k on trial n. Since these are probabilities, they must sum to unity on any given trial:

$$\sum_k p(A_k, n) = 1.$$

The number of trials and the total number of times a word has been recalled must assume non-negative, integral values. We assume that a word can be recalled only once per trial at most, so the number of recalls cannot exceed the number of trials. Therefore, we have

$$p(A_k, n) = 0 \quad \text{for} \quad k < 0, n < 0, n < k.$$

We also assume that none of the words can have been recalled before the first trial, so for $n = 0$,

$$p(A_k, 0) = \begin{cases} 1 & \text{for} \quad k = 0, \\ 0 & \text{for} \quad k \neq 0. \end{cases}$$

For all trials we have the difference equation:

$$p(A_k, n + 1) = p(A_k, n)(1 - \tau_k) + p(A_{k-1}, n)\tau_{k-1}. \tag{1}$$

This equation reflects the fact that a word can get into state A_k on trial $n + 1$ in only two ways: (a) either it is in A_k on trial n and is not recalled on trial $n + 1$, or (b) it is in A_{k-1} on trial n and is recalled on trial $n + 1$.

The following rationalization for this scheme is in the spirit of the statistical theories of learning developed by Bush and Mosteller (1) and by Estes (3). The rationalization is not necessary for the development of the mathematics, but it gives an alternative way of thinking about the present model and helps to clarify its relation to the earlier theories. On the first presentation of the list of words a random sample of stimulus elements is conditioned to the appropriate response for each word. The measure of this set of conditioned elements is τ_0. (The total measure of the set of all stimulus elements for a given word is assumed to be unity, so the measure can be regarded as a probability.) If a word is not recalled, the measure of conditioned elements for that word is unchanged. But if a word is recalled, the proportion of conditioned elements is increased. The effect of recalling a word is to take another random sample of elements from the total set and to condition them. The proportion of elements conditioned when a word in state A_k is recalled is $\tau_{k+1} - \tau_k$. More precise interpretation of this set-theoretical argument will be presented when we consider the special cases of the general theory.

The general solution of (1) when all the τ_k are different is (see Appendix A):

$$p(A_0, n) = (1 - \tau_0)^n, \qquad \text{for} \quad k = 0,$$

$$p(A_k, n) = \tau_0\tau_1 \cdots \tau_{k-1} \sum_{i=0}^{k} \frac{(1 - \tau_i)^n}{\prod_{\substack{j=0 \\ j \neq i}}^{k} (\tau_j - \tau_i)}, \qquad \text{for } k > 0. \qquad (2)$$

The denominator of each of the fractions in the summation includes all differences of the form $(\tau_j - \tau_i)$ except for the zero difference $(\tau_i - \tau_i)$.

The expected number of times a word is recalled, all told, up to and including trial n, is, by definition,

$$E(k, n) = \sum_{k=0}^{n} kp(A_k, n). \qquad (3)$$

The expected proportion of words recalled on trial $n + 1$ is the difference, $E(k, n + 1) - E(k, n)$, between the cumulative values on successive trials. This difference is the theoretical recall score and we symbolize it by ρ_{n+1}. Thus we have the general relation

$$\rho_0 = 0, \qquad\qquad\qquad \text{for } n = 0,$$

$$\rho_{n+1} = E(k, n + 1) - E(k, n), \qquad \text{for } n + 1 > 0. \qquad (4)$$

An alternative expression for ρ_{n+1} can be obtained as follows. On trial n the probability that a word is in state A_k is $p(A_k, n)$. The probability of recall in state A_k is τ_k. The product $\tau_k \cdot p(A_k, n)$ is, therefore, the probability that a word will both be in A_k on trial n and also be recalled on trial $n + 1$. If these joint probabilities are summed over all the states A_k from $k = 0$ to $k = n$, we have the total probability that a word will be recalled on trial $n + 1$. That is to say, we have ρ_{n+1}:

$$\rho_{n+1} = \sum_{k=0}^{n} \tau_k p(A_k, n). \qquad (5)$$

The two expressions (4) and (5) are equivalent, which can be shown as follows. From (3) and (4) together we have

$$\rho_{n+1} = \sum_{k=0}^{n+1} kp(A_k, n + 1) - \sum_{k=0}^{n} kp(A_k, n).$$

The first summation on the right can be rewritten by substituting for $p(A_k, n + 1)$ according to (1):

$$\sum_{k=0}^{n+1} kp(A_k, n + 1) = \sum_{k=0}^{n+1} kp(A_k, n)(1 - \tau_k) + \sum_{k=0}^{n+1} kp(A_{k-1}, n)\tau_{k-1}$$

$$= \sum_{k=0}^{n} kp(A_k, n) - \sum_{k=0}^{n} kp(A_k, n)\tau_k$$

$$+ \sum_{k=0}^{n} (k + 1)p(A_k, n)\tau_k.$$

When this result is substituted into the expression for ρ_{n+1} , we have

$$\rho_{n+1} = -\sum_{k=0}^{n} kp(A_k , n)\tau_k + \sum_{k=0}^{n} (k + 1)p(A_k , n)\tau_k$$

$$= \sum_{k=0}^{n} \tau_k p(A_k , n),$$

which is the desired result.

The asymptotic behavior of the model as n increases without limit can be deduced from the general solution (2). First consider the case in which one or more of the transitional probabilities τ_k is zero. All the words start in state A_0 and have a positive probability of moving along to states A_1 , A_2 , etc., up to the first state, A_h , with zero transitional probability, $\tau_h = 0$. There the words are trapped; eventually all the words are recalled exactly h times and cannot be recalled again. This fact can be seen from (2): If $\tau_i > 0$, then all the terms $(1 - \tau_i)^n$ in (2) go to zero as $n \to \infty$. Thus $p(A_k , n)$ goes to zero for $k < h$. For $k > h$, the product in front of the summation must include $\tau_h = 0$, and so $p(A_k , n) = 0$ for $k > h$. When $k = h$, however, $(1 - \tau_h)^n = (1 - 0)^n = 1$, and so this term in the summation of (2) does not go to zero. Instead, when $\tau_h = 0$ and $\tau_i > 0$ for $i < h$,

$$\lim_{n \to \infty} p(A_h , n) = \frac{\tau_0 \tau_1 \cdots \tau_{h-1}}{(\tau_0 - \tau_h)(\tau_1 - \tau_h) \cdots (\tau_{h-1} - \tau_h)} = 1.$$

The recall score, ρ_{n+1} , then approaches zero as an asymptote; from (5),

$$\lim_{n \to \infty} \rho_{n+1} = \sum_{k=0}^{\infty} \tau_k[\lim_{n \to \infty} p(A_k , n)] = 0,$$

since the probability at the asymptote is concentrated at state A_h , and for this state $\tau_h = 0$. This case is of little interest for an acquisition theory, since the asymptote of the learning curve is at zero. Therefore, in what follows, we shall be concerned only with the case in which all the τ_k are different and greater than zero.

If all the transitional probabilities τ_k are greater than zero, then from (2) we see that as n approaches infinity all the terms in the summation go toward zero for all finite values of k. Consequently the sum of the $p(A_k , n)$ can be made as near zero as we please for any finite k by selecting a large enough value of n. In the limit, therefore, the probability of any finite number of recalls is zero. Since the sum of the $p(A_k , n)$ must equal unity, almost all the probability comes to be concentrated in state A_∞ and we have for the limit when all $\tau_k > 0$,

$$p(A_\infty , \infty) = 1.$$

We are now able to show that a word in state A_k has probability one of moving to state A_{k+1}, if the learning process is continued indefinitely. This happens because almost all words eventually reach state A_∞. Thus we can write, for the probability of leaving state A_k on some trial,

$$\sum_{n=k}^{\infty} \tau_k p(A_k, n) = 1,$$

or,

$$\sum_{n=k}^{\infty} p(A_k, n) = \frac{1}{\tau_k} \qquad \text{for } \tau_k > 0.$$

In all the cases we shall consider in this paper the value of τ_k will approach an asymptote as $k \to \infty$. We are interested in placing the following restrictions on the τ_k:

$$\tau_k \neq \tau_i,$$

$$\tau_k > 0,$$

$$\lim_{k \to \infty} \tau_k = m \leq 1.$$

The first two conditions insure that $p(A_k, n)$ goes toward zero for finite k and large n. The third condition provides the asymptotic value of τ_k for infinite k. In the summation for the limiting value of ρ_{n+1}, all terms are zero out to infinity, and so we have

$$\lim_{n \to \infty} \rho_{n+1} = mp(A_\infty, \infty) = m. \qquad (5')$$

In other words, if we assume that m is the asymptotic value of τ_k as $k \to \infty$, then m is also the asymptotic value of ρ_{n+1} as $n \to \infty$.

In the special cases discussed below, a restriction is placed upon the value of τ_k in the form of the linear difference equation,*

$$\tau_{k+1} = a + \alpha\tau_k, \qquad (6)$$

where $0 \leq a \leq 1$ and $0 \leq \alpha \leq 1 - a$. The limits for α have been chosen so that τ_{k+1} is bounded between zero and one and, since we are interested in acquisition, so that $\tau_{k+1} \geq \tau_k$.

Consider the following development of (5):

$$\rho_{n+2} = \sum_{k=0}^{n+1} \tau_k p(A_k, n + 1).$$

---

*We have tried to observe the convention that parameters are represented by Greek letters and statistical estimates are represented by Roman letters. In the case of a and m, however, we have violated this convention in order to make our symbols coincide with those used by other workers. The symbols m, a, α, and p were originally proposed by Bush and Mosteller.

Now substitute for $p(A_k , n + 1)$ according to (1):

$$\rho_{n+2} = \sum_{k=0}^{n+1} \tau_k p(A_k , n)(1 - \tau_k) + \sum_{k=0}^{n+1} \tau_k p(A_{k-1} , n) \tau_{k-1}$$

$$= \rho_{n+1} - \sum_{k=0}^{n} \tau_k^2 p(A_k , n) + \sum_{k=0}^{n} \tau_{k+1} \tau_k p(A_k , n).$$

Next we substitute for τ_{k+1} according to (6):

$$\rho_{n+2} = \rho_{n+1} - \sum_{k=0}^{n} \tau_k^2 p(A_k , n) + \sum_{k=0}^{n} (a + \alpha \tau_k) \tau_k p(A_k , n)$$

$$= (1 + a) \rho_{n+1} - (1 - \alpha) \sum_{k=0}^{n} \tau_k^2 p(A_k , n)$$

$$= (1 + a) \rho_{n+1} - (1 - \alpha) E(\tau_k^2 , n + 1), \tag{7}$$

where $E(\tau_k^2 , n + 1)$ is the second raw moment of the τ_k (as ρ_{n+1} is the first raw moment) for trial $n + 1$.

Restriction (6) brings the system into direct correspondence with a special case of the theory developed by Bush and Mosteller. In their terminology, an operator Q_1 is applied to the probability of response, p, to give $a_1 + \alpha_1 p$ as the new probability whenever a trial is successful. A second operator Q_2 is applied to give $a_2 + \alpha_2 p$ whenever a trial is unsuccessful. In the present application of this more general theory, Q_1 is preserved intact by restriction (6), but Q_2 is assumed to be the identity operator. That is to say, a_2 is zero and α_2 is unity, so $Q_2 p = p$. In the present application, an unsuccessful trial consists of the omission of the word during recall. It seems reasonable to assume that the non-occurrence of a word has no effect upon its probability of occurrence on the next trial. How successful this simple assumption is will be seen when we examine the data.

Analysis of the Data

At the end of the experiment the experimenter has collected a set of word lists—the words recalled by the learner on successive trials. These recall lists will usually contain a small number of words that did not occur in the presentation. These spontaneous additions by the learner are of some interest in themselves, but we shall ignore them in the present discussion.

We would like to use the data contained in the word lists to obtain an estimate of ρ_{n+1} in (5). We shall refer to the estimate as r_{n+1}. There are, we suppose, N words provided by the experimenter as learning material in the experiment. It seems reasonable to assume that under certain conditions these words are homogeneous. By this we imply that the responses to all of the words in state A_k may be considered as estimates of the same transitional probability of recall, τ_k.

We can then define a convenient statistic,

$$r_{n+1} = \frac{1}{N} \sum_{k=0}^{n} \sum_{i=1}^{N} X_{i,k,n+1} . \tag{8}$$

The numbers, $X_{i,k,n+1}$, are either zero or one. The subscripts k and $n+1$ have the same meaning that we have attached to them previously. They indicate that we are looking at an event that occurs on trial $n+1$ to a word in state A_k. The first summation is carried out over i, the experimental words, with k fixed to show that we count the number of words in each state. The rules that determine whether an $X_{i,k,n+1}$ is zero or one are straight-forward. The $X_{i,k,n+1}$ are zero for all words not in state A_k when summing on i. They are zero for any word in state A_k, if a recall fails to occur on trial $n+1$. Lastly the $X_{i,k,n+1}$ are 1 for any word in state A_k, provided that a recall occurs on trial $n+1$. The second summation extends over k, the various states. This summation goes only up to n because our reference point for determining the number of states is trial n. These rules determine r_{n+1} as the proportion of correct responses to the N experimental words on trial $n+1$.

To show that r_{n+1} is unbiased we observe that

$$E(r_{n+1}) = \frac{1}{N} \sum_{k=0}^{n} \left[E\left(\sum_{i=1}^{N} X_{i,k,n+1} \right) \right].$$

The expectation of any $X_{i,k,n+1}$ in state A_k is τ_k. Thus the expectation of the sum in the brackets is $N \cdot \tau_k \cdot p(A_k, n)$. Substituting this into the expression for $E(r_{n+1})$, we find

$$E(r_{n+1}) = \sum_{k=0}^{n} \tau_k p(A_k, n),$$

$$E(r_{n+1}) = \rho_{n+1} . \tag{9}$$

The sampling variance of r_{n+1} around ρ_{n+1} is determined by the variances of the various $X_{i,k,n+1}$ around the transitional probabilities, τ_k.

$$\text{Var } (r_{n+1}) = \frac{1}{N^2} \sum_{k=0}^{n} \text{Var} \left(\sum_{i=1}^{N} X_{i,k,n+1} \right).$$

The variance of any $X_{i,k,n+1}$ in state A_k is binomial and is given by $\tau_k(1 - \tau_k)$. The variance of $\sum_{i=1}^{N} X_{i,k,n+1}$ thus becomes $N p(A_k, n)\tau_k (1 - \tau_k)$. Substituting this into the expression for Var (r_{n+1}), we obtain

$$\text{Var } (r_{n+1}) = \frac{1}{N} \sum_{k=0}^{n} p(A_k, n)\tau_k(1 - \tau_k). \tag{10}$$

It should be noted that this variance is never larger than the binomial variance

$$\frac{1}{N} \rho_{n+1} \cdot (1 - \rho_{n+1}),$$

since the binomial variance includes in addition to (10) a term that depends on the variance of the τ_k around ρ_{n+1} ,

$$\text{Var} \ (r_{n+1}) = \frac{\rho_{n+1}(1 - \rho_{n+1})}{N} - \frac{1}{N}\left\{ \sum_{k=0}^{n} \tau_k^2 p(A_k \ , \ n) - \rho_{n+1}^2 \right\}. \tag{10'}$$

In order to apply the general theory we must obtain estimates of the transitional probabilities, τ_k . Now τ_k is the probability of moving from state A_k to A_{k+1} and is assumed to be constant from trial to trial. After trial n a certain number of words, $N_{k,n}$, are in state A_k . Of these $N_{k,n}$ words, some go on to A_{k+1} and some remain in A_k on trial $n + 1$. The fraction that moves up to A_{k+1} provides an estimate of τ_k on that trial. Therefore, on every trial we obtain an estimate of τ_k . Call these estimates $t_{k,n+1}$. Then

$$t_{k,n+1} = \frac{\sum_{i=1}^{N} X_{i,k,n+1}}{N_{k,n}} \ .$$

If $N_{k,n}$ is zero, no estimate is possible.

Next we wish to combine the $t_{k,n+1}$ to obtain a single estimate, t_k , of the transitional probability, τ_k . The least-squares solution, obtained by minimizing $(t_{k,n+1} - \tau_k)^2$, is the direct average of the $t_{k,n+1}$. This estimate is unbiased, but it has too large a variance because it places undue emphasis upon the $t_{k,n+1}$ that are based on small values of $N_{k,n}$. We prefer, therefore, to use the maximum-likelihood estimate,

$$t_k = \frac{\sum_{n} N_{k,n} t_{k,n+1}}{\sum_{n} N_{k,n}} \ , \tag{11}$$

which respects the accuracy of the various $t_{k,n+1}$.

For example, after trial 7 there may be 10 words in state A_3 . Of these 10, 6 are recalled on trial 8. This gives the estimate $t_{3,8} = 6/10$. Every trial on which $N_{3,n} \neq 0$ provides a similar estimate, $t_{3,n+1}$. The final estimate of τ_3 is obtained by weighting each of these separate estimates according to the size of the sample on which it is based and then averaging. This procedure is repeated for all the τ_k individually as far as the data permit.

The $t_{k,n+1}$ are also useful to check the basic assumption that τ_k is independent of n. If the $t_{k,n+1}$ show a significant trend, this basic assumption is violated.

The Simplest Case: One Parameter

The computation of $p(A_k \ , \ n)$ from (2) for the general case is exceedingly tedious as n and k become moderately large. We look, therefore, for a simple relation among the τ_k of the form of restriction (6). The first case that we shall consider is

$$\tau_0 = a,$$

$$\tau_{k+1} = a + (1 - a)\tau_k .\tag{12}$$

In this form the model contains only the single parameter, a. The solution of the difference equation (12) is

$$\tau_k = 1 - (1 - a)^{k+1}.\tag{13}$$

The interpretation of (13) in set-theoretical terms runs as follows: On the first presentation of the list a random sample of elements is conditioned for each word. The measure of this sample is a, and it represents the probability, τ_0, of going from state A_0 to state A_1. If a word is not recalled, no change is produced in the proportion of conditioned elements. When a word is recalled, however, the effect is to condition another random sample of elements, drawn independently of the first sample, of measure a to that word. Since some of the elements sampled at recall will have been previously conditioned, after one recall we have (because of our assumption of independence between successive samples):

$$\begin{pmatrix}\text{Elements conditioned}\\ \text{during presentation}\end{pmatrix} + \begin{pmatrix}\text{Elements conditioned}\\ \text{during the recall}\end{pmatrix} - \begin{pmatrix}\text{Common}\\ \text{elements}\end{pmatrix}$$

$$= a + a - a^2 = 1 - (1 - a)^2.$$

This quantity gives us the transitional probability τ_1 of going from A_1 to A_2, from the first to the second recall. The second time a word is recalled another independent random sample of measure a is drawn and conditioned, so we have

$$\tau_2 = [1 - (1 - a)^2] + a - a[1 - (1 - a)^2] = 1 - (1 - a)^3.$$

Continuing in this way generates the relation (13).

With this substitution the general difference equation (1) becomes

$$p(A_k , n + 1) = p(A_k , n)(1 - a)^{k+1} + p(A_{k-1} , n)[1 - (1 - a)^k].$$

The solution of this difference equation can be obtained by the general method outlined in Appendix A or by the appropriate substitution for τ_k in (2). The solution is

$$p(A_0 , n) = (1 - a)^n,$$

$$p(A_k , n) = (1 - a)^{n-k} \prod_{i=0}^{k-1} [1 - (1 - a)^{n-i}].\tag{14}$$

From definition (5) it is possible to obtain the following recursive expression for the recall on trial $n + 1$ (see Appendix B):

$$\rho_{n+1} = a + (1 - a)[1 - (1 - a)^n]\rho_n . \tag{15}$$

The variance of the recall score, r_{n+1}, is

$$\text{Var } (r_{n+1}) = \frac{1}{aN} (\rho_{n+2} - \rho_{n+1}). \tag{16}$$

In order to illustrate the application of these equations, we have taken the data from one subject in an experiment by J. S. Bruner and C. Zimmerman (unpublished). In their experiment a list of 64 monosyllabic English words was read aloud to the subject. At the end of each reading the subject wrote all of the words he could remember. The order of the words was scrambled before each reading. A total of 32 presentations of the list was given.

From the detailed analysis of the estimates of τ_k derived from this subject's data it was determined that a value of $a = 0.22$ would provide a

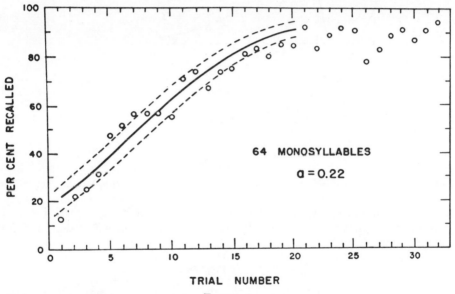

FIGURE 1

Comparison of Theoretical and Observed Values of ρ_n for the One-Parameter Case. Dotted line is drawn ± one standard deviation from ρ_n.

good fit. In Figure 1 the values of ρ_{n+1} computed from (15) are given by the solid function. The data are shown by the open circles. The dotted lines are drawn ± one standard deviation from ρ_{n+1} as computed from the variance in (16). The single parameter gives a reasonably adequate description of these data, at least through the first 20 trials. From the 20th trial on, however, it seems that the subject "forgets as fast as he learns." He seems to reach an asymptote somewhat below the theoretical value at unity. The introduction of an asymptote less than unity will be discussed in connection with the three-parameter case.

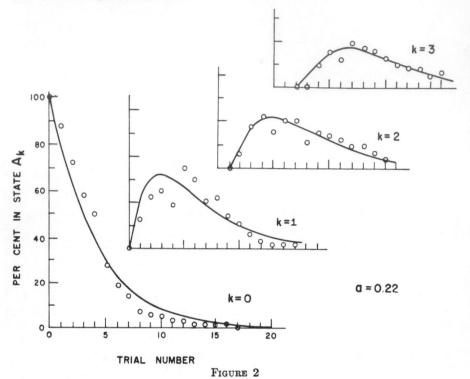

FIGURE 2

Comparison of Theoretical and Observed Values of $p(A_k, n)$ for the One-Parameter Case

As a further check on the correspondence of theory and data, Figure 2 shows the predicted and observed values of $p(A_k, n)$ as a function of n, for $k = 0, 1, 2, 3$.

Second Case: Two Parameters.

In the one-parameter form of the theory it is assumed that the proportion of elements sampled during the presentation of the list is the same as the proportion sampled during each recall. Most data are not adequately described by such a simple model. At the very least, then, it is necessary to consider the situation when these two sampling constants are different. In order to introduce the second parameter, we phrase restriction (6) in the following form:

$$\tau_0 = p_0 ,$$

$$\tau_{k+1} = a + (1 - a)\tau_k , \qquad (17)$$

where p_0 is the proportion of elements conditioned during the presentation. The solution of this difference equation can be written

$$\tau_k = 1 - (1 - p_0)(1 - a)^k. \tag{18}$$

On the first presentation of the list a random sample of measure p_0 is conditioned to every word. When a word is recalled, a random sample of measure a is drawn and conditioned. After one recall, therefore, the measure of conditioned elements is

$$\tau_1 = p_0 + a - ap_0 = 1 - (1 - p_0)(1 - a).$$

After two recalls the measure of conditioned elements is

$$\tau_2 = [1 - (1 - p_0)(1 - a)] + a - a[1 - (1 - p_0)(1 - a)]$$
$$= 1 - (1 - p_0)(1 - a)^2.$$

Continuing in this way generates the relation (18).

With this substitution the general difference equation (1) becomes

$$p(A_k, n + 1) = p(A_k, n)(1 - p_0)(1 - a)^k$$
$$+ p(A_{k-1}, n)[1 - (1 - p_0)(1 - a)^{k-1}]. \tag{19}$$

The solution of (19) is

$$p(A_0, n) = (1 - p_0)^n,$$

$$p(A_k, n) = (1 - p_0)^{n-k} \prod_{i=0}^{k-1} \frac{[1 - (1 - p_0)(1 - a)^i][1 - (1 - a)^{n-i}]}{1 - (1 - a)^{i+1}}. \tag{20}$$

When $p_0 = a$, (20) reduces to (14).

The recursive form for the recall now becomes (see Appendix B)

$$\rho_{n+1} = p_0 + (1 - p_0)[1 - (1 - a)^n]\rho_n. \tag{21}$$

The variance of r_{n+1} is

$$\text{Var}(r_{n+1}) = \frac{1}{aN}(\rho_{n+2} - \rho_{n+1}). \tag{22}$$

In order to illustrate the application of these equations we have selected two sets of data. The first set was collected by Bruner and Zimmerman. A list of 32 monosyllabic words was read aloud. At the end of each reading the subject wrote all of the words he could remember. The order of the words was scrambled before every reading. A total of 32 presentations of the list was given.

From the analysis of the t_k calculated for this particular subject it was found that $a = 0.10$ and $p_0 = 0.27$ gave a good description of the data. In Figure 3 the values of ρ_{n+1} computed from (21) are shown by the solid function. The data are given by the open circles. The dotted lines are drawn

± one standard deviation from ρ_{n+1} as computed from (22). As a further check, Figure 4 shows the predicted and observed values of $p(A_k , n)$ as a function of n for $k = 0, 1, 2, 3$.

The distribution of cumulative recalls on any given trial provides still another way of viewing the data. In Figure 5, the cumulative distribution of k, the number of recalls, is shown for trials 5, 10, 15, 20. The proportion of test words recalled k times or less is plotted for comparison on each trial.

The second set of data was collected by M. Levine. He read aloud a 100-word anecdote. At the end of the reading, the subject wrote down all he could remember. Four such trials were given. The order of the words was not scrambled during the interval between trials.

From the analysis of the data for this particular subject it was found that $a = 0.87$ and $p_0 = 0.61$ gave a good description of the results. Figure 6 shows the comparison of theory and experiment both for ρ_{n+1} and for $p(A_k , n)$ for $k = 0, 1, 2$.

As a general observation, we have noted that when the order of the words is not scrambled between trials, the parameter a is relatively large. This is to say, when the words are not scrambled, there is a much higher probability that the same words will be recalled on successive trials. This effect is related to the serial-position curve. The subject recalls words at the beginning and at the end of the list. If these words remain in their favored positions, they continue to be recalled. New words are added to those recalled at the ends at a rate determined by p_0 , so the learning works from the two ends toward the middle, which is the last to be learned. This effect has been noted with lists of randomly selected English words as well as with anecdotes.

Third Case: Three Parameters

In the one- and two-parameter cases we have assumed that after sufficient practice the subject should eventually reach perfect performance. Some data, however, seem to evade this simple assumption and so it is necessary to consider what happens when a lower asymptote is introduced. Such a parameter may be necessary when, for example, the period of time allowed for recall is limited.

To introduce the third parameter we adopt the general restriction (6)

$$\tau_0 = p_0 ,$$

$$\tau_{k+1} = a + \alpha\tau_k , \quad \text{where} \quad 0 \le a \le 1 - \alpha \le 1. \tag{23}$$

The solution of (23) can be written

$$\tau_k = \frac{a}{1 - \alpha} - \left(\frac{a}{1 - \alpha} - p_0\right)\alpha^k. \tag{24}$$

When $\alpha = 1 - a$, (24) reduces to (18). From (24) we see that as k increases without limit, τ_k approaches $a/(1 - \alpha)$ as an asymptote. From (5') we know

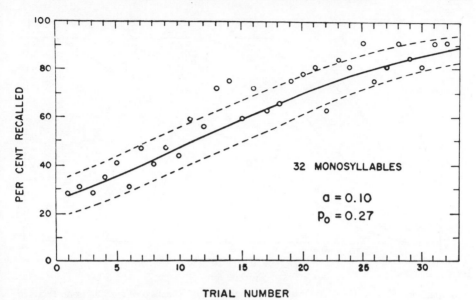

TRIAL NUMBER

FIGURE 3

Comparison of Theoretical and Observed Values of ρ_n for a Two-Parameter Case. Dotted line is drawn ± one standard deviation from ρ_n.

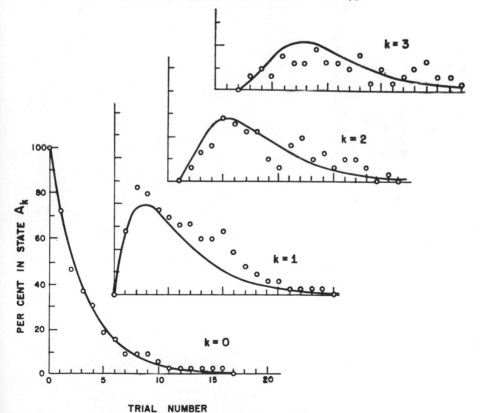

TRIAL NUMBER

FIGURE 4

Comparison of Theoretical and Observed Values of $p(A_k, n)$ for a Two-Parameter Case

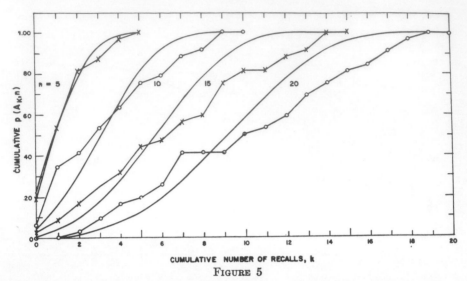

FIGURE 5

Comparison of Theoretical and Observed Distribution of Recalls on Four Different Trials in a Two-Parameter Case

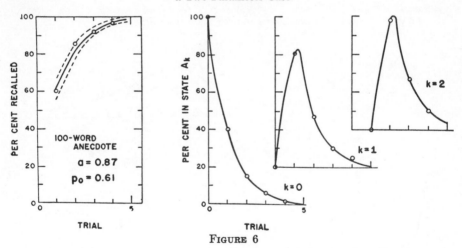

FIGURE 6

Comparison of Theoretical and Observed Values of ρ_n and $p(A_k, n)$ for a Two-Parameter Case

that τ_k and ρ_{n+1} approach the same asymptotic value, m. So we have the equation

$$\lim_{n \to \infty} \rho_{n+1} = m = \frac{a}{1 - \alpha}. \tag{25}$$

Since $1 - \alpha \geq a$, m cannot exceed unity; and since both $a \geq 0$ and $1 - \alpha \geq 0$, m cannot be negative. In general, we are interested in cases where $m > p_0$, for if $p_0 > m$, we obtain forgetting rather than acquisition.

A set-theoretical rationalization for (24) runs as follows. On the presentation of the material a random sample of elements of measure p_0 is conditioned for every word. At the first recall a sample of measure $1 - \alpha$ is drawn. Of these elements, a portion of measure a is conditioned and the remainder, $1 - \alpha - a$, are extinguished. We add the conditioned elements as before, but now we must subtract the measure of the elements conditioned during presentation and extinguished during recall, i.e., $(1 - \alpha - a) p_0$. Thus we have

$$\tau_1 = p_0 + a - ap_0 - (1 - \alpha - a)p_0$$

$$= m - (m - p_0)\alpha.$$

At the second recall the same sampling procedure is repeated:

$$\tau_2 = \tau_1 + a - a\tau_1 - (1 - \alpha - a)\tau_1$$

$$= a + \alpha\tau_1 = m - (m - p_0)\alpha^2.$$

Continuing in this way generates the relation (24).

When (24) is substituted into (1), we obtain the appropriate difference equation, but its solution for the three-parameter case is hardly less cumbersome than (2). It would appear that the simplest way to work with these equations is to take advantage of our solution of the two-parameter case.

First, we introduce a new transitional probability, τ'_k, such that

$$\tau'_k = \tau_k/m$$

$$= 1 - (1 - p_0/m)\alpha^k, \qquad \text{for } p_0 \leq m. \tag{26}$$

This new variable is now the same as in the case of two parameters given in (18), with substitution of p_0/m for p_0 and α for $(1 - a)$. Therefore, from (2) and (20), we know that

$$\tau'_0\tau'_1 \cdots \tau'_{k-1} \sum_{i=0}^{k} \frac{(1 - \tau'_i)^n}{\prod_{\substack{j=0 \\ j \neq i}}^{k} (\tau'_j - \tau'_i)}$$

$$= \left(1 - \frac{p_0}{m}\right)^{n-k} \prod_{i=0}^{k-1} \frac{[1 - (1 - p_0/m)\alpha^i][1 - \alpha^{n-i}]}{1 - \alpha^{i+1}} \tag{27}$$

$$= p'(A_k, n).$$

When $m \tau'_k$ is substituted into (2), the factor m^k in the product in front of the summation cancels the factor m^k in the denominator under the summation. Thus we know that

$$p(A_k, n) = \tau'_0\tau'_1 \cdots \tau'_{k-1} \sum_{i=0}^{k} \frac{(1 - \tau_i)^n}{\prod_{\substack{j=0 \\ j \neq i}}^{k} (\tau'_j - \tau'_i)}, \tag{28}$$

which is the same as $p'(A_k , n)$ in (27) except for the numerator under the summation. This numerator can be written

$$(1 - \tau_i)^n = [(1 - m) + m(1 - \tau'_i)]^n$$

$$= (1 - m)^n + n(1 - m)^{n-1} m(1 - \tau'_i)$$

$$+ \binom{n}{2}(1 - m)^{n-2} m^2 (1 - \tau'_i)^2 + \cdots m^n (1 - \tau'_i)^n. \qquad (29)$$

Now we substitute this sequence for the numerator in (28) and sum term by term. When we consider the last term of this sequence we have

$$\tau'_0 \tau'_1 \cdots \tau'_{k-1} \sum_{i=0}^{k} \frac{m^n (1 - \tau'_i)^n}{\prod_{\substack{j=0 \\ j \neq i}}^{k} (\tau'_j - \tau'_i)} ,$$

which we know from (27) is equal to $m^n p' (A_k , n)$. The next to last term gives

$$\tau'_0 \tau'_1 \cdots \tau'_{k-1} \sum_{i=0}^{k} \frac{n(1 - m)^{n-1} (1 - \tau'_i)^{n-1}}{\prod_{\substack{j=0 \\ j \neq i}}^{k} (\tau'_j - \tau'_i)} ,$$

which we know from (27) is equal to $n(1 - m)m^{n-1} p'(A_k , n - 1)$. Proceeding in this manner brings us eventually to the case where $n < k$, and then we know the term is zero. Consequently, we can write

$$p(A_k , n) = m^n p'(A_k , n) + n(1 - m)m^{n-1} p'(A_k , n - 1) + \cdots$$

$$+ \binom{n}{n - k}(1 - m)^{n-k} m^k p'(A_k , k)$$

$$= \sum_{i=k}^{n} \binom{n}{i} m^i (1 - m)^{n-i} p'(A_k , i). \qquad (30)$$

When the asymptote is unity ($m = 1$), (29) and (30) reduce to the two-parameter case.

We recall that because of the way in which our probabilities were defined in (1), (30) can be written as

$$p(A_k , n) = \sum_{i=0}^{n} \binom{n}{i} m^i (1 - m)^{n-i} p'(A_k , i).$$

Now it is not difficult to find an expression for ρ_{n+1} in terms of the ρ_i' computed in the two-parameter case:

$$\rho_{n+1} = \sum_{k=0}^{n} \tau_k p(A_k, n)$$

$$= m \sum_{k=0}^{n} \tau_k' p(A_k, n)$$

$$= m \sum_{k=0}^{n} \sum_{i=0}^{n} \binom{n}{i} m^i (1-m)^{n-i} \tau_k' p'(A_k, i).$$

If we invert the order of summation, we find that

$$\rho_{n+1} = m \sum_{i=0}^{n} \binom{n}{i} m^i (1-m)^{n-i} \sum_{k=0}^{n} \tau_k' p'(A_k, i)$$

$$= m \sum_{i=0}^{n} \binom{n}{i} m^i (1-m)^{n-i} \rho_{i+1}'. \tag{31}$$

The computation of ρ_{n+1} by this method involves two steps: first, the values of ρ_{n+1}' are calculated as in the two-parameter case with the substitution indicated in (26); second, these values of ρ_{n+1}' are weighted by the binomial expansion of $[m + (1-m)]^n$ and then summed according to (31).

These computations can be abbreviated somewhat by using an approximation developed by Bush and Mosteller (personal communication). It is

$$\rho_{n+2} = (2 + a + 2u\alpha)\rho_{n+1} - [a^2(1-\alpha) + (1+a)(1+2a\alpha)]\rho_n$$
$$+ 3(1-\alpha^2)(1-a)\rho_n^2 - 2(1-\alpha)(1-\alpha^2)\rho_n^3 - 3(1-\alpha^2)\rho_n\rho_{n+1},$$
$$(n \geq 1). \tag{32}$$

The approximation involves permitting the third moment of the distribution of the τ_k around ρ_n to go to zero on every trial.

The variance of r_{n+1} in the three-parameter case is

$$\text{Var}(r_{n+1}) = \frac{m}{aN}[\rho_{n+2} - (a+\alpha)\rho_{n+1}]. \tag{33}$$

This expression for the variance of r_{n+1} follows directly from (7) and (10'). It is easily seen that (10') can be written as follows:

$$\sum_{k=0}^{n} \tau_k^2 p(A_k, n) = \rho_{n+1} - N \text{ Var}(r_{n+1}). \tag{34}$$

Substituting (34) in (7) and solving for $\text{Var}(r_{n+1})$ we find that

$$\text{Var}(r_{n+1}) = \frac{1}{N(1-\alpha)}[\rho_{n+2} - (a+\alpha)\rho_{n+1}],$$

which, except for notation, is (33). The one-parameter and two-parameter variances (16) and (22) are special cases of this expression.

It is of interest to observe that when the limiting value, m, is substituted in (33) for ρ_{n+2} and ρ_{n+1}, the limiting variance is found to be binomial. That is,

$$\lim_{n \to \infty} \text{Var} \ (r_{n+1}) = \frac{m(1 - m)}{N}.$$

This reflects the fact, established earlier in (5'), that as n grows very large the variance of the τ_k around m goes to zero.

In order to obtain a numerical example, we have taken the data from another subject in the experiment by Bruner and Zimmerman. Sixty-four monosyllabic English words were read aloud and the order of the words was scrambled before every presentation. A visual inspection of the data led us to choose an asymptote in the neighborhood of 0.7. This asymptote is drawn on the plot of the t_k in Figure 7 and on the plot of the r_n in Figure 8. Then we

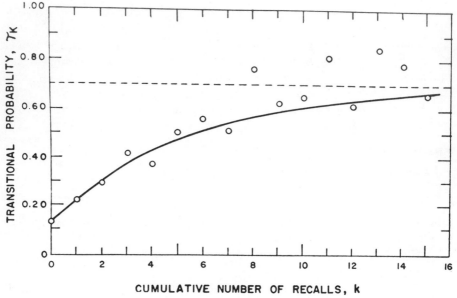

CUMULATIVE NUMBER OF RECALLS, k

FIGURE 7

Transitional Probability of Recall, τ_k, as a Function of Number of Recalls in the Three-Parameter Case. Values of t_k are indicated by open circles. The curve fitted to the t_k is $\tau_k = 0.7 - 0.57 \ (0.83)^k$.

estimated $p_0 = 0.13$ by considering all the trials on which words were in state A_0 and calculating p_0 as the weighted average of the $t_{0,n+1}$ for all those trials. Next we estimated the sampling parameter $\alpha = 0.83$. This was done by obtaining the estimates, t_k, for successive values of k; these estimates, together with (24), give us a set of equations estimating α. We used the weighted average of these estimates (ignoring negative values). Then we obtained $a = 0.12$ from the equation $a = m(1 - \alpha)$. We shall comment on the estimation problems later.

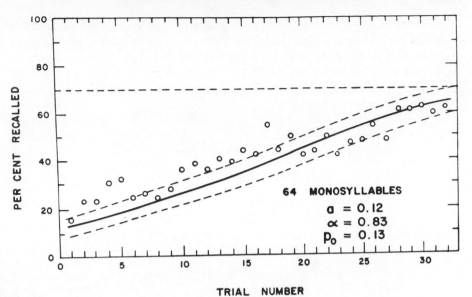

TRIAL NUMBER

FIGURE 8

Comparison of Theoretical and Observed Values of ρ_n for Three-Parameter Case

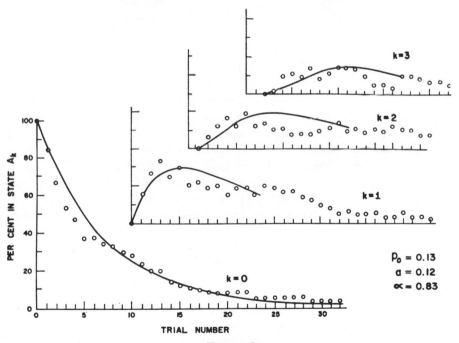

FIGURE 9

Comparison of Theoretical and Observed Values of $p(A_k, n)$ for Three-Parameter Case

When these parameter values were substituted into (24) we obtained the function for τ_k shown in Figure 7. When the values were substituted into (28) for $k = 1, 2, 3, 4$, we obtained the functions for $p(A_k, n)$ shown in Figure 9. When they were substituted into (31) we obtained the function, for ρ_n shown in Figure 8. In Figure 8 the dotted lines are drawn $\pm$ one standard deviation from ρ_n, as computed from (33).

A comparison of the values of ρ_n computed from (31) and from (32) is given for the first eighteen trials in Table 1. With this choice of parameters the Bush-Mosteller approximation seems highly satisfactory.

TABLE 1

Comparison of Exact and Approximate Values of ρ_n for First 18 Trials

Trial	Exact	Approximate	Trial	Exact	Approximate
1	.1300	.1300	10	.2663	.2655
2	.1426	.1426	11	.2837	.2827
3	.1559	.1559	12	.3014	.3000
4	.1700	.1700	13	.3191	.3174
5	.1847	.1846	14	.3369	.3347
6	.2000	.1999	15	.3546	.3520
7	.2159	.2157	16	.3722	.3692
8	.2323	.2319	17	.3896	.3862
9	.2491	.2486	18	.4067	.4030

Discussion

In the preceding pages we have made the explicit assumption that the several words being memorized simultaneously are independent, that memorizing one word does not affect the probability of recalling another word on the list. The assumption can be justified only by its mathematical convenience, because the data uniformly contradict it. The learner's introspective report is that groups of words go together to form associated clusters, and this impression is supported in the data by the fact that many pairs of words are recalled together or omitted together on successive trials. If the theory is used to describe the behavior of 50 rats, independence is a reasonable assumption. But when the theory describes the behavior of 50 words in a list that a single subject must learn, independence is not a reasonable assumption. It is important, therefore, to examine the consequences of introducing covariance.

The difference between the independent and the dependent versions of the theory can best be illustrated in terms of the set-theoretical interpretation of the two-parameter case. Imagine that we have a large ledger with 1000 pages. The presentation of the list is equivalent to writing each of the words at random on 100 pages. Thus $p_0 = 100/1000 = 0.1$. Now we select a page at random. On this page we find written the words A, B, and C. These are responses on the first trial. The rule is that each of these words must be written on 50 pages selected at random. Thus $a = 50/1000 = 0.05$. With the independent model we would first select 50 pages at random and make sure that word A was written on all of them, then select 50 more pages independently for B, and 50 more for C. With a dependent model, however, we could simply make one selection of 50 pages at random and write all three words, A, B, and C, on the same sample of 50 pages. Then whenever A was recalled again it would be likely that B and C would also be recalled at the same time.

The probability that a word will be recalled depends upon the measure of the elements conditioned to it (the number of pages in the ledger on which it is inscribed) and does not depend upon what other words are written on the same pages. Therefore, the introduction of covariance in this way does not change the theoretical recall, ρ_{n+1}. The only effect is to increase the variance of the estimates of ρ_{n+1}. In other words, it is not surprising that the equations give a fair description of the recall scores even though no attention was paid to the probabilities of joint occurrences of pairs of words. Associative clustering should affect the variability, not the rate, of memorization.

The parameters a, p_0, and α obtained from the linear difference equation (6), are assumed to describe each word in the list. Thus data from different words may be combined to estimate the various τ_k. If the parameters vary from word to word, ρ_{n+1} is only an approximation of the mean probability of recall determined by averaging the recall probabilities of all the words. Similarly, the expressions given for ρ_{n+1} cannot be expected to describe the result of averaging several subjects' data together unless all subjects are known to have the same values of the parameters.

The general theory, of course, is not limited to linear restrictions of the form of (6). The data or the theory may force us to consider more complicated functions for τ_k. For all such cases the general solution (2) is applicable, though tedious to use, and will enable us to compute the necessary values of $p(A_k, n)$.

Once a descriptive model of this sort has been used to tease out the necessary parameters, the next step is to vary the experimental conditions and to observe the effects upon these parameters. In order to take this next step, however, we need efficient methods of estimating the parameters from the data. As yet we have found no satisfactory answers to the estimation problem.

There is a sizeable amount of computation involved in determining the functions $p(A_k, n)$ and ρ_n. If a poor choice of the parameters a, p_0, and α is made at the outset, it takes several hours to discover the fact. In the example in the preceding section, we estimated the parameters successively and used different parts of the data for the different estimates. After ρ_n had been computed it seemed to us that our estimates of p_0 and m were both too low. Clearly, the method we have used to fit the theory to the data is not a particularly good one. We have considered least squares in order to use all of the data to estimate all parameters simultaneously. We convinced ourselves that the problem was beyond our abilities. Consequently, we must leave the estimation problem with the pious hope that it will appeal to someone with the mathematical competence to solve it.

Appendix A

Solution for $p(A_k , n)$ in the General Case

The solution of equation (1) with the boundary conditions we have enumerated has been obtained several times in the past (4, 5). We present below our own method of solution because the procedures involved may be of interest in other applications.

Equation (1) may be written explicitly as follows:

$$(1 - \tau_0)p(A_0 , n) = p(A_0 , n + 1)$$

$$\tau_0 p(A_0 , n) + (1 - \tau_1)p(A_1 , n) = p(A_1 , n + 1)$$

$$\tau_1 p(A_1 , n) + (1 - \tau_2)p(A_2 , n) = p(A_2 , n + 1)$$

$$\cdots\cdots\cdots\cdots\cdots\cdots\cdots\cdots\cdots\cdots\cdots\cdots\cdots$$

This system of equations can be written in matrix notation as follows:

$$
\begin{Bmatrix}
1 - \tau_0 & 0 & 0 & 0 & \cdots \\
\tau_0 & 1 - \tau_1 & 0 & 0 & \cdots \\
0 & \tau_1 & 1 - \tau_2 & 0 & \cdots \\
0 & 0 & \tau_2 & 1 - \tau_3 & \cdots \\
\cdot & \cdot & \cdot & \cdot & \cdots \\
\cdot & \cdot & \cdot & \cdot & \cdots \\
\cdot & \cdot & \cdot & \cdot & \cdots
\end{Bmatrix}
\begin{Bmatrix}
p(A_0 , n) \\
p(A_1 , n) \\
p(A_2 , n) \\
p(A_3 , n) \\
\cdot \\
\cdot \\
\cdot
\end{Bmatrix}
=
\begin{Bmatrix}
p(A_0 , n + 1) \\
p(A_1 , n + 1) \\
p(A_2 , n + 1) \\
p(A_3 , n + 1) \\
\cdot \\
\cdot \\
\cdot
\end{Bmatrix}
$$

This infinite matrix of transitional probabilities we shall call T, and the infinite column vectors made up of the state probabilities on trial n and $n + 1$ we shall call d_n and d_{n+1} . So we can write

$$Td_n = d_{n+1} .$$

The initial distribution of state probabilities, d_0 , is the infinite column vector

$\{1, 0, 0, 0, \cdots \}$. The state probabilities on trial one are then given by

$$Td_0 = d_1 .$$

The state probabilities on trial two are given by

$$Td_1 = d_2 ,$$

so by substitution,

$$Td_1 = T(Td_0) = T^2 d_0 = d_2 .$$

Continuing this procedure gives the general relation

$$T^n d_0 = d_n .$$

Therefore, the problem of determining d_n can be equated to the problem of determining T^n.

Since T is a semi-matrix, we know that it can be expressed as

$$T = SDS^{-1},$$

where D is an infinite diagonal matrix with the same elements on its diagonal as are on the main diagonal of T (e.g., **2**). The diagonal elements of S are arbitrary, so we let $S_{ii} = 1$. Now we can write

$$TS = SD$$

$$T \begin{bmatrix} 1 & 0 & 0 & \cdot \\ S_{21} & 1 & 0 & \cdot \\ S_{31} & S_{32} & 1 & \cdot \\ \cdot & \cdot & \cdot & \cdot \end{bmatrix} = \begin{bmatrix} 1 & 0 & 0 & \cdot \\ S_{21} & 1 & 0 & \cdot \\ S_{31} & S_{32} & 1 & \cdot \\ \cdot & \cdot & \cdot & \cdot \end{bmatrix} \begin{bmatrix} 1 - \tau_0 & 0 & 0 & \cdot \\ 0 & 1 - \tau_1 & 0 & \cdot \\ 0 & 0 & 1 - \tau_2 & \cdot \\ \cdot & \cdot & \cdot & \cdot \end{bmatrix} .$$

Now it is a simple matter to solve for S_{ij} term by term. For example, to solve for S_{21} we construct (from row 2 and column 1) the equation

$$\tau_0 + (1 - \tau_1)S_{21} = S_{21}(1 - \tau_0),$$

which gives

$$S_{21} = \tau_0/(\tau_1 - \tau_0).$$

To solve for S_{31} , we use the equation

$$\tau_1 S_{21} + (1 - \tau_2)S_{31} = S_{31}(1 - \tau_0)$$

$$S_{31} = \tau_1 S_{21}/(\tau_2 - \tau_0)$$

$$= \tau_0 \tau_1/(\tau_1 - \tau_0)(\tau_2 - \tau_0).$$

Proceeding in this manner gives the necessary elements of S, and we have

$$
S = \left\{
\begin{array}{ccccc}
1 & 0 & 0 & 0 & \cdots \\[2ex]
\dfrac{\tau_0}{(\tau_1 - \tau_0)} & 1 & 0 & 0 & \cdots \\[3ex]
\dfrac{\tau_0\tau_1}{(\tau_1 - \tau_0)(\tau_2 - \tau_0)} & \dfrac{\tau_1}{(\tau_2 - \tau_1)} & 1 & 0 & \cdots \\[3ex]
\dfrac{\tau_0\tau_1\tau_2}{(\tau_1 - \tau_0)(\tau_2 - \tau_0)(\tau_3 - \tau_0)} & \dfrac{\tau_1\tau_2}{(\tau_2 - \tau_1)(\tau_3 - \tau_1)} & \dfrac{\tau_2}{(\tau_3 - \tau_2)} & 1 & \cdots \\[2ex]
\cdot & \cdot & \cdot & \cdot & \\
\cdot & \cdot & \cdot & \cdot & \\
\cdot & \cdot & \cdot & \cdot & \\
\end{array}
\right\}
$$

The elements of S^{-1} can be obtained term by term from the equation $SS^{-1} = 1$. For example, the element S'_{21} of S^{-1} is given by row two of S times column one of S^{-1}: $\tau_0/(\tau_1 - \tau_0) + S'_{21} = 0$. Continuing in this way we have

$$
S^{-1} = \left\{
\begin{array}{ccccc}
1 & 0 & 0 & 0 & \cdots \\[2ex]
\dfrac{\tau_0}{(\tau_0 - \tau_1)} & 1 & 0 & 0 & \cdots \\[3ex]
\dfrac{\tau_0\tau_1}{(\tau_0 - \tau_2)(\tau_1 - \tau_2)} & \dfrac{\tau_1}{(\tau_1 - \tau_2)} & 1 & 0 & \cdots \\[3ex]
\dfrac{\tau_0\tau_1\tau_2}{(\tau_0 - \tau_3)(\tau_1 - \tau_3)(\tau_2 - \tau_3)} & \dfrac{\tau_1\tau_2}{(\tau_1 - \tau_3)(\tau_2 - \tau_3)} & \dfrac{\tau_2}{(\tau_2 - \tau_3)} & 1 & \cdots \\[2ex]
\cdot & \cdot & \cdot & \cdot & \\
\cdot & \cdot & \cdot & \cdot & \\
\cdot & \cdot & \cdot & \cdot & \\
\end{array}
\right\}
$$

These matrices permit a simple representation of the powers of the matrix T. Thus,

$$
T^2 = (SDS^{-1})(SDS^{-1}) = SD(S^{-1}S)DS^{-1} = SD^2S^{-1},
$$

and in general,

$$
T^n = SD^nS^{-1}.
$$

Since D is a diagonal matrix, D^n is obtained by taking the nth power of every diagonal element. When this equation for T^n is multiplied through, we obtain

$T^n =$

$$
\left\{
\begin{array}{cccc}
(1 - \tau_0)^n & 0 & 0 & \cdots \\[2ex]
\tau_0\left[\dfrac{(1 - \tau_0)^n}{(\tau_1 - \tau_0)} + \dfrac{(1 - \tau_1)^n}{(\tau_0 - \tau_1)}\right] & (1 - \tau_1)^n & 0 & \cdots \\[3ex]
\tau_0\tau_1\left[\dfrac{(1 - \tau_0)^n}{(\tau_1 - \tau_0)(\tau_2 - \tau_0)}\right. & & & \\[2ex]
\quad + \dfrac{(1 - \tau_1)^n}{(\tau_0 - \tau_1)(\tau_2 - \tau_1)} & & & \\[2ex]
\left.\quad + \dfrac{(1 - \tau_2)^n}{(\tau_0 - \tau_2)(\tau_1 - \tau_2)}\right] & \tau_1\left[\dfrac{(1 - \tau_1)^n}{(\tau_2 - \tau_1)} + \dfrac{(1 - \tau_2)^n}{(\tau_1 - \tau_2)}\right] & (1 - \tau_2)^n & \cdots \\[2ex]
\cdot & \cdot & \cdot & \\
\cdot & \cdot & \cdot & \\
\cdot & \cdot & \cdot &
\end{array}
\right.
$$

Since $T^n d_0$ involves only the first column of T^n, it is not actually necessary to obtain more than the first columns of S^{-1} and of T^n. We have presented the complete solution here, however. It can be seen from inspection of the first column of T^n that (2) is the general solution:

$$p(A_0, n) = (1 - \tau_0)^n, \qquad\qquad \text{for } k = 0,$$

$$p(A_k, n) = \tau_0\tau_1 \cdots \tau_{k-1} \sum_{i=0}^{k} \frac{(1 - \tau_i)^n}{\displaystyle\prod_{\substack{j=0 \\ j \neq i}}^{k} (\tau_j - \tau_i)}, \qquad \text{for } k > 0. \tag{2}$$

This general method of solution can be used for the special cases considered in this paper, with the substitution of the appropriate values for τ_k.

Appendix B

Recursive Expression for ρ_{n+1} in Two-Parameter Case

From (20) we obtain the recursive relation

$$p(A_{k+1}, n + 1) = \frac{[1 - (1 - p_0)(1 - a)^k][1 - (1 - a)^{n+1}]}{1 - (1 - a)^{k+1}} p(A_k, n).$$

Rearranging and summing, we have

$$\sum_{k=0}^{n}\left[\frac{1 - (1 - a)^{k+1}}{1 - (1 - a)^{n+1}} p(A_{k+1}, n + 1)\right]$$

$$= \sum_{k=0}^{n} [1 - (1 - p_0)(1 - a)^k]p(A_k, n).$$

The right side of this equation is, from (5) and (18), ρ_{n+1} . The left side can be rewritten

$$\sum_{k=1}^{n+1} \left[\frac{1 - (1 - a)^k}{1 - (1 - a)^{n+1}} \, p(A_k , n + 1) \right] = \rho_{n+1} ,$$

which becomes on trial n (with $n \geq 1$),

$$\sum_{k=1}^{n} \left[\frac{1 - (1 - a)^k}{1 - (1 - a)^n} \, p(A_k , n) \right] = \rho_n .$$

We now have, by adding and subtracting $p(A_0 , n)$,

$$\frac{1}{1 - (1 - a)^n} \left[\sum_{k=0}^{n} p(A_k , n) - \sum_{k=0}^{n} (1 - a)^k p(A_k , n) \right] = \rho_n ,$$

$$1 - \sum_{k=0}^{n} (1 - a)^k p(A_k , n) = [1 - (1 - a)^n] \rho_n .$$

Now we know that

$$\rho_{n+1} = 1 - (1 - p_0) \sum_{k=0}^{n} (1 - a)^k p(A_k , n),$$

and so we obtain

$$\rho_{n+1} = 1 - (1 - p_0)\{1 - [1 - (1 - a)^n] \rho_n\}.$$

Rearranging terms gives

$$\rho_{n+1} = p_0 + (1 - p_0)[1 - (1 - a)^n] \rho_n , \tag{21}$$

which is the desired result.

From this result (15) is obtained directly by equating p_0 and a.

Appendix C

List of Symbols and Their Meanings

a parameter.
A_k state that a word is in after being recalled k times.
α parameter.
d_n infinite column vector, having $p(A_k , n)$ as its elements.
D infinite diagonal matrix similar to T.
k number of times a word has been recalled.
m asymptotic value of τ_k and ρ_n .
n number of trial.
N total number of test words to be learned.
$N_{k,n}$ number of words in state A_k on trial n.
p_0 probability of recalling a word in state A_0 .

$p(A_k, n)$ probability that a word will be in state A_k on trial n.

r_n observed recall score on trial n; estimate of ρ_n.

ρ_n probability of recall on trial n.

S_{ij} elements of S.

S'_{ij} elements of S^{-1}.

S infinite matrix used to transform T into a similar diagonal matrix.

t_k estimate of τ_k.

$t_{k,n}$ observed fraction of words in state A_k that are recalled on trial n.

τ_k probability of recalling a word in state A_k.

T infinite matrix of transition probabilities τ_k.

$\mathrm{Var}\ (r_n)$ variance of the estimate of ρ_n.

$X_{i,k,n+1}$ random variable equal to 1 or 0.

REFERENCES

1. Bush, R. R., and Mosteller, Frederick. A linear operator model for learning. (Paper presented to the Institute for Mathematical Statistics, Boston, December 27, 1951.)
2. Cooke, R. G. Infinite matrices and sequence spaces. London: MacMillan, 1950.
3. Estes, W. K. Toward a statistical theory of learning. *Psychol. Rev.*, 1950, **57**, 94–107.
4. Feller, W. On the theory of stochastic processes with particular reference to applications. Proceedings of the Berkeley Symposium on Mathematical Statistics and Probability, 1949, 403–432.
5. Woodbury, M. A. On a probability distribution. *Ann. math. Statist.*, 1949, **20**, 311–313.

Manuscript received 3/11/52

ULTIMATE CHOICE BETWEEN TWO ATTRACTIVE GOALS: PREDICTIONS FROM A MODEL*

Frederick Mosteller†

HARVARD UNIVERSITY

AND

Maurice Tatsuoka

UNIVERSITY OF HAWAII

A mathematical model for two-choice behavior in situations where both choices are desirable is discussed. According to the model, one or the other choice is ultimately preferred, and a functional equation is given for the fraction of the population ultimately preferring a given choice. The solution depends upon the learning rates and upon the initial probabilities of the choices. Several techniques for approximating the solution of this functional equation are described. One of these leads to an explicit formula that gives good accuracy. This solution can be generalized to the two-armed bandit problem with partial reinforcement in each arm, or the equivalent T-maze problem. Another suggests good ways to program the calculations for a high-speed computer.

The immobility of Buridan's ass, who starved to death between two haystacks, has always seemed unreasonable. No doubt the story was invented to mock an equilibrium theory of behavior. One expects that any such equilibrium in approach-approach situations will be unstable—one of the attractive goals will be chosen. In this paper some properties that flow from a mathematical model for repetitive approach-approach behavior are discussed. In the model for behavior in these choice situations, an organism initially shifts its choices from one to another, but after a while settles upon a single choice.

Thus in the early part of the learning the theoretical organism may give some expression to the notion of an equilibrium by making different choices on different trials, but eventually even this behavior vanishes for the single

*Support for this research has been received from the National Science Foundation (Grant NSF-G2258), the National Institute of Mental Health (Grant M-2293), and the Laboratory of Social Relations, Harvard University.

†We wish to acknowledge and express our appreciation for the cooperation and assistance given by Phillip J. Rulon, Albert Beaton, Wai-Ching Ho, and Donald Spearritt, who set up, programmed, and executed numerous calculations connected with the linear equations method of solution, and by Cleo Youtz for extensive calculations at every stage of the work. We also wish to thank Ray Twery and Robert R. Bush for permission to use in Table 3 some of the unpublished results of their calculations. Those calculations were made on the Illiac through the cooperation of the Digital Computer Laboratory of the University of Illinois, Dr. John P. Nash, Director.

This article appeared in *Psychometrika*, 1960, **25**, 1–18. Reprinted with permission.

organism. On the other hand, some organisms may ultimately choose one goal and others another, so that a notion of equilibrium or balance could be recaptured across a population of organisms. The quantitative aspects of a model for such behavior are investigated. The model employed is one discussed by Bush and Mosteller [1].

A simple situation will be discussed first, then the mathematical problem encountered there will be related to the more complicated two-armed bandit problem with partial reinforcement on each arm. Suppose that on each trial of an infinite sequence an organism may respond (or choose) in one of two ways. For purposes of exposition, specify the ways as R and L (for right and left, say), so that for concreteness one can think of a rat choosing the left-hand or right-hand side in a T-maze, or a person choosing the left-hand or the right-hand button in a two-armed bandit situation. However, R and L are intended to stand for a general pair of attractive objects or responses, mutually exclusive and exhaustive, which lead to attractive goals.

Suppose that on a given trial the probability of choosing R is p, and that of choosing L is $1 - p$, where as usual $0 \leq p \leq 1$. If R is chosen, then the probability of choosing R next time is increased to $\alpha_1 p + 1 - \alpha_1$, but if L is chosen the probability of choosing R next is reduced to $\alpha_2 p$, where $0 \leq \alpha_1 \leq 1, 0 \leq \alpha_2 \leq 1$. The point is that when a reinforcing choice is made, that choice has an increased probability of being chosen next time, and both R and L are regarded as reinforcing. The asymmetry in the formulas comes from the fact that the notation uses the probability of choosing R, and not the probability of choosing the particular side chosen on each trial. The operators used to change the probabilities are discussed by Bush and Mosteller ([1], p. 154 ff.).

Suppose the organism continues making the choices and that his probabilities are adjusted after every trial according to the rules just given. Then it can be shown that sooner or later the organism stops making one of the choices and thereafter chooses only the other. An extreme example occurs if both α_1 and α_2 are zero—then the organism chooses forever what he chooses first (one-trial learning).

One mathematical problem is to discover the probability that the organism eventually chooses R rather than L all the time. If he does choose R all the time, then he is said to be "ultimately attracted by R," or R is "ultimately attracting." The desired probability should be expressible as a function of the initial probability p and of the attractiveness coefficients α_1 and α_2 (the smaller an α, the more attractive the side). For convenience, this will be called the simple approach-approach problem, in contrast to the more complicated partial reinforcement problems.

Consider now as an example a T-maze experiment with paradise fish described by Bush and Wilson [2]. On each trial of this experiment a fish started at one end of a tank and swam to the other, where the left or right side could be chosen. When the right-hand side was chosen, the fish was rewarded on 75 percent of the trials. When the left side was chosen, the fish was rewarded on 25 percent of the trials. The operation was to place the reward on one side or the other every time. In one group a fish was able to see the reward through a transparent divider when he chose the unrewarded side. In the other group an opaque divider was used. The data from these groups showed that the fish tended to stabilize on one side or the other.

Within the framework of the operators described earlier in this paper, if p is the probability of choosing the right-hand side on a given trial, and if the right-hand side is chosen and rewarded, the new probability of choosing the right-hand side might be expressed as $\alpha p + 1 - \alpha$. If the left-hand side were chosen and rewarded, the new probability of choosing the right might be reduced to αp. The parallel with the previous descriptions is very close.

But suppose the side chosen is not rewarded. Then, essentially, three possibilities exist.

(a) The side chosen is more likely to be chosen than it was before. The explanation might be, for example, that the organism is building up a habit pattern, or that he is secondarily reinforced for being in a place that earlier was rewarding.

(b) The side chosen is less likely to be chosen than before. The explanation might be, for example, that information has been received that this side is not paying off.

Whatever the explanation may be, the models corresponding to (a) and to (b) make quite different predictions. The model for (a) says that the probability associated with the side chosen is always increased whether reward is given or not. This ultimately implies—for the operators described here—that one side is chosen every time, that is, that eventually the organism stabilizes on one side. On the other hand, the model for (b) would imply that the organism does not stabilize. To see this, suppose that an organism is certain ($p = 1$) to choose the right-hand side—that is, he has stabilized on the right. Then because of partial reinforcement the organism will experience some nonrewarded trials on the right-hand side. These will reduce the probability of choosing the right-hand side, and so the left-hand side will be chosen sometimes. A similar argument shows that the organism cannot stabilize on the left. Thus under partial reinforcement, a model for assumption (b) would typically have asymptotic instability. A subject does not become attracted by one side or the other, nor does he finally acquire a fixed probability p of choosing R. Instead, his value of p drifts up and down, though in a stochastically stable way. Thus model (a) has attracting and absorbing barriers, while model (b) has reflecting barriers.

(c) The probability is unchanged by a nonreward—then everything depends upon the rewarded trials.

In the experiment with paradise fish the data suggest model (a). In this paper we shall deal with the type (a) model. On the basis of the model, we would like to know (in terms of the learning rates, the initial probabilities, and the probabilities of reward on the two sides) what fraction of the organisms will stabilize on a given side.

Because the numerical problem has turned out to be rather troublesome, and because the general problem has some interest as shown by previous work, we will sketch various solutions that have been tried. Each of them is time-consuming in its development and testing, so a research worker will want to know what ground has already been plowed.

Previous Work

To facilitate discussion of previous work on the simple approach-approach problem, a functional equation for the probability that an organism is ultimately attracted to R will be derived. Let $f(p_1 ; \alpha_1 , \alpha_2)$ be the probability that an infinite sequence of trials ends in choices of R. Here, p_1 is the initial probability of choosing R. The transition rules are: if p_n is the probability of R on trial n, then the probability of R on the next trial is

$$(1) \qquad p_{n+1} = \begin{cases} \alpha_1 p_n + 1 - \alpha_1 , & \text{if } R \text{ is chosen on trial } n, \\ \alpha_2 p_n , & \text{if } L \text{ is chosen on trial } n. \end{cases}$$

In the sequel there is usually no advantage in referring to the trial number associated with p, so the subscript on p_1 is dropped and p stands for the initial probability. Similarly it is always to be understood that the desired function f depends upon α_1 and α_2 ; so except when the full notation is needed, the notation $f(p)$ will be used.

The quantity $f(p)$ may be composed of two parts—the parts corresponding to the choice of R or of L on the initial trial. Assume that each member of a large population has the same initial probability p of choosing R and is faced with the same simple approach-approach problem. Then, on the first choice the fraction p of the individuals choose R, and the new probability of R is $\alpha_1 p + 1 - \alpha_1$ for any member of this group. This means that in this group, the probability of being ultimately attracted by R is $f(\alpha_1 p + 1 - \alpha_1)$. Consequently this group contributes the portion $p f(\alpha_1 p + 1 - \alpha_1)$ to $f(p)$. In the same manner those organisms choosing L first contribute $(1 - p) f(\alpha_2 p)$ to $f(p)$. Thus one derives the basic functional equation for the simple approach-approach problem:

$$(2) \qquad f(p) = pf(\alpha_1 p + 1 - \alpha_1) + (1 - p)f(\alpha_2 p).$$

The boundary conditions are $f(0) = 0$ and $f(1) = 1$. These conditions hold because if $p = 0$, then L occurs, and the new probability for R is $\alpha_2 \cdot 0 = 0$.

Therefore L is always chosen. Similarly if $p = 1$, then R occurs, and the new probability for R is $\alpha_1 \cdot 1 + 1 - \alpha_1 = 1$. Therefore R is always chosen. Thus $f(0) = 0$ and $f(1) = 1$. These conditions for the function are needed because without them (2) only determines f to within a linear transformation. Thus if a certain f satisfies (2), direct substitution shows that $Af + B$ also satisfies it (A and B are constants).

Equation (2) could have had four parts if we related the desired probability to the four terms occurring after two trials, or more generally 2^n terms after n trials. These equations are all equivalent, but they can all be derived by successive applications of (2) to the f's appearing on the right-hand side.

The properties of $f(p)$ have been studied before by Bellman and by Shapiro ([3], Parts II and III), and by Karlin [4] (c.f. [1], p. 163–4). Since not all of their results are readily accessible, those properties of $f(p)$ especially useful here are given below.

i. *Nature of the solution.* Equation (2) has a unique, monotone, analytic solution once the boundary conditions are given. With our boundary conditions the solution is convex for $\alpha_1 \geq \alpha_2$, concave for $\alpha_1 \leq \alpha_2$. The monotonicity is consistent with the probability interpretation given by the learning model—for given α_1 and α_2, the larger the probability of choosing R initially, the more likely that R is ultimately attracting.

ii. *Solutions under special conditions.* In what follows, suppose the relevant boundary conditions $f(0) = 0$ and $f(1) = 1$ to hold. The special conditions have to do with the values assumed by one or both of the α's.

(a) $\alpha_1 = \alpha_2 \neq 1$. The solution is $f(p) = p$, as implied by the fact that $f(p)$ is both convex and concave and by the boundary conditions.

(b) $\alpha_1 = \alpha_2 = 1$. The function f is not defined in our problem unless $p = 1$ or 0, because the probability of R never changes and no attraction occurs.

(c) $\alpha_1 = 1$, $\alpha_2 \neq 1$. The occurrence of R leaves the probability of R unchanged because $\alpha_1 p + 1 - \alpha_1 = p$, so the process can only move toward choosing more L's unless $p = 1$. Thus $f(p; 1, \alpha_2) = 0$, $\alpha_2 \neq 1$, $p \neq 1$, and $f(1; 1, \alpha_2) = 1$.

(d) $\alpha_2 = 1$, $\alpha_1 \neq 1$. Similarly $f(p; \alpha_1, 1) = 1$, $\alpha_1 \neq 1$, $p \neq 0$, and $f(0; \alpha_1, 1) = 0$.

(e) $\alpha_1 = 0$. Here, the only way to be ultimately attracted to L is always to choose L. The probability of the latter behavior is

$$(3) \qquad g(p, \alpha_2) = (1 - p)(1 - \alpha_2 p)(1 - \alpha_2^2 p) \cdots = \prod_{i=0}^{\infty} (1 - \alpha_2^i p).$$

Therefore the probability of ultimate attraction by R is

$$(4) \qquad\qquad f(p; 0, \alpha_2) = 1 - g(p, \alpha_2).$$

(f) $\alpha_2 = 0$. Here to be ultimately attracted by R is never to choose L. In this case

(5)
$$
\begin{aligned}
f(p; \alpha_1, 0) &= p[\alpha_1 p + 1 - \alpha_1][\alpha_1(\alpha_1 p + 1 - \alpha_1) + 1 - \alpha_1] \cdots \\
&= p[\alpha_1 p + 1 - \alpha_1][\alpha_1^2 p + 1 - \alpha_1^2] \cdots \\
&= [1 - (1 - p)][1 - \alpha_1(1 - p)][1 - \alpha_1^2(1 - p)] \cdots \\
&= \prod_{i=0}^{\infty} [1 - \alpha_1^i(1 - p)].
\end{aligned}
$$

In the second step above, note that if R occurs on the first n trials, the probability of R is $\alpha_1^n p + 1 - \alpha_1^n$ (proved in [1], p. 59).

iii. *Iterative properties.* Any continuous initial approximation to $f(p)$ can be iterated successively to obtain in the limit the function $f(p)$. That is, suppose $f_0(p)$ is a first guess at the function $f(p)$, then a better approximation is given by the first iterate

$$ f_1(p) = pf_0(\alpha_1 p + 1 - \alpha_1) + (1 - p)f_0(\alpha_2 p). $$

For example if $f_0(p) = p$, then $f_1(p) = p + (\alpha_2 - \alpha_1) p(1 - p)$. More generally, the $(n + 1)$st iterate is given by

$$ f_{n+1}(p) = pf_n(\alpha_1 p + 1 - \alpha_1) + (1 - p)f_n(\alpha_2 p). $$

Certain initial approximations lead to a monotonic sequence of iterates.

(a) If $f_0(p) = p$, the successive iterates monotonically increase toward $f(p)$ if $\alpha_2 \geq \alpha_1$, monotonically decrease toward $f(p)$ if $\alpha_2 \leq \alpha_1$.

(b) If for the beginning approximation

(6)
$$
f_0(p) =
\begin{cases}
\displaystyle\prod_{i=0}^{\infty} [1 - \alpha_1^i(1 - p)], & \text{for } \alpha_2 \leq \alpha_1, \\[2ex]
\displaystyle 1 - \prod_{i=0}^{\infty} [1 - \alpha_2^i p], & \text{for } \alpha_2 \geq \alpha_1,
\end{cases}
$$

the iterates increase (decrease) monotonically to the function. These results provide two sequences of bounds for $f(p)$ when the approximations mentioned in (a) and (b) are used.

The iteration procedure converges geometrically, that is, after n iterations one can be sure that the nth iterate $f_n(p)$ deviates from the correct answer $f(p)$ by no more than $A\rho^n$, where $A > 0$, and $0 < \rho < 1$. Though geometric convergence sounds speedy, if ρ were near 1, say 0.96, it would take more than 50 iterations to assure being within $0.1A$. The details needed for the calculation of A and ρ will not be provided.

These important results provide a starting point for studying the function $f(p)$, but they do not yield numbers or expressions whose values are close to the true ones. In the remainder of this paper, several techniques for approximating $f(p)$, are provided.

A method designed for high-speed calculation will be considered first, then an excellent approximation obtained from a differential equation will be considered, and then that result will be extended to the two-armed bandit problem. Finally, brief mention of some other methods of approximating this functional equation will be given.

Approximation by Simultaneous Equations

Consider a grid of numbers $0 \, (= p_0), \, p_1 , \, p_2 , \, \cdots , \, p_n , \, 1 \, (= p_{n+1})$ in the unit interval, and write the functional equation (2) as it applies to each of these values of the independent variables. (Lest confusion with earlier notation develop note that p_i still refers to probabilities, but the subscripts no longer correspond to trials as they did in earlier sections.) Then one has the set of equations

$$f(0) \; = 0 \hspace{3cm} + f(0),$$

$$f(p_1) \; = p_1 f(\alpha_1 p_1 + 1 - \alpha_1) + (1 - p_1) f(\alpha_2 p_1),$$

(7) $\hspace{2cm} f(p_2) \; = p_2 f(\alpha_1 p_2 + 1 - \alpha_1) + (1 - p_2) f(\alpha_2 p_2),$

$$\cdots$$

$$f(p_n) \; = p_n f(\alpha_1 p_n + 1 - \alpha_1) + (1 - p_n) f(\alpha_2 p_n),$$

$$f(1) \; = f(1) \hspace{3cm} + 0.$$

The first and last members of this set of equations are, of course, tautologies; there are only n nontrivial equations.

The right-hand sides of the n nontrivial equations of the set (7) each involves the values of $f(p)$ at points that do not ordinarily coincide with any of the chosen grid points. However, by using an interpolation formula, both $f(\alpha_1 p_i + 1 - \alpha_1)$ and $f(\alpha_2 p_i)$, $i = 1, 2, \cdots, n$, may be approximated by linear combinations of the values of $f(p)$ at two or more consecutive grid points $p_i , \, p_{i+1} , \, \cdots$. The number of grid points required depends upon whether one uses linear interpolation (two grid points), interpolation with second differences (three points), third differences (four points), and so forth.

Whatever the number of points may be, each equation of the set (7) can be replaced by an approximate equality involving as unknowns just the values of $f(p)$ at several predetermined grid points, and these unknowns occur only linearly. Thus a system of n linear equations is obtained, approximately satisfied by the n unknown quantities, $f(p_1), \, f(p_2), \, \cdots, \, f(p_n)$. The idea of deriving a system of linear equations whose roots approximate $f(p_i)$, $i = 1, 2, \cdots, n$, was first suggested to us by J. Arthur Greenwood in an unpublished memorandum, in which linear interpolation was used to approximate $f(\alpha_1 p_i + 1 - \alpha_1)$ and $f(\alpha_2 p_i)$.

In this and in the following sections a standard numerical example in which $\alpha_1 = .75$, $\alpha_2 = .80$ is used to illustrate the various methods. This example has the advantage of being easily displayed; further, numbers are fairly easy to compute from it. It has the disadvantage of being relatively easy to fit, so the reader should not be misled into thinking that the precision attained for it is always obtainable.

Example. The method just described is illustrated for a grid of five equally spaced points, using the standard example, $\alpha_1 = 0.75$, $\alpha_2 = 0.80$. Here, the functional equation is

(8) $$f(p) = pf(0.75p + 0.25) + (1 - p)f(0.80p).$$

Taking $p_1 = 0.25$, $p_2 = 0.50$, $p_3 = 0.75$ and writing $f(p_i) = f_i$, for short, in accordance with equations (7),

(9)
$$f_1 = 0.25f(0.4375) + 0.75f(0.20),$$
$$f_2 = 0.50f(0.6250) + 0.50f(0.40),$$
$$f_3 = 0.75f(0.8125) + 0.25f(0.60).$$

First, linear interpolation will be used to approximate $f(0.4375)$, $f(0.20)$, $f(0.6250)$, etc., by means of linear combinations of the five f's: $f_0(= 0)$, f_1, f_2, f_3 and $f_4(= 1)$. Thus,

$$f(0.4375) \simeq \frac{0.5000 - 0.4375}{0.2500} f_1 + \frac{0.4375 - 0.2500}{0.2500} f_2$$
$$= 0.25f_1 + 0.75f_2 ,$$

$$f(0.2\hat{\ }) \simeq \frac{0.25 - 0.20}{0.25} f_0 + \frac{0.20 - 0}{0.25} f_1$$
$$= 0.80f_1 ,$$

and, similarly,

$$f(0.6250) \simeq 0.50f_2 + 0.50f_3 ,$$
$$f(0.40) \simeq 0.40f_1 + 0.60f_2 ,$$
$$f(0.8125) \simeq 0.75f_3 + 0.25f_4 = 0.75f_3 + 0.25,$$
$$f(0.60) \simeq 0.60f_2 + 0.40f_3 .$$

Substituting these approximate expressions for the several functional values in the right-hand sides of (9) and collecting all terms involving the unknowns into the left-hand sides, one obtains

(10)
$$0.3375f_1 - 0.1875f_2 \simeq 0,$$
$$-0.2000f_1 + 0.4500f_2 - 0.2500f_3 \simeq 0,$$
$$- 0.1500f_2 + 0.3375f_3 \simeq 0.1875.$$

Replacing the $\simeq$ by $=$ in the set of approximations (10) and solving the resulting equations, one obtains the following approximations to f_i. (The best available values are also shown for comparison.)

p_i	f_i (approx.)	best values
0.25	0.3385	0.4495
.50	0.6093	0.7286
.75	0.8276	0.8987

The agreement with the best available values is only fair.

Now use second-order interpolation for approximating the non-grid-point values of $f(p)$ that occur in the right-hand sides of (9). The general formula (with equally spaced grid points) is

(11)
$$f(x_i + \epsilon) \simeq \left[1 - \tfrac{1}{2}\frac{\epsilon}{\Delta x}\left(3 - \frac{\epsilon}{\Delta x}\right)\right]f_i + \frac{\epsilon}{\Delta x}\left(2 - \frac{\epsilon}{\Delta x}\right)f_{i+1}$$
$$- \tfrac{1}{2}\frac{\epsilon}{\Delta x}\left(1 - \frac{\epsilon}{\Delta x}\right)f_{i+2},$$

where $x = x_{i+1} - x_i$. Note that (11) gives the interpolated value as a weighted average of the three adjacent tabled values instead of using differences.

Applying (11) to the problem at hand and substituting these approximate expressions into the right-hand sides of (19), one obtains the following system of approximations.

(12)
$$0.2410f_1 - 0.1744f_2 + 0.0235f_3 = 0,$$
$$-0.1400f_1 + 0.3925f_2 - 0.3150f_3 = -0.0625,$$
$$- 0.0497f_2 + 0.1369f_3 = 0.0872,$$

whose roots yield the following approximations.

p_i	f_i (approx.)	best values
.25	0.4279	0.4495
.50	0.7122	0.7286
.75	0.8955	0.8986

These results are a definite improvement over those obtained by linear interpolation.

The above example seems to indicate that a considerable improvement of the approximation can be expected when higher differences are used in the interpolation formula for expressing the non-grid-point values of $f(p)$ in terms of the grid-point values. However, the interpolation formulas become more and more cumbersome to work with numerically as higher differences are included. It therefore is pertinent to see how much improvement can be gained by increasing the number of grid points alone.

TABLE 1

Improvement Obtained by Increasing the Number of
Points in Grid, using Linear Interpolation only;
Entries are Approximate Values of f_i

P_i	Number of points					Best value
	4	5	6	11	21	
.10	.1347	.1473	.1573	.1864	.1984	.2055
.25	.3147	.3388	.3557	.4152	.4375	.4495
.50	.5690	.5955	.6129	.6872	.7133	.7286
.75	.7845	.8007	.8153	.8666	.8856	.8987
.90	.9138	.9203	.9261	.9476	.9586	.9658

Using only linear interpolation, approximations from grids of 4, 5, 6, 11, and 21 points were obtained. These points were not equally spaced because it was hoped that better results would be obtained by spacing the grid so that the functional values would be approximately equally spaced. Information needed for such spacing was available from other methods described later.

Linear interpolations were made in the results for the five grids described above to obtain approximate values at $p = 0.10, 0.25, 0.50, 0.75, 0.90$. The numbers are shown in Table 1, together with the best known values.

Using the difference between the best value and the cell entry for a given p_i as a measure of error, it will be noted that, very roughly, the error decreases linearly with the spacing. On the other hand, with a five-point grid, changing from linear to second-order interpolation gives improvement roughly equivalent to that given by increasing the number of points to 21 and using linear interpolation only. Since simultaneous equations are expensive to solve, it appears that second-order interpolation is well worth the effort, contrary to usual advice.

Calculations, with the aid of an electronic computer, using 21 grid points and second-difference interpolation as well as third-difference interpolation have been made. The results are summarized in Table 2. The results obtained by using second-order differences are hardly distinguishable from those using third-order differences, though in a more sharply curved example they could be more useful. The third-order interpolation column provided numbers labeled "best values" throughout this paper.

In principle, any desired degree of accuracy can be attained by using finer grids, but the cost of the calculations increases roughly as the square of the number of grid points used. A high-speed computer could be programmed to write its own equations and solve them, but such a program

TABLE 2

Approximations Using Second- and Third-Order Interpolations
With 21 Grid Points and the Approximation
By Second Order Differential Equation

p_i	f_i (second-order interpolation)	f_i (third-order interpolation)	f (differential equation)
.00	.00000	.00000	.00000
.05	.10718	.10778	.10325
.10	.20495	.20547	.19839
.15	.29407	.29455	.28601
.20	.37528	.37564	.36648
.25	.44919	.44947	.44035
.30	.51637	.51620	.50774
.35	.57739	.57736	.56982
.40	.63279	.63277	.62626
.45	.68304	.68305	.67764
.50	.72858	.72859	.72435
.55	.76981	.76983	.76672
.60	.80711	.80713	.80504
.65	.84082	.84084	.83967
.70	.87126	.87127	.87088
.75	.89873	.89874	.89891
.80	.92349	.92350	.92402
.85	.94578	.94579	.94648
.90	.96584	.96584	.96648
.95	.98387	.98387	.98425
1.00	1.00000	1.00000	1.00000

was not written. If good accuracy is required, the techniques proposed in this section are recommended.

Approximation by a Differential Equation

An essential feature of the simultaneous-equations approximation discussed in the preceding section was the replacement of non-grid-point values of $f(p)$ by linear combinations of grid-point values. The continuous variable analogue of this procedure is the expansion of $f(\alpha_1 p + 1 - \alpha_1)$ and $f(\alpha_2 p)$ as Taylor's series in the neighborhood of p. This approach will now be used to derive a differential equation whose solution yields an approximation to the desired function, $f(p)$.

Rewriting $f(\alpha_1 p + 1 - \alpha_1)$ as $f(p + (1 - \alpha_1)(1 - p))$, and expanding the latter as a Taylor's series,

$$f(p + (1 - \alpha_1)(1 - p)) = f(p) + (1 - \alpha_1)(1 - p)f'(p)$$

(13)
$$+ \frac{(1 - \alpha_1)^2(1 - p)^2}{2!} f''(p) + \cdots,$$

where f' and f'' are the first and second derivatives of f with respect to p.
Similarly, expand $f(\alpha_2 p)$ as follows:

$$f(\alpha_2 p) = f(p - (1 - \alpha_2)p) = f(p) - (1 - \alpha_2)pf'(p)$$

(14)
$$+ \frac{(1 - \alpha_2)^2 p^2}{2!} f''(p) - \cdots .$$

Using only through the term in $f''(p)$ in the two series (13) and (14), substitute these expressions for the functions in the right-hand side of the functional equation (2). The result is a differential equation

(15)
$$f(p) = p[f(p) + (1 - \alpha_1)(1 - p)f'(p) + \tfrac{1}{2}(1 - \alpha_1)^2(1 - p)^2 f''(p)]$$
$$+ (1 - p)[f(p) - (1 - \alpha_2)pf'(p) + \tfrac{1}{2}(1 - \alpha_2)^2 p^2 f''(p)].$$

By rearranging terms in (15),

$$\tfrac{1}{2}\{(1 - \alpha_1)^2 - [(1 - \alpha_1)^2 - (1 - \alpha_2)^2]p\}f''(p) + (\alpha_2 - \alpha_1)f'(p) = 0.$$

Hence,

(16)
$$\frac{f''(p)}{f'(p)} = \frac{2(\alpha_2 - \alpha_1)}{[(1 - \alpha_1)^2 - (1 - \alpha_2)^2]p - (1 - \alpha_1)^2} ,$$

which is integrated to yield

(17)
$$f'(p) = C_1 \left[\frac{(1 - \alpha_1)^2}{(1 - \alpha_1)^2 - (1 - \alpha_2)^2} - p \right]^{1/(1-\bar{\alpha})} ,$$

where C_1 is a constant of integration, and $\bar{\alpha}$ is an abbreviation for $(\alpha_1 + \alpha_2)/2$.
Integrating both sides of (17),

(18)
$$f(p) = C_1' \left[\frac{(1 - \alpha_1)^2}{(1 - \alpha_1)^2 - (1 - \alpha_2)^2} - p \right]^{1+1/(1-\bar{\alpha})} + C_2 ,$$

where C_1' and C_2 are new constants of integration.
Determining C_1' and C_2 from the boundary conditions $f(0) = 0$ and $f(1) = 1$, the final form of $f(p)$ is

(19)
$$f(p) = \frac{A^B - (A - p)^B}{A^B - (A - 1)^B} ,$$

where

$$A = \frac{(1 - \alpha_1)^2}{(1 - \alpha_1)^2 - (1 - \alpha_2)^2}$$

and

$$B = \frac{1}{1 - (\alpha_1 + \alpha_2)/2} + 1.$$

Example: Taking $\alpha_1 = 0.75$, $\alpha_2 = 0.80$, as before, calculate the constants occurring in (19).

$$A = \frac{0.25^2}{(0.25)^2 - (0.20)^2} = 2.7778,$$

$$B = \frac{1}{1 - 1.55/2} + 1 = 5.4444.$$

Hence, from (19),

(20) $$f(p) = \frac{260.42 - (2.7778 - p)^{5.4444}}{237.49}.$$

Using (20), calculate the values of $f(p)$ for $p = 0.25$, 0.50, and 0.75.

p_i	f_i (approx.)	best values
.25	0.4403	0.4495
.50	0.7244	0.7286
.75	0.8989	0.8987

Values of $f(p)$ in intervals of 0.05 for p are shown in Table 2, where they may be compared with the best values so far obtained. Among the various approximate methods which can be easily carried out with desk calculators, the differential equation method yields results in closest agreement with those obtained by the simultaneous equations using 21 grid points and third-difference interpolation.

The Two-Armed Bandit

The differential equation approach can equally easily be applied to the more general model appropriate to the two-armed bandit problem with partial reinforcement on each arm (or the equivalent T-maze experiment).

Suppose that there are two responses R and L, and whichever occurs a reward or a nonreward follows. If R occurs, reward follows with probability π_1 ; if L occurs, reward follows with probability π_2 . If p is the probability of R on a given trial, the new probability for R is as follows.

New probability for R		Probability of happening
$\alpha_1 p + 1 - \alpha_1$	if R and reward occur	$\pi_1 p$
$\alpha_2 p + 1 - \alpha_2$	if R and nonreward	$(1 - \pi_1)p$
$\alpha_1 p$	if L and reward	$\pi_2(1 - p)$
$\alpha_2 p$	if L and nonreward	$(1 - \pi_2)(1 - p)$

These results represent a special case of those presented in ([1], p. 118, 286) and discussed briefly on p. 287 in the paragraph following equation (13.22) in [1].

It has been assumed that reward is equally effective on either side and that nonreward is also equally effective on either side. It should be recalled that these transition rules imply that nonreward improves the probability of choosing a given side, as discussed in the opening section of this paper.

Now in the same way that the basic functional equation (2) for the simple approach-approach problem was derived, the basic functional equation for the two-armed bandit problem with partial reinforcement can be derived. The functional equation for the proportion $f(p)$ of organisms who eventually learn to make only response R is

(21)
$$f(p) = p\pi_1 f(\alpha_1 p + 1 - \alpha_1) + p(1 - \pi_1)f(\alpha_2 p + 1 - \alpha_2)$$
$$+ (1 - p)\pi_2 f(\alpha_1 p) + (1 - p)(1 - \pi_2)f(\alpha_2 p).$$

No generality is lost, and there is some gain in the sequel, if it is assumed that $\alpha_1 \leq \alpha_2$ and $\pi_1 \geq \pi_2$. If $\pi_1 = 1$ and $\pi_2 = 0$, (21) reduces to (2).

Using the approximations (13) and (14) for $f(\alpha_i p + 1 - \alpha_i)$ and $f(\alpha_i p)$, respectively, (21) can be rewritten, after rearrangement of terms, as

(22)
$$[(\pi_1 - \pi_2)\{(1 - \alpha_1)^2 - (1 - \alpha_2)^2\}p - \{\pi_1(1 - \alpha_1)^2$$
$$+ (1 - \pi_1)(1 - \alpha_2)^2\}]f''(p) = 2(\pi_1 - \pi_2)(\alpha_2 - \alpha_1)f'(p).$$

The boundary conditions are $f(0) = 0$, $f(1) = 1$, as before.

Comparing (22) with the corresponding differential equation, (16), for the simpler model, the general solution of (22) has the form

(23)
$$f(p) = \frac{A^B - (A - p)^B}{A^B - (A - 1)^B} ,$$

where the constant A is now defined as

$$A = \frac{\pi_1(1 - \alpha_1)^2 + (1 - \pi_1)(1 - \alpha_2)^2}{(\pi_1 - \pi_2)[(1 - \alpha_1)^2 - (1 - \alpha_2)^2]} , \qquad (\alpha_1 \neq \alpha_2 , \pi_1 \neq \pi_2)$$

while

$$B = \frac{1}{1 - (\alpha_1 + \alpha_2)/2} + 1,$$

as before. Note that the expression for A for the simple approach-approach problem is obtained by substituting $\pi_1 = 1$, $\pi_2 = 0$ in the present A.

The expression for A is undefined when either $\alpha_1 = \alpha_2$ or $\pi_1 = \pi_2$, hence (23) cannot be used. In each of these cases, however, it can be argued from first principles that the function sought is $f(p) = p$. This result is also given by the differential equation (22), which reduces to $f''(p) = 0$ under these special conditions.

Monte Carlo Calculations for Two-Armed Bandits

Twery and Bush made a series of Monte Carlo calculations on Illiac of $f(0.50)$ for two-armed bandit experiments with $\pi_1 = 0.75$, $\pi_2 = 0.25$ for various combinations of α-values. The case of $\alpha_1 = 0.90$, $\alpha_2 = 0.95$ will be used to calculate the value of $f(0.50)$ from (23).

For the stated parameter values,

$$A = \frac{(0.75)(0.10)^2 + (0.25)(0.05)^2}{(0.50)[(0.10)^2 - (0.05)^2]} = 2.1667,$$

$$B = \frac{1}{1 - (1.85/2)} + 1 = 14.3333.$$

Hence, (23) in this case becomes

(24) $$f(p) = \frac{65015.7 - (2.1667 - p)^{43/3}}{65006.6}.$$

From this formula,

$$f(0.50) = 0.977,$$

compared with Twery and Bush's result, 0.970.

The values of $f(0.50)$, calculated from (23) for the various combinations of alpha values used by Twery and Bush, are shown in Table 3 along with

TABLE 3

Comparison of Differential Equation Results (first entry)
With Those of Twery and Bush (second entry)
Obtained from the Mean Probability Level of 100 Sequences
At the 800th Trial for Various α_1, α_2, for $p = 0.5$
And $\pi_1 = 1 - \pi_2 = 0.75$

α_1 \ α_2	.91	.92	.93	.94	.95	.96	.97
.90	.634	.770	.878	.944	.977	---	---
	.610	.780	.880	.960	.970	---	---
.91		.665	.820	.923	.972	---	---
		.700	.840	.900	.970	---	---
.92			.707	.877	.962	.990	---
			.669	.880	.980	.997	---
.93				.763	.933	.987	.988
				.834	.960	.990	1.000
.94					.835	.975	---
					.787	.990	---
.95						.916	.996
						.826	.999
.96							.979
							.932

the Monte Carlo result obtained by these authors. Their numbers were obtained in a pseudo-experiment in which 100 sequences of 800 trials each were run with random numbers. The entry itself is the average value of p for the 100 sequences at trial 800. Thus it has some random variation and is pre-asymptotic to the extent that 800 trials is not an infinite number. The agreement is quite encouraging for the use of the differential-equation method. The agreement between the Monte Carlo results and the differential equation is surprisingly close, considering that only 100 sequences were used and that the differential equation is only an approximation. On the other hand, both learning parameters are near unity in these examples; in that neighborhood the differential equation should be quite a good approximation.

T-maze Experiment with Paradise Fish

In the first section of this paper, a T-maze experiment by Bush and Wilson [2] using paradise fish was described. The rate of reward was 0.75 for response R and 0.25 for response L. In the notation of our model, $\pi_1 = 0.75$ and $\pi_2 = 0.25$. The learning-rate parameters were estimated to be $\alpha_1 = 0.916$ and $\alpha_2 = 0.942$ for the group in which the fish could see the reward through a transparent divider when they chose the unrewarded side. The initial probability for response R (estimated from results on the first 10 of the 140 trials) varied considerably from one fish to another, the average value being 0.496, or nearly 0.50. Bush and Wilson report that the initial distribution of p approximately followed the symmetrical Beta distribution

$$(25) \qquad y = 3.61[p(1 - p)]^{0.7}.$$

This initial distribution was used to calculate the expected fraction attracted by R. The relative areas under the curve (25) in the ten intervals

$$[0, 0.1], \ [0.1, 0.2], \ \cdots, \ [0.9, 1.0]$$

were found, the values of $f(p)$ at the midpoints of these intervals were calculated, and their weighted average was obtained. The result was $f(p) = 0.800$.

In the experiment, Bush and Wilson found 15 of the 22 fish in the experimental group making nearly all R responses after about 100 trials. This leads to the estimate 0.68 for the proportion ultimately attracted to the R response. That result is only about one standard error away from the fitted value 0.80. That small deviation does not even take any account of the unreliability of the original estimates of the α's.

Other Methods

Several other methods of approximating the function have been explored. One that was rather successful employed the function $f(p; \alpha, 0)$ or $f(1 - p; 0, \alpha)$, choosing a value of α that made the iterate change very little. This method was superior to an iteration technique beginning with $f_0(p) = p$.

Since one knows exactly the solution to the functional equation in the special case $\alpha_1 = \alpha_2$, the notion of expanding $f(p; \alpha_1, \alpha_2)$ as a power series in α_2 in the neighborhood of α_1 suggests itself. Robert R. Bush, in an unpublished note, developed such a technique.

REFERENCES

[1] Bush, R. R. and Mosteller, F. *Stochastic models for learning.* New York: Wiley, 1955.
[2] Bush, R. R. and Wilson, T. R. Two-choice behavior of paradise fish. *J. exp. Psychol.*, 1956, **51**, 315–322.
[3] Harris, T. E., Bellman, R., and Shapiro, H. N. Studies in functional equations occurring in decision processes. Res. Memo. P-382, The RAND Corp., Santa Monica, Calif., 1953.
[4] Karlin, S. Some random walks arising in learning models I. *Pacific J. Math.*, 1953, **3**, 725–756.

Manuscript received 1/9/59

Revised manuscript received 6/29/59

A THEORY OF DISCRIMINATION LEARNING [1]

FRANK RESTLE

Stanford University [2]

This paper presents a theory of two-choice discrimination learning. Though similar in form to earlier theories of simple learning by Estes (5) and Bush and Mosteller (2,3), this system introduces a powerful new assumption which makes definite quantitative predictions easier to obtain and test. Several such predictions dealing with learning and transfer are derived from the theory and tested against empirical data.

The stimulus situation facing a subject in a trial of discrimination learning is thought of as a set of cues. A subset of these cues may correspond to any thing—concrete or abstract, present, past, or future, of any description—to which the subject can learn to make a differential response. In this definition it does not matter whether the subject actually makes a differential response to the set of cues as long as he has the capacity to learn one. An individual cue is thought of as "indivisible" in the sense that different responses cannot be learned to different parts of it. Informally, the term "cue" will occasionally be used to refer to any set of cues, all of which are manipulated in the same way during a whole experiment.

[1] This paper is adapted from part of a Ph.D. dissertation submitted to Stanford University. The author is especially indebted to Dr. Douglas H. Lawrence and to Dr. Patrick Suppes for encouragement and criticism. Thanks are also due Dr. W. K. Estes who loaned prepublication manuscripts and Dr. R. R. Bush who pointed out some relations between the present theory and the Bush-Mosteller model (3).

[2] Now at the Human Resources Research Office, The George Washington University.

In problems to be analyzed by this theory, every individual cue is either "relevant" or "irrelevant." A cue is relevant if it can be used by the subject to predict where or how reward is to be obtained. For example, if food is always found behind a black card in a rat experiment, then cues aroused by the black card are relevant. A cue aroused by an object uncorrelated with reward is "irrelevant." For example, if the reward is always behind the black card but the black card is randomly moved from left to right, then "position" cues are irrelevant. These concepts are discussed by Lawrence (6).

In experiments to be considered, the subject has just two choice responses. No other activities are considered in testing the theory. Any consistent method of describing these two responses which can be applied throughout a complete experiment is acceptable in using this theory.

THEORY

In solving a two-choice discrimination problem the subject learns to relate his responses correctly to the relevant cues. At the same time his responses become independent of the irrelevant cues. These two aspects of discrimination learning are represented by two hypothesized processes, "conditioning" and "adaptation."

Intuitively, a conditioned cue is one which the subject knows how to use in getting reward. If k is a relevant cue and $c(k,n)$ is the probability that k has been conditioned at the beginning of the nth trial, then

$$c(k,n+1)=c(k,n)+\theta[1-c(k,n)] \quad [1]$$

This article appeared in *Psychol. Rev.*, 1955, **62**, 11–19. Reprinted with permission.

is the probability that it will be conditioned by the beginning of the next trial. On each trial of a given problem a constant proportion, θ, of unconditioned relevant cues becomes conditioned.

To the extent that a conditioned cue affects performance, it contributes to a correct response only, whereas an unconditioned relevant cue contributes equally to a correct and to an incorrect response.

Intuitively, an adapted cue is one which the subject does not consider in deciding upon his choice response. If a cue is thought of as a "possible solution" to the problem, an adapted cue is a possible solution which the subject rejects or ignores. If $a(k,n)$ is the probability that irrelevant cue k has been adapted at the beginning of the nth trial, then

$$a(k,n+1) = a(k,n) + \theta[1-a(k,n)] \quad [2]$$

is the probability that it will be adapted by the beginning of the next trial. On each trial of a given problem a constant proportion of unadapted irrelevant cues becomes adapted. An adapted cue is nonfunctional in the sense that it contributes neither to a correct nor to an incorrect response.

It will be noticed that the same constant θ appears in both equations 1 and 2. The *fundamental simplifying assumption* of this theory deals with θ. This assumption is that

$$\theta = \frac{r}{r+i}, \quad [3]$$

where r is the number of relevant cues in the problem and i is the number of irrelevant cues. Thus, θ is the proportion of relevant cues in the problem. This proportion is the same as the fraction of unconditioned cues conditioned on each trial, and the fraction of unadapted cues adapted on each trial.

The performance function $p(n)$, representing the probability of a correct response on the nth trial, is in accord with the definitions of conditioning and adapting given above. The function is in the form of a ratio, with the total number of unadapted cues in the denominator and the number of conditioned cues plus one-half times the number of other cues in the numerator. Thus conditioned cues contribute their whole effect toward a correct response, adapted cues contribute nothing toward either response, and other cues contribute their effect equally toward correct and incorrect responses. Formally,

$$p(n) = \frac{\sum^{r} c(k,n) + \frac{1}{2}\sum^{r}[1-c(k,n)] + \frac{1}{2}\sum^{i}[1-a(k,n)]}{r + \sum^{i}[1-a(k,n)]}. \quad [4]$$

Here $\sum^{r}$ is the sum taken over the r relevant cues and $\sum^{i}$ is the sum taken over the i irrelevant cues.

Some Consequences Regarding Simple Learning

If the subject is naive at the beginning of training, so that for any relevant cue k, $c(k,1) = 0$, and for any irrelevant cue k, $a(k,1) = 0$, and if he receives n trials on a given problem, then by mathematical induction it can be shown that if k is relevant,

$$c(k,n+1) = 1 - (1-\theta)^n \quad [5]$$

and if k is irrelevant,

$$a(k,n+1) = 1 - (1-\theta)^n. \quad [6]$$

Under these circumstances we can substitute equations 5 and 6 into equation 4 and, taking advantage of the simplifying effects of equation 3, we have

$$p(n) = 1 - \tfrac{1}{2} \frac{(1 - \theta)^{n-1}}{\theta + (1 - \theta)^n}. \quad [7]$$

Plotting equation 7 shows that p is an S-shaped function of n with an asymptote (for $\theta > 0$) at 1.00. Also, $p(1) = \tfrac{1}{2}$. Since $p(n)$ is a monotonic increasing function of θ we can estimate θ from observations of performance. If we want to know the theoretical proportion of relevant cues in a problem for a particular subject, we have the subject work on the problem, record his performance curve, and solve equation 7 for θ. This result depends directly upon the simplifying assumption of equation 3.

Since the instability of individual learning curves makes it difficult to fit curves to them, it is fortunate that θ can be determined in a different way. Suppose a subject makes F errors in the course of solving the problem to a very rigorous criterion and it is assumed for practical purposes that he has made all the errors he is going to make. Theoretically, the total number of errors made on a problem can be written

$$E = \sum_{n=1}^{\infty} [1 - p(n)].$$

Under the conditions satisfying equation 7, this can be evaluated approximately by using the continuous time variable t in place of the discrete trial variable n, and integrating. The result of this integration is that

$$E \simeq \tfrac{1}{2} + \tfrac{1}{2} \frac{\log \theta}{(1 - \theta) \log (1 - \theta)}. \quad [8]$$

By equation 8, which relates the total number of errors made on a problem to θ, it is possible to make relatively stable estimates of θ.

An Empirical Test of the Simple Learning Theory— Combination of Cues

Consider three problems, s_1, s_2, and s_3, all of which involve the same irrelevant cues. Two of the problems, s_1 and s_2, have entirely separate and different relevant cues, while in problem s_3 all the relevant cues of s_1 and s_2 are present and relevant. That is, $r_3 = r_1 + r_2$ and $i_1 = i_2 = i_3$. If we know θ_1 and θ_2 we can compute θ_3, since by equation 3

$$\theta_1 = r_1/(r_1 + i)$$
$$\theta_2 = r_2/(r_2 + i)$$
$$\theta_3 = (r_1 + r_2)/(r_1 + r_2 + i).$$

Solving these equations for θ_3 in terms of θ_1 and θ_2 we get

$$\theta_3 = (\theta_1 + \theta_2 - 2\theta_1\theta_2)/(1 - \theta_1\theta_2). \quad [9]$$

This theorem answers the following question: Suppose we know how many errors are made in learning to use differential cue X and how many are used to learn cue Y, then how many errors will be made in learning a problem in which either X or Y can be used (if X and Y are entirely discrete)?

Eninger (4) has run an experiment which tests equation 9. Three groups of white rats were run in a T maze on successive discrimination problems. The first group learned a visual discrimination, *black-white*, the second group learned an auditory discrimination, *tone–no-tone*, and the third group had both cues available and relevant.

Since each group was run to a rigorous criterion, total error scores are used to estimate θ_1 and θ_2 by equation 8.[3] The values estimated are

[3] Total error scores do not appear in Eninger's original publication and are no longer known. However, trials-to-criterion scores were reported. Total error scores were

$\theta_1 = .020$, based on an estimated average of 98.5 errors made on the auditory-cue problem, and $\theta_2 = .029$, based on an estimated average of 64.5 errors on the visual-cue problem. Putting these two values into equation 9 we get

$$\theta_3 = .029 + .020 + 2(.020)(.029)/ 1 - (.020)(.029)$$
$$= .049.$$

This value of θ_3 substituted into equation 8 leads to the expectation of about 33 total errors on the combined cues problem. In fact, an average of 26 errors was made by the four subjects on this problem. The prediction is not very accurate. However, only 14 animals were employed in the entire experiment, in groups of five, five, and four. Individual differences among animals within groups were considerable. If account is taken of sampling variability of the two single-cue groups and of the combined-cue group of subjects, the prediction is not significantly wrong. Further experimentation is needed to determine whether the proposed law is tenable.

It is easily seen that θ_3 will always be larger than θ_1 or θ_2 if all three problems are solved. Learning will always be faster in the combined-cues problem. Eninger (4) in his paper points out that this qualitative statement is a consequence of Spence's theory of discrimination. However, Spence's theory gives no quantitative law.

TRANSFER OF TRAINING

In order to apply this theory to transfer-of-training experiments in which more than one problem is used, certain assumptions are made. It is

estimated from trials-to-criterion scores by using other, comparable data collected by Amsel (1). Dr. Amsel provided detailed results in a personal communication.

assumed that if a cue is conditioned in one problem and appears immediately thereafter as a relevant cue in a new problem, it is still conditioned. Likewise, an adapted cue appearing as an irrelevant cue in a new problem is adapted. However, if a conditioned cue is made irrelevant it is obviously no longer conditioned, since it cannot serve as a predictor of reward. Similarly, it is assumed that if an adapted cue is made relevant in a new problem, it becomes unadapted and available for conditioning.

According to the present definition of conditioning, a conditioned cue contributes to a correct response. Therefore the above assumptions will not hold if the relation between a cue and a reward is reversed in changing the problem. This theory cannot be used to analyze reversal learning, and is applicable only in cases in which relevant cues maintain an unchanging significance.

If two problems are run under the same conditions and in the same apparatus, and differ only in the degree of difference between the discriminanda (as where one problem is a *black-white* and the other a *dark gray-light gray* discrimination), it is assumed that both problems involve the same cues; but the greater the difference to be discriminated, the more cues are relevant and the less are irrelevant.

EMPIRICAL TESTS OF THE TRANSFER-OF-TRAINING THEORY

As Lawrence (7) has pointed out, it seems that a difficult discrimination is more easily established if the subjects are first trained on an easy problem of the same type than if all training is given directly on the difficult discrimination. The experimental evidence on this point raises the question of predicting transfer performance from one problem to another, where the two problems involve the same stimulus dimension but differ in difficulty.

Suppose that problems s_1 and s_2 both require a discrimination along the same stimulus dimension and differ only in that s_2 is more difficult than s_1. Let θ_1 be the proportion of relevant cues in problem s_1 and θ_2 be the proportion of relevant cues in s_2. Suppose that the training schedule involves n trials on problem s_1 followed by j trials on problem s_2. Then the probability of a correct response on trial $n + j$ is

lem without prior experience, their performance on the first problem serves to estimate θ_1, the proportion of relevant cues in the easier pretraining problem. Lawrence replicated the experiment, having two experimental groups, ATG No. 1 and ATG No. 2, each of which transferred abruptly from an easy pretraining problem to the test problem. Group ATG No. 1 had a very easy problem for which we estimate $\theta_1 = .14$. Group ATG No. 2 had a more difficult problem for which $\theta_1' = .07$.

For group ATG No. 1, $\theta_1 = .14$, $\theta_2 = .04$, and $n = 30$ since thirty

$$p(n + j) = \frac{\theta_2 + \frac{1}{2}(1 - \theta_2)^{j-1}[\theta_1 - \theta_2 + (1 - \theta_1)^n(1 - \theta_1 - \theta_2)]}{\theta_2 + (1 - \theta_2)^{j-1}[\theta_1 - \theta_2 + (1 - \theta_1)^{n+1}]}. \quad [10]^4$$

This theorem can be tested against the results of experiments reported by Lawrence (7). He trained white rats in one brightness discrimination and transferred them to a more difficult problem for further training. A control group, which Lawrence called "HDG," learned the hard test problem without work on any other problem. The performance of this control group is used to estimate θ_2, the proportion of relevant cues in the test problem. The value found was .04.[5] Since the experimental subjects first worked on the pretraining prob-

trials of pretraining were given. From this information we can compute $p(n + j)$ for all j, using equation 10. The predicted transfer performance is compared with observed performance in Table 1. For group ATG No. 2, $\theta_1' = .07$, $\theta_2 = .04$, and $n = 50$ since fifty trials of pretraining were given. Here also, $p(n + j)$ can be computed. Prediction is compared with observed performance in Table 1, from which it can be seen that the predictions are

[4] The justification of equation 10 involves no mathematical difficulties. On the first trial of transfer we know the probability that any cue relevant in the second problem is conditioned, since all cues relevant in the second problem were relevant in the first. Similarly, we know the probability that i_1 of the i_2 irrelevant cues are adapted. The other $i_2 - i_1$ cues are unadapted. Equations 1 and 2 can be applied at this point, and all terms divided by $r_1 + i_1 (= r_2 + i_2)$.

[5] These estimates were made by the unsatisfactory method of fitting equation 7 to group average learning curves. Therefore the results regarding Lawrence's experiment are approximate.

TABLE 1

PREDICTION OF EASY-TO-HARD TRANSFER IN RATS*

| Trials of Transfer Training | Proportion of Correct Responses | | | |
| | Group ATG 1 | | Group ATG 2 | |
	Observed	Predicted	Observed	Predicted
1–10	.66	.63	.81	.71
11–20	.70	.68	.83	.77
21–30	.74	.72	.81	.81
31–40	.84	.78		
41–50	.86	.83		

* Data from Lawrence (7).

relatively accurate, though performance is higher than predicted.

Lawrence also considered the possibility that a gradual transition from
easy through successively harder problems would result in rapid mastery of
the difficult problem. He tested this
proposition by giving another group
of subjects a series of three pretest
problems before the final test problem.
The problems in order of ease of learning were, first, the problem learned by
ATG No. 1 with $\theta_1 = .14$, an intermediate problem which was not otherwise used, the difficult pretest problem
with $\theta_3 = .07$, and finally the test
problem with $\theta_4 = .04$.

To estimate θ_2 in Lawrence's experiment where problem s_2 never was
used separately in simple learning,
we notice the relation of θ to differences between discriminanda in apparent foot-candles for problems s_1, s_3,
and s_4 whose θ values are known.
We know that if the problems are
properly controlled, and the stimulus
difference is zero foot-candles, there
are no relevant cues and θ is zero. It
was found that this assumption, along
with available data, made it possible
to write a tentative empirical function
relating θ to the difference between
discriminanda in foot-candles. This
equation presumably holds only in the
case of Lawrence's apparatus, train-

TABLE 2

THE RELATION OF "DIFFERENCE BETWEEN
STIMULI" AND θ VALUE OF PROBLEM*

Difference Between Discriminanda in Apparent Foot-Candles	Corresponding θ Value of Problem
67.7	.14
35.2	.113**
14.0	.07
5.9	.04
0.0	.00†

* Data from Lawrence (7).
** Estimated by interpolation from empirical equa-
tion 16.
† Theoretical—see text for explanation.

TABLE 3

PREDICTION OF TRANSFER PERFORMANCE OF
RATS AFTER A SERIES OF PRETRAINING
PROBLEMS*

Trials Working on Final Test Problem	Proportion of Correct Responses	
	Observed	Predicted
1–10	.73	.73
11–20	.82	.79
21–30	.87	.84
31–40	.89	.87
41–50	.90	.90

* Data from Lawrence (7).

ing procedure, subjects, etc. The
equation adopted is

$$\theta = .0988 \log_{10}(.4\,d) \qquad [11]$$

where d is the difference between discriminanda in foot-candles. It is emphasized that this equation has no
theoretical significance and is merely
expedient. From equation 11 it is
possible to determine the θ value of
the intermediate pretraining problem
by interpolation. Table 2 gives the
data and results of this interpolation.

Ten trials were given on each of the
first three problems and fifty trials
on the final test problem. Using the
θ values in Table 2 it is possible to
predict the test problem performance
of subjects who have gone through
gradual transition pretraining.[6] This
prediction is compared with observed
performance in Table 3. It may be
noted that the correspondence between prediction and observation is
in this case very close. Again, however, the prediction is consistently a
little lower than observed performance.

[6] The general prediction for transfer through
a series of problems which get successively
more difficult can be derived by following
through and repeating the reasoning in footnote 4. Since the resulting equations are
extremely large and can be derived rather
easily, they are not given here.

NEW DATA

The theory has thus far been tested against the behavior of rats. Its generality is now tested with college students in a simple discrimination learning task.

Subjects and procedure. The subjects in this experiment were 23 students in the elementary psychology course at Stanford University. The S was seated at one end of a table and told that his responses could be either "A" or "B". On each trial S saw a single stimulus, which was a black square on a circular white background. The two squares used on alternate trials differed in size. In problem s_1 the squares differed in height by $\frac{1}{4}$ in., in problem s_2 they differed by $\frac{1}{8}$ in. The mean height of each pair of squares was 3 in. The squares were viewed at a distance of about 6 ft.

For half the Ss in each experimental group, the problem was to say "A" to the smaller square and "B" to the larger one. The other Ss had the converse problem. The S was never told that the problem was a size discrimination. Stimuli were alternated randomly. A rest period was called after each ten trials and S was asked what he thought the correct solution to the problem was, and to outline possible solutions which had occurred to him. This method of questioning is a modification of Prentice's method (8).

Twelve Ss were trained first on problem s_1 to a criterion of 15 successive correct responses and then transferred to problem s_2 and run to the same criterion. These Ss made up the "Easy-Hard Transfer Group" called EH. The other 11 Ss were trained first on s_2 and then transferred to s_1. This was the "Hard-Easy Transfer Group" called HE. The two groups were approximately equated for age, sex, and known special visual skills.

Results. Using the pretraining performance of the EH group, the average proportion of relevant cues, θ_1, was estimated at .254 by equation 8. Using the pretraining performance of the HE group, the average proportion of relevant cues in problem s_2 was estimated at $\theta_2 = .138$.

The transfer performance of group EH, which first learned the easy and then the hard problem, is predictable by equation 10. Since these subjects

worked to a high criterion in pretraining, we can assume that $p(n)$ is negligibly different from one at the end of pretraining. Then by equation 7 we see that $(1 - \theta_1)^{n-1}$ is small, and equation 10 simplifies to

$$p(n+j) = \frac{\theta_2 + \frac{1}{2}(1-\theta_2)^{j-1}(\theta_1-\theta_2)}{\theta_2 + (1-\theta_2)^{j-1}(\theta_1-\theta_2)}. \quad [12]$$

This theoretical function of j is compared with observed transfer performance in Table 4. It is seen that the correspondence is quite close with a negligible constant error.

This prediction is based on the formula which also predicted Lawrence's rat data. This confirmation suggests that the law can be applied to human as well as rat performance on this type of task.

Using the line of reasoning which developed equation 10 we can produce an equation to predict transfer performance from hard to easier problems of the same sort. Certain cues are relevant in the easy problem which were irrelevant in the harder one. These cues cannot be identified in the hard problem. For performance to be perfect in the easier problem all relevant cues must be identified. Therefore, when the subject transfers from the hard to the easier

TABLE 4

PREDICTION OF TRANSFER OF TRAINING FROM EASIER TO HARDER PROBLEM IN HUMAN SUBJECTS

Trials after Transfer to Second Problem	Proportion of Correct Responses	
	Observed	Predicted
1–5	.817	.821
6–10	.933	.895
11–15	.926	.941
16–20	.933	.966
21–25	.966	.988
26–30	.983	.994
31–35	1.000	1.000

TABLE 5

PREDICTION OF TRANSFER OF TRAINING FROM
HARDER TO EASIER PROBLEM IN
HUMAN SUBJECTS

Trials After Transfer to Second Problem	Proportion of Correct Responses	
	Observed	Predicted
1–4	.932	.883
5–8	.955	.960
9–12	.955	.984
13–16	1.000	.995

problem we should expect some small number of errors to be made. On the assumption that the hard problem was completely learned in pretraining, the formula for transfer performance on the easy problem is

$$p(n+j) = \frac{\theta_2 + (\theta_1 - \theta_2)(1 - \theta_1)^{j-1}}{\theta_1} \quad [13]$$

where θ_1 is the proportion of relevant cues in the easy problem and θ_2 is the proportion of relevant cues in the harder problem. The proof of this theorem is similar to that of equation 12 above, and is not given here.

Equation 13 yields the prediction for transfer performance of the *HE* subjects. In Table 5 the prediction is compared with observed transfer performance.

Despite the very small frequencies predicted and observed, the prediction is quite accurate. In all, seven errors were made by eleven subjects, whereas a total of eight were expected. This is an average of .64 errors per subject observed, and .73 predicted.

DISCUSSION

The definition of a "cue" in terms of possible responses is selected because the theoretical results do not depend critically upon the nature of the stimulating agent. While cues are thought of as stimulus elements, these elements need not be of the nature of "points of color" or "elementary tones." If a subject can learn a consistent response to a certain configuration despite changes in its constituents, then the configuration is by definition a cue separate from its constituents. The intention is to accept any cue which can be demonstrated to be a possible basis for a differential response.

The process of conditioning described in this paper is formally similar to the processes of conditioning of Estes (5) and Bush and Mosteller (2,3). In the present theory conditioning takes place at each trial, not only on "reinforced" trials. In earlier theories conditioning is said to occur only on such reinforced trials. In two-choice discrimination the incorrect response has a high initial probability (one-half) because of the nature of the physical situation and the way of recording responses. Therefore, a theory of two-choice learning must account for the consistent weakening of such responses through consistent nonreinforcement.

The notion of adaptation used here is formally analogous to the operation of Bush and Mosteller's Discrimination Operator "*D*" (3). However, whereas Bush and Mosteller's operator is applied only on trials in which the reward condition is reversed for a cue, the present theory indicates that this process takes place each trial. In addition, while the Discrimination Operator and the process of adaptation are both exponential in form, Bush and Mosteller introduce a new exponential constant k for this purpose and the present theory uses the conditioning constant θ.

The major point differentiating the present theory from similar earlier theories is the use of the strong simplifying assumption identifying the exponential constant θ with the proportion of relevant cues. This assumption may appear intuitively unlikely, but if it should be shown by further experiment to be tenable, the predictive power of discrimination learning theory is enhanced. There seems to be no reason for abandoning so useful an assumption unless experimental results require it.

SUMMARY

A theory of two-choice discrimination learning has been presented. The theory is formally similar to earlier theories of Estes (5) and Bush and Mosteller (3) but differs somewhat in basic concepts and uses a new simplifying assumption.

From this theory three empirical laws are derived: one dealing with the combination of relevant cues, and two dealing with a special type of transfer of training. These laws permitted quantitative predictions of the behavior of four groups of rats and two groups of human subjects. Five of these six predictions were quite accurate, and the sixth was within the range of reasonable sampling deviation.

REFERENCES

1. AMSEL, A. Rate of learning a visual brightness discrimination as a function of discriminanda durations. *J. comp. physiol. Psychol.*, 1952, **45**, 341–346.
2. BUSH, R. R., & MOSTELLER, F. A mathematical model for simple learning. *Psychol. Rev.*, 1951, **58**, 313–323.
3. BUSH, R. R., & MOSTELLER, F. A model for stimulus generalization and discrimination. *Psychol. Rev.*, 1951, **58**, 413–423.
4. ENINGER, M. U. Habit summation in a selective learning problem. *J. comp. physiol. Psychol.*, 1952, **45**, 511–516.
5. ESTES, W. K. Toward a statistical theory of learning. *Psychol. Rev.*, 1950, **57**, 94–107.
6. LAWRENCE, D. H. Acquired distinctiveness of cues: II. Selective association in a constant stimulus situation. *J. exp. Psychol.*, 1950, **40**, 175–188.
7. LAWRENCE, D. H. The transfer of a discrimination along a continuum. *J. comp. physiol. Psychol.*, 1952, **45**, 511–516.
8. PRENTICE, W. C. H. Continuity in human learning. *J. exp. Psychol.*, 1949, **39**, 187–194.

(Received January 14, 1954)

THE ROLE OF OBSERVING RESPONSES IN
DISCRIMINATION LEARNING [1]

PART I

BY L. BENJAMIN WYCKOFF, JR.

University of Wisconsin

Theorists in the area of discrimination learning have often had occasion to refer to a set or predisposition of S to learn differential responses to a particular pair of stimuli. Such a predisposition has often been attributed to some reaction of S such as an attending response, orienting response, perceiving response, sensory organizational activity, etc. To implement the discussion of the role of such reactions in discrimination learning we shall adopt the term "observing response" (R_o) to refer to any response which results in exposure to the pair of discriminative stimuli involved. The probability of occurrence of an observing response will be denoted by p_o. These responses are to be distinguished from the responses upon which reinforcement is based; that is, running, turning right or left, lever pressing, etc., which, for convenience, we shall term "effective responses."

Spence (19) has proposed a theory of discrimination which is specifically intended to deal with situations where no observing response is required of S, that is to say, to situations in which S is certain to be exposed to the discriminative stimuli on each trial or prior to each effective response ($p_o = 1$). The fact that in some discrimination experiments this condition has not been satisfied has become an issue

[1] This paper is submitted in partial fulfillment of the requirements for the degree of Doctor of Philosophy, in the Department of Psychology, Indiana University. The writer wishes to express his appreciation to Dr. C. J. Burke for his invaluable guidance and stimulation.

in the literature, largely because it became necessary to delimit clearly the situations to which Spence's theory is intended to apply.

Spence's theory of discrimination states that stimulus-response connections are strengthened or weakened during discrimination training in essentially the same way as these changes would occur during conditioning or extinction. When a response is reinforced the connections between it and all aspects of the stimulus situation impinging on S at the time the response occurred will be strengthened. These connections will be weakened when the response is not reinforced. Certain implications of this theory were questioned by Krechevsky (11) and other theorists, and became the subject matter of the "continuity-discontinuity" controversy. This material has been reviewed a number of times (2, 5) and need not be repeated in detail here. One aspect of the controversy is pertinent to the present discussion. Krechevsky (12) presented experimental findings which indicated that rats learned nothing with respect to two stimulus patterns during the first 20 trials of a discrimination experiment even though they were systematically reinforced for approaching a particular pattern during this interval. Failure to learn was established by showing a lack of interference when Ss were tested on a reversed discrimination. These findings were in apparent disagreement with the data obtained by McCulloch and Pratt (13) in a similar experiment in which differing weights were used as discriminative stimuli. Here interference was obtained, indicating that some cumulative learning had occurred in the early portion of the experiment.

In interpreting these results, Spence (20, p. 277) argued that the stimuli (patterns) used by Krechevsky were not sufficiently

This article appeared in *Psychol. Rev.*, 1952, **59**, 431–442. Reprinted with permission.

conspicuous to provide a legitimate test of his theory. He suggested that Ss had not learned to orient toward the stimuli within the first 20 trials. He points out that in such cases, ". . . the animal must learn to orient and fixate its head and eyes so as to receive the critical stimuli." He then suggests a way in which this learning may occur. "These reactions are learned . . . because they are followed within a short temporal interval by the final goal response."

This interpretation was put to an experimental test by Ehrenfreund (5). In his experiment the likelihood of S's receiving the critical stimuli was manipulated by changing the position of the stimuli (upright and inverted triangles) with respect to the landing platform of a jumping stand. The design of the experiment was essentially the same as Krechevsky's. The results conform to Spence's interpretation. When the stimuli were placed relatively high, no learning occurred within the first 40 trials, whereas when the stimuli were placed closer to the landing platform learning did occur. Learning was again measured in terms of interference in the learning of a subsequent reversed discrimination.

The analysis of discrimination situations in which some observing response is required is of interest for several reasons. First, discrimination learning in situations other than laboratory experiments, such as human learning in the course of every day events, is largely of this kind. Secondly, even in the most closely controlled laboratory experiments it is seldom, if ever, possible to say with certainty that S is exposed to the discriminative stimuli prior to each effective response. In the case of pattern discriminations it has been demonstrated by Ehrenfreund (5) that relatively small differences in the position of the discriminative stimuli will effect discrimination learning, indicating that relatively precise fixation of the stimulus is required.

In the present paper an attempt will be made to develop a more extensive theory of discrimination which will include situations in which some observing response (hereafter referred to as R_o) is required before S is exposed to the discriminative stimuli. An example of such a situation would be an experiment in which stimulus cards were placed overhead. In this case the response of raising the head would be the R_o).

If we accept the notion that changes in p_o can be accounted for within the framework of reinforcement learning theory, it should be possible to devise a theory of discrimination which will include those cases where some R_o is necessary. The purpose of this paper is to outline such a theory. We shall see that by analyzing discrimination learning in this way it will be possible to account for stimulus generalization and also changes in generalization during discrimination learning without postulating any direct interaction between stimuli. Several hypotheses will be derived from this theory which have been tested in an experiment by the author presented in detail elsewhere (22). Finally we shall outline a way in which the present theory can be integrated with existing quantitative theories of conditioning and extinction to form a quantitative theory of discrimination.

To simplify this discussion let us consider a hypothetical experiment using a situation similar to that used by Wilcoxon, Hays, and Hull (21), and later used by Hull (10) for a discrimination experiment. In this experiment a rat was placed in a small compartment with a single exit through a door into a goal compartment. A measure of the latency of the response of running through this door was obtained. The discriminative stimuli consisted of a black or a white door, either one of which was present on each trial. During discrimination training the running response was reinforced with food when one color was present, whereas reinforcement was withheld when the other color was present. Each stimulus was present on an average of 50 per cent of the trials.

For purposes of the present discussion let us consider a slightly different situation in which the discriminative stimuli are placed overhead rather than directly in front of S. In this case an observing response, raising the head, will be necessary if S is to be exposed to the discriminative stimuli. On each trial, when S is placed in the apparatus, there will be a certain probability that the R_o of looking up will occur. When R_o does occur S will be exposed either to a black or a white card. When the R_o fails to occur S will not be exposed to either card, but rather to a neutral population of stimuli (walls, floor, etc.). Note that in this situation S does not improve its chances of ultimate reinforcement by making the R_o. The food is placed in the goal compartment whenever the white card is present whether S actually looks up or not. In a sense then, S gains only information by making the R_o.

We are now in a position to examine the relation between observing responses and stimulus generalization. In general it is apparent that if p_o has a low value, S will seldom be exposed to the discriminative stimuli (the black and white cards). S therefore, will have minimum opportunity to learn discrimination or to manifest any discrimination already learned. On the other hand, if p_o has a high value, the opportunity to learn or manifest discrimination will be large.

Stimulus generalization between two stimuli is usually defined either in terms of S's tendency to respond

similarly to the two stimuli, or in terms of failure to learn differential responses readily. Thus we can see that stimulus generalization will decrease as p_o increases.

If we assume that p_o changes as a result of learning processes we can see that these changes would give rise to changes in generalization between the stimuli involved. More specifically, if we assume that p_o will increase during discrimination learning (differential reinforcement), generalization between the discriminative stimuli will decrease. Similarly, we might assume that p_o will decrease if we introduce a procedure in which the subject is reinforced equally often in the presence of either stimulus (non-differential reinforcement). This decrease in p_o would give rise to an increase in generalization between the stimuli.

In the case of the hypothetical experiment suggested above, generalization will be shown in a "crossover" effect between positive and negative trials. Reinforcements on positive trials (positive stimulus card present but not necessarily observed) will tend to strengthen the effective response on negative trials, while unreinforced responses on negative trials will tend to weaken the effective response on positive trials. If S's tendency to look up increases during differential reinforcement, this "crossover" effect will decrease. If during non-differential reinforcement the tendency to look up decreases, the "crossover" effect will increase.

It should be emphasized that these statements regarding increases and decreases in p_o are, at this point, assumptions which may or may not be true in a particular experimental situation. We shall present experimental findings which suggest that these assumptions are quite generally true below.

In the above discussion we have considered the effects of R_o on discrimination and generalization. At this point we turn our attention to the problem of accounting for changes in p_o within the framework of reinforcement learning theory. Our problem will be to identify possible reinforcing conditions which may account for increases in p_o during differential reinforcement.

First we note that, by definition, the observing response results in exposure to a pair of discriminative stimuli. If exposure to these stimuli is in some way reinforcing, we shall expect p_o to increase or remain high. The problem at hand is to show how exposure to discriminative stimuli may have a reinforcing effect under the condition of differential reinforcement, while the same stimuli do not have this effect under the condition of non-differential reinforcement. Reinforcement theory provides two ways of accounting for this reinforcing effect.

The first method is the mechanism suggested by Spence when he states that observing responses are learned "because they are followed within a short temporal interval by the final goal response" (19). This mechanism will operate in experiments such as a "jumping stand" experiment, in which exposure to discriminative stimuli may serve to increase the probability of prompt reinforcement, that is to say, the probability of the "correct" jump may be increased. Spence offered this suggestion in relation to a jumping stand experiment.

The second method of accounting for the reinforcing effect is by appeal to the principles of secondary reinforcement. Here we suggest that the discriminative stimuli themselves take on secondary reinforcing value during the course of discrimination learning.

It has been demonstrated that an originally neutral stimulus which accompanies reinforcement may acquire secondary reinforcing properties. That is, it may serve to strengthen a response upon which it is made contingent. Skinner (18, p. 246) has demonstrated that whenever a stimulus becomes a discriminative stimulus for some response in a chain leading ultimately to reinforcement, this stimulus will serve as a secondary reinforcing stimulus. The conditions necessary for the formation of secondary reinforcing properties are further considered by Notterman (16), Schoenfeld et al. (17) and Dinsmoor (4). They point out that in all cases where secondary reinforcement has been demonstrated, the conditions were also appropriate for the establishment of the stimulus in question as a discriminative stimulus. They suggest that this may be a necessary (as well as sufficient) condition for the establishment of secondary reinforcing properties. In the present formulation it is apparent that the positive stimulus is presented in the appropriate temporal position to become both a discriminative stimulus (for the effective response) and a secondary reinforcing stimulus (for the observing response).

This mechanism may operate in any situation whatever where an R_o is involved, since it is a defining characteristic of the R_o that it leads to exposure to discriminative stimuli. Specifically it should apply to the hypothetical experiment suggested above. Here the effective response (running) will always be reinforced when S is exposed to the white card. Hence the white card could be expected to acquire secondary reinforcing value. It is not sufficient to show simply that the positive stimulus will acquire secondary reinforcing value. We must also consider two other factors. First, R_o results in exposure to the positive stimulus only 50 per cent of the time. It results in exposure to the negative stimulus the other 50 per cent. Second, the running response is reinforced sometimes when S is exposed to the neutral stimulus population, since, on positive trials, the running response is reinforced even though S does not look up. The effective response is reinforced most consistently when S is exposed to the positive stimulus. Therefore, it is still plausible to postulate that the intermittent exposure to the positive and negative stimuli will have a net reinforcing effect on R_o.

It is true of both of these mechanisms that, before any increase in p_o can be expected to occur, S must learn differential effective responses, that is to say, S must learn to respond differently to the two discriminative stimuli. In the case of the "jumping stand" experiment, if S does not have differential jumping tendencies toward the discriminative stimuli, the probability of reinforcement will always be 50 per cent, and will not be improved by the occurrence of R_o.

When we apply the secondary reinforcement principle we can see that the positive stimulus must appear in the proper temporal relation to reinforcement a number of times before this stimulus will acquire secondary reinforcing properties. In terms of Notterman, Schoenfeld, and Dinsmoor's interpretation it will be necessary for S to learn differential effective responses to the discriminative stimuli before secondary reinforcing properties are acquired by these stimuli.

In view of these considerations we introduce the following general hypothesis: Exposure to discriminative stimuli will have a reinforcing effect on the observing response to the extent that S has learned to respond differently to the two discriminative stimuli.

Hereafter we shall refer to the magnitude of the difference between

Ss' tendencies to respond to the two discriminative stimuli as the "degree of discrimination."

Earlier it was pointed out that the probability of occurrence of R_o is one of the factors determining the rate of formation of discrimination. According to the present hypothesis the opposite relationship is also true. The resulting picture is one of a circular interrelationship, in which R_o affects the formation of discrimination because of its effect on exposure to discriminative stimuli, while the degree of discrimination affects R_o through another mechanism involving either secondary reinforcement or changes in the probability of reinforcement.

We now present four propositions which are implied by this general hypothesis. The hypothesis was formulated partly on the basis of experimental evidence already available, which suggested that these propositions were true (22). At present we shall consider them as specific hypotheses. The first two of these have already been introduced as assumptions.

1. p_o will increase (or remain high) under conditions of differential reinforcement.

2. p_o will decrease (or remain low) under conditions of non-differential reinforcement.

It is apparent that these hypotheses are consistent with the general hypothesis since the degree of discrimination will tend to increase (or remain high) under differential reinforcement, while it will tend to decrease (or remain low) under nondifferential reinforcement. In other words, S will learn to respond differently to the two stimuli under differential reinforcement, but will learn to respond in the same way to them under nondifferential reinforcement. Additional hypotheses of interest can be derived from this general hypothesis.

3. When a well established discrimination is reversed p_o will decrease temporarily and then return to a high value.

We shall expect this change in p_o because, following a reversal, the degree of discrimination will decrease as the original discrimination vanishes. It will then increase as the new discrimination is formed.

4. If at some point in an experiment the degree of discrimination is low and at the same time p_o is low (but greater than zero), we shall expect the formation of discrimination to be retarded for some interval, but finally to occur quite rapidly.

This hypothesis arises from the fact that increases in the degree of discrimination, and increases in p_o, are dependent upon each other. Early in the process S will be exposed to the discriminative stimuli only a small proportion of the time and hence the degree of discrimination cannot increase rapidly. At the same time p_o will not increase because of the low degree of discrimination. Then, as the degree of discrimination becomes sufficiently great to bring about an increase in p_o the entire learning process will be accelerated.

Krechevsky (11) presents data obtained in discrimination experiments in a jumping stand situation which correspond in some respects to the predictions of the present formulation. Curves for individual Ss show relatively abrupt discrimination formation. In general the curves also show a slight improvement in discrimination prior to the abrupt change. A curve presented for discrimination reversal shows a rapid decrease in the degree of discrimination to a chance level, followed by an interval during which improvement was much less rapid. Finally the process accelerated as the reversed discrimination formed.

Krechevsky also noted that during the interval while S was responding approximately according to chance with respect to the discriminative stimuli, he showed a strong position preference. These findings are in complete agreement with hypotheses 3 and 4 in the present formulation.

The four hypotheses presented so far were tested in an experiment by the writer (22) which is presented in detail elsewhere. In this experiment direct measures of an R_o were obtained during differential reinforcement, nondifferential reinforcement and during discrimination reversal. Pigeons were used in a Skinner-box situation in which the effective response was striking a single translucent key. The discriminative stimuli were colored lights (red and green) projected on the back of the key one at a time. The colored lights were withheld and the key was lighted white until the R_o occurred. The R_o consisted of stepping on a pedal on the floor of the compartment. The reasons for using this response as an observing response are discussed in detail elsewhere (22). Here it will suffice to say that this response falls within our definition of an observing response in that it resulted in exposure to the discriminative stimuli. As in the case of the hypothetical experiment discussed above, the observing response had no effect on the probability of reinforcement at any given moment.

All of the above hypotheses were supported by the results of this experiment. Concerning the first three hypotheses, p_o was higher under differential reinforcement than under nondifferential reinforcement. When Ss were shifted from differential to nondifferential reinforcement a marked decrease in p_o occurred. All of these differences were significant at a 5 per cent level of confidence or better.

The fourth hypothesis does not apply unless at some point in the experiment the degree of discrimination and p_o are both low. This condition was not satisfied consistently since the operant (or base) level of the pedal response turned out to be relatively high for Ss. However, in several cases this condition was satisfied and in these cases the results conformed to the hypothesis.

We can now illustrate some ways in which this theory might be useful in interpreting behavior in other experiments.

1. If this theory is applied to situations in which more than one pair of discriminative stimuli is involved we can make some predictions regarding changes in the readiness of S to form discriminations based on some particular pair of stimuli.

2. It has been demonstrated that when a discrimination is reversed repeatedly Ss tend to learn the reversed discrimination more and more rapidly (15, 8). According to the present theory, during discrimination reversal the observing response is partially extinguished and reconditioned. Thus, during repeated reversals, the R_o is, in effect, reinforced intermittently. Studies of intermittent reinforcement have indicated that when a response is intermittently extinguished and reconditioned, the strength of the response tends to attain a relatively constant high value (18). On the first reversal p_o might drop to a low value, and recover slowly, but with repeated reversals we would expect this drop to become less prominent, and finally, p_o would remain high throughout the reversal. It is apparent that if p_o remained high, a reversed discrimination would be learned more rapidly than otherwise.

In the preceding discussion we have examined some of the ways in which discrimination learning may be affected when some observing response is required of S. We shall now derive some quantitative statements to supplement the above analysis. We shall attempt to set down the relationships involved in such a way that the present theory can be readily integrated into existing quantitative theories of learning such as Hull's (9), Estes' (6) or Bush and Mosteller's (3). The potential applications of this development could proceed along two different lines.

First, we could attempt to state the relationships between observing responses and measurable aspects of the effective responses in such a way that p_o could be estimated in situations where direct measurement of R_o is not feasible. This might be the case, for example, if the R_o involved focusing of the eye. If we apply the present development in this way, p_o would become an intervening variable, which could be used to account for and predict behavior in situations where (1) the apparent generalization between stimuli changes, or (2) where the ease of formation of discrimination changes as a function of training. Berlyne (1) suggests that "attention" be treated in a similar way.

Secondly, we could predict discrimination learning functions by adopting some set of assumptions regarding the component learning processes involved. These assumptions could be adopted from some existing theory which treats the simpler processes of conditioning and extinction. The main obstacle to this endeavor at the moment is the absence of any quantitative function for predicting changes in p_o. However, we shall be able to set down the relationships involved in such a way that any acceptable function can immediately be inserted.

QUANTITATIVE ANALYSIS

For purposes of this analysis let us return to consideration of the hypothetical experiment discussed above. There it was pointed out that we must take into consideration three different stimulus populations which may effect Ss' behavior. We shall adopt the following notation to represent these stimuli. Let S_1 represent the stimulus population to which S is exposed on trials when the R_o occurs and when the positive stimulus card (white) is present, S_2 represent the stimulus population on trials when the R_o occurs and when the negative stimulus card (black) is present, and S_3 the stimulus population to which S is exposed when the R_o fails to occur.

In this analysis we shall use the symbol p to represent the probability of occurrence of the effective response at any given moment during a trial. This variable can be related to the variable of response latency as follows. Estes (6) has shown that if a response can be expected to occur with a given probability at any moment during a trial, the mean latency of the response will be proportional to the reciprocal of the probability; that is to say, $L = k/p$, where L is the mean latency, p the probability, and k a constant of proportionality which will depend on the units of measurement used. In the present case we must consider the probability of occurrence of the effective response for each of three stimulus populations. Let us adopt the symbols p_1, p_2, and p_3 to represent the probability of occurrence of the effective response when S is exposed to S_1, S_2, and S_3, respectively. We shall also wish to refer to the net probability of occurrence of the effective response on a given trial, taking into account that S may be exposed to different stimuli during the trial depending on the occurrence or non-oc-

currence of the R_o. We shall use the symbols p_+ and p_- to represent the net probability on trials when the positive or negative stimuli are present.

To summarize:

$S_1 =$ the population of stimuli to which S is exposed if (1) the positive stimulus is present and (2) the R_o occurs.

$S_2 =$ the population of stimuli to which S is exposed if (1) the negative stimulus is present and (2) the R_o occurs.

$S_3 =$ the population of stimuli to which S is exposed if the observing response fails to occur.

$p =$ the probability that the effective response will occur at any given moment during a trial $(= k/L)$

$p_1 =$ the value of p when S is exposed to S_1

$p_2 =$ the value of p when S is exposed to S_2

$p_3 =$ the value of p when S is exposed to S_3

$p_+ =$ the net value of p for a trial on which the positive stimulus is present

$p_- =$ the net value of p for a trial on which the negative stimulus is present

$p_o =$ the probability of occurrence of R_o at any given moment during a trial.

We shall now express certain functional relationships among these variables. First we shall express p_+ and p_- as two functions of the variables p_1, p_2, p_3, and p_o. p_+ and p_- are variables which can be evaluated from experimental measures, such as latency of the effective response, without reference to direct measures of R_o. They correspond to the measures of response tendency usually obtained in discrimination experiments.

However, in the present framework p_+ and p_- are assumed to be the net result of the operation of the variables p_1, p_2, p_3, and p_o. Our task will be to express this dependence as a pair of functional relationships. This can be done as follows.

Consider a selected moment during a positive trial. At this moment S will be exposed to either S_1, with a probability of p_o, or to S_3, with a probability of $(1 - p_o)$. If S is exposed to S_1 he will make the effective response with a proabability of p_1. If the effective response and R_o are independent of each other the probability that both R_o and the effective response will occur will be the product $p_1 p_o$. If S is exposed to S_3 he will make the effective response with a probability of p_3, and the probability that both will occur will be the product $(1 - p_o) p_3$. The total probability that the effective response will occur at this moment will be the sum of these products. Thus:

$$p_+ = p_o p_1 + (1 - p_o) p_3. \quad (1)$$

By exactly parallel reasoning with respect to a selected moment during a negative trial we obtain:

$$p_- = p_o p_2 + (1 - p_o) p_3. \quad (2)$$

The next step will be to derive expressions for predicting the values of p_1, p_2, and p_3. The reinforcement contingencies for the effective response in the presence of S_1, S_2, and S_3 can be readily ascertained. It will be possible to predict changes in the values of p_1, p_2, and p_3 on the basis of learning functions for the simpler processes of conditioning and extinction if we assume that learning with respect to each of these stimuli, proceeds independently of learning with respect to the others. This assumption implies that interaction between stimuli will have a negligible effect.

However, in making this assumption we do not forfeit the ability to handle stimulus generalization within the present framework, since, as we have already pointed out, stimulus generalization can be accounted for without postulating any such direct interaction.

In the present paper we do not adopt a particular set of functions for conditioning and extinction, but attempt to set down the relationships in such a way that any acceptable set of functions can be immediately inserted.

The assumption of "negligible direct interaction" implies that changes in the probability of occurrence of the effective response with respect to a particular stimulus population S_i ($i = 1$, 2, or 3) will occur only during the time in which S is exposed to S_i, and that the rate of change with respect to time will depend on:

1. Whether or not the effective response is reinforced.
2. The value of p_i at the time.

If we let r_i represent the proportion of the time during which S is exposed to S_i, the rate of change of p_i can be approximated by two functions as follows:

$$dp_i/dt = r_i f_c(p_i) \quad (3)$$

if the effective response is reinforced, and

$$dp_i/dt = r_i f_e(p_i) \quad (4)$$

if the effective response is not reinforced.

The functions f_c and f_e represent any acceptable set of analytic functions which approximate the rate of change of probability of occurrence of an effective response during conditioning and extinction, respectively. It will be noted that if we assign a value of 1 to r we will obtain expressions for simple cases of conditioning or extinction. In the present model the values of r_i can be expressed as functions of p_o as follows. The positive and negative stimuli are each to be present 50 per cent of the time. During this time the subject will be exposed to S_1 or S_2 with a probability of p_o. Hence:

$$r_1 = r_2 = .5p_o.$$

S will be exposed to S_3 with a probability of $(1 - p_o)$. Hence:

$$r_3 = (1 - p_o).$$

We also know that all effective responses in the presence of S_1 are reinforced, effective responses in the presence of S_2 are not reinforced, and effective responses in the presence of S_3 are reinforced an average of one-half of the time. Using the above values of r and appropriate functions for reinforced and non-reinforced responses we obtain:

$$dp_1/dt = .5p_o f_c(p_1) \qquad (5)$$

$$dp_2/dt = .5p_o f_e(p_2) \qquad (6)$$

$$dp_3/dt = .5(1 - p_o)f_c(p_3) + .5(1 - p_o)f_e(p_3). \qquad (7)$$

We can now outline the steps which would be necessary to predict p_+ and p_- (measurable aspects of effective responses) if we can predict the values of p_o as a function of time. Such a function could be derived empirically or through some theoretical statement regarding the factors which bring about changes in p_o. If p_o can be expressed as a function of time we can rewrite equations 5, 6, and 7 to obtain expressions involving only dp_i, dt, p_i and t. If these differential equations can be solved we will obtain $p_i = f_i(t)$. Thus we can obtain values of p_1, p_2, p_3, and p_o for any point in time. These values can be substituted in equations 1 and 2 to give the desired prediction of p_+ and p_-.

On the other hand if we wish to estimate the values of p_o from known values of p_+ and p_-, we can proceed as follows.

Equations 1 and 2 state:

$$p_+ = p_o p_1 + (1 - p_o)p_3, \qquad (1)$$

$$p_- = p_o p_2 + (1 - p_o)p_3. \qquad (2)$$

Differentiating with respect to time we obtain:

$$dp_+/dt = p_o(dp_1/dt) + p_1(dp_o/dt) + (1 - p_o)(dp_3/dt) - p_3(dp_o/dt), \qquad (8)$$

$$dp_-/dt = p_o(dp_2/dt) + p_2(dp_o/dt) + (1 - p_o)(dp_3/dt) - p_3(dp_o/dt). \qquad (9)$$

Substituting values for dp_1/dt, dp_2/dt and dp_3/dt from equations 5, 6, and 7 and rearranging terms we obtain:

$$dp_+/dt = .5p_o^2 f_c(p_1) + .5(1 - p_o)^2[f_c(p_3) + f_e(p_3)] + (p_1 - p_3)(dp_o/dt), \qquad (10)$$

$$dp_-/dt = .5p_o^2 f_e(p_2) + .5(1 - p_o)^2[f_c(p_3) + f_e(p_3)] + (p_2 - p_3)(dp_o/dt). \qquad (11)$$

Equations 1, 2, 10, and 11 represent four simultaneous equations. By combining these equations we can express p_1, p_2, and p_3 as functions of the other variables and obtain a single expression:

$$dp_o/dt = G(p_+, p_-, dp_+/dt, dp_-/dt, p_o), \qquad (12)$$

where the function G will depend on the functions f_c and f_e adopted for the conditioning and extinction functions.

Now, if the curves representing the values of p_+ and p_- are determined experimentally, we can express these variables as analytic functions of time. We can also obtain expressions for dp_+/dt and dp_-/dt as functions of time. Substituting the functions for p_+,

p_-, dp_+/dt and dp_-/dt in equation 12 we obtain:

$$dp_o/dt = G'(t, p_o). \qquad (13)$$

If this differential equation can be solved we obtain:

$$p_o = f_o(t). \qquad (14)$$

This equation will give us the desired value of p_o for any point in time during the experiment.

SUMMARY

In many discrimination learning situations some response, such as an orienting response, will be required of S before he is exposed to the discriminative stimuli. We call these responses "observing responses" (R_o), and indicate their probability of occurrence as p_o. Increases in p_o will result in increased exposure to the discriminative stimuli, and hence increased opportunity for S to learn or manifest discrimination. Decreased p_o will have the opposite effect. These results are operationally equivalent to decreases or increases in stimulus generalization between the discriminative stimuli. The following general hypothesis regarding changes in p_o can be derived from the principle of secondary reinforcement.

Hypothesis: Exposure to discriminative stimuli will have a reinforcing effect on the observing response to the extent that S has learned to respond differently to the two discriminative stimuli.

From this general hypothesis we derive the following specific hypotheses:

1. p_o will increase (or remain high) under conditions of differential reinforcement (discrimination training);

2. p_o will decrease (or remain low) under conditions of nondifferential reinforcement;

3. When a well established discrimination is reversed, p_o will decrease temporarily and then recover;

4. If the degree of discrimination and p_o are both low, the formation of discrimination will be retarded for some interval but will finally occur quite rapidly.

Evidence in support of these specific hypotheses was obtained in an experiment in which an R_o was measured directly.

This formulation may be useful for interpreting behavior in cases where changes in generalization between stimuli occur, and where the ease of formation of discrimination on the basis of some particular set of stimuli, changes as a function of training. Ss learn reversed discriminations more and more rapidly if reversals are presented repeatedly. The present formulation offers a relatively simple and readily testable interpretation of this phenomenon.

This formulation lends itself to precise quantitative statement. A quantitative analysis could be used in two ways: (1) to make quantitative predictions of behavior based on some set of theoretical statements regarding the component learning processes, and (2) to evaluate p_o from observations of measurable aspects of effective responses. The steps required for such an analysis are outlined.

REFERENCES

1. BERLYNE, D. E. Attention, perception and behavior theory. PSYCHOL. REV., 1951, **58**, 137–146.
2. BITTERMAN, M. E., & COATE, W. B. Some new experiments on the nature of discrimination learning in the rat. *J. comp. Psychol.*, 1950, **43**, 198–210.
3. BUSH, R. R., & MOSTELLER, F. A mathematical model for learning. PSYCHOL. REV., 1951, **58**, 313–323.
4. DINSMOOR, J. A. A quantitative comparison of the discriminative and reinforc-

ing functions of a stimulus. *J. exp. Psychol.*, 1950, **40**, 458–472.

5. EHRENFREUND, D. An experimental test of the continuity theory of discrimination learning with pattern vision. *J. comp. Psychol.*, 1948, **41**, 408–422.

6. ESTES, W. K. Toward a statistical theory of learning. PSYCHOL. REV., 1950, **57**, 94–107.

7. FRICK, F. C. An analysis of an operant discrimination. *J. Psychol.*, 1948, **26**, 93–123.

8. HARLOW, H. F. Studies in discrimination learning by monkeys: I. The learning of discrimination series and the reversal of a discrimination series. *J. gen. Psychol.*, 1944, **30**, 3–12.

9. HULL, C. L. *Principles of behavior.* New York: D. Appleton-Century Co., Inc., 1943.

10. ——. Simple qualitative discrimination learning. PSYCHOL. REV., 1950, **57**, 303–313.

11. KRECHEVSKY, I. "Hypotheses" in rats. PSYCHOL. REV., 1932, **39**, 516–532.

12. ——. A study of the continuity of the problem-solving process. PSYCHOL. REV., 1938, **45**, 107–133.

13. McCULLOCH, T. L., & PRATT, J. C. A study of the pre-solution period in weight discrimination by white rats. *J. comp. Psychol.*, 1934, **18**, 271–290.

14. NORTH, A. J. Improvement in successive discrimination reversals. *J. comp. Psychol.*, 1950, **43**, 422–460.

15. ——. Performance during an extended series of discrimination reversals. *J. comp. Psychol.*, 1950, **43**, 461–470.

16. NOTTERMAN, J. M. A study of some relations among aperiodic reinforcement, discrimination training, and secondary reinforcement. *J. exp. Psychol.*, 1951, **41**, 161–169.

17. SCHOENFELD, W. N., ANTONITIS, J. J., & BERSH, P. J. A preliminary study of training conditions necessary for secondary reinforcement. *J. exp. Psychol.*, 1950, **40**, 40–45.

18. SKINNER, B. F. *The behavior of organisms.* New York: Appleton-Century, 1938.

19. SPENCE, K. W. The nature of discrimination learning in animals. PSYCHOL. REV., 1936, **43**, 427–449.

20. ——. Continuous versus non-continuous interpretations of discrimination learning. PSYCHOL. REV., 1940, **47**, 271–288.

21. WILCOXON, H. C., HAYS, RUTH, & HULL, C. L. A preliminary determination of the function relationship of effective reaction potential ($_s\bar{E}_R$) to the ordinal number of vincentized extinction reactions ($\dot{n}$). *J. exp. Psychol.*, 1950, **40**, 194–199.

22. WYCKOFF, L. B. The role of observing responses in discrimination learning: Part II. Unpublished Ph.D. thesis, Indiana Univ., 1951.

[MS. received September 19, 1951]